Stochastic Processes and the Wiener Integral

PURE AND APPLIED MATHEMATICS

A Series of Monographs and Textbooks

1. K. YANO. Integral Formulas in Riemannian Geometry (1970)
2. S. KOBAYASHI. Hyperbolic Manifolds and Holomorphic Mappings (1970)
3. V. S. VLADIMIROV. Equations of Mathematical Physics (A. Jeffrey, editor; A. Littlewood, translator) (1970)
4. B. N. PSHENICHNYI. Necessary Conditions for an Extremum (L. Neustadt, translation editor; K. Makowski, translator) (1971)
5. L. NARICI, E. BECKENSTEIN, and G. BACHMAN. Functional Analysis and Valuation Theory (1971)
6. D. S. PASSMAN. Infinite Group Rings (1971)
7. L. DORNHOFF. Group Representation Theory (in two parts). Part A: Ordinary Representation Theory. Part B: Modular Representation Theory (1971, 1972)
8. W. BOOTHBY and G. L. WEISS (eds.). Symmetric Spaces: Short Courses Presented at Washington University (1972)
9. Y. MATSUSHIMA. Differential Manifolds (E. T. Kobayashi, translator) (1972)
10. L. E. WARD, JR. Tropology: An Outline for a First Course (1972)
11. A. BABAKHANIAN. Cohomological Methods in Group Theory (1972)
12. R. GILMER. Multiplicative Ideal Theory (1972)
13. J. YEH. Stochastic Processes and the Wiener Integral (1973)
14. J. BARROS-NETO. An Introduction to the Theory of Distributions (1973)

In Preparation:

J. DIEUDONNE. Introduction to the Theory of Formal Groups

R. LARSEN. Functional Analysis: An Introduction

C. PROCESI. Rings with Polynomial Identities

I. VAISMAN. Cohomology and Differential Forms

N. WALLACH. Differential Operators on Homogeneous Spaces

K. YANO and S. ISHIHARA. Differential Geometry of Tangent and Cotangent Bundles

STOCHASTIC PROCESSES AND THE WIENER INTEGRAL

J. Yeh

Department of Mathematics
University of California, Irvine
Irvine, California

MARCEL DEKKER, INC. New York 1973

MARCEL DEKKER, INC.
95 Madison Avenue, New York, New York 10016

LIBRARY OF CONGRESS CATALOG CARD NUMBER: 72-91439
ISBN: 0-8247-1809-7

Printed in the United States of America

PREFACE

The present book is an introduction to stochastic processes, Brownian motion processes, Gaussian processes, Wiener measure and Wiener integrals. Below is a brief outline of its contents.

In Chapter 1, it is shown that a stochastic process on an arbitrary probability space induces a probability measure in the space of all real valued functions and that the process can then be represented by a process on the function space. This is done by means of the Kolmogorov extension theorem, a detailed proof of which is given here. Separability, measurability and continuity of a stochastic process are discussed in this chapter. There is also a study of infinite dimensional random vectors. Chapter 2 is a brief treatise of martingales. The main objects here are the martingale convergence theorem and the martingale closing theorem. Chapter 3 begins with an existence proof of additive processes (i.e., processes with independence increments). This is followed by a discussion of sample function properties of additive processes. The Brownian motion process is then characterized as an additive process with continuous sample functions. In Chapter 4 the existence of a Gaussian process having an arbitrarily given pair of real valued function and positive definite symmetric function as its mean and covariance function is proved. In Chapter 5, the stochastic integral of stepwise stochastic process with respect to a continuous Brownian motion process is defined as a random variable which is the Riemann-Stieltjes integrals of sample functions of the former process with respect to those of the latter. This definition is then extended to a wider class of stochastic processes satisfying certain measurability and integrability conditions. In Chapter 6, Hájek's proof of the Feldman-Hájek dichotomy that two Gaussian measures on a function space are either equivalent or singular is given. In Chapter 7 the Wiener measure is first constructed on the space of all real valued functions. Then it is shown that the subspace consisting of the continuous functions has an outermeasure equal to 1 and thus inherits a probability measure from the containing space of all real valued functions. Chapter 8 contains the Cameron-Martin translation theorem of Wiener integrals. The translation theorem in § 34 is a particular case of a more general theorem in Cameron and Martin [2]. I presented it here because of the relative brevity of its proof and because of its application.

The bibliography is not intended to be complete. Rather, it is a list of publications which I referred to or drew material from in writing this book. Gelfand and Yaglom [1], Kovalchik [1], Yaglom [1] and Shepp [1] contain longer lists of publications in Wiener integrals and the Feldman-Hájek dichotomy up to the times of their publication.

The prerequisite for reading this book is a good background in real analysis and some knowledge of measure theoretic probability theory. In the Appendix I collected the theorems in probability theory along with definitions needed in stating them. The numberings of these definitions and theorems are preceded by the letter A. Thus for instance Theorem A4.2 appears in § 4 of the Appendix. Proofs of these theorems can be found in most standard works in probability theory and real analysis.

In writing the present book I am indebted to Doob [2] and Itô [2] from which I taught in the past. The influence of these two works are evident in many parts of the present book. I take this opportunity to express my gratitude to Professor Robert H. Cameron from whom I learned integration in functions spaces. Drs. William Hudson, Richard Brooks, Edward Kerlin, Martin Walter and Wesley Masenten contributed in improving the text. For the expert typing of the text I thank Lillian White, Linda Husak and Grace Koo the first of whom typed most of the manuscript. My thanks are due to the editorial board of the series Pure and Applied Mathematics, and in particular Professor Howard G. Tucker, for inviting me to write this book.

J. Yeh

Irvine, California

CONTENTS

Stochastic Processes and the Wiener Integral

Chapter 1
STOCHASTIC PROCESSES

§1. STOCHASTIC PROCESSES

A stochastic process is by definition a collection of random variables $\{X_t, t \in D\}$ defined on a probability space $(\Omega, \mathfrak{B}, P)$ where the index set D is a subset of the real line R^1. Thus a stochastic process X is a real-valued function $X(t, \omega)$ on $D \times \Omega$ which is a $\mathfrak{B}$-measurable function on Ω for each $t \in D$. We shall occasionally use the notation $X(t)$ to mean the random variable $X(t, \cdot)$. The index set D is called the domain of definition of the stochastic process. For each $\omega \in \Omega$, the real-valued function $X(\cdot, \omega)$ is called a sample function or a sample path of the stochastic process. Sometimes it is necessary to permit some of the random variables $X(t, \cdot)$, $t \in D$, to assume extended real values, and then we speak of an extended real-valued stochastic process. Otherwise a stochastic process is always real valued.

Definition 1.1 Two stochastic processes X and Y on a probability space $(\Omega, \mathfrak{B}, P)$ and $D \subset R^1$ are said to be equivalent if, for every $t \in D$, $X(t, \omega) = Y(t, \omega)$ for a.e. ω, i.e., there exists $\Lambda_t \in \mathfrak{B}$ with $P(\Lambda_t) = 0$ such that $X(t, \omega) = Y(t, \omega)$ for $\omega \in \Lambda_t^c$. X and Y are said to be almost surely equal if the sample functions of X and Y are identical for a.e. ω, i.e., there exists $\Lambda \in \mathfrak{B}$ with $P(\Lambda) = 0$ such that $X(\cdot, \omega) = Y(\cdot, \omega)$ for $\omega \in \Lambda^c$.

Definition 1.2 A stochastic process X on a probability space $(\Omega, \mathfrak{B}, P)$ and $D \subset R^1$ is said to be almost surely continuous if a.e. sample function is continuous on D, i.e., there exists

$\Lambda \in \mathfrak{B}$ with $P(\Lambda) = 0$ such that $X(\cdot, \omega)$ is a continuous function on D for $\omega \in \Lambda^c$.

Remark 1.3 Two almost surely continuous stochastic processes which are equivalent are in fact almost surely equal.

Proof Let X and Y be almost surely continuous and equivalent stochastic processes on $(\Omega, \mathfrak{B}, P)$ and D. Let $\Lambda \in \mathfrak{B}$ with $P(\Lambda) = 0$ be such that $X(\cdot, \omega)$ and $Y(\cdot, \omega)$ are continuous on D for $\omega \in \Lambda^c$. Let $S = \{s_n, n = 1, 2, \cdots\}$ be a countable dense subset of D whose elements are numbered in an arbitrary way. By the equivalence of X and Y, for every n there exists $\Lambda_n \in \mathfrak{B}$ with $P(\Lambda_n) = 0$ such that

$$X(s_n, \omega) = Y(s_n, \omega) \quad \text{for} \quad \omega \in \Lambda_n^c.$$

Let $\Lambda_\infty = \bigcup_{n=1}^{\infty} \Lambda_n$. Then $\Lambda_\infty \in \mathfrak{B}$ with $P(\Lambda_\infty) = 0$ and

$$X(s_n, \omega) = Y(s_n, \omega) \quad \text{for} \quad n = 1, 2, \cdots \quad \text{when} \quad \omega \in \Lambda_\infty^c.$$

On the other hand for an arbitrary $t \in D$ and $\omega \in \Lambda^c$, $X(t, \omega) = \lim_{k\to\infty} X(s_{n_k}, \omega)$ and $Y(t, \omega) = \lim_{k\to\infty} Y(s_{n_k}, \omega)$ for every subsequence $\{s_{n_k}\} \subset \{s_n\}$ such that $\lim_{k\to\infty} s_{n_k} = t$. Then from the fact that $X(s_{n_k}, \omega) = Y(s_{n_k}, \omega)$, $k = 1, 2, \cdots$, for $\omega \in \Lambda_\infty^c$ we have $X(t, \omega) = Y(t, \omega)$ for $\omega \in (\Lambda \cup \Lambda_\infty)^c$. □

Definition 1.4 Given a stochastic process X on a probability space $(\Omega, \mathfrak{B}, P)$ and $D \subset R^1$. Let $T = \{t_1, t_2, \cdots, t_n\}$ be a finite sequence of distinct elements of D. Consider the transformation $X_T = X_{t_1 \cdots t_n} = \big(X(t_1, \cdot), \cdots, X(t_n, \cdot)\big)$ of Ω into R^n and let $\Phi_{X_T} = \Phi_{X_{t_1 \cdots t_n}}$ be the n-dimensional probability distribution determined by X_T, i.e., the probability measure on the σ-field of

Borel sets in R^n, $\mathfrak{B}^n$, defined by

$$\Phi_{X_T}(E) = P\left(X_T^{-1}(E)\right) \quad \text{for} \quad E \in \mathfrak{B}^n.$$

Let $\mathfrak{T}$ be the collection of all the T's. Then $\{\Phi_{X_T}, T \in \mathfrak{T}\}$ is called the system of finite dimensional probability distributions determined by X.

Remark 1.5 For two equivalent stochastic processes X and Y on a probability space $(\Omega, \mathfrak{B}, P)$ and $D \subset R^1$ we have $\Phi_{X_T} = \Phi_{Y_T}$ for every $T \in \mathfrak{T}$.

Proof Let $T = \{t_1, t_2, \cdots, t_n\}$. Since a probability measure on $\mathfrak{B}^n$ is uniquely determined by its values for intervals in R^n of the type $I = (\alpha_1, b_1] \times \cdots \times (\alpha_n, b_n]$, to show that $\Phi_{X_T} = \Phi_{Y_T}$ it suffices to show that $\Phi_{X_T}(I) = \Phi_{Y_T}(I)$ for every I. Now at each t_k, $k = 1,2, \cdots, n$, from the equivalence of X and Y there exists $\Lambda_k \in \mathfrak{B}$ with $P(\Lambda_k) = 0$ such that $X(t_k, \omega) = Y(t_k, \omega)$ when $\omega \in \Lambda_k^c$. Let $\Lambda = \bigcup_{k=1}^n \Lambda_k$. Then $P(\Lambda) = 0$ so that

$$\begin{aligned}
\Phi_{X_T}(I) &= P\left\{\omega \in \Omega\,;\, X(t_k, \omega) \in (\alpha_k, b_k],\ k = 1,2, \cdots, n\right\} \\
&= P\left\{\omega \in \Lambda^c\,;\, X(t_k, \omega) \in (\alpha_k, b_k],\ k = 1,2, \cdots, n\right\} \\
&= P\left\{\omega \in \Lambda^c\,;\, Y(t_k, \omega) \in (\alpha_k, b_k],\ k = 1,2, \cdots, n\right\} \\
&= P\left\{\omega \in \Omega\,;\, Y(t_k, \omega) \in (\alpha_k, b_k],\ k = 1,2, \cdots, n\right\} \\
&= \Phi_{Y_T}(I).
\end{aligned}$$

□

§2. EXISTENCE OF A STOCHASTIC PROCESS WITH A GIVEN SYSTEM OF FINITE DIMENSIONAL PROBABILITY DISTRIBUTIONS

In §1 we saw that a stochastic process X on a probability space $(\Omega, \mathfrak{B}, P)$ and $D \subset R^1$ determines a system of finite dimensional probability distributions $\{\Phi_{X_T}, T \in \mathfrak{T}\}$ where $\mathfrak{T}$ is the collection of all finite sequences of distinct elements $T = \{t_1, t_2, \cdots, t_n\}$ from D. We also saw that if X and Y are two equivalent stochastic processes on $(\Omega, \mathfrak{B}, P)$ and D then $\Phi_{X_T} = \Phi_{Y_T}$ for every $T \in \mathfrak{T}$. It is natural to ask the question: Given a system of finite dimensional probability distributions $\{\Phi_T, T \in \mathfrak{T}\}$ does a stochastic process X on some probability space $(\Omega, \mathfrak{B}, P)$ and D exist which has $\{\Phi_T, T \in \mathfrak{T}\}$ as its system of finite dimensional probability distributions, that is, $\Phi_{X_T} = \Phi_T$ for every $T \in \mathfrak{T}$? The answer to this question is in the affirmative provided that the system $\{\Phi_T, T \in \mathfrak{T}\}$ satisfies certain consistency conditions. To prove this we need the Kolmogorov Extension Theorem.

[I] The Kolmogorov Extension Theorem

Given an arbitrary set A and the collection R^A of all real-valued functions defined on A. An element of R^A is denoted by $\omega = \left(\omega(\alpha), \alpha \in A\right)$ and the real number $\omega(\alpha)$ is called the α-coordinate of ω. For a finite sequence of distinct elements of A, $\{\alpha_1, \cdots, \alpha_n\}$, the projection of R^A onto R^n with index $\{\alpha_1, \cdots, \alpha_n\}$, namely, $p_{\alpha_1 \cdots \alpha_n}$, is defined by

$$p_{\alpha_1 \cdots \alpha_n}(\omega) = \left(\omega(\alpha_1), \cdots, \omega(\alpha_n)\right) \in R^n \quad \text{for every } \omega \in R^A.$$

The Borel cylinder in R^A with index $\{\alpha_1, \cdots, \alpha_n\}$ and base $B \in \mathfrak{B}^n$ is a subset of R^A defined by

$$p_{\alpha_1 \cdots \alpha_n}^{-1}(B) = \left\{\omega \in R^A ;\ p_{\alpha_1 \cdots \alpha_n}(\omega) \in B\right\}.$$

Let $\mathfrak{Z}_{\alpha_1 \cdots \alpha_n}$ be the collection of all Borel cylinders in R^A with index $\{\alpha_1, \cdots, \alpha_n\}$, i.e.,

$$\mathfrak{Z}_{\alpha_1 \cdots \alpha_n} = p_{\alpha_1 \cdots \alpha_n}^{-1}(\mathfrak{B}^n) = \left\{p_{\alpha_1 \cdots \alpha_n}^{-1}(B),\ B \in \mathfrak{B}^n\right\}$$

and let

$$\mathfrak{Z} = \cup\, \mathfrak{Z}_{\alpha_1 \cdots \alpha_n}$$

where the union is over all finite sequences of distinct elements of A. As we shall show in Remark 2.2, $\mathfrak{Z}_{\alpha_1 \cdots \alpha_n}$ is a σ-field and $\mathfrak{Z}$ is a field of subsets of R^A.

<u>Theorem 2.1</u> Kolmogorov Extension Theorem. Let μ be a set function defined on the field $\mathfrak{Z} = \cup\, \mathfrak{Z}_{\alpha_1 \cdots \alpha_n}$ of subsets of R^A satisfying the condition that, for every $\{\alpha_1, \cdots, \alpha_n\}$, μ is a probability measure on the σ-field $\mathfrak{Z}_{\alpha_1 \cdots \alpha_n}$. Then μ can be extended uniquely to be a probability measure on the σ-field $\sigma(\mathfrak{Z})$ generated by $\mathfrak{Z}$.

Before we prove Theorem 2.1 let us enumerate some pertinent properties of $\mathfrak{Z}_{\alpha_1 \cdots \alpha_n}$ and $\mathfrak{Z}$ in the form of a remark.

<u>Remark 2.2</u> 1°. $\mathfrak{Z}_{\alpha_1 \cdots \alpha_n}$ is a σ-field of subsets of R^A.

<u>Proof</u> (1) $R^A = p_{\alpha_1 \cdots \alpha_n}^{-1}(R^n)$. Thus $R^A \in \mathfrak{Z}_{\alpha_1 \cdots \alpha_n}$.

(2) Let $E \in \mathfrak{Z}_{\alpha_1 \cdots \alpha_n}$. Then $E = p_{\alpha_1 \cdots \alpha_n}^{-1}(B)$ for some $B \in \mathfrak{B}^n$ so that $E^c = p_{\alpha_1 \cdots \alpha_n}^{-1}(B^c) \in \mathfrak{Z}_{\alpha_1 \cdots \alpha_n}$.

(3) Let $\{E_i,\ i = 1, 2, \cdots\} \subset \mathfrak{Z}_{\alpha_1 \cdots \alpha_n}$. Then $E_i = p_{\alpha_1 \cdots \alpha_n}^{-1}(B_i)$ for some $B_i \in \mathfrak{B}^n$ so that

$$\bigcup_{i=1}^{\infty} E_i = \bigcup_{i=1}^{\infty} p_{\alpha_1 \cdots \alpha_n}^{-1}(B_i) = p_{\alpha_1 \cdots \alpha_n}^{-1}\left(\bigcup_{n=1}^{\infty} B_i\right) \in \mathfrak{F}_{\alpha_1 \cdots \alpha_n}. \quad \square$$

2°. If $E \in \mathfrak{F}_{\alpha_1 \cdots \alpha_n}$ then by the definition of $\mathfrak{F}_{\alpha_1 \cdots \alpha_n}$ there exists some $B \in \mathfrak{B}^n$ such that $E = p_{\alpha_1 \cdots \alpha_n}^{-1}(B)$. The set B is uniquely determined by E, i.e., if $B_1, B_2 \in \mathfrak{B}^n$, $B_1 \neq B_2$, then $p_{\alpha_1 \cdots \alpha_n}^{-1}(B_1) \neq p_{\alpha_1 \cdots \alpha_n}^{-1}(B_2)$ or, equivalently, if $E_1, E_2 \in \mathfrak{F}_{\alpha_1 \cdots \alpha_n}$ and $E_1 = p_{\alpha_1 \cdots \alpha_n}^{-1}(B_1)$, $E_2 = p_{\alpha_1 \cdots \alpha_n}^{-1}(B_2)$ with $B_1, B_2 \in \mathfrak{B}^n$ then $E_1 = E_2$ implies $B_1 = B_2$. This is from the fact that $p_{\alpha_1 \cdots \alpha_n}(E_1) = B_1$, $p_{\alpha_n \cdots \alpha_n}(E_2) = B_2$ so that $E_1 = E_2$ implies $B_1 = B_2$.

3°. Consider $\mathfrak{F} = \bigcup \mathfrak{F}_{\alpha_1 \cdots \alpha_n}$. If $E \in \mathfrak{F}$ then $E \in \mathfrak{F}_{\alpha_1 \cdots \alpha_n}$ for some index $\{\alpha_1, \cdots, \alpha_n\}$ and $E = p_{\alpha_1 \cdots \alpha_n}^{-1}(B)$ for some $B \in \mathfrak{B}^n$ which is uniquely determined as long as $\{\alpha_1, \cdots, \alpha_n\}$ is fixed according to 2°. However E may belong to other σ-fields than $\mathfrak{F}_{\alpha_1 \cdots \alpha_n}$. For instance if $E = p_{\alpha_1 \cdots \alpha_n}^{-1}(B)$ then certainly $E = p_{\alpha_1 \cdots \alpha_{n+1}}^{-1}(B \times R^1)$ with an arbitrary $\alpha_{n+1} \in A$, $\alpha_{n+1} \neq \alpha_1, \cdots, \alpha_n$, so that $E \in \mathfrak{F}_{\alpha_1 \cdots \alpha_n \alpha_{n+1}}$.

Also if $\Pi = \{\Pi_1, \cdots, \Pi_n\}$ is a permutation of $\{1, \cdots, n\}$ and $\Pi(B) \in \mathfrak{B}^n$ is the permuted set of $B \in \mathfrak{B}^n$ by Π, i.e., the set in R^n traced by $(\xi_{\Pi_1} \cdots \xi_{\Pi_n}) \in R^n$ when $(\xi_1, \cdots, \xi_n) \in R^n$ traces B, then certainly $E = p_{\alpha_1 \cdots \alpha_n}^{-1}(B) = p_{\alpha_{\Pi_1} \cdots \alpha_{\Pi_n}}^{-1}\left(\Pi(B)\right)$ so that

$E \in \mathfrak{J}_{\alpha_{\Pi_1} \cdots \alpha_{\Pi_n}}$ also. Note also that $\mathfrak{J}_{\alpha_1 \cdots \alpha_n} = \mathfrak{J}_{\alpha_{\Pi_1} \cdots \alpha_{\Pi_n}}$.

4°. Let $E \in \mathfrak{J}$. As we saw in 3°, E has more than one representation by finite dimensional Borel sets. A representation $E = p_{\alpha_1 \cdots \alpha_n}^{-1}(B)$, $B \in \mathfrak{B}^n$, is called a minimal representation for E if B is not the Cartesian product of R^1 with an $n-1$ dimensional Borel set. The space R^A, for any index $\{\alpha_1, \cdots, \alpha_n\}$, being representable as $p_{\alpha_1 \cdots \alpha_n}^{-1}(R^n)$ only, has no minimal representation. For any $E \in \mathfrak{J}$, $E \neq R^A$, any representation $E = p_{\alpha_1 \cdots \alpha_n}^{-1}(B)$, $B \in \mathfrak{B}^n$, which is not already a minimal representation can be reduced to a minimal representation since E can also be given as $E = p_{\alpha_{\Pi_1} \cdots \alpha_{\Pi_n}}^{-1}\left(\Pi(B)\right)$ where $\Pi(B) = B' \times R^1$ with an $n-1$ dimensional Borel set B' and consequently $E = p_{\alpha_{\Pi_1} \cdots \alpha_{\Pi_{n-1}}}^{-1}(B')$. If this last representation is not yet a minimal representation we repeat the process of reduction until we arrive at a minimal representation.

5°. Let $E \in \mathfrak{J}$, $E \neq R^A$, and let $p_{\alpha_1 \cdots \alpha_n}^{-1}(B_1)$, $B_1 \in \mathfrak{B}^n$, $p_{\beta_1 \cdots \beta_m}^{-1}(B_2)$, $B_2 \in \mathfrak{B}^m$, be two minimal representations of E. Then $m = n$ and $\{\beta_1, \cdots, \beta_m\} = \{\alpha_{\Pi_1}, \cdots, \alpha_{\Pi_n}\}$ for some permutation $\Pi = \{\Pi_{\alpha_1}, \cdots, \Pi_{\alpha_n}\}$ of $\{1, \cdots, n\}$ and $B_2 = \Pi(B_1)$.

<u>Proof</u> (1) To show $m = n$, assume for instance $n < m$. Then for some j_0 we have $\beta_{j_0} \neq \alpha_1, \cdots \alpha_n$. Then B_2 must be the Cartesian product of R^1 and an $m-1$ dimensional Borel set contradicting the minimality of the representation $p_{\beta_1 \cdots \beta_m}^{-1}(B_2)$.

Thus $n \geq m$. Similarly we have $m \geq n$ and hence $m = n$.

(2) The argument in (1) shows not only that $m = n$ but also that as two point sets $\{\alpha_1, \cdots, \alpha_n\}$ and $\{\beta_1, \cdots, \beta_n\}$ are equal.

(3) Now that $\{\alpha_1, \cdots, \alpha_n\}$ and $\{\beta_1, \cdots, \beta_n\}$ are equal as point sets, there exists a permutation $\Pi = \{\Pi_1, \cdots, \Pi_n\}$ of $\{1, \cdots, n\}$ so that $\{\beta_1, \cdots, \beta_n\} = \{\alpha_{\Pi_1}, \cdots, \alpha_{\Pi_n}\}$. Then

$$E = p_{\alpha_1 \cdots \alpha_n}^{-1}(B_1) = p_{\alpha_{\Pi_1} \cdots \alpha_{\Pi_n}}^{-1}\left(\Pi(B_1)\right) = p_{\beta_1 \cdots \beta_n}^{-1}\left(\Pi(B_1)\right).$$

But $E = p_{\beta_1 \cdots \beta_n}^{-1}(B_2)$ also. Thus by 2°, $B_2 = \Pi(B_1)$. □

6°. $\mathfrak{Z}$ is a field of subsets of R^A.

Proof (1) $R^A \in \mathfrak{Z}$. In fact $R^A = p_{\alpha_1 \cdots \alpha_n}^{-1}(R^n) \in \mathfrak{Z}_{\alpha_1 \cdots \alpha_n}$ for every $\{\alpha_1, \cdots, \alpha_n\}$.

(2) If $E \in \mathfrak{Z}$ then $E \in \mathfrak{Z}_{\alpha_1 \cdots \alpha_n}$ for some $\{\alpha_1, \cdots, \alpha_n\}$ and hence $E^c \in \mathfrak{Z}_{\alpha_1 \cdots \alpha_n} \subset \mathfrak{Z}$ since $\mathfrak{Z}_{\alpha_1 \cdots \alpha_n}$ is a σ-field.

(3) Let $E_1, E_2 \in \mathfrak{Z}$. Then $E_1 = p_{\alpha_1 \cdots \alpha_n}^{-1}(B_1)$, $B_1 \in \mathfrak{B}^n$, and $E_2 = p_{\beta_1 \cdots \beta_m}^{-1}(B_2)$, $B_2 \in \mathfrak{B}^m$. If $\{\alpha_1 \cdots \alpha_n\}$ and $\{\beta_1, \cdots, \beta_m\}$ are disjoint as point sets then we have

$$E_1 = p_{\alpha_1 \cdots \alpha_n \beta_1 \cdots \beta_m}^{-1}(B_1 \times R^m), \quad E_2 = p_{\alpha_1 \cdots \alpha_n \beta_1 \cdots \beta_m}^{-1}(R^n \times B_2)$$

and hence

$$E_1 \cup E_2 = p_{\alpha_1 \cdots \alpha_n \beta_1 \cdots \beta_m}^{-1}(B_1 \times R^m \cup R^n \times B_2) \in \mathfrak{Z}_{\alpha_1 \cdots \alpha_n \beta_1 \cdots \beta_m} \subset \mathfrak{Z}.$$

If $\{\alpha_1, \cdots, \alpha_n\}$ and $\{\beta_1, \cdots, \beta_m\}$ are not disjoint as point sets then permute $\{\alpha_1, \cdots, \alpha_n\}$, $\{\beta_1, \cdots, \beta_m\}$, B_1 and B_2 if necessary so that

$$\alpha_i = \beta_i \text{ for } i = 1,2,\cdots,\ell \text{ and } \alpha_i \neq \beta_j \text{ for } i = \ell+1,\cdots,n,\ j=\ell+1,\cdots,m.$$

Then

$$E_1 = p_{\alpha_1\cdots\alpha_n}^{-1}(B_1) = p_{\alpha_1\cdots\alpha_\ell\ \alpha_{\ell+1}\cdots\alpha_n\ \beta_{\ell+1}\cdots\beta_m}^{-1}(B_1 \times R^{m-\ell})$$

$$E_2 = p_{\beta_1\cdots\beta_m}^{-1}(B_2) = p_{\alpha_1\cdots\alpha_\ell\ \beta_{\ell+1}\cdots\beta_m\ \alpha_{\ell+1}\cdots\alpha_n}^{-1}(B_2 \times R^{n-\ell})$$

$$= p_{\alpha_1\cdots\alpha_\ell\ \alpha_{\ell+1}\cdots\alpha_n\ \beta_{\ell+1}\cdots\beta_m}^{-1}\left(\Pi(B_2 \times R^{n-\ell})\right)$$

with a suitable permutation Π. Then $E_1 \cup E_2 \in \mathfrak{J}_{\alpha_1\cdots\alpha_n\beta_{\ell+1}\cdots\beta_m} \subset \mathfrak{J}$. □

<u>Lemma 2.3</u> Given a k-dimensional probability space $(R^k, \mathfrak{B}^k, \Phi)$. For every $A \in \mathfrak{B}^k$ and $\varepsilon > 0$ there exist compact sets C and D such that $C \subset A$, $D \subset A^c$, and $\Phi(A - C)$, $\Phi(A^c - D) < \varepsilon$.

<u>Proof</u> Let $\mathfrak{K}$ be the collection of members of $\mathfrak{B}^k$ for which the statement of the lemma holds. Let $\mathfrak{J}^k$ be the collection of subsets of R^k of the type $(a_1, b_1] \times \cdots \times (a_k, b_k]$ which generates the σ-field $\mathfrak{B}^k$. If we show that $\mathfrak{J}^k \subset \mathfrak{K}$ and that $\mathfrak{K}$ is a σ-field then $\mathfrak{B}^k \subset \mathfrak{K}$, and the proof is complete.

We show first that $\mathfrak{J}^k \subset \mathfrak{K}$. Now if $A \in \mathfrak{J}^k$ then clearly both A and A^c are limits of monotone increasing sequences of compact sets $\{C_n, n = 1,2,\cdots\}$ and $\{D_n, n = 1,2,\cdots\}$ so that, for sufficiently large n, we have $\Phi(A - C_n)$, $\Phi(A^c - D_n) < \varepsilon$ and $A \in \mathfrak{K}$.

Next we show that $\mathfrak{K}$ is a σ-field. First of all, $R^k \in \mathfrak{J}^k \subset \mathfrak{K}$. Secondly by the definition of $\mathfrak{K}$, $A \in \mathfrak{K}$ implies $A^c \in \mathfrak{K}$. Finally let

$\{A_n, n=1,2,\cdots\} \subset \mathfrak{K}$. We proceed to show that $\bigcup_{n=1}^{\infty} A_n \in \mathfrak{K}$. Now for every $\epsilon > 0$ there exist compact sets $C_n \subset A_n$ and $D_n \subset A_n^c$ such that $\Phi(A_n - C_n)$, $\Phi(A_n^c - D_n) < \epsilon/2^{n+1}$. Then

$$\bigcup_{n=1}^{\infty} C_n \subset \bigcup_{n=1}^{\infty} A_n, \quad \bigcup_{n=1}^{\infty} A_n - \bigcup_{n=1}^{\infty} C_n \subset \bigcup_{n=1}^{\infty} (A_n - C_n)$$

and

$$\Phi\left(\bigcup_{n=1}^{\infty} A_n - \bigcup_{n=1}^{\infty} C_n\right) \leq \sum_{n=1}^{\infty} \Phi(A_n - C_n) \leq \frac{\epsilon}{2}.$$

On the other hand for sufficiently large N we have $\Phi\left(\bigcup_{n=1}^{\infty} C_n - \bigcup_{n=1}^{N} C_n\right) \leq \epsilon/2$. The set $\bigcup_{n=1}^{N} C_n$ is a compact set contained in $\bigcup_{n=1}^{\infty} A_n$ and

$$\bigcup_{n=1}^{\infty} A_n - \bigcup_{n=1}^{N} C_n = \left(\bigcup_{n=1}^{\infty} A_n - \bigcup_{n=1}^{\infty} C_n\right) \cup \left(\bigcup_{n=1}^{\infty} C_n - \bigcup_{n=1}^{N} C_n\right)$$

and consequently

$$\Phi\left(\bigcup_{n=1}^{\infty} A_n - \bigcup_{n=1}^{N} C_n\right) \leq \frac{\epsilon}{2} + \frac{\epsilon}{2} = \epsilon.$$

Regarding $\left(\bigcup_{n=1}^{\infty} A_n\right)^c$ we have $\bigcap_{n=1}^{\infty} D_n \subset \bigcap_{n=1}^{\infty} A_n^c$ so that

$$\left(\bigcup_{n=1}^{\infty} A_n\right)^c - \bigcap_{n=1}^{\infty} D_n = \bigcap_{n=1}^{\infty} A_n^c - \bigcap_{n=1}^{\infty} D_n$$

$$= \text{complement of } \bigcap_{n=1}^{\infty} D_n \text{ in } \bigcap_{n=1}^{\infty} A_n^c$$

$$= \bigcup_{n=1}^{\infty} \left\{\bigcap_{n=1}^{\infty} A_n^c - D_n\right\} \subset \bigcup_{n=1}^{\infty} \left(A_n^c - D_n\right)$$

and hence

$$\Phi\left(\left(\bigcup_{n=1}^{\infty} A_n\right)^c - \bigcap_{n=1}^{\infty} D_n\right) \le \sum_{n=1}^{\infty} \Phi\left(A_n^{\,c} - D_n\right) \le \epsilon.$$

Thus we have found the required compact sets $\bigcup_{n=1}^{N} C_n$ and $\bigcap_{n=1}^{\infty} D_n$ for $\bigcup_{n=1}^{\infty} A_n$ and $\left(\bigcup_{n=1}^{\infty} A_n\right)^c$ respectively and $\bigcup_{n=1}^{\infty} A_n \in \mathfrak{R}$. □

Proof of Theorem 2.1 Since μ is a probability measure on $\mathfrak{Z}_{\alpha_1 \cdots \alpha_n}$ for every $\{\alpha_1, \cdots, \alpha_n\}$ it has the following properties on the field $\mathfrak{Z}$:

1°. $0 \le \mu(E) \le 1$ for every $E \in \mathfrak{Z}$.

2°. $\mu(\emptyset) = 0$ and $\mu(R^A) = 1$.

3°. μ is additive on $\mathfrak{Z}$. (This follows from the fact that if $E_1, E_2 \in \mathfrak{Z}$ then $E_1, E_2 \in \mathfrak{Z}_{\alpha_1 \cdots \alpha_n}$ for some $\{\alpha_1, \cdots, \alpha_n\}$ as we saw in 6°, Remark 2.2.)

Now in general a nonnegative additive set function μ on a field $\mathfrak{A}$ of subsets of a space X can be extended to be a measure on the σ-field generated by $\mathfrak{A}$ if and only if μ is countably additive on $\mathfrak{A}$ to start with, i.e.,

$$\{A_n, n = 1, 2, \cdots\} \subset \mathfrak{A}, \text{ disjoint, } \bigcup_{n=1}^{\infty} A_n \in \mathfrak{A} \Rightarrow \mu\left(\bigcup_{n=1}^{\infty} A_n\right) = \sum_{n=1}^{\infty} \mu(A_n). \tag{1}$$

The extension is unique if $\mu(X) < \infty$. Furthermore if $\mu(X) < \infty$ then (1) is equivalent to

$$\{A_n, n = 1, 2, \cdots\} \subset \mathfrak{A}, \; A_n \downarrow, \; \lim_{n\to\infty} A_n = \emptyset \Rightarrow \lim_{n\to\infty} \mu(A_n) = 0. \tag{2}$$

To prove our theorem we show that a contrapositive of (2)

holds, namely,

$$\{E_n, n=1,2,\cdots\} \subset \mathfrak{F},\ E_n \downarrow,\ \mu(E_n) \geq \epsilon_0 > 0 \text{ for all } n \Rightarrow \bigcap_{n=1}^{\infty} E_n \neq \phi. \quad (3)$$

Note that the additivity of μ on $\mathfrak{F}$ implies the monotonicity of μ on $\mathfrak{F}$ so that $E_n \downarrow$ implies $\mu(E_n)\downarrow$ and consequently the condition that $\mu(E_n)$ does not converge to 0 is equivalent to the existence of some $\epsilon_0 > 0$ such that $\mu(E_n) \geq \epsilon_0$ for all n.

Now take any monotone decreasing sequence $\{E_n, n=1,2,\cdots\} \subset \mathfrak{F}$. Let $E_n = p_{\alpha_{n,1}\cdots\alpha_{n,m_n}}^{-1}(B_n'),\ B' \in \mathfrak{B}^{m_n}$. Let $\{\alpha_\nu, \nu=1,2,\cdots\}$ be a finite or infinite sequence of distinct elements of A which, as a point set, contains all the sets $\{\alpha_{n,1}, \cdots, \alpha_{n,m_n}\}$, $n=1,2,\cdots$. Then we can represent E_n as

$$E_n = p_{\alpha_1\alpha_2\cdots\alpha_{\sigma(n)}}^{-1}(B_n'') \text{ where } B_n'' \in \mathfrak{B}^{\sigma(n)},\ \sigma(n)\uparrow \text{ as } n\uparrow \text{ and } n \leq \sigma(n).$$

When $\{\alpha_\nu, \nu=1,2,\cdots\}$ is a finite sequence then $\{E_n, n=1,2,\cdots\}$ is contained in one σ-field and (3) holds from the fact that μ is a probability measure on the σ-field. Assume then that $\{\alpha_\nu, \nu=1,2,\cdots\}$ is an infinite sequence. Let $E_0 = R^A$. Repeat some of the entries in the sequence $\{E_n, n=0,1,\cdots\}$ if necessary so that for the new sequence we have

$$E_n = p_{\alpha_1\cdots\alpha_n}^{-1}(B_n), \quad B_n \in \mathfrak{B}^n, \quad n=1,2,\cdots.$$

Let $\Phi_n(B) = \mu\left(p_{\alpha_1\cdots\alpha_n}^{-1}(B)\right)$, $B \in \mathfrak{B}^n$, i.e. Φ_n is the n-dimensional probability measure on $(R^n, \mathfrak{B}^n)$ determined by the probability measure μ on $\left(R^A, \mathfrak{F}_{\alpha_1\cdots\alpha_n}\right)$. According to Lemma 2.3 for our

B_n there exists a compact set $C_n \subset B_n$ such that $\Phi_n(B_n - C_n) < \epsilon_0/2^{n+1}$. Let $K_n = p_{\alpha_1 \cdots \alpha_n}^{-1}(C_n)$. Then

$$\mu(E_n - K_n) = \mu\left(p_{\alpha_1 \cdots \alpha_n}^{-1}(B_n - C_n)\right) = \Phi_n(B_n - C_n) < \frac{\epsilon_0}{2^{n+1}} .$$

Now $K_n \subset E_n$ but $\{K_n, n = 1,2, \cdots\}$ may not be a monotone decreasing sequence. So let $L_n = K_1 \cap \cdots \cap K_n$. Then $\{L_n, n = 1,2, \cdots\}$ is a monotone decreasing sequence and

$$E_n - L_n = E_n - \bigcap_{i=1}^{n} K_i = E_n - \bigcap_{i=1}^{n} (K_i \cap E_n) = \bigcup_{i=1}^{n} \left\{E_n - (K_i \cap E_n)\right\} \subset \bigcup_{i=1}^{n} (E_i - K_i)$$

so that

$$\mu(E_n - L_n) \leq \sum_{i=1}^{n} \mu(E_i - K_i) < \sum_{i=1}^{n} \frac{\epsilon_0}{2^{n+1}} < \frac{\epsilon_0}{2} .$$

Thus $L_n \subset K_n \subset E_n$ and

$$\mu(L_n) = \mu(E_n) - \mu(E_n - L_n) > \mu(E_n) - \frac{\epsilon_0}{2} \geq \frac{\epsilon_0}{2}$$

so that $L_n \neq \emptyset$. Take an arbitrary element $\omega^{(n)} \in L_n$, $n = 1,2, \cdots$.

Let us show first that $\{\omega^{(n)}, n = 1,2, \cdots\}$ is such that, for every ν, the sequence $\left\{\omega^{(n)}(\alpha_\nu), n = 1,2, \cdots\right\}$ has a convergent subsequence. Now given ν let $n \geq \nu$. Then

$$\omega^{(n+p)} \in L_{n+p} \subset L_n \subset K_n \quad \text{for} \quad p = 0,1,2, \cdots$$

so that

$$\left(\omega^{(n+p)}(\alpha_1), \cdots, \omega^{(n+p)}(\alpha_n)\right) = p_{\alpha_1 \cdots \alpha_n}\left(\omega^{(n+p)}\right) \in C_n, \quad p = 0,1,2, \cdots$$

and in particular $\{\omega^{(n+p)}(\alpha_\nu),\ p = 0,1,2,\cdots\}$ is a bounded sequence and hence $\{\omega^{(n)}(\alpha_\nu),\ n = 1,2,\cdots\}$ has a convergent subsequence. Consider now $\{\omega^{(n)}(\alpha_\nu),\ n,\nu = 1,2,\cdots\}$. For each ν there exists a subsequence $\{n_k\}$ of $\{n\}$, depending on ν, such that $\omega^{(n_k)}(\alpha_\nu)$ converges as $k\to\infty$. Then by the diagonal procedure we can select a subsequence $\{n_m\}$ of $\{n\}$ such that $\lim_{m\to\infty}\omega^{(n_m)}(\alpha_\nu)$ exists for every ν. Let $\omega^{(0)}(\alpha_\nu) = \lim_{m\to\infty}\omega^{(n_m)}(\alpha_\nu)$ and define

$$\omega^{(0)} = \left(\omega^{(0)}(\alpha_\nu),\ \nu = 1,2,\cdots \quad \text{and} \quad \omega^{(0)}(\alpha) = 0 \ \text{ if } \ \alpha \neq \alpha_\nu,\ \nu = 1,2,\cdots\right)$$

Since C_n is closed, $\left(\omega^{(0)}(\alpha_1), \cdots, \omega^{(0)}(\alpha_n)\right) \in C_n$. Thus $\omega^{(0)} \in K_n \subset E_n$ for all n and $\omega^{(0)} \in \bigcap_{n=1}^{\infty} E_n$, proving $\bigcap_{n=1}^{\infty} E_n \neq \emptyset$.

□

<u>Theorem 2.4</u> Kolmogorov Existence Theorem. Given a system of finite dimensional probability distributions $\{\Phi_T, T \in \mathfrak{T}\}$ where $\mathfrak{T}$ is the collection of finite sequences $T = \{t_1, \cdots, t_n\}$ of distinct elements of $D \subset R^1$ and Φ_T is an n-dimensional probability distribution. There exists a stochastic process on some probability space and D which has $\{\Phi_T, T \in \mathfrak{T}\}$ as its system of finite dimensional probability distributions if the system $\{\Phi_T, T \in \mathfrak{T}\}$ satisfies the following consistency conditions:

(a) if $T_1 = \{t_1, \cdots, t_n\}$ and $T_2 = \{t_1, \cdots, t_n, t_{n+1}\}$ then $\Phi_{T_1}(B) = \Phi_{T_2}(B \times R^1)$ for every $B \in \mathfrak{B}^n$;

(b) if $T_1 = \{t_1, \cdots, t_n\}$, $T_2 = \{s_1, \cdots, s_n\}$, $B_1, B_2 \in \mathfrak{B}^n$ and

$\{s_1, \cdots, s_n\} = \{t_{\Pi_1}, \cdots, t_{\Pi_n}\}$, $B_2 = \Pi(B_1)$ for some permutation $\Pi = \{\Pi_1, \cdots, \Pi_n\}$ of $\{1, \cdots, n\}$ then $\Phi_{T_1}(B_1) = \Phi_{T_2}(B_2)$.

Proof (1) Let $\Omega = R^D$, the collection of all real-valued functions $x(t)$, $t \in D$ and let $p_{t_1 \cdots t_n}$ be the projection of R^D onto R^n defined by $p_{t_1 \cdots t_n}(x) = \big(x(t_1), \cdots, x(t_n)\big)$. Let $\mathfrak{Z}_{t_1 \cdots t_n} = p_{t_1 \cdots t_n}^{-1}(\mathfrak{B}^n)$ and $\mathfrak{Z} = \bigcup \mathfrak{Z}_{t_1 \cdots t_n}$. We define a set function μ on $\mathfrak{Z}$ which is a probability measure on $\mathfrak{Z}_{t_1 \cdots t_n}$ for every $\{t_1, \cdots, t_n\}$ as follows. For $E \in \mathfrak{Z}_{t_1 \cdots t_n}$ given by $E = p_{t_1 \cdots t_n}^{-1}(B)$, $B \in \mathfrak{B}^n$, let $\mu(E) = \Phi_{t_1 \cdots t_n}(B)$. From the one-to-one correspondence between the members of $\mathfrak{Z}_{t_1 \cdots t_n}$ and $\mathfrak{B}^n$, as we saw in 2°, Remark 2.2, μ is well defined on $\mathfrak{Z}_{t_1 \cdots t_n}$.

We show next that μ is a probability measure on $\mathfrak{Z}_{t_1 \cdots t_n}$. Since $0 \le \Phi_{t_1 \cdots t_n}(B) \le 1$ for every $B \in \mathfrak{B}^n$, $\emptyset = p_{t_1 \cdots t_n}^{-1}(\emptyset)$ and $R^D = p_{t_1 \cdots t_n}^{-1}(R^n)$ we have $0 \le \mu(E) \le 1$ for every $E \in \mathfrak{Z}_{t_1 \cdots t_n}$, $\mu(\emptyset) = 0$ and $\mu(R^D) = 1$. To show the countable additivity of μ on $\mathfrak{Z}_{t_1 \cdots t_n}$ let $\{E_i, i = 1, 2, \cdots\} \subset \mathfrak{Z}_{t_1 \cdots t_n}$ be a disjoint collection and let $E_i = p_{t_1 \cdots t_n}^{-1}(B_i)$, $B_i \in \mathfrak{B}^n$, $i = 1, 2, \cdots$. Since $p_{t_1 \cdots t_n}$ covers R^n, the disjointness of $\{E_i, i = 1, 2, \cdots\}$ implies that of $\{B_i, i = 1, 2, \cdots\}$. For $E = \bigcup_{i=1}^{\infty} E_i \in \mathfrak{Z}_{t_1 \cdots t_n}$ let $E = p_{t_1 \cdots t_n}^{-1}(B)$, $B \in \mathfrak{B}^n$.

Now

$$E = \bigcup_{i=1}^{\infty} E_i = \bigcup_{i=1}^{\infty} p_{t_1 \cdots t_n}^{-1}(B_i) = p_{t_1 \cdots t_n}^{-1}\left(\bigcup_{n=1}^{\infty} B_i\right)$$

so that by 2°, Remark 2.2, $B = \bigcup_{i=1}^{\infty} B_i$. Then

$$\mu(E) = \Phi_{t_1 \cdots t_n}(B) = \Phi_{t_1 \cdots t_n}\left(\bigcup_{n=1}^{\infty} B_i\right) = \sum_{i=1}^{\infty} \Phi_{t_1 \cdots t_n}(B_i) = \sum_{i=1}^{\infty} \mu(E_i).$$

(2) We show that μ is well defined on $\mathfrak{F}$. Let $E \in \mathfrak{F}$. If $E = R^D$ then $E = p_{t_1 \cdots t_n}^{-1}(R^n)$ for every $\{t_1, \cdots, t_n\}$ so that $\mu(E) = \Phi_{t_1 \cdots t_n}(R^n) = 1$. Suppose $E \neq R^D$. The values of $\mu(E)$ corresponding to two minimal representations of E are equal by 5°, Remark 2.2, and our condition (b). On the other hand the value of $\mu(E)$ corresponding to a nonminimal representation of E is equal to that corresponding to a minimal representation according to 4°, Remark 2.2, and the conditions (b) and (a). Thus for every $E \in \mathfrak{F}$, $\mu(E)$ is independent of the representation of E and μ is well defined on $\mathfrak{F}$. According to Theorem 2.1, μ can be extended uniquely to be a probability measure on $\sigma(\mathfrak{F})$. Thus we have constructed a probability space $(\Omega, \mathfrak{B}, P) = \left(R^D, \sigma(\mathfrak{F}), \mu\right)$.

(3) Let us define a stochastic process X on $\left(R^D, \sigma(\mathfrak{F}), \mu\right)$ and D by

$$X(t, x) = x(t), \qquad t \in D,\ x \in R^D.$$

The fact that, for every $t \in D$, $X(t, \cdot)$ is $\sigma(\mathfrak{F})$ measurable is obvious since

$$\{x \in R^D;\ X(t,x) \in B\} = \{x \in R^D;\ x(t) \in B\}$$

$$= p_t^{-1}(B) \in \mathfrak{Z}_t \subset \sigma(\mathfrak{Z}) \quad \text{for every} \quad B \in \mathfrak{B}^1.$$

The fact that $\Phi_{X_{t_1 \cdots t_n}} = \Phi_{t_1 \cdots t_n}$ follows from

$$\Phi_{X_{t_1 \cdots t_n}}(B) = \mu\{x \in R^D;\ (x(t_1), \cdots, x(t_n)) \in B\}$$

$$= \mu\left(p_{t_1 \cdots t_n}^{-1}(B)\right) = \Phi_{t_1 \cdots t_n}(B) \quad \text{for every} \quad B \in \mathfrak{B}^n.$$

This completes the proof of the theorem. □

[II] Representation of a Stochastic Process by One on R^D

Let Y be a stochastic process on a probability space $(\Omega, \mathfrak{B}, P)$ and $D \subset R^1$. The system of finite dimensional probability distributions of Y, $\{\Phi_{Y_T}, T \in \mathfrak{T}\}$, clearly satisfies the consistency conditions (a), (b) of Theorem 2.4 so that according to the theorem the triple $(R^D, \sigma(\mathfrak{Z}), \mu)$ where μ is defined by

$$\mu(E) = \Phi_{Y_{t_1 \cdots t_n}}(B) \quad \text{for} \quad E = p_{t_1 \cdots t_n}^{-1}(B), \quad B \in \mathfrak{B}^n$$

is a probability space, and the real-valued function X on $D \times R^D$ defined by

$$X(t, x) = x(t) \qquad t \in D, \quad x \in R^D$$

is a stochastic process on $\left(R^D, \sigma(\mathfrak{Z}), \mu\right)$ and D which has $\{\Phi_{Y_T}, T \in \mathfrak{T}\}$ as its system of finite dimensional probability distributions, i.e., $\Phi_{X_T} = \Phi_{Y_T}$ for every $T \in \mathfrak{T}$. Thus for $T = \{t_1, \cdots, t_n\}$ we have, for every $B \in \mathfrak{B}^n$,

$$\mu\left\{x \in R^D;\ \left(x(t_1), \cdots, x(t_n)\right) \in B\right\} = \Phi_{X_T}(B) = \Phi_{Y_T}(B)$$
$$= P\left\{\omega \in \Omega;\ \left(Y(t_1,\omega), \cdots, Y(t_n,\omega)\right) \in B\right\}.$$

Among all the stochastic processes which have D as its domain of definition and have the same system of finite dimensional probability distributions as Y, the process X is distinguished by the fact that the sample space is R^D, the σ-field of the probability space is $\sigma(\mathfrak{Z})$ which is defined independently of any stochastic process, and the fact that $X(t,x) = x(t)$, $x \in R^D$, so that the space of sample functions coincides with the sample space.

[III] Induction of a Probability Measure on a Function Space by a Stochastic Process

Given a stochastic process Y on a probability space $(\Omega, \mathfrak{B}, P)$ and $D \subset R^1$. Consider a transformation S of Ω into R^D defined by

$$S(\omega) = Y(\cdot,\omega) \in R^D, \qquad \omega \in \Omega.$$

In general the space R^D is not covered by S, nor does $\omega_1 \neq \omega_2$ imply $S(\omega_1) \neq S(\omega_2)$. Let $p_{t_1 \cdots t_n}$ be the projection of R^D onto R^n defined by

$$p_{t_1\cdots t_n}(x) = \left(x(t_1),\cdots, x(t_n)\right) \in R^n, \qquad x \in R^D$$

and let $\mathfrak{Z}_{t_1\cdots t_n} = p_{t_1\cdots t_n}^{-1}(\mathfrak{B}^n)$. For $E \in \mathfrak{Z}_{t_1\cdots t_n}$, $E = p_{t_1\cdots t_n}^{-1}(B)$, $B \in \mathfrak{B}^n$ let

$$\begin{aligned}\mu_Y(E) &= P\{\omega \in \Omega; (p_{t_1\cdots t_n} S)(\omega) \in B\}\\ &= P\{\omega \in \Omega; \left(Y(t_1,\omega),\cdots, Y(t_n,\omega)\right) \in B\}\\ &= \Phi_{Y_{t_1\cdots t_n}}(B). \qquad (1)\end{aligned}$$

As we saw in the proof of Theorem 2.4, μ_Y is well defined on $\mathfrak{Z} = \bigcup \mathfrak{Z}_{t_1\cdots t_n}$ and is a probability measure on $\mathfrak{Z}_{t_1\cdots t_n}$ for each $\{t_1,\cdots, t_n\}$ so that it can be extended uniquely to be a probability measure on $\sigma(\mathfrak{Z})$. The measure μ_Y is called the probability measure induced on $\left(R^D, \sigma(\mathfrak{Z})\right)$ by the stochastic process Y.

Consider the transformations

$$\Omega \xrightarrow{S} R^D \xrightarrow{p_{t_1\cdots t_n}} R^n,$$

i.e.,

$$\omega \rightarrow Y(\cdot,\omega) \rightarrow \left(Y(t_1,\omega), \cdots, Y(t_n,\omega)\right).$$

For $E \in \mathfrak{Z}$, $E = p_{t_1\cdots t_n}^{-1}(B)$, $B \in \mathfrak{B}^n$ we have

$$S^{-1}(E) = S^{-1} p_{t_1\cdots t_n}^{-1}(B) = (p_{t_1\cdots t_n} S)^{-1}(B) =$$

$$= \left\{\omega \in \Omega ; \left(Y(t_1, \omega), \cdots, Y(t_n, \omega)\right) \in B\right\} \in \mathfrak{B} \tag{2}$$

and thus by our definition of μ_Y by (1)

$$\mu_Y(E) = P\left(S^{-1}(E)\right), \qquad E \in \mathfrak{Z}. \tag{3}$$

Actually (2) and (3) hold for every $E \in \sigma(\mathfrak{Z})$. To show this let

$$\mathfrak{G} = \left\{G \subset R^D ; S^{-1}(G) \in \mathfrak{B}\right\}.$$

From the fact that $\mathfrak{B}$ is a σ-field follows immediately that $\mathfrak{G}$ too is a σ-field. By (2), $\mathfrak{Z} \subset \mathfrak{G}$ and hence $\sigma(\mathfrak{Z}) \subset \mathfrak{G}$. If we define a set function on $\mathfrak{G}$ by $P\left(S^{-1}(G)\right)$ then from the fact that P is a probability measure follows immediately that PS^{-1} is a probability measure on $\mathfrak{G}$. Since on the field $\mathfrak{Z}$, μ_Y and PS^{-1} agree according to (3) they agree on $\sigma(\mathfrak{Z})$ also. Thus we have shown that

$$S^{-1}(E) \in \mathfrak{B} \quad \text{for} \quad E \in \sigma(\mathfrak{Z})$$

and

$$\mu_Y(E) = P\left(S^{-1}(E)\right) \quad \text{for} \quad E \in \sigma(\mathfrak{Z}).$$

Therefore we have

$$\left(R^D, \sigma(\mathfrak{Z}), \mu_Y\right) \subset (R^D, \mathfrak{G}, PS^{-1}).$$

Note also that for $S(\Omega) \subset R^D$ we have $S^{-1}S(\Omega) = \Omega \in \mathfrak{B}$ so that $S(\Omega) \in \mathfrak{G}$ and $(PS^{-1})\, S(\Omega) = P(\Omega) = 1$. Although $\mathfrak{G}$ is a greater σ-field than $\sigma(\mathfrak{Z})$, it depends on $(\Omega, \mathfrak{B}, P)$ and Y. On the other hand $\sigma(\mathfrak{Z})$ is defined without any regard to $(\Omega, \mathfrak{B}, P)$ and Y. For

for this reason the measurable space $\left(R^D, \sigma(\mathfrak{J})\right)$ is preferable to $(R^D, \mathfrak{G})$ when we consider probability measures induced on the function space R^D by more than one stochastic processes.

§3. STOCHASTICALLY CONTINUOUS PROCESSES

The concept of stochastic continuity of a process is the extension of the concept of convergence in probability of a sequence of random variables.

[I] Stochastic Continuity

Definition 3.1 A stochastic process X on a probability space $(\Omega, \mathfrak{B}, P)$ and $D \subset R^1$ is said to be stochastically continuous at $t_0 \in D$ if $X(t, \cdot)$ converges to $X(t_0, \cdot)$ in probability as $t \to t_0$ in the sense that

$$\lim_{t \to t_0} P\left\{\omega \in \Omega; |X(t,\omega) - X(t_0,\omega)| \geq \epsilon\right\} = 0 \quad \text{for every } \epsilon > 0.$$

We shall write $P - \lim_{t \to t_0} X(t, \cdot) = X(t_0, \cdot)$ when this condition is satisfied. We say that X is stochastically continuous when it is stochastically continuous at every $t_0 \in D$.

Remark 3.2 $P - \lim_{t \to t_0} X(t, \cdot) = X(t_0, \cdot)$ if and only if for every sequence $\{t_n, n = 1, 2, \cdots\} \subset D$ which converges to t_0 we have $P - \lim_{n \to \infty} X(t_n, \cdot) = X(t_0, \cdot)$.

Proof For $\epsilon > 0$ define a real-valued function on D by

$$\psi_\epsilon(t) = P\left\{\omega \in \Omega; |X(t,\omega) - X(t_0,\omega)| \geq \epsilon\right\}, \qquad t \in D.$$

Then $\psi_\varepsilon(t_0) = 0$ so that the condition $P - \lim_{t \to t_0} X(t, \cdot) = X(t_0, \cdot)$ is equivalent to the condition $\lim_{t \to t_0} \psi_\varepsilon(t) = \psi_\varepsilon(t_0)$, namely, the continuity of ψ_ε at t_0. But ψ_ε is continuous at t_0 if and only if for every sequence $\{t_n, n = 1, 2, \cdots\} \subset D$ which converges to t_0 we have $\lim_{n \to \infty} \psi_\varepsilon(t_n) = \psi_\varepsilon(t_0)$, in other words, $P - \lim_{n \to \infty} X(t_n, \cdot) = X(t_0, \cdot)$. □

[II] Metrization of Convergence in Probability

We say that a sequence of random variables $\{X_n, n = 1, 2, \cdots\}$ on a probability space $(\Omega, \mathfrak{B}, P)$ is a Cauchy sequence with respect to convergence in probability if for every $\varepsilon > 0$ there exists N such that

$$P\left\{\omega \in \Omega ; \left|X_m(\omega) - X_n(\omega)\right| \geq \varepsilon\right\} < \varepsilon \quad \text{for} \quad m, n \geq N.$$

It is well known that the space of all random variables on $(\Omega, \mathfrak{B}, P)$ is complete with respect to convergence in probability in the sense that if $\{X_n, n = 1, 2, \cdots\}$ is a Cauchy sequence with respect to convergence in probability then there exists a random variable X_0 on $(\Omega, \mathfrak{B}, P)$, determined up to a set of probability measure 0, such that $X_0 = P - \lim_{n \to \infty} X_n$.

Let $\mathfrak{X}$ be the space of all random variables on $(\Omega, \mathfrak{B}, P)$ where two random variables which are equal a.e. are identified. The space $\mathfrak{X}$ is a linear space with respect to the algebraic operations defined by

$$(X + Y)(\omega) = X(\omega) + Y(\omega), \qquad X, Y \in \mathfrak{X}$$

$$(\alpha X)(\omega) = \alpha X(\omega) \qquad X \in \mathfrak{X}, \ \alpha \in R^1.$$

Theorem 3.3 The real-valued function $\|X\|$ defined on the linear space $\mathfrak{X}$ of all random variables X on a probability space $(\Omega, \mathfrak{B}, P)$ by

$$\|X\| = \int_\Omega \frac{|X(\omega)|}{1 + |X(\omega)|} P(d\omega), \qquad X \in \mathfrak{X}$$

is a quasi norm on $\mathfrak{X}$, i.e.,

1°. $0 \le \|X\| < \infty$ for every $X \in \mathfrak{X}$ and $\|X\| = 0$ if and only if $X = 0$;

2°. $\|-X\| = \|X\|$ for every $X \in \mathfrak{X}$;

3°. $\|X + Y\| \le \|X\| + \|Y\|$ for every $X, Y \in \mathfrak{X}$

and consequently $\rho(X, Y) = \|X - Y\|$, $X, Y \in \mathfrak{X}$, is a metric on $\mathfrak{X}$.

Proof 1° and 2° are obvious from the definition of $\|\cdot\|$. For 3° let us observe that

$$\frac{\gamma_1}{1 + \gamma_1} \le \frac{\gamma_2}{1 + \gamma_2} \quad \text{for} \quad 0 \le \gamma_1 \le \gamma_2 \tag{1}$$

and hence

$$\frac{|\alpha + \beta|}{1 + |\alpha + \beta|} \le \frac{|\alpha| + |\beta|}{1 + |\alpha| + |\beta|} \le \frac{|\alpha|}{1 + |\alpha|} + \frac{|\beta|}{1 + |\beta|} \quad \text{for } \alpha, \beta \in R^1. \tag{2}$$

□

Theorem 3.4 A sequence $\{X_n, n = 1, 2, \cdots\} \subset \mathfrak{X}$ is a Cauchy sequence with respect to the metric ρ defined in the last theorem if and only if it is a Cauchy sequence with respect to convergence in probability. For $X_0 \in \mathfrak{X}$, $\lim_{n\to\infty} \rho(X_n, X_0) = 0$ if and only if $P\text{-}\lim_{n\to\infty} X_n = X_0$. Thus in view of the completeness of $\mathfrak{X}$ with respect to convergence in probability the space $\mathfrak{X}$ is complete with respect to the metric ρ.

Proof For $X \in \mathfrak{X}$ and $\eta > 0$ let $A_\eta = \{\omega \in \Omega; |X(\omega)| \geq \eta\}$. By the inequality (1) in the proof of Theorem 3.3 we have

$$\frac{\eta}{1+\eta} P(A_\eta) \leq \int_{A_\eta} \frac{|X(\omega)|}{1+|X(\omega)|} P(d\omega) \leq \|X\| \tag{1}$$

and

$$\|X\| = \int_{A_\eta} \frac{|X(\omega)|}{1+|X(\omega)|} P(d\omega) + \int_{A_\eta^c} \frac{|X(\omega)|}{1+|X(\omega)|} P(d\omega)$$

$$\leq P(A_\eta) + \frac{\eta}{1+\eta} P(A_\eta^c) . \tag{2}$$

From (1) we have

$$\frac{\eta}{1+\eta} P\{\omega \in \Omega; |X_m(\omega) - X_n(\omega)| \geq \eta\} \leq \rho(X_m, X_n) \tag{3}$$

so that if $\{X_n, n = 1,2,\cdots\}$ is a Cauchy sequence with respect to the metric ρ then it is a Cauchy sequence with respect to convergence in probability. From (2) we have

$$\rho(X_m, X_n) \leq P\{\omega \in \Omega; |X_m(\omega) - X_n(\omega)| \geq \eta\} + \frac{\eta}{1+\eta} . \tag{4}$$

If $\{X_n, n = 1,2,\cdots\}$ is a Cauchy sequence with respect to convergence in probability then for $\epsilon > 0$ let $\eta > 0$ be such that $\eta/(1+\eta) < \epsilon/2$ and let N be such that the first term on the right side of (4) is less than $\epsilon/2$ for $m,n \geq N$. Then $\rho(X_m, X_n) < \epsilon$ for $m,n \geq N$ so that the sequence is a Cauchy sequence with respect to the metric ρ.

Finally the fact that for $X_0 \in \mathfrak{X}$, $\lim_{n\to\infty} (X_n, X_0) = 0$ if and only if $P - \lim_{n\to\infty} X_n = X_0$ also follows from (3) and (4). □

Theorem 3.5 Given a stochastic process X on a probability space $(\Omega, \mathfrak{B}, P)$ and $D \subset R^1$. If X is stochastically continuous on D then it is uniformly stochastically continuous on every compact subset $K \subset D$ i.e., for every $\epsilon > 0$ and $\eta > 0$ there exists $\delta > 0$ such that

$$P\left\{\omega \in \Omega ;\ |X(t', \omega) - X(t'', \omega)| \ge \epsilon\right\} < \eta$$

whenever $t', t'' \in K$, $|t' - t''| < \delta$.

Proof Metrize the space $\mathfrak{X}$ of all random variables on $(\Omega, \mathfrak{B}, P)$ by the metric ρ introduced in Theorem 3.3. According to Remark 3.2 and Theorem 3.4, X is stochastically continuous at $t_0 \in D$ if and only if $\lim_{t\to t_0} \rho\left(X(t),\ X(t_0)\right) = 0$. Consider a transformation A of the metric space D into the metric space $\mathfrak{X}$ defined by $A(t) = X(t)$, $t \in D$. Then the stochastic continuity of X on D is equivalent to the continuity of A on D. Thus under the assumption of stochastic continuity of X on D we have the continuity of A on D and hence its uniform continuity on every compact subset $K \subset D$ so that for every $\epsilon > 0$ and $\eta > 0$ there exists $\delta > 0$ such that

$$\rho\left(X(t'),\ X(t'')\right) < \frac{\epsilon}{1+\epsilon}\,\eta \quad \text{whenever} \quad t', t'' \in K,\ |t' - t''| < \delta.$$

On the other hand by means of (1) in the proof of Theorem 3.3 we have for $E = \left\{\omega \in \Omega ;\ |X(t',\omega) - X(t'',\omega)| \ge \epsilon\right\}$

$$\rho\left(X(t'),\ X(t'')\right) \ge \int_E \frac{|X(t',\omega) - X(t'',\omega)|}{1 + |X(t',\omega) - X(t'',\omega)|}\, P(d\omega) \ge \frac{\epsilon}{1+\epsilon}\, P(E).$$

Thus

$$P(E) < \eta \quad \text{whenever} \quad t', t'' \in K,\ |t' - t''| < \delta.$$

□

§4. SEPARABLE PROCESSES

Let X be a stochastic process on a probability space $(\Omega, \mathfrak{B}, P)$ and an uncountable subset $D \subset R^1$. For $\gamma \in R^1$, the set

$$\{\omega \in \Omega ; X(t,\omega) \leq \gamma \text{ for all } t \in D\} = \bigcap_{t \in D} \{\omega \in \Omega ; X(t,\omega) \leq \gamma\}$$

as the intersection of uncountably many $\mathfrak{B}$-measurable sets may not be $\mathfrak{B}$-measurable. To make this set $\mathfrak{B}$-measurable J. L. Doob introduced the separability condition on X.

[I] Separability and Equivalent Conditions

Definition 4.1 Given a stochastic process X on a probability space $(\Omega, \mathfrak{B}, P)$ and $D \subset R^1$. Let $\mathfrak{A}$ be an arbitrary subcollection of the σ-field of Borel sets in $R^1, \mathfrak{B}^1$, and let $\mathfrak{J}_O$ be the collection of open intervals in R^1. The process X is said to be separable with respect to $\mathfrak{A}$ if there exists a countable dense subset $S \subset D$ such that for every $A \in \mathfrak{A}$ and $I \in \mathfrak{J}_O$ we have

$$\{\omega \in \Omega ; X(t,\omega) \in A \text{ for all } t \in D \cap I\}$$
$$= \{\omega \in \Omega ; X(s,\omega) \in A \text{ for all } s \in S \cap I\}.$$

When X is separable with respect to the collection of closed intervals $\mathfrak{J}_C$ in R^1 we say simply that X is separable.

Example As an example of inseparable process take $(\Omega, \mathfrak{B}, P) = \left([0,1], \mathfrak{M}_{[0,1]}, m_L\right)$ where $\mathfrak{M}_{[0,1]}$ is the σ-field of Lebesgue measurable sets contained in $[0,1]$, m_L is the Lebesgue measure, and $D = [0,1]$. Let A be a non-Lebesgue measurable set contained in $[0,1]$ and define a real-valued function X on $D \times \Omega$ by

$$X(t, \omega) = \begin{cases} 1 & \text{when } t \in A \text{ and } \omega = t \\ 0 & \text{otherwise.} \end{cases}$$

For each $t \in D$, $t \notin A$, we have $X(t,\omega) = 0$ for all $\omega \in \Omega$, and for each $t \in D$, $t \in A$, we have $X(t,\omega) = 0$ for all $\omega \in \Omega$ except for $\omega = t$ for which $X(t,\omega) = 1$. Thus for every $t \in D$, $X(t,\omega)$ is $\mathfrak{B}$-measurable and X is a stochastic process. Note also that for each $\omega \in \Omega$, $\omega \notin A$, we have $X(t,\omega) = 0$ for all $t \in D$ and for each $\omega \in \Omega$, $\omega \in A$, we have $X(t,\omega) = 0$ except for $t = \omega$ for which $X(t,\omega) = 1$. Thus every sample function is a Lebesgue measurable function. If X were separable then there would be a countable dense subset $S \subset D$ such that for every $J \in \mathfrak{J}_C$ and $I \in \mathfrak{J}_O$

$$\{\omega \in \Omega ; X(t,\omega) \in J \text{ for all } t \in D \cap I\}$$
$$= \{\omega \in \Omega ; X(s,\omega) \in J \text{ for all } s \in S \cap I\} \in \mathfrak{M}_{[0,1]} .$$

But with $J = [0, \frac{1}{2}]$ and $I = R^1$ we have

$$\{\omega \in \Omega ; X(t,\omega) \in [0, \tfrac{1}{2}] \text{ for all } t \in D\} = [0,1] - A \notin \mathfrak{M}_{[0,1]} .$$

Thus X is inseparable. However X has an equivalent process which is separable, namely, $Y(t,\omega) = 0$ for $t \in D$, $\omega \in \Omega$. The equivalence of X and Y follows from

$$\{\omega \in \Omega ; X(t,\omega) = Y(t,\omega)\} = \begin{cases} \Omega & \text{if } t \notin A \\ \Omega - \{t\} & \text{if } t \in A \end{cases}$$

Equivalent conditions for separability will be given now in terms of limit inferior, limit superior, lower envelop, and upper envelop of sample functions of the process as $t \to t_0 \in \overline{D}$. We define for $\omega_0 \in \Omega$, $t_0 \in \overline{D}$

$$\operatorname*{low\ env}_{t \to t_0} X(t,\omega_0) = \lim_{\delta \downarrow 0} \inf_{t \in (t_0 - \delta,\, t_0 + \delta) \cap D} X(t,\omega_0)$$

$$\operatorname*{low\ env}_{s \to t_0} X(s,\omega_0) = \lim_{\delta \downarrow 0} \inf_{s \in (t_0 - \delta,\, t_0 + \delta) \cap S} X(s,\omega_0)$$

$$\operatorname*{upp\ env}_{t \to t} X(t,\omega_0) = \lim_{\delta \downarrow 0} \sup_{t \in (t_0 - \delta,\, t_0 + \delta) \cap D} X(t,\omega_0)$$

$$\operatorname*{low\ env}_{s \to t_0} X(s,\omega_0) = \lim_{\delta \downarrow 0} \sup_{s \in (t_0 - \delta,\, t_0 + \delta) \cap S} X(s,\omega_0).$$

Thus

$$\operatorname*{low\ env}_{t \to t_0} X(t,\omega_0) = \min\left\{ \liminf_{t \to t_0} X(t,\omega_0),\ X(t_0,\omega) \right\}$$

provided $t_0 \in D$

$$\operatorname*{low\ env}_{s \to t_0} X(s,\omega_0) = \min\left\{ \liminf_{s \to t_0} X(s,\omega_0),\ X(t_0,\omega) \right\}$$

provided $t_0 \in S$

and similarly for $\operatorname{upp}_{t \to t_0} \operatorname{env} X(t,\omega_0)$ and $\operatorname{upp}_{s \to t_0} \operatorname{env} X(s,\omega_0)$.

<u>Theorem 4.2</u> Given a stochastic process X on a probability space $(\Omega, \mathfrak{B}, P)$ and $D \subset R^1$. Let $\mathfrak{J}_O$ and $\mathfrak{J}_C$ be the collections of open intervals and closed intervals in R^1, respectively. Then with a fixed countable dense subset $S \subset D$ the following conditions (S_0), (S_1), (S_2), (S_3), (S_4) are all equivalent. Also $(S_1) \Rightarrow (S_5)$. When $t_0 \in S$, $(S_5) \Rightarrow (S_4)$.

(S_0) X is separable, i.e., for every $J \in \mathfrak{J}_C$ and every $I \in \mathfrak{J}_O$

$$\{\omega \in \Omega ;\ X(t,\omega) \in J \text{ for all } t \in D \cap I\}$$
$$= \{\omega \in \Omega ;\ X(s,\omega) \in J \text{ for all } s \in S \cap I\}.$$

(S_1) For every $\omega_0 \in \Omega$ and every $I \in \mathfrak{J}_O$

$$\inf_{D \cap I} X(t,\omega_0) = \inf_{S \cap I} X(s,\omega_0), \quad \sup_{D \cap I} X(t,\omega_0) = \sup_{S \cap I} X(s,\omega_0).$$

(S_2) For every $\omega_0 \in \Omega$, every $t_0 \in D$ and every $I \in \mathfrak{J}_O$ containing t_0

$$\inf_{S \cap I} X(s,\omega_0) \le X(t_0,\omega_0) \le \sup_{S \cap I} X(s,\omega_0)$$

(S_3) For every $\omega_0 \in \Omega$ and every $t_0 \in D$

$$\operatorname*{low\ env}_{s \to t_0} X(s,\omega_0) \le X(t_0,\omega_0) \le \operatorname*{upp\ env}_{s \to t_0} X(s,\omega_0)$$

(S_4) For every $\omega_0 \in \Omega$ and every $t_0 \in \overline{D}$

$$\operatorname*{low\ env}_{t \to t_0} X(t,\omega_0) = \operatorname*{low\ env}_{s \to t_0} X(s,\omega_0),$$

$$\operatorname*{upp\ env}_{t \to t_0} X(t,\omega_0) = \operatorname*{upp\ env}_{s \to t_0} X(s,\omega_0)$$

(S_5) For every $\omega_0 \in \Omega$ and every $t_0 \in \overline{D}$

$$\liminf_{t \to t_0} X(t,\omega_0) = \liminf_{s \to t_0} X(s,\omega_0),$$

$$\limsup_{t \to t_0} X(t,\omega_0) = \limsup_{s \to t_0} X(s,\omega_0).$$

Proof The equivalence of the conditions (S_0), (S_1), (S_2), (S_3), (S_4) can be established by showing $(S_0) \Rightarrow (S_1)$, $S_1) \Rightarrow (S_0)$, $(S_1) \Rightarrow (S_2)$, $(S_2) \Rightarrow (S_1)$, $(S_2) \Rightarrow (S_3)$, $(S_3) \Rightarrow (S_2)$, $(S_3) \Rightarrow (S_4)$, $(S_4) \Rightarrow (S_3)$. These implications are immediate. Let us show only $(S_3) \Rightarrow (S_4)$.

For $\omega_0 \in \Omega$ and $t_0 \in \overline{D}$ let $\alpha = \text{low}_{t \to t_0} \text{ env } X(t, \omega_0)$ and $\beta = \text{low}_{s \to t_0} \text{ env } X(s, \omega_0)$. Clearly $\alpha \leq \beta$. From the definition of α as lower envelop we can select a sequence $\{t_n, n = 1, 2, \cdots\} \subset D$ such that $\lim_{n \to \infty} t_n = t_0$ and $\lim_{n \to \infty} X(t_n, \omega_0) = \alpha$. Applying (S_3) to each t_n we can select a sequence $\{s_n, n = 1, 2, \cdots\} \subset S$ such that $|s_n - t_n| < 1/n$ and $X(s_n, \omega_0) \leq X(t_n, \omega_0) + 1/n$. Then

$$\beta = \underset{s \to t_0}{\text{low env}}\, X(s, \omega_0) = \lim_{\delta \downarrow 0} \inf_{s \in (t_0 - \delta, t_0 + \delta) \cap S} X(s, \omega_0)$$

$$\leq \liminf_{n \to \infty} X(s_n, \omega_0) \leq \alpha. \qquad \square$$

[II] Existence of a Separable Equivalent Process

For every stochastic process there exists a separable extended real-valued stochastic process which is equivalent to it. The following lemma is the key to this theorem.

Lemma 4.3 For an arbitrary stochastic process X on a probability space $(\Omega, \mathfrak{B}, P)$ and $D \subset R^1$ the following hold:

(1) Corresponding to each $A \in \mathfrak{B}^1$ there exists a countable subset $S_A \subset D$ such that for every $t \in D$

$$P\{\omega \in \Omega;\, X(s, \omega) \in A \text{ for all } s \in S_A\}$$

$$= P\{\omega \in \Omega;\, X(s, \omega) \in A \text{ for all } s \in S_A \text{ and } X(t, \omega) \in A\} \qquad (1)$$

or equivalently, for every $t \in D$,

$$P\{\omega \in \Omega ; X(s,\omega) \in A \text{ for all } s \in S_A \text{ and } X(t,\omega) \in A^c\} = 0. \quad (2)$$

The set S_A can be chosen to be dense in D.

(2) If $\mathfrak{A}_0$ is a countable subcollection of $\mathfrak{B}^1$ and $\mathfrak{A}_\delta$ is the collection of all intersections of countably many members of $\mathfrak{A}_0$ then there exists a countable subset $S \subset D$ such that for every $t \in D$ and $A \in \mathfrak{A}_\delta$

$$P\{\omega \in \Omega ; X(s,\omega) \in A \text{ for all } s \in S\}$$

$$= P\{\omega \in \Omega ; X(s,\omega) \in A \text{ for all } s \in S \text{ and } X(t,\omega) \in A\} \quad (3)$$

and for every $t \in D$ there exists $\Lambda_t \in \mathfrak{B}$ with $P(\Lambda_t) = 0$ such that

$$\{\omega \in \Omega ; X(s,\omega) \in A \text{ for all } s \in S \text{ and } X(t,\omega) \in A^c\} \subset \Lambda_t$$

$$\text{for every } A \in \mathfrak{A}_\delta . \quad (4)$$

Again the set S can be chosen to be dense in D.

Proof The equivalence of (1) and (2) is obvious. Regarding (4), note that $\mathfrak{A}_\delta$ need not be a countable collection so that the union of the set on the left side of (4) corresponding to $A \in \mathfrak{A}_\delta$ may not be in $\mathfrak{B}$. Nevertheless according to (4) this union can be contained in some $\Lambda_t \in \mathfrak{B}$ with $P(\Lambda_t) = 0$.

(1) Given $A \in \mathfrak{B}^1$. Let $\mathfrak{E} = \{E_t, t \in D\}$ where $E_t = \{\omega \in \Omega ; X(t,\omega) \in A\}$, let $\mathfrak{E}_\delta$ be the collection of all intersections of countably many members of $\mathfrak{E}$ and let $\rho = \inf_{F \in \mathfrak{E}_\delta} P(F)$. We show first that ρ is attained by some $F_0 \in \mathfrak{E}_\delta$. From the definition of ρ, for every positive integer n there exists $F_n \in \mathfrak{E}_\delta$ such that

$\rho \le P(F_n) \le \rho + 1/n$. Let $F_0 = \bigcap_{n=1}^{\infty} F_n$. Then $F_0 \in \mathfrak{E}_\delta$ and $\rho \le P(F_0) \le P(F_n) \le \rho + 1/n$ for every n so that $P(F_0) = \rho$. Since F_0 is the intersection of countable members of $\mathfrak{E}$ there exists a countable subset $S_A \subset D$ such that $F_0 = \bigcap_{s \in S_A} E_s = \{\omega \in \Omega ; X(s,\omega) \in A$ for all $s \in S_A\}$. If S_A is not a dense subset of D yet, add countably many points from D to S_A so that S_A is dense in D. The new $F_0 = \bigcap_{s \in S_A} E_s$ is still in $\mathfrak{E}_\delta$ and $P(F_0) = \rho$ still holds. Now for any $t \in D$ we have $F_0 \cap E_t \in \mathfrak{E}_\delta$ so that by the definition of ρ we have $\rho \le P(F_0 \cap E_t) \le P(F_0) = \rho$, i.e., $P(F_0 \cap E_t) = P(F_0)$, which is (1).

(2) For $A \in \mathfrak{A}_0$ let S_A be a countable dense subset of D for which (1) holds. Let $S = \bigcup_{A \in \mathfrak{A}_0} S_A$, a countable dense subset of D. Then for every $A \in \mathfrak{A}_0$ and $t \in D$, we have by (2)

$$P\{\omega \in \Omega ; X(s,\omega) \in A \text{ for all } s \in S \text{ and } X(t,\omega) \in A^c\} = 0.$$

Let

$$\Lambda_t = \bigcup_{A \in \mathfrak{A}_0} \{\omega \in \Omega ; X(s,\omega) \in A \text{ for all } s \in S \text{ and } X(t,\omega) \in A^c\}.$$

Since $\mathfrak{A}_0$ is countable, $\Lambda_t \in \mathfrak{B}$ and $P(\Lambda_t) = 0$. Now if $A \in \mathfrak{A}_\delta$ then $A = \bigcap_{n=1}^{\infty} A_n$ where $A_n \in \mathfrak{A}_0$ and $A^c = \bigcup_{n=1}^{\infty} A_n^{\,c}$. Thus, if ω_0 is in the set on the left side of (4) then $X(t,\omega_0) \in A^c$ and hence $X(t,\omega_0) \in A_n^{\,c}$ for some n so that

$$\omega_0 \in \{\omega \in \Omega ; X(s,\omega) \in A \text{ for all } s \in S \text{ and } X(t,\omega) \in A_n^{\,c}\} \subset \Lambda_t$$

which proves (4). □

To state the existence theorem of a separable extended

real-valued stochastic process equivalent to a given process let us fix the notations first. Thus let $\overline{R}$ be the two-point compactification of R, i.e., $\overline{R} = \{-\infty\} \cup R \cup \{\infty\}$ topologized by the collection of unions of countably many sets of the types (a,b), $[-\infty,c)$, $(d,\infty]$, and $\emptyset$ where a, b, c, d are rational numbers. This collection satisfies the open set axioms. Let $\mathfrak{A}_0$ be the collection of unions of finitely many intervals of any kind (i.e., open, closed, open at one end and closed at the other) whose endpoints are rational numbers or $\pm\infty$. Clearly $\mathfrak{A}_0$ is a countable collection. Let $\mathfrak{A}_\delta$ be the collection of intersections of countable members of $\mathfrak{A}_0$ and let $\mathfrak{C}$ be the collection of closed sets in $\overline{R}$. Then clearly $\mathfrak{C} \subset \mathfrak{A}_\delta$.

Theorem 4.4 Let X be a stochastic process on a probability space $(\Omega, \mathfrak{B}, P)$ and $D \subset R^1$. There exists an extended real-valued stochastic process Y on $(\Omega, \mathfrak{B}, P)$ and D which is equivalent to X and is separable with respect to the collection $\mathfrak{C}$ of closed sets in $\overline{R}$.

Proof Let $\{I_r, r = 1,2,\cdots\}$ be the collection of open intervals in $\overline{R}$ with rational or infinite endpoints and let $D_r = D \cap I_r$. For each r let us apply (4) of Lemma 4.3 to the stochastic process X restricted to D_r. Then there exists a countable dense subset $S_r \subset D_r$ such that for every $t \in D_r$ there exists $\Lambda_{t,r} \in \mathfrak{B}$ with $P(\Lambda_{t,r}) = 0$ for which

$$\left\{\omega \in \Omega;\, X(s,\omega) \in A \text{ for all } s \in S_r \text{ and } X(t,\omega) \in A^c\right\} \subset \Lambda_{t,r}$$

for every $A \in \mathfrak{A}_\delta$.

Then

$$t \in D_r,\ \omega \notin \Lambda_{t,r}\ A \in \mathfrak{A}_\delta,\ X(s, \omega) \in A \text{ for all } s \in S_r$$

$$\Rightarrow X(t, \omega) \in A. \tag{1}$$

For each $t \in D$ let Λ_t be the union of all $\Lambda_{t,r}$ with such r that $t \in I_r$. Then $\Lambda_t \in \mathfrak{B}$ and $P(\Lambda_t) = 0$. Let $S = \bigcup_{r=1}^{\infty} S_r$, a countable dense subset of D. Thus

$$\left.\begin{array}{ll} \text{a)} & I \in \mathfrak{J}_0 \\ \text{b)} & t \in D \cap I \left(\text{and hence } t \in D_{r_0} \text{ for some } r_0\right) \\ \text{c)} & \omega \notin \Lambda_t \left(\text{and hence } \omega \notin \Lambda_{t,r_0}\right) \\ \text{d)} & C \in \mathfrak{C} \subset \mathfrak{A}_\delta \\ \text{e)} & X(s,\omega) \in C \text{ for all } s \in S \cap I \\ & \left(\text{and hence for all } s \in S_{r_0}\right) \end{array}\right\} \Rightarrow X(t,\omega) \in C.$$

Let us define an extended real-valued stochastic process Y on $(\Omega, \mathfrak{B}, P)$ and D by

$$Y(s,\omega) = X(s,\omega) \qquad \text{for} \quad s \in S,\ \omega \in \Omega \tag{3}$$

$$Y(t,\omega) = X(t,\omega) \qquad \text{for} \quad t \in D - S,\ \omega \notin \Lambda_t \tag{4}$$

$$Y(t,\omega) = \liminf_{s \to t} X(s,\omega) \quad \text{for} \quad t \in D - S,\ \omega \in \Lambda_t. \tag{5}$$

Clearly, $Y(t,\cdot)$ is $\mathfrak{B}$-measurable for each $t \in D$. Since $P(\Lambda_t) = 0$, the two stochastic processes X and Y are equivalent. To show the separability of Y with respect to $\mathfrak{C}$ we show that for every $C \in \mathfrak{C}$ and $I \in \mathfrak{J}_0$

$$\begin{aligned} &\{\omega \in \Omega;\ Y(t,\omega) \in C \text{ for all } t \in D \cap I\} \\ &= \{\omega \in \Omega;\ Y(s,\omega) \in C \text{ for all } s \in S \cap I\}. \end{aligned} \tag{6}$$

For (6) it suffices to show that for $\omega_0 \in \Omega$

$$Y(x,\omega_0) \in C \text{ for all } s \in S \cap I \Rightarrow Y(t,\omega_0) \in C \text{ for all } t \in (D-S) \cap I.$$

Let us observe first that if $Y(s,\omega_0) \in C$ for all $s \in S \cap I$ then by (3) $X(s,\omega_0) = Y(s,\omega_0) \in C$ for all $s \in S \cap I$ so that the last condition in the hypothesis of (2) is satisfied. Now for $t \in (D-S) \cap I$, if $\omega_0 \notin \Lambda_t$ then $Y(t,\omega_0) = X(t,\omega_0) \in C$ by (4) and (2) and if $\omega_0 \in \Lambda_t$ then by (5) $Y(t,\omega_0) = \lim\inf_{s \to t} X(s,\omega_0) \in C$ since $X(s,\omega_0) \in C$ for all $s \in S \cap I$ and C is a closed set. Thus for $t \in (D-S) \cap I$ we have $Y(t,\omega_0) \in C$. This completes the proof. □

[III] Almost Sure Separability

Definition 4.5 A stochastic process X on a probability space $(\Omega, \mathfrak{B}, P)$ and $D \subset R^1$ is said to be almost surely separable with respect to $\mathfrak{A} \subset \mathfrak{B}^1$ if there exist a countable dense subset $S \subset D$ and $\Lambda \in \mathfrak{B}$ with $P(\Lambda) = 0$ such that the restriction of X to $\Omega - \Lambda$ is a separable process with respect to $\mathfrak{A}$ relative to S.

Thus X is almost surely separable (with respect to $\mathfrak{J}_C$) if and only if there exists a countable dense subset $S \subset D$ and $\Lambda \in \mathfrak{B}$ with $P(\Lambda) = 0$ such that one, and hence all, of the conditions (S_1) to (S_4) in Theorem 4.2 holds for every $\omega \in \Omega - \Lambda$.

Lemma 4.6 Let X be an almost surely separable stochastic process on a probability space $(\Omega, \mathfrak{B}, P)$ and $D \subset R^1$, i.e., there exist a countable dense subset $S \subset D$ and $\Lambda \in \mathfrak{B}$ with $P(\Lambda) = 0$ such that according to (S_3) of Theorem 4.2

$$\operatorname*{low\,env}_{s \to t} X(s,\omega) \leq X(t,\omega) \leq \operatorname*{upp\,env}_{s \to t} X(s,\omega)$$

for all $t \in D$ when $\omega \notin \Lambda$. (1)

If there exists a countable dense subset $\Sigma = \{\sigma\} \subset D$ such that for every $t \in D$ there exists $\Lambda_t \in \mathfrak{B}$ with $P(\Lambda_t) = 0$ for which

$$\operatorname*{low\,env}_{\sigma \to t} X(\sigma, \omega) \le X(t, \omega) \le \operatorname*{upp\,env}_{\sigma \to t} X(\sigma, \omega) \quad \text{for every } \omega \notin \Lambda_t \tag{2}$$

then there exists $\Lambda' \in \mathfrak{B}$ with $P(\Lambda') = 0$ such that

$$\operatorname*{low\,env}_{\sigma \to t} X(\sigma, \omega) \le X(t, \omega) \le \operatorname*{upp\,env}_{\sigma \to t} X(\sigma, \omega)$$
$$\text{for all } t \in D \text{ when } \omega \notin \Lambda', \tag{3}$$

i.e., X is almost surely separable relative to Σ.

<u>Proof</u> Applying (2) to each $s \in S$ we obtain

$$\operatorname*{low\,env}_{\sigma \to s} X(\sigma, \omega) \le X(s, \omega) \le \operatorname*{upp\,env}_{\sigma \to s} X(\sigma, \omega), \qquad \omega \notin \Lambda_s. \tag{4}$$

Let $\Lambda' = \Lambda \cup (\bigcup_{s \in S} \Lambda_s)$. Then $\Lambda' \in \mathfrak{B}$ and $P(\Lambda') = 0$. Furthermore (1) and (4) hold for $\omega \notin \Lambda'$. Thus from (1) and (4) we have for $\omega \notin \Lambda'$

$$X(t, \omega) \ge \operatorname*{low\,env}_{s \to t} X(s, \omega) \ge \operatorname*{low\,env}_{s \to t} \left\{ \operatorname*{low\,env}_{\sigma \to t} X(\sigma, \omega) \right\}$$

$$= \lim_{\delta \downarrow 0} \inf_{s \in (t-\delta, t+\delta)} \left\{ \lim_{\eta \downarrow 0} \inf_{\sigma \in (s-\eta, s+\eta)} X(\sigma, \omega) \right\}$$

$$\ge \lim_{\delta \downarrow 0} \inf_{s \in (t-\delta, t+\delta)} \inf_{\sigma \in (t-\delta, t+\delta)} X(\sigma, \omega)$$

$$= \lim_{\delta \downarrow 0} \inf_{\sigma \in (t-\delta, t+\delta)} X(\sigma, \omega)$$

$$= \operatorname*{low\,env}_{\sigma \to t} X(\sigma, \omega). \qquad \square$$

Theorem 4.7 If a stochastic process X on a probability space $(\Omega, \mathfrak{B}, P)$ and $D \subset R^1$ is separable and stochastically continuous then it is almost surely separable relative to every countable dense subset $\Sigma \subset D$.

Proof We show that every countable dense subset $\Sigma \subset D$ satisfies (2) of Lemma 4.6. Let $t \in D$ and let $\{\sigma_n, n = 1, 2, \cdots\} \subset \Sigma$ be so chosen that $\lim_{n\to\infty} \sigma_n = t$. From the stochastic continuity of X at t we have $X(t, \cdot) = P - \lim_{n\to\infty} X(\sigma_n, \cdot)$ and consequently there exist a subsequence $\{n_k\}$ of $\{n\}$ and $\Lambda_t \in \mathfrak{B}$ with $P(\Lambda_t) = 0$ such that $X(t,\omega) = \lim_{k\to\infty} X(\sigma_{n_k}, \omega)$ for $\omega \notin \Lambda_t$. Then for $\omega \notin \Lambda_t$

$$\operatorname*{low\,env}_{\sigma\to t} X(\sigma,\omega) = \lim_{\delta\downarrow 0} \inf_{\sigma\in(t-\delta, t+\delta)} X(\sigma,\omega) \le \lim_{\delta\downarrow 0} \inf_{\sigma_{n_k}\in(t-\delta, t+\delta)} X(\sigma_{n_k},\omega)$$

$$\le \liminf_{k\to\infty} X(\sigma_{n_k},\omega) = \lim_{k\to\infty} X(\sigma_{n_k},\omega) = X(t,\omega)$$

proving the first inequality in (2) of Lemma 4.6. The second inequality can be proved likewise. □

Theorem 4.8 Let X be a stochastic process on a probability space $(\Omega, \mathfrak{B}, P)$ and $D \subset R^1$ which is separable relative to a countable dense subset $S \subset D$. For $t_0 \in D$, $\omega_0 \in \Omega$, $I \in \mathfrak{I}_O$, $I \ni t_0$ let $A(I,\omega_0)$ be the closure of the range of $X(t,\omega_0)$ for $t \in I$, i.e.,

$$A(I,\omega_0) = \overline{\{X(t,\omega_0),\ t \in I\}}$$

and let

$$A(t_0,\omega_0) = \bigcap_{\substack{I\ni t_0 \\ I\in\mathfrak{I}_O}} A(I, \omega_0)$$

Let Y be a stochastic process on $(\Omega, \mathfrak{B}, P)$ and D satisfying

$$Y(s,\omega) = X(s,\omega) \qquad \text{for a.e. } \omega \text{ for all } s \in S \tag{1}$$

$$Y(t_0,\omega_0) \in A(t_0,\omega_0) \qquad \text{for } t_0 \in D,\ \omega_0 \in \Omega . \tag{2}$$

Then Y is an almost surely separable process relative to S.

Proof By (1), there exists $\Lambda \in \mathfrak{B}$ with $P(\Lambda) = 0$ such that

$$Y(s,\omega) = X(s,\omega) \qquad \text{for } \omega \in \Omega - \Lambda \text{ for all } s \in S. \tag{3}$$

To show that Y is an almost surely separable process relative to S we show that (S_2) of Theorem 4.2 is satisfied for every $\omega_0 \in \Omega - \Lambda$, i.e., for $t_0 \in D$, $I \in \mathfrak{J}_O$, $I \ni t_0$ we have

$$\inf_{S \cap I} Y(s,\omega_0) \leq Y(t_0,\omega_0) \leq \sup_{S \cap I} Y(s,\omega_0). \tag{4}$$

According to (2), for $\omega_0 \in \Omega$, $t_0 \in D$, $I \in \mathfrak{J}_O$, $I \ni t_0$ we have

$$\inf_{D \cap I} X(t,\omega_0) \leq Y(t_0,\omega_0) \leq \sup_{D \cap I} X(t,\omega_0). \tag{5}$$

But X is separable relative to S and hence by (S_1) of Theorem 4.2 we have for $\omega_0 \in \Omega$, $I \in \mathfrak{J}_O$

$$\inf_{D \cap I} X(t,\omega_0) = \inf_{S \cap I} X(s,\omega_0), \qquad \sup_{D \cap I} X(t,\omega_0) = \sup_{S \cap I} X(s,\omega_0). \tag{6}$$

Combining (5), (6), (3) we have (4). □

§5. MEASURABLE PROCESSES

A stochastic process X on a probability space $(\Omega, \mathfrak{B}, P)$ and $D \subset R^1$ is a $\mathfrak{B}$-measurable function of $\omega \in \Omega$ for each $t \in D$. However X may not be a measurable function of $(t, \omega) \in D \times \Omega$ with respect to the product of the probability measure and the Lebesgue measure. If it is measurable and integrable with respect to the product measure then we can apply the Fubini theorem.

Let $\mathfrak{M}_D$ be the σ-field of Lebesgue measurable sets contained in $D \subset R^1$ when D is Lebesgue measurable and let $\mathfrak{B}_D$ be the σ-field of Borel sets contained in D when D is a Borel set. Let $\sigma(\mathfrak{M}_D \times \mathfrak{B})$ be the σ-field generated by the Cartesian product of $\mathfrak{M}_D$ and $\mathfrak{B}$. We define $\sigma(\mathfrak{B}_D \times \mathfrak{B})$ likewise. We write m_L for the Lebesgue measure on $\mathfrak{M}_D$ or $\mathfrak{B}_D$.

Definition 5.1 Given a probability space $(\Omega, \mathfrak{B}, P)$ and a Lebesgue or Borel measurable set $D \subset R^1$. A real-valued function X on $D \times \Omega$ is called a Lebesgue or Borel measurable process if it is measurable with respect to $\sigma(\mathfrak{M}_D \times \mathfrak{B})$ or $\sigma(\mathfrak{B}_D \times \mathfrak{B})$, respectively.

If X is a Lebesgue or Borel measurable process on $D \times \Omega$ according to Definition 5.1, then for every $t \in D$, $X(t, \cdot)$ is $\mathfrak{B}$-measurable so that X is indeed a stochastic process on $(\Omega, \mathfrak{B}, P)$ and D. Similarly for every $\omega \in \Omega$, $X(\cdot, \omega)$ is a Lebesgue or Borel measurable function on D. If one of the two iterated integrals $\int_D E\left[|X(t, \cdot)|\right] m_L(dt)$ and $E\left[\int_D |X(t, \cdot)| m_L(dt)\right]$ is finite so is the other and

$$\int_D E\left[X(t,\cdot)\right] m_L(dt) = \int_{D\times\Omega} X(t,\omega)(m_L \times P)\big(d(t,\omega)\big) = E\left[\int_D X(t,\cdot)\, m_L(dt)\right]$$

according to Fubini's theorem. On the other hand if a given stochastic process X on $(\Omega, \mathfrak{B}, P)$ and D is equal to a $\sigma(\mathfrak{M}_D \times \mathfrak{B})$- or $\sigma(\mathfrak{B}_D \times \mathfrak{B})$-measurable function on $D \times \Omega$ except on a $\sigma(\mathfrak{M}_D \times \mathfrak{B})$- or $\sigma(\mathfrak{B}_D \times \mathfrak{B})$-measurable set with $m_L \times P$ measure 0, that is, if X is measurable with respect to the completion of the measure space $\big(D \times \Omega, \sigma(\mathfrak{M}_D \times \mathfrak{B}), m_L \times P\big)$ or of the measure space $\big(D \times \Omega, \sigma(\mathfrak{B}_D \times \mathfrak{B}), m_L \times P\big)$, then the last equality still holds under the assumption that one of the two iterated integrals of $|X|$ is finite. The following theorems concerning measurable processes are due to J. L. Doob.

Theorem 5.2 Let X be a stochastic process on a probability space $(\Omega, \mathfrak{B}, P)$ and a Lebesgue measurable set $D \subset R^1$. If X is stochastically continuous at every $t \in D - D_0$ where $D_0 \in \mathfrak{M}_D$ with $m_L(D_0) = 0$ then there exists an extended real-valued stochastic process Y on $(\Omega, \mathfrak{B}, P)$ and D which is equivalent to X, almost surely separable and measurable with respect to the completion of $\big(D \times \Omega, \sigma(\mathfrak{M}_D \times \mathfrak{B}), m_L \times P\big)$.

Proof According to Theorem 4.4 there exists an extended real-valued stochastic process X^* on $(\Omega, \mathfrak{B}, P)$ and D which is equivalent to X and is separable with respect to the collection of closed sets in $\overline{R}$. From its equivalence to X, X^* is stochastically continuous at every $t \in D - D_0$.

The transformation $\eta = T\xi = (2/\pi) \arctan \xi$ transforms $\overline{R}$ one-to-one bicontinuously onto $[-1, 1]$, preserves ordering by $<$ and is abolutely continuous on every finite closed interval in R^1 since the derivative is continuous. Recall that a real-valued function on a finite closed interval is absolutely continuous if and only if it is continuous, of bounded variation and transforms every Lebesgue measurable set with Lebesgue measure 0 into such a set again. Also a function which has the first and the last of the above three properties transforms a Lebesgue measurable set into a Lebesgue measurable set. Thus for $E = T(D)$ and $E_0 = T(D_0)$ we have $E, E_0 \in \mathfrak{M}_{[-1,1]}$ and $m_L(E_0) = 0$.

For $t \in D$, let $u = Tt$ and $X^{**}(u,\omega) = T\left[X^*(T^{-1}u,\omega)\right]$ for $\omega \in \Omega$. Clearly X^{**} is a stochastic process on $(\Omega, \mathfrak{B}, P)$ and E, satisfies $|X^{**}(u,\omega)| \le 1$ for $u \in E$, $\omega \in \Omega$, is stochastically continuous at every $u \in E - E_0$ and separable with respect to the collection of closed sets in $[-1,1]$. The separability of X^{**} follows from that of X^* by means of the condition (S_4) of Theorem 4.2 and the fact that T preserves ordering by $<$.

We may now assume that $D \in \mathfrak{M}_{[-1,1]}$, X is a stochastic process on $(\Omega, \mathfrak{B}, P)$ and D, satisfies $|X(t,\omega)| \le 1$ for $t \in D$, $\omega \in \Omega$, is stochastically continuous at every $t \in D - D_0$ where $D_0 \in \mathfrak{M}_{[-1,1]}$ with $m_L(D_0) = 0$, and is separable with respect to the collection of closed sets in $[-1,1]$.

Let $S = \{s_n, n = 1, 2, \cdots\}$ be a countable dense subset of D relative to which X is separable. For each $t \in D$ and positive integer n let

$$s(t,n) = \begin{cases} \max\{s_1, \dots, s_n\} & \text{if } \max\{s_1, \dots, s_n\} < t, \\ \text{the one among } s_1, \dots, s_n \text{ on the right side of and} \\ \text{nearest to } t & \text{if } \max\{s_1, \dots, s_n\} \ge t. \end{cases}$$

Since every neighborhood of t contains some members of S,

$\lim_{n\to\infty} s(t,n) = t$. Let

$$Y_n(t,\omega) = X\Big(s(t,n), \omega\Big) \qquad t \in D,\ \omega \in \Omega,\ n = 1,2,\cdots .$$

Clearly Y_n is a stochastic process on $(\Omega, \mathfrak{B}, P)$ and D. Since all sample functions of Y_n are step functions with at most n points of discontinuity which occur on a subset of $\{s_1, \cdots, s_n\}$, Y_n is separable and measurable with respect to $\sigma(\mathfrak{M}_D \times \mathfrak{B})$.

From the stochastic continuity of X at $t \in D - D_0$ and from $\lim_{n\to\infty} s(t,n) = t$ we have

$$X(t,\cdot) = P - \lim_{n\to\infty} X\Big(s(t,n), \cdot\Big) = P - \lim_{n\to\infty} Y_n(t,\cdot), \qquad t \in D - D_0. \tag{1}$$

Since $|Y_n(t,\omega) - X(t,\omega)| \le 2$, the Bounded Convergence Theorem under convergence in probability applies and we have from $P - \lim_{n\to\infty} |Y_n(t,\cdot) - X(t,\cdot)| = 0$

$$\lim_{n\to\infty} \int_\Omega |Y_n(t,\omega) - X(t,\omega)|\, P(d\omega) = 0, \qquad t \in D - D_0 .$$

By means of the Triangle Inequality we have then

$$\lim_{m,n\to\infty} \int_\Omega |Y_m(t,\omega) - Y_n(t,\omega)|\, P(d\omega) = 0, \qquad t \in D - D_0 .$$

Since $|Y_n(t,\omega)| \le 1$ for $t \in D$, $\omega \in \Omega$, $n = 1,2,\cdots$ the last integral as a function of t is bounded by 2 for all m and n. Integrating both sides of the last equation over D, then applying the Bounded Convergence Theorem and finally using Fubini's theorem we obtain

$$\lim_{m,n\to\infty} \int_{D\times\Omega} |Y_m(t,\omega) - Y_n(t,\omega)|\, (m_L \times P)\Big(d(t,\omega)\Big) = 0.$$

According to the Riesz-Fischer theorem there exist $E \in \sigma(\mathfrak{M}_D \times \mathfrak{B})$ with $(m_L \times P)(E) = 0$, a subsequence $\{n_k\}$ of $\{n\}$ and a real-valued $\sigma(\mathfrak{M}_D \times \mathfrak{B})$ - measurable function Y_∞ on $D \times \Omega - E$ such that

$$\lim_{n\to\infty} \int_{D\times\Omega} |Y_n(t,\omega) - Y_\infty(t,\omega)|(m_L \times P)\big(d(t,\omega)\big) = 0.$$

and

$$\lim_{k\to\infty} Y_{n_k}(t,\omega) = Y_\infty(t,\omega) \qquad (t,\omega) \in D \times \Omega - E. \tag{2}$$

Since $(m_L \times P)(E) = 0$ there exists $D_1 \in \mathfrak{M}_D$ with $m_L(D_1) = 0$ such that the section of E at $t \in D - D_1$ has P measure 0, i.e.,

$$\lim_{k\to\infty} Y_{n_k}(t,\omega) = Y_\infty(t,\omega) \qquad \text{for a.e. } \omega \text{ when } t \in D - D_1. \tag{3}$$

Let $D_2 = S \cup D_0 \cup D_1$. Then by (1) and (3)

$$X(t,\omega) = Y_\infty(t,\omega) \qquad \text{for a.e. } \omega \text{ when } t \in D - D_2. \tag{4}$$

Define Y on $D \times \Omega$ by

$$Y(t,\omega) = \begin{cases} X(t,\omega) & \text{if } t \in D_2 \text{ or if } (t,\omega) \in E \\ Y_\infty(t,\omega) & \text{if } t \in D - D_2 \text{ and } (t,\omega) \in D \times \Omega - E \end{cases}. \tag{5}$$

Clearly for each $t \in D$, $Y(t,\cdot)$ is $\mathfrak{B}$-measurable so that Y is a stochastic process on $(\Omega, \mathfrak{B}, P)$ and D. To show the equivalence of Y to X let us observe that if $t \in D_2$ then $Y(t,\omega) = X(t,\omega)$ for all $\omega \in \Omega$ and if $t \in D - D_2$ then $Y(t,\omega) = Y_\infty(t,\omega)$ for a.e. ω so that, by (4), $X(t,\omega) = Y(t,\omega)$ for a.e. ω. The almost sure separability of Y is from Theorem 4.8. Observe that (2) of Theorem 4.8 is satisfied by our Y at every $(t,\omega) \in D \times \Omega$. Finally from (5) and the fact that Y_∞ is defined and $\sigma(\mathfrak{M}_D \times \mathfrak{B})$ - measurable on $D \times \Omega - E$

and $(m_L \times P)(E) = 0$, Y is measurable with respect to the completion of $\left((D \times \Omega), \sigma(\mathfrak{M}_D \times \mathfrak{B}), m_L \times P\right)$. □

To show that the continuity of sample functions implies measurability of the process we show first that there exist two measurable processes whose sample functions are limit inferior and limit superior of the sample functions of the tiven process at each time point.

For $t_0 \in R^1$ let us write $[t_0]$ for the integral part of t_0 i.e., $t_0 = [t_0] + \epsilon$ where $0 \le \epsilon < 1$. For $t_0 \in R^1$ and a positive integer n let

$$I_{t_0,n} = \left\{t \in R^1 ; [2^n t] = [2^n t_0]\right\} .$$

Since for every $t \in R^1$

$$[2^n t] = [2^n t_0] \Leftrightarrow \frac{[2^n t_0]}{2^n} \le t < \frac{[2^n t_0] + 1}{2^n}$$

we have $I_{t_0,n} = \left[j\, 2^{-n}, (j+1)\, 2^{-n}\right)$ where j is an integer depending on t_0 and is in fact given by $j = [2^n t_0]$. Clearly $I_{t_0,n}$ contains t_0. Note also that the collection $\left\{I_{t_0,n}, t_0 \in R^1\right\}$ is a decomposition of R^1 into disjoint intervals whose endpoints are binary rationals of denomination 2^{-n}. Since $I_{t_0, n+1} = \left[k\, 2^{-(n+1)}, (k+1)\, 2^{-(n+1)}\right)$ with $k = [2^{n+1} t_0]$ and since both $I_{t_0,n}$ and $I_{t_0, n+1}$ contain t_0, we have $I_{t_0, n+1} \subset I_{t_0,n}$.

Lemma 5.3 Let X be a separable stochastic process on a probability space $(\Omega, \mathfrak{B}, P)$ and a Lebesgue or Borel measurable set $D \subset R^1$. For each $t_0 \in D$ and positive integer n let

$$I_{t_0,n} = \left\{ t \in R^1 ; [2^n t] = [2^n t_0] \right\} \tag{1}$$

$$\begin{aligned} L_n(t_0, \omega) &= \inf_{D \cap I_{t_0,n}} X(t, \omega) \qquad t_0 \in D, \ \omega \in \Omega \\ U_n(t_0, \omega) &= \sup_{D \cap I_{t_0,n}} X(t, \omega) \qquad t_0 \in D, \ \omega \in \Omega \end{aligned} \tag{2}$$

Then L_n and U_n are extended real-valued stochastic processes on $(\Omega, \mathfrak{B}, P)$ and D, satisfy

$$L_n(t_0, \omega) \le X(t_0, \omega) \le U_n(t_0, \omega), \qquad t_0 \in D, \ \omega \in \Omega \tag{3}$$

and are measurable with respect to $\sigma(\mathfrak{M}_D \times \mathfrak{B})$ or $\sigma(\mathfrak{B}_D \times \mathfrak{B})$. If we admit ∞ and $-\infty$ as limits then

$$\begin{aligned} L_\infty(t, \omega) &= \lim_{n\to\infty} L_n(t_0, \omega) \quad \text{and} \\ U_\infty(t_0, \omega) &= \lim_{n\to\infty} U_n(t_0, \omega) \quad \text{exist for } t_0 \in D, \ \omega \in \Omega \end{aligned} \tag{4}$$

and

$$L_\infty(t_0, \omega) \le X(t_0, \omega) \le U_\infty(t_0, \omega), \qquad t_0 \in D, \ \omega \in \Omega. \tag{5}$$

The extended real-valued stochastic processes L_∞ and U_∞ are measurable with respect $\sigma(\mathfrak{M}_D \times \mathfrak{B})$ or $\sigma(\mathfrak{B}_D \times \mathfrak{B})$. Finally if for $\omega_0 \in \Omega$, $X(\cdot, \omega_0)$ is continuous at t_0 then

$$L_\infty(t_0, \omega_0) = X(t_0, \omega_0) = U_\infty(t_0, \omega_0). \tag{6}$$

Proof Let X be separable relative to a countable dense subset $S \subset D$. We may assume without loss of generality that S contains all the rational numbers in D. Then, for every open interval $I \subset R^1$,

$$\inf_{D \cap I} X(t, \omega) = \inf_{S \cap I} X(s, \omega), \qquad \omega \in \Omega$$

and in particular when I is the interior of $I_{t_0, n}$. Since $\left[2^n t_0\right] 2^{-n}$ is a rational number, if it is in D then it is in S as well. Thus

$$L_n(t_0, \omega) = \inf_{D \cap I_{t_0, n}} X(t, \omega) = \inf_{S \cap I_{t_0, n}} X(s, \omega) \qquad t_0 \in D, \ \omega \in \Omega .$$

As the infimum of countably many random variables on $(\Omega, \mathfrak{B}, P)$, $L_n(t_0, \omega)$ is an extended real-valued random variable on $(\Omega, \mathfrak{B}, P)$ and L_n is an extended real-valued stochastic process on $(\Omega, \mathfrak{B}, P)$ and D. Since $t_0 \in I_{t_0, n}$ we have $L_n(t_0, \omega) \leq X(t_0, \omega)$ for $\omega \in \Omega$ by (2). This proves (3). The measurability of L_n with respect to $\sigma(\mathfrak{M}_D \times \mathfrak{B})$ or $\sigma(\mathfrak{B}_D \times \mathfrak{B})$ follows from the fact that if $S = \{s_m, m = 1, 2, \cdots\}$ and $S_m = \{s_1, \cdots, s_m\}$ then

$$L_n(t_0, \omega) = \lim_{m \to \infty} L_{n,m}(t_0, \omega) \qquad t_0 \in D, \ \omega \in \Omega$$

where

$$L_{n,m}(t_0, \omega) = \begin{cases} \inf_{S_m \cap I_{t_0, n}} X(s, \omega) & \text{when } S_m \cap I_{t_0, n} \neq \emptyset \\ 0 & \text{when } S_m \cap I_{t_0, n} = \emptyset . \end{cases}$$

Since $L_{n,m}$ is a stepwise stochastic process it is measurable with respect to $\sigma(\mathfrak{M}_D \times \mathfrak{B})$ or $\sigma(\mathfrak{B}_D \times \mathfrak{B})$. Then so is L_n.

Since $I_{t_0,n} \downarrow$ as $n \uparrow \infty$, $L_n(t_0, \omega) \uparrow$ as $n \uparrow \infty$ so that $L_\infty(t_0, \omega) = \lim_{n\to\infty} L_n(t_0, \omega)$ exists and is measurable with respect to $\sigma(\mathfrak{M}_D \times \mathfrak{B})$ or $\sigma(\mathfrak{B}_D \times \mathfrak{B})$ for $t_0 \in D$, $\omega \in \Omega$. The inequalities (5) follow from (3).

To prove (6), suppose that for $\omega_0 \in \Omega$, $X(\cdot, \omega_0)$ is continuous at t_0. According to (5), $L_\infty(t_0, \omega_0) \le X(t_0, \omega_0)$. Assume $c = X(t_0, \omega_0) - L_\infty(t_0, \omega_0) > 0$. From the continuity of $X(\cdot, \omega_0)$ at t_0 there exists an open interval $I \subset R^1$ such that

$$\inf_{D \cap I} X(t, \omega_0) \ge L_\infty(t_0, \omega_0) + \frac{c}{2} .$$

For sufficiently large n, $I_{t_0,n} \subset I$ so that

$$L_n(t_0, \omega_0) = \inf_{S \cap I_{t_0,n}} X(s, \omega_0) \ge \inf_{D \cap I} X(t, \omega_0) \ge L_\infty(t_0, \omega_0) + \frac{c}{2}$$

contradicting $L_n(t_0, \omega_0) \uparrow L_\infty(t_0, \omega_0)$. □

<u>Theorem 5.4</u> Let X be a separable stochastic process on a probability space $(\Omega, \mathfrak{B}, P)$ and a Lebesgue or Borel measurable set $D \subset R^1$. Suppose there exists $D_0 \in \mathfrak{M}_D$ or $\mathfrak{B}_D$ with $m_L(D_0) = 0$ such that for every $t_0 \in D - D_0$

$$P\left\{\omega \in \Omega ; \lim_{t \to t_0} X(t, \omega) = X(t_0, \omega)\right\} = 1$$

(i.e., for every $t_0 \in D - D_0$, there exists $\Lambda_{t_0} \in \mathfrak{B}$ with $P(\Lambda_{t_0}) = 0$ such that $X(\cdot, \omega)$ is continuous at t_0 for $\omega \in \Lambda_{t_0}^c$) then there exists $E \in \sigma(\mathfrak{M}_D \times \mathfrak{B})$ or $\sigma(\mathfrak{B}_D \times \mathfrak{B})$ with $(m_L \times P)(E) = 0$ such that on $D \times \Omega - E$, X is measurable with respect to $\sigma(\mathfrak{M}_D \times \mathfrak{B})$ or $\sigma(\mathfrak{B}_D \times \mathfrak{B})$.

<u>Proof</u> Let us assume $m_L(D) < \infty$. When $m_L(D) = \infty$ we decompose D into countably many Lebesgue or Borel measurable sets with finite measures and apply the argument below to each of

them. Now according to Lemma 5.3, $L_\infty(t,\omega) \le X(t,\omega) \le U_\infty(t,\omega)$ for $t \in D$, $\omega \in \Omega$. From the measurability of L_∞ and U_∞ with respect to $\sigma(\mathfrak{M}_D \times \mathfrak{B})$ or $\sigma(\mathfrak{B}_D \times \mathfrak{B})$ we have

$$E = \{(t,\omega) \in D \times \Omega ; L_\infty(t,\omega) \neq U_\infty(t,\omega)\} \in \sigma(\mathfrak{M}_D \times \mathfrak{B}) \text{ or } \sigma(\mathfrak{B}_D \times \mathfrak{B})$$

and $(m_L \times P)(E) < \infty$. To show that $(m_L \times P)(E) = 0$ we use the fact that $(m_L \times P)(E) = 0$ if and only if for a.e. $t \in D$ the section of E at t, i.e., $E_t = \{\omega \in \Omega ; (t,\omega) \in E\}$, has $P(E_t) = 0$. But for every $t \in D - D_0$, $X(\cdot,\omega)$ is continuous at t for a.e. ω so that by Lemma 5.3 $L_\infty(t,\omega) = X(t,\omega) = U_\infty(t,\omega)$ for a.e. ω and hence

$$P(E_t) = P\{\omega \in \Omega ; L_\infty(t,\omega) \neq U_\infty(t,\omega)\} = 0.$$

Therefore $(m_L \times P)(E) = 0$. Now on $D \times \Omega - E$ we have $L_\infty(t,\omega) = U_\infty(t,\omega)$ so that $X(t,\omega) = L_\infty(t,\omega) = U_\infty(t,\omega)$ and is hence measurable with respect to $\sigma(\mathfrak{M}_D \times \mathfrak{B})$ or $\sigma(\mathfrak{B}_D \times \mathfrak{B})$. □

<u>Theorem 5.5</u> Let X be a stochastic process on a probability space $(\Omega, \mathfrak{B}, P)$ and a Lebesgue or Borel measurable set $D \subset R^1$. If every sample function of X is continuous on D then X is separable relative to every countable dense subset $S \subset D$ and is measurable with respect to $\sigma(\mathfrak{M}_D \times \mathfrak{B})$ or $\sigma(\mathfrak{B}_D \times \mathfrak{B})$.

<u>Proof</u> Let $S \subset D$ be an arbitrary countable dense subset. For every open interval I and closed interval J in R^1

$$\{\omega \in \Omega ; X(t,\omega) \in J \text{ for all } t \in D \cap I\}$$
$$\subset \{\omega \in \Omega ; X(s,\omega) \in J \text{ for all } s \in D \cap I\}.$$

To prove the reversed inclusion let ω_0 be an element in the second set. For any $t \in D \cap I$ we can select $\{s_n, n = 1, 2, \cdots\} \subset S \cap I$ with

$\lim_{n\to\infty} s_n = t$. From the continuity of $X(\cdot,\omega_0)$ at t we have

$$X(t,\omega_0) = \lim_{n\to\infty} X(s_n,\omega_0) \in J$$

since $X(s_n,\omega_0) \in J$ for $n = 1,2,\cdots$ and J is a closed set. Thus ω_0 is in the first set also. This proves the equality of the two sets and hence the separability of X relative to S.

Since $X(\cdot,\omega)$ is continuous on D for every $\omega \in \Omega$, we have $L_\infty(t,\omega) = X(t,\omega) = U_\infty(t,\omega)$ on $D \times \Omega$ by Lemma 5.3. The measurability of X on $D \times \Omega$ then follows from that of L_∞ and U_∞. □

§6. CONTINUOUS PROCESSES

In Theorem 5.5 we showed that the continuity of the sample functions of a stochastic process implies its separability and measurability. Let us now derive some conditions on a stochastic process that ensure the continuity of its sample functions. We shall present first a theorem due to M. Loève which gives a sufficient condition for the continuity of the sample functions of a stochastic process in terms of the probability distributions of the increments of the process. A. N. Kolmogorov's condition for the continuity of sample functions in terms of the continuity in the mean of the process is then derived from Loève's theorem.

Definition 6.1 A stochastic process X on a probability space $(\Omega, \mathfrak{B}, P)$ and $D \subset R^1$ is said to be continuous if $X(\cdot,\omega)$ is continuous on D for every $\omega \in \Omega$. It is said to be almost surely continuous if $X(\cdot,\omega)$ is continuous on D for a.e. $\omega \in \Omega$.

Theorem 6.2 Let X be a stochastic process on a probability space $(\Omega, \mathfrak{B}, P)$ and $D = [0,1]$. Let $g(h)$ and $q(h)$ be arbitrary nonnegative even functions defined for $0 < |h| < h_0$

with some $h_0 > 0$ which are monotone increasing for $h \in (0, h_0)$ and satisfy

$$\sum_{n=1}^{\infty} g\left(\frac{1}{2^n}\right) < \infty \tag{1}$$

$$\sum_{n=1}^{\infty} 2^n q\left(\frac{1}{2^n}\right) < \infty . \tag{2}$$

If X satisfies the condition that

$$P\left\{\omega \in \Omega ; \left|X(t+h,\omega) - X(t,\omega)\right| \geq g(h)\right\} \leq q(h)$$

$$\text{wherever } t, t+h \in [0,1], \ 0 < |h| < h_0 \tag{3}$$

then there exists a stochastic process Y on $(\Omega, \mathfrak{B}, P)$ and D which is equivalent to X and is continuous.

<u>Proof</u> For $n = 1, 2, \cdots$, we consider the polygonalization X_n of X with 2^n equal subintervals of $[0,1]$ by polygonalizing each sample function of X. Thus we let $t_{n,r} = r2^{-n}$, $r = 0, 1, 2, \cdots, 2^n$ and for each $t \in [t_{n,r}, t_{n,r+1}]$ define a random variable $X_n(t, \cdot)$ on $(\Omega, \mathfrak{B}, P)$ by

$$\frac{X_n(t,\omega) - X(t_{n,r},\omega)}{t - t_{n,r}} = \frac{X(t_{n,r+1},\omega) - X(t_{n,r},\omega)}{2^{-n}}$$

i.e.,

$$X_n(t,\omega) = X(t_{n,r},\omega) + 2^n(t - t_{n,r})\left\{X(t_{n,r+1},\omega) - X(t_{n,r},\omega)\right\}$$

Thus for $t \in [t_{n,r}, t_{n,r+1}]$, from the fact that $X_n(t,\omega)$ is a polygonal function we have

$$|X_{n+1}(t, \omega) - X_n(t, \omega)|$$

$$\leq \left| X(t_{n+1,2r+1}, \omega) - \tfrac{1}{2}\left\{X(t_{n+1,2r}, \omega) + X(t_{n+1,2r+2}, \omega)\right\} \right|$$

$$\leq \tfrac{1}{2} A_{n,r}(\omega) + \tfrac{1}{2} B_{n,r}(\omega)$$

where

$$A_{n,r}(\omega) = |X(t_{n+1,2r+1}, \omega) - X(t_{n+1,2r}, \omega)|$$

and

$$B_{n,r}(\omega) = |X(t_{n+1,2r+1}, \omega) - X(t_{n+1,2r+2}, \omega)|.$$

Then

$$\max_{[t_{n,r}, t_{n,r+1}]} |X_{n+1}(t,\omega) - X_n(t,\omega)| \leq \tfrac{1}{2} A_{n,r}(\omega) + \tfrac{1}{2} B_{n,r}(\omega)$$

and

$$P\left\{\omega \in \Omega;\ \max_{[t_{n,r}, t_{n,r+1}]} |X_{n+1}(t, \omega) - X_n(t, \omega)| \geq g\left(\frac{1}{2^{n+1}}\right)\right\}$$

$$\leq P\left\{\omega \in \Omega;\ A_{n,r}(\omega) \geq g\left(\frac{1}{2^{n+1}}\right)\right\} + P\left\{\omega \in \Omega;\ B_{n,r}(\omega) \geq g\left(\frac{1}{2^{n+1}}\right)\right\}$$

$$\leq 2q\left(\frac{1}{2^{n+1}}\right)$$

for n so large that $2^{-(n+1)} < h_0$ according to (3). The $\mathfrak{B}$-measurability of the maximum is from the fact that it is equal to the supremum over the rational numbers in the subinterval on account of the continuity of the sample functions of $X_{n+1} - X_n$. Now since

$$\left\{\omega\in\Omega;\ \max_{[0,1]}|X_{n+1}(t,\omega)-X_n(t,\omega)|\geq g\left(\frac{1}{2^{n+1}}\right)\right\}$$

$$\subset\bigcup_{r=0}^{2^n-1}\left\{\omega\in\Omega;\ \max_{[t_{n,r},\,t_{n,r+1}]}|X_{n+1}(t,\omega)-X_n(t,\omega)|\geq g\left(\frac{1}{2^{n+1}}\right)\right\}$$

we have, for sufficiently large n,

$$P\left\{\omega\in\Omega;\ \max_{[0,1]}|X_{n+1}(t,\omega)-X_n(t,\omega)|\geq g\left(\frac{1}{2^{n+1}}\right)\right\}$$

$$\leq 2^n\cdot 2q\left(\frac{1}{2^{n+1}}\right). \tag{4}$$

A well-known consequence of the Borel-Cantelli theorem is that if a sequence of random variables $\{Z_n, n=1,2,\cdots\}$ on $(\Omega, \mathfrak{B}, P)$ satisfies $\sum_{n=1}^{\infty} P\{\omega\in\Omega;\ |Z_n(\omega)|>\epsilon_n\}<\infty$ for a convergent series $\sum_{n=1}^{\infty}\epsilon_n$ of positive numbers then $\sum_{n=1}^{\infty}|Z_n(\omega)|$ converges for a.e. ω. Thus by (1), (4), and (2) there exists $\Lambda\in\mathfrak{B}$ with $P(\Lambda)=0$ such that

$$\sum_{n=1}^{\infty}\max_{[0,1]}|X_{n+1}(t,\omega)-X_n(t,\omega)| \text{ converges for } \omega\in\Lambda^c.$$

Then for $\omega\in\Lambda^c$, corresponding to every $\epsilon>0$ there exists $N(\omega,\epsilon)$ such that

$$\max_{[0,1]}|X_{n+p}(t,\omega)-X_n(t,\omega)|\leq\sum_{i=n}^{n+p-1}\max_{[0,1]}|X_{i+1}(t,\omega)-X_i(t,\omega)|<\epsilon$$

for $p=1,2,\cdots$, whenever $n\geq N(\omega,\epsilon)$. According to the Cauchy criterion $\{X_n(t,\omega), n = 1,2, \cdots\}$ converges uniformly for $t \in [0,1]$ when $\omega \in \Lambda^c$.

Let us define for each $t \in D$

$$Y(t,\omega) = \begin{cases} \lim_{n\to\infty} X_n(t,\omega) & \omega \in \Lambda^c \\ 0 & \omega \in \Lambda . \end{cases}$$

Then for each $t \in D$, $Y(t,\cdot)$ is a random variable on $(\Omega, \mathfrak{B}, P)$ so that Y is a stochastic process on $(\Omega, \mathfrak{B}, P)$ and D. For $\omega \in \Lambda^c$, $Y(\cdot,\omega)$ is continuous on D from the fact that $X_n(\cdot,\omega)$ is continuous on D and converges uniformly on D to $Y(\cdot,\omega)$ as $n \to \infty$ when $\omega \in \Lambda^c$. Thus Y is a continuous process.

It remains to show that Y is equivalent to X. Let $t \in D$. If $t = t_{n,r}$ for some n and r then $X_{n+p}(t,\omega) = X(t,\omega)$ for $p = 0,1,2,\cdots$ so that $Y(t,\omega) = \lim_{n\to\infty} X_n(t,\omega) = X(t,\omega)$ for $\omega \in \Lambda^c$, i.e., $Y(\cdot,\omega) = X(\cdot,\omega)$ for a.e. ω. On the other hand if $t \neq t_{n,r}$ for all n and r we have $t = \lim_{n\to\infty} t_{n,r_n}$ where $0 < t - t_{n,r_n} < 1/2^n$ from the denseness of $\{t_{n,r}, r = 0,1,2,\cdots,2^n, n = 1,2,\cdots\}$ in D. For sufficiently large n we have $2^{-n} < h_0$ so that

$$P\left\{\omega \in \Omega ; |X(t_{n,r_n},\omega) - X(t,\omega)| \geq g\left(\frac{1}{2^n}\right)\right\}$$

$$\leq P\left\{\omega \in \Omega ; |X(t_{n,r_n},\omega) - X(t,\omega)| \geq g(t - t_{n,r_n})\right\}$$

$$\leq q(t - t_{n,r_n}) \leq q\left(\frac{1}{2^n}\right)$$

by the fact that g(h) is monotone increasing and by (3). Let

$$\Gamma_n = \left\{ \omega \in \Omega ;\ |X(t_{n,r_n}, \omega) - X(t, \omega)| \geq g\left(\frac{1}{2^n}\right) \right\} .$$

Since $\sum_{n=1}^{\infty} q(2^{-n}) < \infty$ by (2) we have by the Borel-Cantelli theorem that $P\left(\lim_{n\to\infty} \inf \Gamma_n^{\,c}\right) = 1$, i.e., there exists $\Lambda_t \in \mathfrak{B}$ with $P(\Lambda_t) = 0$ such that for $\omega \in \Lambda_t^{\,c}$

$$|X(t_{n,r_n}, \omega) - X(t, \omega)| < g\left(\frac{1}{2^n}\right) \quad \text{for all but finitely many } n.$$

Since $\lim_{n\to\infty} g(2^{-n}) = 0$ from (1), we have $\lim_{n\to\infty} X(t_{n,r_n}, \omega) = X(t, \omega)$ for $\omega \in \Lambda_t^{\,c}$. Thus for $\omega \in (\Lambda \cup \Lambda_t)^c$ we have from the continuity of $Y(\cdot, \omega)$ on D

$$Y(t, \omega) = \lim_{n\to\infty} Y(t_{n,r_n}, \omega) = \lim_{n\to\infty} X(t_{n,r_n}, \omega) = X(t, \omega)$$

i.e., $Y(t, \omega) = X(t, \omega)$ for a.e. ω. This establishes the equivalence of Y to X and completes the proof of the theorem. □

Theorem 6.3 Let X be a stochastic process on a probability space $(\Omega, \mathfrak{B}, P)$ and $D = [0,1]$. If there exist $\alpha, \beta, K, h_0 > 0$ such that

$$E\left(|X(t+h, \cdot) - X(t, \cdot)|^{\alpha}\right) \leq K|h|^{1+\beta}$$

$$\text{whenever } t, t+h \in [0,1],\ |h| < h_0 \tag{1}$$

then there exists a stochastic process Y on $(\Omega, \mathfrak{B}, P)$ and D which is equivalent to X and is continuous.

Proof We show that there exist nonnegative even functions $g(h)$ and $q(h)$ defined for $0 < |h| < h_0$ and monotone increasing for $h \in (0, h_0)$ which satisfy (1) and (2) of Theorem 6.2 and with which X satisfies (3) of the same theorem. For an arbitrary positive even function $g(h)$, $0 < |h| < h_0$, we have by the Markov inequality and (1)

$$P\left\{\omega \in \Omega;\ |X(t+h,\cdot) - X(t,\cdot)| \geq g(h)\right\}$$

$$\leq \frac{E\left(|X(t+h,\cdot) - X(t,\cdot)|^{\alpha}\right)}{\left[g(h)\right]^{\alpha}} \leq \frac{K|h|^{1+\beta}}{\left[g(h)\right]^{\alpha}}$$

for $t, t+h \in [0,1]$ and $0 < |h| < h_0$. (2)

Let $\gamma \in (0, \beta/\alpha)$ and define positive even functions $g(h)$ and $q(h)$ for $0 < |h| < h_0$ by

$$g(h) = |h|^{\gamma} \quad \text{and} \quad q(h) = \frac{K|h|^{1+\beta}}{\left[g(h)\right]^{\alpha}} = K|h|^{1+\epsilon}$$

where $\epsilon = \beta - \alpha\gamma > 0$.

Then g and h are monotone increasing for $h > 0$,

$$\sum_{n=1}^{\infty} g(2^{-n}) = \sum_{n=1}^{\infty} (2^{-\gamma})^n \quad \text{and} \quad \sum_{n=1}^{\infty} 2^n q(2^{-n}) = K \sum_{n=1}^{\infty} (2^{-\epsilon})^n$$

both of which are convergent geometric series. Finally by (2) and the definition of q

$$P\{\omega \in \Omega;\ |X(t+h,\cdot) - X(t,\cdot)| \geq g(h)\} \leq q(h)$$

for $t, t+h \in [0,1]$, $0 < |h| < h_0$.

Thus g, q, and X satisfy the conditions of Theorem 6.2 and by its conclusion Theorem 6.3 holds. □

Theorem 6.4 Let X be a stochastic process on a probability space $(\Omega, \mathfrak{B}, P)$ and $D = [0,1]$. If there exist $\alpha, \beta, K, h_0 > 0$, $0 < \alpha < \beta$, such that

$$E\left(|X(t+h,\cdot) - X(t,\cdot)|^{\alpha}\right) \leq \frac{K|h|}{|\log|h||^{1+\beta}}$$

whenever $t, t+h \in [0,1]$, $0 < |h| < h_0$

then there exists a stochastic process Y on $(\Omega, \mathfrak{B}, P)$ and D which is equivalent to X and is continuous.

Proof Let $g(h)$, $0 < |h| < h_0$, be an arbitrary positive even function. For t, $t+h \in [0,1]$, $0 < |h| < h_0$, we have, by the Markov inequality and (1),

$$P\{\omega \in \Omega;\ |X(t+h,\cdot) - X(t,\cdot)| \geq g(h)\} \leq \frac{E\left(|X(t+h,\cdot) - X(t,\cdot)|^{\alpha}\right)}{[g(h)]^{\alpha}}$$

$$\leq \frac{K|h|}{|\log|h||^{1+\beta}[g(h)]^{\alpha}}$$

Let $\gamma \in (1, \beta/\alpha)$. Assume $h_0 \leq 1$ so that $\log|h| \neq 0$ for $|h| < h_0$. Define positive even functions $g(h)$ and $q(h)$ for

$0 < |h| < h_0$ by

$$g(h) = \frac{1}{|\log |h||^{\gamma}}$$

and

$$q(h) = \frac{K|h|}{|\log |h||^{1+\beta}\left[g(h)\right]^{\alpha}} = K|h|\,|\log |h||^{-1-\epsilon}$$

where $\epsilon = \beta - \alpha\gamma > 0$.

For $h \in (0,h_0)$, $h_0 < 1$, $|\log h|$ is monotone decreasing so that $g(h)$ and $q(h)$ are monotone increasing. Also the two series

$$\sum_{n=1}^{\infty} g\left(\frac{1}{2^n}\right) = \sum_{n=1}^{\infty} \frac{1}{|\log 2^{-n}|^{\gamma}} = \frac{1}{(\log 2)^{\gamma}} \sum_{n=1}^{\infty} \frac{1}{n^{\gamma}}$$

$$\sum_{n=1}^{\infty} 2^n q\left(\frac{1}{2^n}\right) = \sum_{n=1}^{\infty} 2^n \frac{K2^{-n}}{|\log 2^{-n}|^{1+\epsilon}} = \frac{K}{(\log 2)^{1+\epsilon}} \sum_{n=1}^{\infty} \frac{1}{n^{1+\epsilon}}$$

converge since $\gamma > 1$ and $\epsilon > 0$. Thus g, q, and X satisfy the conditions of Theorem 6.2 and by its conclusion Theorem 6.4 holds.

□

The last three theorems gave sufficient conditions for the existence of a continuous equivalent process. We shall show that if in addition the given process is separable then it is itself almost surely continuous.

Theorem 6.5 Let X be a stochastic process on a probability space $(\Omega, \mathfrak{B}, P)$ and $D \subset R^1$. If X is almost surely separable and has an almost surely continuous equivalent process Y then X is itself almost surely continuous.

Proof From the almost sure separability of X there exist a countable dense subset $S \subset D$ and $\Lambda_1 \in \mathfrak{B}$ with $P(\Lambda_1) = 0$ such that for every open interval $I \subset R^1$

$$\inf_{D \cap I} X(t, \omega) = \inf_{S \cap I} X(s, \omega) \quad \text{and}$$

$$\sup_{D \cap I} X(t, \omega) = \sup_{S \cap I} X(s, \omega) \quad \text{when} \quad \omega \in \Lambda_1^c. \tag{1}$$

Since Y is almost surely continuous there exists $\Lambda_2 \in \mathfrak{B}$ with $P(\Lambda_2) = 0$ such that

$$Y(\cdot, \omega) \text{ is continuous on } D \text{ when } \omega \in \Lambda_2^c. \tag{2}$$

From the equivalence of X and Y we have in particular for every $s \in S$ a set $\Lambda_s \in \mathfrak{B}$ with $P(\Lambda_s) = 0$ such that

$$Y(s, \omega) = X(s, \omega) \text{ when } \omega \in \Lambda_s. \tag{3}$$

Let $\Lambda = \Lambda_1 \cup \Lambda_2 \cup \left(\bigcup_{s \in S} \Lambda_s\right)$. Then $\Lambda \in \mathfrak{B}$ and $P(\Lambda) = 0$. For every $\omega \in \Lambda^c$, (1), (2), and (3) hold. We proceed to show that, for every $\omega \in \Lambda^c$, $X(\cdot, \omega)$ is continuous on D. Let $t_0 \in D$. From the continuity of $Y(\cdot, \omega)$ on D, for every $\epsilon > 0$ there exists $\delta > 0$ such that

$$|Y(t, \omega) - Y(t_0, \omega)| < \epsilon \quad \text{when} \quad t \in D, \ |t - t_0| < \delta.$$

With $I = (t_0 - \delta, t_0 + \delta)$ we have

$$X(t_0, \omega) \geq \inf_{D \cap I} X(t, \omega) = \inf_{S \cap I} X(s, \omega) = \inf_{S \cap I} Y(s, \omega) \geq Y(t_0, \omega) - \epsilon.$$

From the arbitrariness of $\epsilon > 0$ we have $X(t_0, \omega) \geq Y(t_0, \omega)$. Similarly we have $X(t_0, \omega) \leq Y(t_0, \omega)$ so that $X(t_0, \omega) = Y(t_0, \omega)$. From the arbitrariness of $t_0 \in D$ we have $X(t, \omega) = Y(t, \omega)$ for all $t \in D$ when $\omega \in \Lambda^c$. Thus X is almost surely continuous. □

Combining Theorem 6.2 and Theorem 6.5 we have the following: If a stochastic process X on a probability space $(\Omega, \mathfrak{B}, P)$ and $D = [0,1]$ is almost surely separable and satisfies the conditions of Theorem 6.2 then it is almost surely continuous. This result can be extended easily to domains D which are infinite intervals. For instance when $D = R^1$ and

$$P\{\omega \in \Omega ;\ |X(t+h, \omega) - X(t, \omega)| \geq g(h)\} \leq q(h)$$

$$\text{whenever} \quad t, t+h \in R^1, \ 0 < |h| < h_0$$

then restricted to each of the countably many overlapping intervals $[n, n+1]$, $[n - \frac{1}{2}, n + \frac{1}{2}]$, $n = 0, \pm 1, \pm 2, \cdots$, X is almost surely continuous so that it is almost surely continuous on the entire R^1.

§7. INFINITE DIMENSIONAL RANDOM VECTORS

[I] Borel Sets and Baire Functions in Infinite Dimensional Spaces

In preparation for a study of Borel sets in infinite dimensional spaces let us consider the inverse transformation of the σ-field $\sigma(\mathfrak{E})$ generated by a collection $\mathfrak{E}$ of subsets of a set X_1 when this set is transformed into a set X_2.

Lemma 7.1 Let f be a transformation defined on a set X_1 into a set X_2. If $\mathfrak{A}_1$ is a σ-field of subsets of X_1 then

$$\mathfrak{A}_2 = \left\{E \subset X_2 \,;\, f^{-1}(E) \in \mathfrak{A}_1\right\}$$

is a σ-field of subsets of X_2.

Proof First of all $f^{-1}(X_2) = X_1 \in \mathfrak{A}_1$ so that $X_2 \in \mathfrak{A}_2$. Secondly if $E \in \mathfrak{A}_2$ then $f^{-1}(E) \in \mathfrak{A}_1$ and

$$f^{-1}(E^c) = f^{-1}(X_2 - E) = X_1 - f^{-1}(E) \in \mathfrak{A}_1$$

so that $E^c \in \mathfrak{A}_2$. Finally for $\{E_n, n = 1, 2, \cdots\} \subset \mathfrak{A}_2$ we have $f^{-1}(E_n) \in \mathfrak{A}_1$, $n = 1, 2, \cdots$, and

$$f^{-1}\left(\bigcup_{n=1}^{\infty} E_n\right) = \bigcup_{n=1}^{\infty} f^{-1}(E_n) \in \mathfrak{A}_1$$

so that $\bigcup_{n=1}^{\infty} E_n \in \mathfrak{A}_2$. This completes the proof that $\mathfrak{A}_2$ is a σ-field of subsets of X_2. □

Lemma 7.2 Let X_1, X_2, f, and $\mathfrak{A}_1$ be as in Lemma 7.1. Let $\mathfrak{E}$ be an arbitrary collection of subsets of X_2. Then $\mathfrak{A}_1 \supset f^{-1}(\mathfrak{E})$ implies $\mathfrak{A}_1 \supset f^{-1}\left(\sigma(\mathfrak{E})\right)$.

Proof For $\mathfrak{A}_2$ as defined in Lemma 7.1 we have $\mathfrak{A}_1 \supset f^{-1}(\mathfrak{A}_2)$. On the other hand from the assumption that $\mathfrak{A}_1 \supset f^{-1}(\mathfrak{E})$ we have $\mathfrak{A}_2 \supset \mathfrak{E}$ and consequently $\mathfrak{A}_2 \supset \sigma(\mathfrak{E})$. Thus $\mathfrak{A}_1 \supset f^{-1}(\mathfrak{A}_2) \supset f^{-1}\left(\sigma(\mathfrak{E})\right)$.

Theorem 7.3 Let f be a transformation defined on a set X_1 into a set X_2. If $\mathfrak{E}$ is an arbitrary collection of subsets of X_2 then

$$\sigma\left(f^{-1}(\mathfrak{E})\right) = f^{-1}\left(\sigma(\mathfrak{E})\right).$$

Proof Since $\sigma(\mathfrak{C})$ is a σ-field of subsets of X_2, $f^{-1}\big(\sigma(\mathfrak{C})\big)$ is a σ-field of subsets of X_1. This σ-field contains $f^{-1}(\mathfrak{C})$. Thus $\sigma\big(f^{-1}(\mathfrak{C})\big) \subset f^{-1}\big(\sigma(\mathfrak{C})\big)$. The reverse inclusion is a particular case of Lemma 7.2. □

We are now ready to consider Borel sets in an infinite dimensional space. As before let $\mathfrak{B}^n$ be the σ-field of Borel sets in the n-dimensional Euclidean space R^n. Let $\mathfrak{O}^n$ and $\mathfrak{C}^n$ be, respectively, the collection of open sets and the collection of closed sets in R^n in the usual topology. Let $\mathfrak{J}_O{}^n$ and $\mathfrak{J}_C{}^n$ be, respectively, the collection of open intervals $\Pi_{i=1}^n (a_i, b_i)$, $-\infty \le a_i < b_i \le \infty$, and the collection of closed intervals. Let $\mathfrak{G}^n$ be an arbitrary collection of subsets of R^n such that $\sigma(\mathfrak{G}^n) = \mathfrak{B}^n$. Thus $\mathfrak{O}^n, \mathfrak{C}^n, \mathfrak{J}_O{}^n$, and $\mathfrak{J}_C{}^n$ are examples of $\mathfrak{G}^n$.

Given an arbitrary linearly ordered set Λ, let R^Λ be the collection of all real-valued functions x on Λ where $x = [x_\lambda, \lambda \in \Lambda]$, $x_\lambda \in R^1$. For $M \subset \Lambda$ let p_M be the projection of R^Λ onto R^M, i.e.,

$$p_M[x_\lambda, \lambda \in \Lambda] = [x_\lambda, \lambda \in M].$$

Let $L = \{\lambda_1, \cdots, \lambda_n\}$ where $\lambda_1, \cdots, \lambda_n \in \Lambda$ and $\lambda_1 < \cdots < \lambda_n$ and let $\mathfrak{L}$ be the collection of finite strictly increasing sequences L of elements of Λ. For $L = \{\lambda_1, \cdots, \lambda_n\} \in \mathfrak{L}$ the projection $p_L = p_{\{\lambda_1, \cdots, \lambda_n\}}$ will be abbreviated as $p_{\lambda_1, \cdots, \lambda_n}$.

We define collections $\mathfrak{N}^\Lambda, \mathfrak{O}^\Lambda, \mathfrak{J}_O{}^\Lambda$ of subsets of R^Λ by

$$\mathfrak{N}^\Lambda = \left\{p_L{}^{-1}(\mathfrak{O}^L),\ L \in \mathfrak{L}\right\},$$

$\mathfrak{O}^\Lambda$ = the collection of arbitrary unions of members of $\mathfrak{N}^\Lambda$,

$\mathfrak{J}_O{}^\Lambda = \left\{p_L{}^{-1}(\mathfrak{J}_O{}^L), L \in \mathfrak{L}\right\}$.

Clearly $\mathfrak{J}_O{}^\Lambda \subset \mathfrak{N}^\Lambda \subset \mathfrak{O}^\Lambda$. If $x \in R^\Lambda, N \in \mathfrak{N}^\Lambda$, and $x \in N$, we say that N is a neighborhood of x. The collection $\mathfrak{N}^\Lambda$ satisfies the axioms of neighborhood system for a topological space and $\mathfrak{O}^\Lambda$ satisfies the axioms of open sets. The topology on R^Λ defined by $\mathfrak{O}^\Lambda$ is called the product topology.

Definition 7.4 By the σ-field of Borel sets in R^Λ we mean $\mathfrak{B}^\Lambda = \sigma(\mathfrak{J}_O{}^\Lambda)$ and by the σ-field of Borel sets in R^Λ in the topological sense we mean $\mathfrak{B}_T{}^\Lambda = \sigma(\mathfrak{O}^\Lambda)$.

Clearly $\mathfrak{B}^\Lambda \subset \mathfrak{B}_T{}^\Lambda$. When Λ is a finite set the collection of open sets $\mathfrak{O}^\Lambda$ in the product topology of R^Λ is the collection of open sets in the usual topology of a finite dimensional Euclidean space so that $\sigma(\mathfrak{J}_O{}^\Lambda) = \sigma(\mathfrak{O}^\Lambda)$ and hence $\mathfrak{B}^\Lambda = \mathfrak{B}_T{}^\Lambda$. We show below that this equality holds when Λ is a countable set.

Lemma 7.5 For any choice of $\mathfrak{G}^L$ with $\sigma(\mathfrak{G}^L) = \mathfrak{B}^L$ for $L \in \mathfrak{L}$ we have

$$\sigma\left\{p_L{}^{-1}(\mathfrak{G}^L), L \in \mathfrak{L}\right\} = \sigma\left\{p_L{}^{-1}(\mathfrak{B}^L), L \in \mathfrak{L}\right\}$$

and in particular

$$\mathfrak{B}^\Lambda = \sigma\left\{p_L{}^{-1}(\mathfrak{J}_O{}^L), L \in \mathfrak{L}\right\} = \sigma\left\{p_L{}^{-1}(\mathfrak{J}_C{}^L), L \in \mathfrak{L}\right\} = \sigma\left\{p_L{}^{-1}(\mathfrak{B}^L), L \in \mathfrak{L}\right\}.$$

Proof Since $\mathfrak{G}^L \subset \mathfrak{B}^L$ we have $\sigma\left\{p_L{}^{-1}(\mathfrak{G}^L), L \in \mathfrak{L}\right\} \subset \sigma\left\{p_L{}^{-1}(\mathfrak{B}^L), L \in \mathfrak{L}\right\}$. To prove the reversed inclusion, note that for each $L \in \mathfrak{L}$ we have by Theorem 7.3

$$p_L^{-1}(\mathfrak{B}^L) = p_L^{-1}\left(\sigma(\mathfrak{G}^L)\right) = \sigma\left(p_L^{-1}(\mathfrak{G}^L)\right) \subset \sigma\left\{p_L^{-1}(\mathfrak{G}^L), L \in \mathfrak{L}\right\}$$

so that

$$\sigma\left\{p_L^{-1}(\mathfrak{B}^L), L \in \mathfrak{L}\right\} \subset \sigma\left\{p_L^{-1}(\mathfrak{G}^L), L \in \mathfrak{L}\right\}. \qquad \square$$

Theorem 7.6 If Λ is a countable set then $\mathfrak{B}^\Lambda = \mathfrak{B}_T^\Lambda$.

Proof It suffices to show that $\mathfrak{B}^\Lambda \supset \mathfrak{B}_T^\Lambda$, i.e., $\sigma(\mathfrak{J}_O^\Lambda) \supset \sigma(\mathfrak{D}^\Lambda)$ when Λ is a countable set. Now when Λ is countable so is $\mathfrak{L}$. Let $\mathfrak{L} = \{L_k, k = 1,2, \cdots\}$. Since every member S of $\mathfrak{D}^\Lambda$ is an arbitrary union of members of $\mathfrak{N}^\Lambda = \left\{p_L^{-1}(\mathfrak{D}^L), L \in \mathfrak{L}\right\}$ we can write

$$S = \bigcup_{k=1}^{\infty} \bigcup_{\alpha_k \in A_k} p_{L_k}^{-1}\left(O_{L_k, \alpha_k}\right) = \bigcup_{k=1}^{\infty} p_{L_k}^{-1}\left(\bigcup_{\alpha_k \in A_k} O_{L_k, \alpha_k}\right)$$

where A_k is an index set which depends on L_k and $O_{L_k, \alpha} \in \mathfrak{D}^{L_k}$. Since an arbitrary union of open sets is open, $O_{L_k} \equiv \bigcup_{\alpha_k \in A_k} O_{L_k, \alpha_k} \in \mathfrak{D}^{L_k}$ so that

$$p_{L_k}^{-1}\left(\bigcup_{\alpha_k \in A_k} O_{L_k, \alpha_k}\right) = p_{L_k}^{-1}\left(O_{L_k}\right) \in p_{L_k}^{-1}\left(\mathfrak{B}^{L_k}\right).$$

Since S is a countable union

$$S \in \sigma\left\{p_{L_k}^{-1}(\mathfrak{B}^{L_k}), \ k = 1,2, \cdots\right\} = \mathfrak{B}^\Lambda$$

where the last equality is from Lemma 7.5. Thus $\sigma(\mathfrak{D}^\Lambda) \subset \mathfrak{B}^\Lambda$. This completes the proof. $\square$

Definition 7.6a A real-valued function f on R^Λ is called a Baire function or a Borel measurable function on R^Λ if it is $\mathfrak{B}^\Lambda$-measurable, i.e.,

$$f^{-1}(E) \in \mathfrak{B}^\Lambda \text{ for every } E \in \mathfrak{B}^1.$$

[II] Infinite Dimensional Random Vectors

Definition 7.7 Given a probability space $(\Omega, \mathfrak{B}, P)$. For an arbitrary linearly ordered index set Λ the transformation X of Ω into R^Λ defined by

$$X(\omega) = \left(X_\lambda(\omega), \lambda \in \Lambda\right), \qquad \omega \in \Omega$$

where X_λ is a random variable on $(\Omega, \mathfrak{B}, P)$ for each $\lambda \in \Lambda$ is called a random vector with values in R^Λ.

Theorem 7.8 Given a probability space $(\Omega, \mathfrak{B}, P)$. A transformation X of Ω into R^Λ is a random vector if and only if it is a measurable transformation of $(\Omega, \mathfrak{B})$ into $(R^\Lambda, \mathfrak{B}^\Lambda)$, i.e., $X^{-1}(E) \in \mathfrak{B}$ for every $E \in \mathfrak{B}^\Lambda$.

Proof (1) Suppose X is a random vector. Let $\mathfrak{A}^\Lambda$ be the collection of all subsets $A \subset R^\Lambda$ such that $X^{-1}(A) \in \mathfrak{B}$. From the fact that $\mathfrak{B}$ is a σ-field of subsets of Ω follows immediately that $\mathfrak{A}^\Lambda$ is a σ-field of subsets of R^Λ. Recall that, according to Lemma 7.5, $\mathfrak{B}^\Lambda = \sigma\left\{p_L^{-1}(\mathfrak{B}^L), L \in \mathfrak{L}\right\}$. To show that $\mathfrak{B}^\Lambda \subset \mathfrak{A}^\Lambda$ it suffices to show that $p_L^{-1}(\mathfrak{B}^L) \subset \mathfrak{A}^\Lambda$ for each $L \in \mathfrak{L}$. Now

$$\begin{aligned} X^{-1}\left(p_L^{-1}(\mathfrak{B}^L)\right) &= (p_L X)^{-1}(\mathfrak{B}^L) = X_L^{-1}(\mathfrak{B}^L) \\ &= X_L^{-1}\left(\sigma(\mathfrak{J}_O^L)\right) = \sigma\left(X_L^{-1}(\mathfrak{J}_O^L)\right) \end{aligned}$$

where we used Theorem 7.3 in obtaining the last of the above equalities. If we write $L = \{\lambda_1, \cdots, \lambda_n\}$ then each $I \in \mathfrak{J}_O^L$ has the form $I = \Pi_{i=1}^n (a_i, b_i)$ so that

$$X_L^{-1}(I) = \left\{\omega \in \Omega ; X_{\lambda_i}(\omega) \in (a_i, b_i),\ i = 1,2, \cdots, n\right\} \in \mathfrak{B}.$$

Thus $X_L^{-1}(\mathfrak{J}_0^L) \subset \mathfrak{B}$ and consequently $\sigma\left(X_L^{-1}(\mathfrak{J}_0^L)\right) \subset \mathfrak{B}$.

Therefore $\mathfrak{B}^\Lambda \subset \mathfrak{A}^\Lambda$ and X_Λ is a measurable transformation of $(\Omega, \mathfrak{B})$ imto $(R^\Lambda, \mathfrak{B}^\Lambda)$.

(2) Conversely suppose that X_Λ is a measurable transformation of $(\Omega, \mathfrak{B})$ into $(R^\Lambda, \mathfrak{B}^\Lambda)$. Then for every $\lambda \in \Lambda$, $X_\lambda = p_\lambda X_\Lambda$ is a random variable on $(\Omega, \mathfrak{B}, P)$ since it is the composition of the measurable transformation X_Λ of $(\Omega, \mathfrak{B})$ into $(R^\Lambda, \mathfrak{B}^\Lambda)$ and the measurable transformation p_λ of $(R^\Lambda, \mathfrak{B}^\Lambda)$ into $(R^1, \mathfrak{B}^1)$. □

Definition 7.9 Let X be a random vector defined on a probability space $(\Omega, \mathfrak{B}, P)$ with values in R^Λ, i.e., X is a measurable transformation of $(\Omega, \mathfrak{B})$ into $(R^\Lambda, \mathfrak{B}^\Lambda)$. The probability measure Φ_X on $(R^\Lambda, \mathfrak{B}^\Lambda)$ defined by

$$\Phi_X(E) = P\left(X^{-1}(E)\right), \qquad E \in \mathfrak{B}^\Lambda$$

is called the probability measure determined by X.

Theorem 7.10 Let X be a random vector defined on a probability space $(\Omega, \mathfrak{B}, P)$ with values in R^Λ and let Φ_X be the probability measure on $(R^\Lambda, \mathfrak{B}^\Lambda)$ determined by X. If f is a Baire function on R^Λ, i.e., a measurable transformation of $(R^\Lambda, \mathfrak{B}^\Lambda)$ into $(R^1, \mathfrak{B}^1)$, then $Y = f(X)$ is a random variable on $(\Omega, \mathfrak{B}, P)$ and

$$E(Y) = \int_{R^\Lambda} f(x)\, \Phi_X(dx), \text{ i.e., } \int_\Omega f\left(X(\omega)\right)P(d\omega) = \int_{R^\Lambda} f(x)\Phi_X(dx)$$

in the sense that the existence of one side of the equality implies that of the other and the equality of the two.

Proof Consider first the case where $f(x) \geq 0$ on R^{Λ}. Then both $\int_{R^k} f(x)\, \Phi_X(dx)$ and $\int_\Omega f(X(\omega))\, P(d\omega)$ exist. We show the equality of the two as follows. Let $I_{n,k} = \left[(k-1)2^{-n}, k2^{-n}\right)$, $n = 0, 1, 2, \cdots$, $k = 1, 2, \cdots$. Then

$$\int_\Omega f(X(\omega))\, P(d\omega) = \lim_{n\to\infty} \sum_{k=1}^{\infty} \frac{k-1}{2^n} P\{\omega \in \Omega; f(X(\omega)) \in I_{n,k}\}$$

$$= \lim_{n\to\infty} \sum_{k=1}^{\infty} \frac{k-1}{2^n} P\{\omega \in \Omega; X(\omega) \in f^{-1}(I_{n,k})\}.$$

Since f is a Baire function on R^{Λ}, $f^{-1}(I_{n,k}) \in \mathfrak{B}^{\Lambda}$ and

$$P\{\omega \in \Omega; X(\omega) \in f^{-1}(I_{n,k})\} = P\left(X^{-1} f^{-1}(I_{n,k})\right) = \Phi_X\left(f^{-1}(I_{n,k})\right).$$

Thus

$$\int_\Omega f(X(\omega))\, P(d\omega) = \lim_{n\to\infty} \sum_{k=1}^{\infty} \frac{k-1}{2^n} \Phi_X\left(f^{-1}(I_{n,k})\right)$$

$$= \lim_{n\to\infty} \sum_{k=1}^{\infty} \frac{k-1}{2^n} \Phi_X\{x \in R^{\Lambda}; f(x) \in I_{n,k}\}$$

$$= \int_{R^k} f(x)\, \Phi_X(dx)$$

This proves the theorem for nonnegative f. For the general case we decompose f into its positive and negative parts and apply the above result. □

Definition 7.11 A finite system of random vectors $\{(X_\lambda, \lambda \in \Lambda_1), \cdots, (X_\lambda, \lambda \in \Lambda_n)\}$ on a probability space is said to be independent if, for arbitrary $\lambda_{1,1}, \cdots, \lambda_{1,p(1)} \in \Lambda_1; \cdots; \lambda_{n,1}, \cdots, \lambda_{n,p(n)} \in \Lambda_n$, the system of finite dimensional random vectors $\{(X_{\lambda_{1,1}}, \cdots, X_{\lambda_{1,p(1)}}), \cdots, (X_{\lambda_{n,1}}, \cdots, X_{\lambda_{n,p(n)}})\}$ is an independent system. An infinite system of random vectors is said to be independent if every finite subcollection is independent.

Theorem 7.12 Let $\{X_{\Lambda_1}, \cdots, X_{\Lambda_n}\}$ be an independent system of random vectors on a probability space $(\Omega, \mathfrak{B}, P)$. Let T_j be a Baire transformation of R^{Λ_j} into R^{M_j} and let $Y_{M_j} = T_j(X_{\Lambda_j})$ for $j = 1, 2, \cdots, n$. Then $\{Y_{M_1}, \cdots, Y_{M_n}\}$ is an independent system of random vectors.

Proof This theorem is an immediate consequence of Definition 7.11 and Theorem A6.6. □

Theorem 7.13 A system of random variables $\{X_\lambda, \lambda \in \Lambda\}$ on a probability space $(\Omega, \mathfrak{B}, P)$ is independent if and only if $(R^\Lambda, \mathfrak{B}^\Lambda, \Phi_X)$ where X is the random vector $X(\omega) = \left(X_\lambda(\omega), \lambda \in \Lambda\right)$, $\omega \in \Omega$, is the product measure space of $(R^1, \mathfrak{B}^1, \Phi_{X_\lambda})$, $\lambda \in \Lambda$.

Proof (1) Suppose $\{X_\lambda, \lambda \in \Lambda\}$ is an independent system. Then for every $\{\lambda_1, \cdots, \lambda_n\} \subset \Lambda$, $\{X_{\lambda_1}, \cdots, X_{\lambda_n}\}$ is an independent system. Thus for $E_i \in \mathfrak{B}^1$, $i = 1,2,\cdots,n$, and

$$E = \prod_{\lambda\in\Lambda} E_\lambda$$

where $E_\lambda = E_i$ when $\lambda = \lambda_i$ for $i = 1,2,\cdots,n$ and $E_\lambda = R^1$ when $\lambda \neq \lambda_i$ for $i = 1,2,\cdots,n$, we have

$$\begin{aligned}\Phi_X(E) &= P\left(X^{-1}(E)\right) = P\left\{\omega \in \Omega; X_{\lambda_i}(\omega) \in E_i, i = 1,2,\cdots n\right\}\\ &= \prod_{i=1}^{n} P\left\{\omega \in \Omega; X_{\lambda_i}(\omega) \in E_i\right\} = \prod_{i=1}^{n} P\left(X_{\lambda_i}^{-1}(E_i)\right)\\ &= \prod_{i=1}^{n} \Phi_{X_{\lambda_i}}(E_i).\end{aligned}$$

But according to the theory of infinite product of measures there exists a unique probability measure on $(R^\Lambda, \mathfrak{B}^\Lambda)$ with the above property, namely, the product of Φ_{X_λ}, $\lambda \in \Lambda$. Thus $\Phi_X = \Pi_{\lambda\in\Lambda} \Phi_{X_\lambda}$.

(2) Conversely suppose $(R^\Lambda, \mathfrak{B}^\Lambda, \Phi_X)$ is the product of $(R^1, \mathfrak{B}^1, \Phi_{X_\lambda})$, $\lambda \in \Lambda$. Then for $L = \{\lambda_1, \cdots, \lambda_n\} \subset \Lambda$, $(R^L, \mathfrak{B}^L, \Phi_{X_L})$ is the product of $(R^1, \mathfrak{B}^1, \Phi_{\lambda_i})$, $i = 1,2,\cdots,n$, so that $\{X_{\lambda_1}, \cdots, X_{\lambda_n}\}$ is an independent system. This proves the independence of the system $\{X_\lambda, \lambda \in \Lambda\}$. □

[III] σ-field Generated by a System of Random Variables

Definition 7.14 By the σ-field $\sigma\{X_\lambda, \lambda\in \Lambda\}$ generated by a system of random variables $\{X_\lambda, \lambda\in \Lambda\}$ on a probability space $(\Omega, \mathfrak{B}, P)$ we mean the smallest σ-field of subsets of Ω with respect to which every X_λ, $\lambda \in \Lambda$, is measurable. Similarly by the

σ-field $\sigma\{X_L, L \in \mathfrak{L}\}$ generated by the system of finite dimensional random vectors $\{X_L, L \in \mathfrak{L}\}$ we mean the smallest σ-field of subsets of Ω with respect to which every $X_L, L \in \mathfrak{L}$, is measurable. Clearly

$$\sigma\{X_\lambda, \lambda \in \Lambda\} = \sigma\left\{X_\lambda^{-1}(\mathfrak{B}^1), \lambda \in \Lambda\right\} \subset \mathfrak{B}$$

and

$$\sigma\{X_L, L \in \mathfrak{L}\} = \sigma\left\{X_L^{-1}(\mathfrak{B}^L), L \in \mathfrak{L}\right\} \subset \mathfrak{B}.$$

Lemma 7.15 Let $\{X_\lambda, \lambda \in \Lambda\}$ be a system of random variables on a probability space. Then the following σ-fields of subsets of Ω are all equal

(1) $\sigma\left\{X_\lambda^{-1}(\mathfrak{B}^1), \lambda \in \Lambda\right\}$ (2) $\sigma\left\{X_\lambda^{-1}(\mathfrak{G}^1), \lambda \in \Lambda\right\}$

(3) $\sigma\left\{X_L^{-1}(\mathfrak{B}^L), L \in \mathfrak{L}\right\}$ (4) $\sigma\left\{X_L^{-1}(\mathfrak{G}^L), L \in \mathfrak{L}\right\}$

(5) $X_\Lambda^{-1}(\mathfrak{B}^\Lambda)$

Proof By Theorem 7.3

$$\begin{aligned}\sigma\left\{X_\lambda^{-1}(\mathfrak{B}^1), \lambda \in \Lambda\right\} &= \sigma\left\{X_\lambda^{-1}\left(\sigma(\mathfrak{G}^1)\right), \lambda \in \Lambda\right\} \\ &= \sigma\left\{\sigma\left(X_\lambda^{-1}(\mathfrak{G}^1)\right), \lambda \in \Lambda\right\} \\ &\supset \sigma\left\{X_\lambda^{-1}(\mathfrak{G}^1), \lambda \in \Lambda\right\}\end{aligned}$$

On the other hand for each $\lambda \in \Lambda$, $\sigma\left(X_\lambda^{-1}(\mathfrak{G}^1)\right) \subset \sigma\left\{X_\lambda^{-1}(\mathfrak{G}^1), \lambda \in \Lambda\right\}$ and hence

$$\sigma\left\{\sigma\left(X_\lambda^{-1}(\mathfrak{G})^1)\right), \lambda \in \Lambda\right\} \subset \sigma\left\{X_\lambda^{-1}(\mathfrak{G}^1), \lambda \in \Lambda\right\}.$$

Thus (1) and (2) are equal.

Similarly (3) and (4) are equal.

Clearly (3) contains (1). We show that (4) is contained in (1). For $\mathfrak{G}^L$ in (4) we may take $\mathfrak{G}^L = \mathfrak{J}_0^{\ L}$. Then for every $I \in \mathfrak{J}_0^{\ L}$, namely, $I = \Pi_{i=1}^n (a_i, b_i)$, we have

$$X_L^{-1}(I) = \bigcap_{i=1}^n \left\{\omega \in \Omega\, ; X_{\lambda_i}(\omega) \in (a_i, b_i)\right\}$$

which is contained in (1). Thus (4) is contained in (1).

Finally we show that (5) is equal to (4). Now

$$\begin{aligned} X_\Lambda^{-1}(\mathfrak{B}^\Lambda) &= X_\Lambda^{-1}\left(\sigma(\mathfrak{J}_0^{\ \Lambda})\right) = X_\Lambda^{-1}\left\{\sigma\left\{P_L^{-1}(\mathfrak{J}_0^{\ L}), L \in \mathfrak{L}\right\}\right\} \\ &= \sigma\left\{X_\Lambda^{-1}\left\{P_L^{-1}(\mathfrak{J}_0^{\ L}), L \in \mathfrak{L}\right\}\right\} = \left\{(P_L X_\Lambda)^{-1}\mathfrak{J}_0^{\ L}, L \in \mathfrak{L}\right\} \\ &= \sigma\left\{X_L^{-1}(\mathfrak{J}_0^{\ L}), L \in \mathfrak{L}\right\} \end{aligned}$$

where the third equality is by Theorem 7.3. □

<u>Definition 7.16</u> A random variable Y on a probability space $(\Omega, \mathfrak{B}, P)$ is said to be a Baire function, or Borel measurable function, of a system of random variables $\{X_\lambda, \lambda \in \Lambda\}$ on $(\Omega, \mathfrak{B}, P)$ if there exists a $\mathfrak{B}^\Lambda$-measurable function $\varphi(\xi_\lambda, \lambda \in \Lambda)$ on R^Λ such that

$$Y(\omega) = \varphi\left(X_\lambda(\omega), \lambda \in \Lambda\right), \qquad \omega \in \Omega.$$

Theorem 7.17 A random variable Y on a probability space $(\Omega, \mathfrak{B}, P)$ is a Baire function of a system of random variables $\{X_\lambda, \lambda \in \Lambda\}$ on $(\Omega, \mathfrak{B}, P)$ if and only if Y is $\sigma\{X_\lambda, \lambda \in \Lambda\}$-measurable.

Proof (1) Let Y be a Baire function of $\{X_\lambda, \lambda \in \Lambda\}$. Then there exists a $\mathfrak{B}$-measurable function $\varphi(\xi_\lambda, \lambda \in \Lambda)$ on R^Λ such that

$$Y(\omega) = \varphi\left(X_\lambda(\omega), \lambda \in \Lambda\right), \qquad \omega \in \Omega. \tag{1}$$

With the transformation X_Λ of Ω into R^Λ defined by $X_\Lambda(\omega) = \left(X_\lambda(\omega), \lambda \in \Lambda\right)$ and the transformation φ of R^Λ into R^1, the random variable Y can be given as a composite transformation $Y = \varphi \circ X_\Lambda$ of Ω into R^1. Then

$$Y^{-1}(E) = X_\Lambda^{-1}\left(\varphi^{-1}(E)\right), \qquad E \in \mathfrak{B}^1.$$

But $\varphi^{-1}(E) = \mathfrak{B}^\Lambda$ and hence

$$X_\Lambda^{-1}\left(\varphi^{-1}(E)\right) \in \sigma\left\{X_\lambda^{-1}(\mathfrak{B}^1), \lambda \in \Lambda\right\} = \sigma\{X_\lambda, \lambda \in \Lambda\}$$

by Lemma 7.15. Thus Y is $\sigma\{X_\lambda, \lambda \in \Lambda\}$-measurable.

(2) Conversely suppose Y is $\sigma\{X_\lambda, \lambda \in \Lambda\}$-measurable. We proceed to construct a $\mathfrak{B}^\Lambda$-measurable function $\varphi(\xi_\lambda, \lambda \in \Lambda)$ on R^Λ with which (1) holds. Now from the $\sigma\{X_\lambda, \lambda \in \Lambda\}$-measurability of Y we have

$$S_{m,j} \equiv Y^{-1}\left(\left(\frac{j}{2^m}, \frac{j+1}{2^m}\right]\right) \in \sigma\{X_\lambda, \lambda \in \Lambda\},$$

$$\text{for } m = 1, 2, \cdots;\ j = 0, \pm 1, \pm 2, \cdots . \tag{2}$$

According to Lemma 7.15

$$\sigma\{X_\lambda, \lambda \in \Lambda\} = \sigma\left\{X_\lambda^{-1}(\mathfrak{B}^1), \lambda \in \Lambda\right\} = X_\Lambda^{-1}(\mathfrak{B}^\Lambda) .$$

Thus there exists $E_{m,j} \in \mathfrak{B}^\Lambda$ such that

$$S_{m,j} = X_\Lambda^{-1}(E_{m,j}) .$$

For fixed m, $S_{m,j}$, $j = 0, \pm 1, \pm 2, \cdots$, are disjoint and their union is equal to Ω. But $E_{m,j}$, $j = 0, \pm 1, \pm 2, \cdots$, may not have this property. However, if we let

$$F_{m,j} = E_{m,j} - \bigcup_{j' \neq j} \left(E_{m,j} \cap E_{m,j'}\right) \in \mathfrak{B}^\Lambda \tag{3}$$

then $F_{m,j}$, $j = 0, \pm 1, \pm 2, \cdots$ are disjoint for fixed m since

$$X_\Lambda^{-1}\left(E_{m,j_1} \cap E_{m,j_2}\right) = X_\Lambda^{-1}\left(E_{m,j_1}\right) \cap X_\Lambda^{-1}\left(E_{m,j_2}\right) = \phi$$

for $j_1 \neq j_2$. Now

$$X_\Lambda^{-1}(F_{m,j}) = S_{m,j} = Y^{-1}\left(\left(\frac{j}{2^m}, \frac{j+1}{2^m}\right]\right) \tag{4}$$

Define a $\mathfrak{B}^\Lambda$-measurable function $\varphi_m(\xi_\lambda, \lambda \in \Lambda)$ on R^Λ by

$$\varphi_m(\xi_\lambda, \lambda \in \Lambda) = \begin{cases} \dfrac{j}{2^m} & \text{on } F_{m,j},\ j = 0, \pm 1, \pm 2, \cdots \\ 0 & \text{otherwise.} \end{cases}$$

Then from (3) and (4)

$$0 < Y(\omega) - \varphi_m\left(X_\lambda(\omega), \lambda \in \Lambda\right) \le \frac{1}{2^m}, \quad \omega \in \Omega$$

and consequently

$$\lim_{n\to\infty} \varphi_m\left(X_\lambda(\omega), \lambda \in \Lambda\right) = Y(\omega), \qquad \omega \in \Omega. \tag{5}$$

Each φ_m is a $\mathfrak{B}^\Lambda$-measurable function on R^Λ. Let R_∞^Λ be the subset of R^Λ where the following limit exists:

$$\varphi(\xi_\lambda, \lambda \in \Lambda) = \lim_{m\to\infty} \varphi_m(\xi_\lambda, \lambda \in \Lambda). \tag{6}$$

We define

$$\varphi(\xi_\lambda, \lambda \in \Lambda) \equiv 0 \qquad \text{on} \qquad R^\Lambda - R_\infty^\Lambda .$$

Then φ is a $\mathfrak{B}^\Lambda$-measurable function on R^Λ. Let K be the subset of R^Λ covered by the transformation X_Λ of Ω into R^Λ. To show that $K \subset R_\infty^\Lambda$, let $(\xi_\lambda, \lambda \in \Lambda) \in K$. Then for some $\omega \in \Omega$ we have $(\xi_\lambda, \lambda \in \Lambda) = \left(X_\lambda(\omega), \lambda \in \Lambda\right)$ so that

$$\lim_{m\to\infty} \varphi_m(\xi_\lambda, \lambda \in \Lambda) = \lim_{m\to\infty} \varphi_m\left(X_\lambda(\omega), \lambda \in \Lambda\right)$$

which exists by (5). This proves that $K \subset R_\infty^\Lambda$. Then by (5) and (6)

$$Y(\omega) = \lim_{m\to\infty} \varphi_m\left(X_\lambda(\omega), \lambda \in \Lambda\right) = \varphi\left(X_\lambda(\omega), \lambda \in \Lambda\right), \qquad \omega \in \Omega.$$

This completes the proof of the theorem. □

<u>Lemma 7.18</u> A real-valued function f defined on a measurable space $(X, \mathfrak{F})$ is $\mathfrak{F}$-measurable if and only if for every rational number $r, f^{-1}\left((-\infty, r)\right) \in \mathfrak{F}$.

<u>Proof</u> If f is $\mathfrak{F}$-measurable then $f^{-1}\left((-\infty, r)\right) \in \mathfrak{F}$ for

every real number r and in particular for every rational number r. Conversely suppose that $f^{-1}\big((-\infty, r)\big) \in \mathfrak{F}$ for every rational number r. Given a real number α let $\{r_n, n = 1, 2, \cdots\}$ be a sequence of rational numbers such that $r_n \uparrow \alpha$. Then $(-\infty, \alpha) = \bigcup_{n=1}^{\infty} (-\infty, r_n)$ and

$$f^{-1}\big((-\infty, r)\big) = f^{-1}\Big(\bigcup_{n=1}^{\infty} (-\infty, r_n)\Big) = \bigcup_{n=1}^{\infty} f^{-1}\big((-\infty, r_n)\big) \in \mathfrak{F}$$

since $f^{-1}\big((-\infty, r_n)\big) \in \mathfrak{F}$ for $n = 1, 2, \cdots$ and $\mathfrak{F}$ is a σ-field. □

Theorem 7.19 Let $\{X_\lambda, \lambda \in \Lambda\}$ be a system of random variables on a probability space $(\Omega, \mathfrak{B}, P)$. If $E \in \sigma\{X_\lambda, \lambda \in \Lambda\}$ then there exists a countable subset $M_E \subset \Lambda$ depending on E such that $E \in \sigma\{X_\lambda, \lambda \in M_E\}$. If Y is a $\sigma\{X_\lambda, \lambda \in \Lambda\}$-measurable random variable on $(\Omega, \mathfrak{B}, P)$ then there exists a countable subset $M_Y \subset \Lambda$ depending on Y such that Y is $\sigma\{X_\lambda, \lambda \in M_Y\}$-measurable.

Proof (1) Recall that $\sigma\{X_\lambda, \lambda \in \Lambda\} = \sigma\big\{X_\lambda^{-1}(\mathfrak{B}^1), \lambda \in \Lambda\big\}$. Let $\mathfrak{A}$ be the collection of members E of $\sigma\{X_\lambda, \lambda \in \Lambda\}$ such that $E \in \sigma\{X_\lambda, \lambda \in M_E\}$ for some countable subset $M_E \subset \Lambda$ depending on E. The fact that $\mathfrak{A}$ is not $\emptyset$ and is a σ-field can be seen as follows. First of all $\Omega = X_\lambda^{-1}(R^1) \in X_\lambda^{-1}(\mathfrak{B}^1) = \sigma(X_\lambda) \subset \mathfrak{A}$ for any $\lambda \in \Lambda$. Secondly if $E \in \sigma\{X_\lambda, \lambda \in M_E\}$ where $M_E \subset \Lambda$ is a countable subset then $E^c \in \sigma\{X_\lambda, \lambda \in M_E\}$ since $\sigma\{X_\lambda, \lambda \in M_E\}$ is a σ-field so that $E^c \in \mathfrak{A}$. Finally let $\{E_n, n = 1, 2, \cdots\} \subset \mathfrak{A}$. Then $E_n \in \sigma\{X_\lambda, \lambda \in M_{E_n}\}$ where $M_{E_n} \subset \Lambda$ is a countable subset for $n = 1, 2, \cdots$. Then $M = \bigcup_{n=1}^{\infty} E_n \subset \Lambda$ is a countable subset and

$E_n \in \sigma\{X_\lambda, \lambda \in M\}$. From the fact that $\sigma\{X_\lambda, \lambda \in M\}$ is a σ-field we have $\bigcup_{n=1}^\infty E_n \in \sigma\{X_\lambda, \lambda \in M\}$ so that $\bigcup_{n=1}^\infty E_n \in \mathfrak{A}$. This completes the proof that $\mathfrak{A}$ is a σ-field. Now $\sigma(X_\lambda) \subset \mathfrak{A}$ for every $\lambda \in \Lambda$ and hence $\sigma\{X_\lambda, \lambda \in \Lambda\} \subset \mathfrak{A}$ since $\mathfrak{A}$ is a σ-field.

(2) Let Y be a $\sigma\{X_\lambda, \lambda \in \Lambda\}$-measurable random variable on $(\Omega, \mathfrak{B}, P)$. Let $\{r_n, n = 1, 2, \cdots\}$ be the collection of all rational numbers. Then $Y^{-1}\big((-\infty, r_n)\big) \in \sigma\{X_\lambda, \lambda \in \Lambda\}$ for each n and hence $Y^{-1}\big((-\infty, r_n)\big) \in \sigma\{X_\lambda, \lambda \in M_n\}$ for some countable subset $M_n \subset \Lambda$ by (1). Let $M = \bigcup_{n=1}^\infty M_n \subset \Lambda$, a countable subset. Then $Y^{-1}\big((-\infty, r_n)\big) \in \sigma\{X_\lambda, \lambda \in M\}$ for each n. Thus by Lemma 7.18, Y is $\sigma\{X_\lambda, \lambda \in M\}$-measurable. □

Chapter 2

MARTINGALES

§8. CONDITIONAL EXPECTATION AND CONDITIONAL PROBABILITY

[I] Conditional Expectation

Given a probability space $(\Omega, \mathfrak{B}, P)$ and a random variable $X \in L_1(\Omega)$. By the conditional expectation of X given $A \in \mathfrak{B}$ we mean the real number

$$E\left(X|A\right) = \frac{1}{P(A)} \int_A X(\omega)\, P(d\omega)$$

provided $P(A) > 0$. Given a sub-σ-field $\mathfrak{A} \subset \mathfrak{B}$ we shall define the conditional expectation of X given $\mathfrak{A}$, written $E\left(X|\mathfrak{A}\right)$, as an $\mathfrak{A}$-measurable random variable such that

$$\int_A E\left(X|\mathfrak{A}\right)(\omega)\, P(d\omega) = \int_A X(\omega)\, P(d\omega), \qquad A \in \mathfrak{A}.$$

We shall show that $E\left(X|\mathfrak{A}\right)$ always exists and is unique up to an $\mathfrak{A}$-measurable set of P-measure 0. Note that when $\mathfrak{A}$ is a finite field, $E\left(X|\mathfrak{A}\right)$ is a simple function on $(\Omega, \mathfrak{A})$.

Theorem 8.1 Given a probability space $(\Omega, \mathfrak{B}, P)$, a random variable $X \in L_1(\Omega)$ and a sub-σ-field $\mathfrak{A} \subset \mathfrak{B}$. There exists an $\mathfrak{A}$-measurable function φ on Ω such that

$$\int_A \varphi(\omega)\, P(d\omega) = \int_A X(\omega)\, P(d\omega), \qquad A \in \mathfrak{A}. \tag{1}$$

If φ_1 and φ_2 are $\mathfrak{A}$-measurable random variables on $(\Omega, \mathfrak{B}, P)$ each satisfying (1) then $\varphi_1(\omega) = \varphi_2(\omega)$ for a.e. ω with respect to $(\mathfrak{A}, P)$.

Proof Let $X \in L_1(\Omega)$ and $X \geq 0$. If $E(X) = 0$ then $X(\omega) = 0$ for a.e. ω so that the identically vanishing function on Ω will do as φ. Assume then that $E(X) > 0$. The set function on $\mathfrak{A}$ defined by

$$Q(A) = \frac{1}{E(X)} \int_A X(\omega)\, P(d\omega), \qquad A \in \mathfrak{A} \tag{2}$$

is a probability measure on $(\Omega, \mathfrak{A})$ which is absolutely continuous with respect to P. By the Radon-Nikodym theorem there exists an $\mathfrak{A}$-measurable function ψ on Ω such that

$$Q(A) = \int_A \psi(\omega)\, P(d\omega), \qquad A \in \mathfrak{A}$$

Then

$$\int_A X(\omega)\, P(d\omega) = E(X)\, Q(A) = \int_A E(X)\, \psi(\omega)\, P(d\omega), \qquad A \in \mathfrak{A}$$

and $\varphi(\omega) = E(X)\, \psi(\omega)$ is an $\mathfrak{A}$-measurable function on Ω which satisfies (1). For a general $X \in L_1(\Omega)$ we apply the above result to its positive and negative parts.

If φ_1 and φ_2 are $\mathfrak{A}$-measurable random variables satisfying (1), let

$$A_0 = \left\{\omega \in \Omega;\ \varphi_1(\omega) > \varphi_2(\omega)\right\} \in \mathfrak{A}\,.$$

By (1)

$$\int_{A_0} \left\{\varphi_1(\omega) - \varphi_2(\omega)\right\} P(d\omega) = 0\,.$$

Since $\varphi_1(\omega) - \varphi_2(\omega) > 0$ on A_0 we have $P(A_0) = 0$. Thus $\varphi_1(\omega) \leq \varphi_2(\omega)$ for a.e. ω with respect to $(\mathfrak{A}, P)$. Reversing the roles of φ_1 and φ_2 we have $\varphi_2(\omega) \leq \varphi_1(\omega)$ for a.e. ω with respect to $(\mathfrak{A}, P)$ and hence $\varphi_1(\omega) = \varphi_2(\omega)$ for a.e. ω with respect to $(\mathfrak{A}, P)$. □

<u>Definition 8.2</u> Given a probability space $(\Omega, \mathfrak{B}, P)$, a random variable $X \in L_1(\Omega)$ and a sub-σ-field $\mathfrak{A} \subset \mathfrak{B}$. The equivalence class of $\mathfrak{A}$-measurable random variables φ on Ω satisfying

$$\int_A \varphi(\omega)\, P(d\omega) = \int_A X(\omega)\, P(d\omega), \qquad A \in \mathfrak{A}$$

is called the conditional expectation of X given $\mathfrak{A}$ and written $E(X|\mathfrak{A})$, the equivalence relation being that of a.e. equality with respect to $(\mathfrak{A}, P)$. Each member of this equivalence class is called a version of the conditional expectation. We shall use $E(X|\mathfrak{A})(\omega)$ to mean the value at ω of an arbitrary version. For $X_1, X_2 \in L_1(\Omega)$, by $E(X_1|\mathfrak{A}) = E(X_2|\mathfrak{A})$ we mean the equality of the two equivalence classes, i.e., every version of $E(X_1|\mathfrak{A})$ is a version of $E(X_2|\mathfrak{A})$ and vice versa.

<u>Theorem 8.3</u> Given a probability space $(\Omega, \mathfrak{B}, P)$, random variables $X, X_1, \cdots, X_n \in L_1(\Omega)$, a sub-$\sigma$-field $\mathfrak{A} \subset \mathfrak{B}$ and $c_1, \cdots, c_n \in R^1$. We have

$$E\left(\sum_{i=1}^{n} c_i X_i \,|\, \mathfrak{A}\right) = \sum_{i=1}^{n} c_i E(X_i \,|\, \mathfrak{A}) \tag{1}$$

$$X(\omega) \geq 0 \text{ for a.e. } \omega \text{ with respect to } (\mathfrak{B}, P)$$
$$\Rightarrow E(X|\mathfrak{A})(\omega) \geq 0 \text{ for a.e. } \omega \text{ with respect to } (\mathfrak{A}, P) \tag{2}$$

$$X_1(\omega) \leq X_2(\omega) \text{ for a.e. } \omega \text{ with respect to } (\mathfrak{B}, P)$$
$$\Rightarrow E(X_1|\mathfrak{A})(\omega) \leq E(X_2|\mathfrak{A})(\omega) \text{ for a.e. } \omega \text{ with respect to } (\mathfrak{A}, P) \tag{3}$$

$$\left|E(X|\mathfrak{A})(\omega)\right| \leq E(|X| \,|\, \mathfrak{A})(\omega) \text{ for a.e. } \omega \text{ with respect to } (\mathfrak{A}, P). \tag{4}$$

Proof (1) is obvious from Definition 8.2. To prove (2), let $X(\omega) \geq 0$ for a.e. ω with respect to $(\mathfrak{B}, P)$. Then for every $A \in \mathfrak{A}$

$$\int_A E\left(X \mid \mathfrak{A}\right)(\omega)\; P(d\omega) = \int_A X(\omega)\; P(d\omega) \geq 0$$

so that $E\left(X \mid \mathfrak{A}\right)(\omega) \geq 0$ for a.e. ω with respect to $(\mathfrak{A}, P)$. (3) follows from (2) and (1). To prove (4), note that $X, -X \leq |X|$ and (3) imply

$$E\left(X \mid \mathfrak{A}\right)(\omega) \leq E\left(|X| \mid \mathfrak{A}\right)(\omega) \quad \text{for a.e. } \omega \text{ with respect to } (\mathfrak{A}, P)$$

and

$$-E\left(X \mid \mathfrak{A}\right)(\omega) = E\left(-X \mid \mathfrak{A}\right)(\omega) \leq E\left(|X| \mid \mathfrak{A}\right)(\omega) \quad \text{for a.e. } \omega \text{ with respect to } (\mathfrak{A}, P)$$

so that

$$\left|E\left(X \mid \mathfrak{A}\right)(\omega)\right| \leq E\left(|X| \mid \mathfrak{A}\right)(\omega) \quad \text{for a.e. } \omega \text{ with respect to } (\mathfrak{A}, P). \quad \square$$

Theorem 8.4 Given a probability space $(\Omega, \mathfrak{B}, P)$, random variables X and Y where $X, XY \in L_1(\Omega)$ and a sub-σ-field $\mathfrak{A} \subset \mathfrak{B}$. If Y is $\mathfrak{A}$-measurable then

$$E\left(XY \mid \mathfrak{A}\right) = YE\left(X \mid \mathfrak{A}\right). \tag{1}$$

In particular if $Y \in L_1(\Omega)$ and is $\mathfrak{A}$-measurable then

$$E\left(Y \mid \mathfrak{A}\right) = Y. \tag{2}$$

Proof To prove (1) we show that $Y(\omega)\,E\left(X \mid \mathfrak{A}\right)(\omega)$ is a version of $E\left(XY \mid \mathfrak{A}\right)$. The $\mathfrak{A}$-measurability of $Y(\omega)\,E\left(X \mid \mathfrak{A}\right)(\omega)$ follows from that of $Y(\omega)$ and $E\left(X \mid \mathfrak{A}\right)(\omega)$. It remains to show

$$\int_A Y(\omega)\, E\left(X \mid \mathfrak{A}\right)(\omega)\, P(d\omega) = \int_A Y(\omega)\, X(\omega)\, P(d\omega), \qquad A \in \mathfrak{A}. \qquad (3)$$

Assume $X \geq 0$. The measure on $(\Omega, \mathfrak{A})$ defined by

$$\mu(A) = \int_A X(\omega)\, P(d\omega) = \int_A E\left(X \mid \mathfrak{A}\right)(\omega)\, P(d\omega), \qquad A \in \mathfrak{A} \qquad (4)$$

is absolutely continuous with respect to P so that each of the two sides of (3) is equal to $\int_A Y(\omega)\, \mu(d\omega)$. For the general X we apply the above result to the positive and negative parts of X. □

Theorem 8.5 Given a probability space $(\Omega, \mathfrak{B}, P)$, a random variable $X \in L_1(\Omega)$ and sub-σ-fields $\mathfrak{A}_1, \mathfrak{A}_2$ of $\mathfrak{B}$ where $\mathfrak{A}_1 \subset \mathfrak{A}_2$, we have

$$E\left[E\left(X \mid \mathfrak{A}_1\right) \mid \mathfrak{A}_2\right] = E\left(X \mid \mathfrak{A}_1\right) \qquad (1)$$

$$E\left[E\left(X \mid \mathfrak{A}_2\right) \mid \mathfrak{A}_1\right] = E\left(X \mid \mathfrak{A}_1\right). \qquad (2)$$

Proof Since $E\left(X \mid \mathfrak{A}_1\right)$ is $\mathfrak{A}_1$-measurable it is also $\mathfrak{A}_2$-measurable. Then (1) follows from (2) of Theorem 8.4. To prove (2) let $A \in \mathfrak{A}_1 \subset \mathfrak{A}_2$. By repeated application of Definition 8.2

$$\int_A E\left[E\left(X \mid \mathfrak{A}_2\right) \mid \mathfrak{A}_1\right](\omega)\, P(d\omega) = \int_A E\left(X \mid \mathfrak{A}_2\right)(\omega)\, P(d\omega) = \int_A X(\omega)\, P(d\omega).$$

Thus $E\left[E\left(X \mid \mathfrak{A}_2\right) \mid \mathfrak{A}_1\right]$ is the conditional expectation of X given $\mathfrak{A}_1$ and (2) holds. □

Theorem 8.6 Dominated Convergence Theorem for Conditional Expectation. Given a probability space $(\Omega, \mathfrak{B}, P)$ and a sequence of random variables $\{X_n, n = 1, 2, \cdots\} \subset L_1(\Omega)$. If $X_n(\omega)$

converges to $X(\omega)$ for a.e. ω as $n \to \infty$ and $|X_n(\omega)| \le Z(\omega)$ for a.e. ω for $n = 1,2,\cdots$ where $Z \in L_1(\Omega)$ then for an arbitrary sub-σ-field $\mathfrak{A} \subset \mathfrak{B}$ we have

$$\lim_{n\to\infty} E\left(X_n|\mathfrak{A}\right)(\omega) = E\left(X|\mathfrak{A}\right)(\omega) \quad \text{for a.e. } \omega \text{ with respect to } (\mathfrak{A},P).$$

<u>Proof</u> Let

$$Y_n(\omega) = \sup_{k\ge n} |X_k(\omega) - X(\omega)| \qquad n = 1,2,\cdots.$$

Then $Y_n(\omega) \ge 0$, $Y_n(\omega) \downarrow$ as $n \to \infty$ for every $\omega \in \Omega$ and $Y_n(\omega) \le 2Z(\omega)$ for a.e. ω for $n = 1,2,\cdots$ so that $\{Y_n, n = 1,2,\cdots\} \subset L_1(\Omega)$. Also from the convergence of $X_n(\omega)$ to $X(\omega)$ for a.e. ω $Y_n(\omega)$ converges to 0 for a.e. ω. By Theorem 8.5

$$|E\left(X_n|\mathfrak{A}\right)(\omega) - E\left(X|\mathfrak{A}\right)(\omega)| \le |E\left(|X_n - X|\,|\mathfrak{A}\right)(\omega)| \le E\left(Y_n|\mathfrak{A}\right)(\omega)$$

for a.e. ω with respect to $(\mathfrak{A}, P)$. Thus it suffices to show that $\lim_{n\to\infty} E\left(Y_n|\mathfrak{A}\right)(\omega) = 0$ for a.e. ω with respect to $(\mathfrak{A}, P)$. From the fact that $Y_n(\omega) \ge 0$ and $Y_n(\omega) \downarrow$ and from Theorem 8.5 follows that $E\left(Y_n|\mathfrak{A}\right)(\omega) \ge 0$ and $E\left(Y_n|\mathfrak{A}\right)(\omega) \downarrow$ and consequently $W(\omega) = \lim_{n\to\infty} E\left(Y_n|\mathfrak{A}\right)(\omega)$ exists for a.e. ω with respect to $(\mathfrak{A}, P)$ and

$$E(W) \le E\left[\left(Y_n|\mathfrak{A}\right)\right] = E(Y_n).$$

But $\lim_{n\to\infty} Y_n(\omega) = 0$ and $Y_n(\omega) \le 2Z(\omega)$ for a.e. ω so that by the Dominated Convergence Theorem $\lim_{n\to\infty} E(Y_n) = 0$. □

<u>Corollary 8.7</u> Monotone Convergence Theorem for Conditional Expectation. Given a probability space $(\Omega, \mathfrak{B}, P)$, a sequence of random variables $\{X_n, n = 0,1,2,\cdots\} \subset L_1(\Omega)$ and a sub-σ-field $\mathfrak{A} \subset \mathfrak{B}$. If $X_n(\omega) \uparrow X_0(\omega)$ as $n \to \infty$ for a.e. ω then

$E(X_n|\mathfrak{A})(\omega) \uparrow E(X_0|\mathfrak{A})(\omega)$ for a.e. ω with respect to $(\mathfrak{A}, P)$. Similarly if $X_n(\omega) \downarrow X_0(\omega)$ for a.e. ω then $E(X_n|\mathfrak{A})(\omega) \downarrow E(X_0|\mathfrak{A})(\omega)$ for a.e. ω with respect to $(\mathfrak{A}, P)$.

Proof When the sequence of random variables is monotone increasing use X_0 as Z in Theorem 8.6. When it is monotone decreasing, the sequence $\{|X_n - X_0|, n = 1,2,\cdots\}$ converges to 0 for a.e. ω and $|X_n(\omega) - X_0(\omega)| \le |X_1(\omega) - X_0(\omega)|$ for a.e. ω for $n = 1,2,\cdots$. Also $\{X_n - X_0, n = 1,2,\cdots\} \subset L_1(\Omega)$. Using $X_1 - X_0$ as Z in Theorem 8.6 we have

$$\lim_{n\to\infty} |E(X_n|\mathfrak{A})(\omega) - E(X_0|\mathfrak{A})(\omega)| \le E(|X_n - X_0|\,|\mathfrak{A})(\omega) = 0$$

for a.e. ω with respect to $(\mathfrak{A}, P)$. □

[II] Conditional Probability

Given a probability space $(\Omega, \mathfrak{B}, P)$ and $M, A \in \mathfrak{B}$. By the conditional probability of M given A we mean

$$P(M|A) = \frac{1}{P(A)} P(M \cap A)$$

provided $P(A) > 0$. To define the conditional probability of M given a sub-σ-field $\mathfrak{A} \subset \mathfrak{B}$ we prove the following theorem:

Theorem 8.8 Given a probability space $(\Omega, \mathfrak{B}, P)$, $M \in \mathfrak{B}$ and a sub-σ-field $\mathfrak{A} \subset \mathfrak{B}$. There exists an $\mathfrak{A}$-measurable function φ on Ω such that

$$\int_A \varphi(\omega)\, P(d\omega) = P(M \cap A), \qquad A \in \mathfrak{A}. \tag{1}$$

In fact every version of $E(\chi_M|\mathfrak{A})$ will do. If φ_1 and φ_2 are $\mathfrak{A}$-measurable random variables on $(\Omega, \mathfrak{B}, P)$ each satisfying (1) then

$\varphi_1(\omega) = \varphi_2(\omega)$ for a.e. ω with respect to $(\mathfrak{A}, P)$.

Proof   Every version of $E(\chi_M|\mathfrak{A})$ is $\mathfrak{A}$-measurable and

$$\int_A E(\chi_M|\mathfrak{A})(\omega)P(d\omega) = \int_A \chi_M(\omega)P(d\omega) = P(M\cap A), \quad A\in\mathfrak{A}$$

which is (1). The rest of the theorem can be proved as in Theorem 8.1. □

Definition 8.9   Given a probability space $(\Omega, \mathfrak{B}, P)$, $M\in\mathfrak{B}$ and a sub-σ-field $\mathfrak{A}\subset\mathfrak{B}$. By the conditional probability of M given $\mathfrak{A}$, written $P(M|\mathfrak{A})$, we mean the equivalence class of $\mathfrak{A}$-measurable random variables φ on Ω satisfying

$$\int_A \varphi(\omega)P(d\omega) = P(M\cap A), \quad A\in\mathfrak{A}.$$

We write $P(M|\mathfrak{A})(\omega)$ for the value at ω of some version of $P(M|\mathfrak{A})$. For $M_1, M_2\in\mathfrak{B}$ we write $P(M_1|\mathfrak{A}) = P(M_2|\mathfrak{A})$ to mean the equality of the two equivalence classes.

Theorem 8.10   Given a probability space $(\Omega, \mathfrak{B}, P)$ and a sub-σ-field $\mathfrak{A}\subset\mathfrak{B}$, we have

$$0 \le P(M|\mathfrak{A})(\omega) \le 1 \text{ for } M\in\mathfrak{B},\ P(\phi|\mathfrak{A})(\omega) = 0 \text{ and}$$
$$P(\Omega|\mathfrak{A})(\omega) = 1 \tag{1}$$

for a.e. ω with respect to $(\mathfrak{A}, P)$. For any disjoint collection $\{M_n n = 1, 2, \cdots\} \subset \mathfrak{B}$

$$P\left(\bigcup_{n=1}^{\infty} M_n|\mathfrak{A}\right) = \sum_{n=1}^{\infty} P(M_n|\mathfrak{A}). \tag{2}$$

Proof (1) follows by using the version $E\left(\chi_M \middle| \mathfrak{A}\right)$ of $P\left(M \middle| \mathfrak{A}\right)$ and applying (2) of Theorem 8.3 and (2) of Theorem 8.4. To prove (2) use $\chi_{\bigcup_{n=1}^{\infty} M_n} = \sum_{n=1}^{\infty} \chi_{M_n}$ and Corollary 8.7. □

[III] Conditional Probability Distribution

According to Theorem 8.10 if $\{M_n, n=1,2,\cdots\} \subset \mathfrak{B}$ is a disjoint collection then

$$P\left(\bigcup_{n=1}^{\infty} M_n \middle| \mathfrak{A}\right)(\omega) = \sum_{n=1}^{\infty} P\left(M_n \middle| \mathfrak{A}\right)(\omega)$$ for a.e. ω with respect to $(\mathfrak{A}, P)$. The exceptional $\mathfrak{A}$-measurable set of P-measure 0 depends on the collection $\{M_n, n=1,2,\cdots\}$. For this reason, for fixed $\omega \in \Omega$, $P\left(\cdot \middle| \mathfrak{A}\right)(\omega)$ is in general not a measure on $\mathfrak{B}$.

Definition 8.11 Given a probability space $(\Omega, \mathfrak{B}, P)$ and a sub-σ-field $\mathfrak{A} \subset \mathfrak{B}$. A real-valued function $\psi(M, \omega)$ defined on $\mathfrak{B} \times \Omega$ satisfying the conditions

1° for every $\omega \in \Omega$, $\psi(\cdot, \omega)$ is a probability measure on $\mathfrak{B}$.

2° for every $M \in \mathfrak{B}$, $\psi(M, \omega) = P\left(M \middle| \mathfrak{A}\right)(\omega)$ except on an $\mathfrak{A}$-measurable set of P-measure 0

is called a conditional probability distribution given $\mathfrak{A}$ and written $\pi\left(\mathfrak{B} \middle| \mathfrak{A}\right)(M, \omega)$.

For each $M \in \mathfrak{B}$, while $P\left(M \middle| \mathfrak{A}\right)$ is $\mathfrak{A}$-measurable, $\psi(M, \cdot)$ may not be $\mathfrak{A}$-measurable although it is measurable with respect to the completion of $(\Omega, \mathfrak{A}, P)$.

Theorem 8.12 Given a probability space $(\Omega, \mathfrak{B}, P)$ and a sub-σ-field $\mathfrak{A} \subset \mathfrak{B}$. Let $\psi(M, \omega)$, $(M, \omega) \in \mathfrak{B} \times \Omega$, be a conditional probability distribution given $\mathfrak{A}$. Then for every $X \in L_1(\Omega)$

$$E\left(X|\mathfrak{A}\right)(\omega) = \int_\Omega X(\omega')\psi(d\omega', \omega)$$

for a.e. ω with respect to $(\mathfrak{A}, P)$. (1)

Proof Let $H \subset L_1(\Omega)$ be the collection of members of $L_1(\Omega)$ for which (1) holds. Then for every $M \in \mathfrak{B}$, $\chi_M \in H$ since

$$E\left(\chi_M|\mathfrak{A}\right)(\omega) = P\left(M|\mathfrak{A}\right)(\omega) = \psi(M, \omega)$$
$$= \int_M \psi(d\omega', \omega) = \int_\Omega \chi_M(\omega)\psi(d\omega', \omega)$$

for a.e. ω with respect to $(\mathfrak{A}, P)$. Also, H contains every linear combination of its members. Thus H contains every simple function on $(\Omega, \mathfrak{B})$. Let $X \in L_1(\Omega)$. Suppose $X \geq 0$. Then there exists a monotone increasing sequence of nonnegative simple functions $\{X_n, n=1, 2, \cdots\}$ on $(\mathfrak{A}, \mathfrak{B})$ which converges to X a.e. By Corollary 8.7 and the fact that (1) holds for simple functions on $(\Omega, \mathfrak{B})$ we have

$$E\left(X|\mathfrak{A}\right)(\omega) = \lim_{n\to\infty} E\left(X_n|\mathfrak{A}\right)(\omega) = \lim_{n\to\infty}\int_\Omega X_n(\omega')\psi(d\omega', \omega) = \int_\Omega X(\omega')\psi(d\omega', \omega)$$

for a.e. ω with respect to $(\mathfrak{A}, P)$ so that $X \in H$. For the general $X \in L_1(\Omega)$ we apply the above result to its positive and negative parts.

Example Given a probability space $(\Omega, \mathfrak{B}, P)$. Let $\{\Lambda_1, \cdots, \Lambda_\ell\} \subset \mathfrak{B}$ be a disjoint collection with $\bigcup_{k=1}^{\ell} \Lambda_k = \Omega$ and $P(\Lambda_k) > 0$ for $k = 1, 2, \cdots, \ell$. Let $\mathfrak{A}$ be the collection of all arbitrary unions of members of $\{\Lambda_1, \cdots, \Lambda_\ell\}$, which is a σ-field. Define a real-valued function $\psi(M, \omega)$ on $\mathfrak{B} \times \Omega$ by

$$\psi(M, \omega) = \frac{P(M \cap \Lambda_k)}{P(\Lambda_k)} \quad \text{for } M \in \mathfrak{B} \text{ and}$$

$$\omega \in \Lambda_k, \ k = 1, 2, \cdots, \ell .$$

For every $\omega \in \Omega$, $\psi(\cdot, \omega)$ is a probability measure on $(\Omega, \mathfrak{B})$. In fact $0 \le \psi(M, \omega) \le 1$ for $M \in \mathfrak{B}$, $\psi(\phi, \omega) = 0$, $\psi(\Omega, \omega) = 1$ and for any disjoint collection $\{M_n, n=1, 2, \cdots\} \subset \mathfrak{B}$ we have

$$\psi\Big(\bigcup_{n=1}^{\infty} M_n, \omega\Big) = \frac{P\Big(\bigcup_{n=1}^{\infty} M_n \cap \Lambda_k\Big)}{P(\Lambda_k)} = \frac{\sum_{n=1}^{\infty} P\Big(M_n \cap \Lambda_k\Big)}{P(\Lambda_k)} = \sum_{n=1}^{\infty} \psi(M_n, \omega) \text{ for } w \in \Lambda_k .$$

For each $M \in \mathfrak{B}$, $\psi(M, \cdot)$ is $\mathfrak{A}$-measurable. Furthermore if $A \in \mathfrak{A}$, $A = \Lambda_{k_1} \cup \ldots \cup \Lambda_{k_p}$ then

$$\int_A \psi(M, \omega) P(d\omega) = \sum_{q=1}^{p} \frac{P\Big(M \cap \Lambda_{k_q}\Big)}{P\Big(\Lambda_{k_q}\Big)} P\Big(\Lambda_{k_q}\Big) = \sum_{q=1}^{p} P\Big(M \cap \Lambda_{k_q}\Big) = P(M \cap A)$$

so that $\psi(M, \cdot)$ is in fact a version of the conditional probability of M given $\mathfrak{A}$. Thus $\psi(M, \omega)$ is a conditional distribution given $\mathfrak{A}$.

[IV] Conditioning by a System of Random Variables

Definition 8.13 Given a probability space $(\Omega, \mathfrak{B}, P)$, a system of random variables $\{X_\lambda, \lambda \in \Lambda\}$ on $(\Omega, \mathfrak{B}, P)$ and a random variable $Y \in L_1(\Omega)$. By the conditional expectation of Y given $\{X_\lambda, \lambda \in \Lambda\}$, written $E\Big(Y | X_\lambda, \lambda \in \Lambda\Big)$, we mean the conditional expectation $E\Big(Y | \sigma\{X_\lambda, \lambda \in \Lambda\}\Big)$. (Recall that according to Lemma 7.15, $\sigma\{X_\lambda, \lambda \in \Lambda\} = X_\Lambda^{-1}(\mathfrak{B}^\Lambda)$ where $X_\Lambda(\omega) = \left(X_\lambda(\omega), \lambda \in \Lambda\right)$.)

As an example consider a probability space $(\Omega, \mathfrak{B}, P)$, a finite system of random variables $\{X_1, \cdots, X_n\}$ on $(\Omega, \mathfrak{B}, P)$ and a random variable $Y \in L_1(\Omega)$ and

$$E\left(Y|X_1, \cdots, X_n\right) = E\left(Y|\sigma\{X_1, \ldots, X_n\}\right)$$

where $\sigma\{X_1, \cdots, X_n\} = X^{-1}(\mathfrak{B}^n)$ with $X(\omega) = \left(X_1(\omega), \cdots, X_n(\omega)\right)$ according to Lemma 7.15. Since $E\left(Y|\sigma\{X_1, \cdots, X_n\}\right)$ is $\sigma\{X_1, \cdots, X_n\}$-measurable, it is a Baire function of $(X_1, \cdots, X_n)$, i.e., there exists a Baire function $\varphi(\xi_1, \cdots, \xi_n)$ on R^n such that

$$E\left(Y|\sigma\{X_1, \cdots, X_n\}\right)(\omega) = \varphi\left[X_1(\omega), \cdots, X_n(\omega)\right], \quad \omega \in \Omega \tag{1}$$

according to Theorem 7.17, φ depending on the particular version of the conditional expectation. Let

$$Z(\omega) = \left(X_1(\omega), \cdots, X_n(\omega), Y(\omega)\right)$$

and P_Z be the $n+1$-dimensional probability distribution determined by Z, i.e.,

$$P_Z(F) = P\left(Z^{-1}(F)\right), \quad F \in \mathfrak{B}^{n+1} .$$

Now from (1) and Definition 8.2

$$\int_A \varphi\left[X_1(\omega), \cdots, X_n(\omega)\right] P(d\omega) = \int_A Y(\omega) P(d\omega) ,$$

$$\text{for } A \in \sigma\{X_1, \cdots, X_n\} . \tag{2}$$

On the other hand for $F \in \mathfrak{B}^{n+1}$ from the definition of P_Z

$$\int_{Z^{-1}(F)} \varphi\left[X_1(\omega), \cdots, X_n(\omega)\right] P(d\omega)$$

$$= \int_F \varphi(\xi_1, \cdots, \xi_n)\, P_Z\left(d(\xi_1, \cdots, \xi_n, \eta)\right) \tag{3}$$

and

$$\int_{Z^{-1}(F)} Y(\omega)\, P(d\omega) = \int_F \eta\, P_Z\left(d(\xi_1, \cdots, \xi_n, \eta)\right). \tag{4}$$

In particular when $F \in \mathfrak{B}^{n+1}$ is such that $Z^{-1}(F) \in \sigma\{X_1, \cdots, X_n\} = X^{-1}(\mathfrak{B}^n)$ then by (2), (3), (4)

$$\int_F \varphi(\xi_1, \cdots, \xi_n)\, P_Z\left(d(\xi_1, \cdots, \xi_n, \eta)\right) = \int_F \eta P_Z\left(d(\xi_1, \cdots, \xi_n, \eta)\right). \tag{5}$$

Thus for $F = E \times R^1$, $E \in \mathfrak{B}^n$, for which we have $Z^{-1}(F) = X^{-1}(E) \in \sigma\{X_1, \cdots, X_n\}$,

$$\int_{E\times R^1} \varphi(\xi_1, \cdots, \xi_n) P_Z\left(d(\xi_1, \cdots, \xi_n, \eta)\right) = \int_{E\times R^1} \eta P_Z\left(d(\xi_1, \cdots, \xi_n, \eta)\right). \tag{6}$$

Assume that P_Z is absolutely continuous with respect to the Lebesgue measure m_L on $(R^n, \mathfrak{B}^{n+1})$ and let $f(\xi_1, \cdots, \xi_n, \eta)$ be the Radon-Nikodym derivative. From the fact that m_L is a product measure, (6) can be written as

$$\int_E \varphi(\xi_1, \cdots, \xi_n) \left[\int_{R^1} f(\xi_1, \cdots, \xi_n, \eta) m_L(d\eta)\right] m_L\left(d(\xi_1, \cdots, \xi_n)\right)$$

$$= \int_E \left[\int_{R^1} \eta f(\xi_1, \cdots, \xi_n, \eta) m_L(d\eta)\right] m_L\left(d(\xi_1, \cdots, \xi_n)\right). \tag{7}$$

Since the integrand on each side of (7) is $\mathfrak{B}^n$-measurable and (7) holds for every $E \in \mathfrak{B}^n$,

$$\varphi(\xi_1, \cdots, \xi_n)\int_{R^1} f(\xi_1, \cdots, \xi_n, \eta) m_L(d\eta) = \int_{R^1} \eta f(\xi_1, \cdots, \xi_n, \eta) m_L(d\eta) \tag{8}$$

on R^n for a.e. $(\xi_1, \cdots, \xi_n)$ with respect to $(\mathfrak{B}^n, m_L)$. In particular at those points $(\xi_1, \cdots, \xi_n)$ where (8) holds and furthermore the integral on the left side of (8) does not vanish we have

$$\varphi(\xi_1, \cdots, \xi_n) = \frac{\int_{R^1} \eta f(\xi_1, \cdots, \xi_n, \eta) m_L(d\eta)}{\int_{R^1} f(\xi_1, \cdots, \xi_n) m_L(d\eta)} . \tag{9}$$

§9. MARTINGALES

[I] Definition of Martingale, Submartingale, and Supermartingale

Definition 9.1 Given a probability space $(\Omega, \mathfrak{B}, P)$. A system of sub-$\sigma$-fields of $\mathfrak{B}$, $\{\mathfrak{F}_\lambda, \lambda \in \Lambda\}$ where Λ is a linearly ordered index set is said to be a monotone increasing system if $\mathfrak{F}_{\lambda'} \subset \mathfrak{F}_{\lambda''}$ whenever $\lambda', \lambda'' \in \Lambda$ and $\lambda' < \lambda''$. When the index set Λ is a subset of R^1 the linear ordering is that of increasing magnitude unless otherwise specified. A system of random variables $\{X_\lambda, \lambda \in \Lambda\}$ on $(\Omega, \mathfrak{B}, P)$ is said to be adapted to $\{\mathfrak{F}_\lambda, \lambda \in \Lambda\}$ if X_λ is $\mathfrak{F}_\lambda$-measurable for each $\lambda \in \Lambda$.

Note that if $\{X_\lambda, \lambda \in \Lambda\}$ is adapted to $\{\mathfrak{F}_\lambda, \lambda \in \Lambda\}$ and $\{X_\lambda, \lambda \in \Lambda\} \subset L_1(\Omega)$ then $E\left(X_\lambda | \mathfrak{F}_\lambda\right) = X_\lambda$.

Definition 9.2 Given a probability space $(\Omega, \mathfrak{B}, P)$, a monotone increasing system of sub-σ-fields of $\mathfrak{B}$, $\{\mathfrak{F}_\lambda, \lambda \in \Lambda\}$, and a system of random variables $\{X_\lambda, \lambda \in \Lambda\}$ adapted to $\{\mathfrak{F}_\lambda, \lambda \in \Lambda\}$. If

1° $X_\lambda \in L_1(\Omega)$ for every $\lambda \in \Lambda$

2° $E\left(X_{\lambda''} \mid \mathfrak{F}_{\lambda'}\right)(\omega) =, \geq$ or $\leq X_{\lambda'}(\omega)$ for a.e. ω with respect to $(\mathfrak{F}_{\lambda'}, P)$ whenever $\lambda' \leq \lambda''$

then we say that $\{X_\lambda, \lambda \in \Lambda\}$ is a martingale, submartingale, or supermartingale, respectively, with respect to $\{\mathfrak{F}_\lambda, \lambda \in \Lambda\}$, or briefly, that $\{X_\lambda, \mathfrak{F}_\lambda, \lambda \in \Lambda\}$ is a martingale, submartingale, or supermartingale.

Note that if $\{X_\lambda, \mathfrak{F}_\lambda, \lambda \in \Lambda\}$ is a submartingale or a supermartingale then $\{-X_\lambda, \mathfrak{F}_\lambda, \lambda \in \Lambda\}$ is a supermartingale or a submartingale respectively.

Definition 9.3 We say that a system of random variables $\{X_\lambda, \lambda \in \Lambda\}$ on a probability space is a martingale, submartingale, or supermartingale if the system is a martingale, submartingale, or supermartingale, respectively, with respect to the monotone increasing system of sub-σ-fields $\left\{\sigma\{X_\rho, \rho \leq \lambda\}, \lambda \in \Lambda\right\}$.

Remark 9.4 Given a probability space $(\Omega, \mathfrak{B}, P)$ and two monotone increasing systems of sub-σ-fields of $\mathfrak{B}$, $\{\mathfrak{F}_\lambda, \lambda \in \Lambda\}$ and $\{\mathfrak{G}_\lambda, \lambda \in \Lambda\}$ where $\mathfrak{G}_\lambda \subset \mathfrak{F}_\lambda$ for $\lambda \in \Lambda$. If a system of random variables $\{X_\lambda, \lambda \in \Lambda\}$ adapted to both of the two systems is a martingale, submartingale, or supermartingale with respect to $\{\mathfrak{F}_\lambda, \lambda \in \Lambda\}$ then so is it with respect to $\{\mathfrak{G}_\lambda, \lambda \in \Lambda\}$ and in particular with respect to $\left\{\sigma\{X_\rho, \rho \leq \lambda\}, \lambda \in \Lambda\right\}$ since $\{X_\lambda, \lambda \in \Lambda\}$ is adapted to this system and furthermore $\sigma\{X_\rho, \rho \leq \lambda\} \subset \mathfrak{F}_\lambda$ for every $\lambda \in \Lambda$.

Proof Let us prove the remark for the case of submartingale as an example. Thus suppose that $\{X_\lambda, \lambda \in \Lambda\}$ is a submartingale with respect to $\{\mathfrak{F}_\lambda, \lambda \in \Lambda\}$. Since $\{X_\lambda, \lambda \in \Lambda\}$ is adapted to $\{\mathfrak{G}_\lambda, \lambda \in \Lambda\}$ by assumption, it suffices to show that

$$E\left(X_{\lambda''} \mid \mathfrak{G}_{\lambda'}\right)(\omega) \geq X_{\lambda'}(\omega)$$

for a.e. ω with respect to $(\mathfrak{G}_{\lambda'}, P)$ when $\lambda' \leq \lambda''$. (1)

Now

$$\int_A X_{\lambda''}(\omega) P(d\omega) = \int_A E\left(X_{\lambda''} | \mathfrak{F}_{\lambda'}\right)(\omega) P(d\omega)$$

$$\geq \int_A X_{\lambda'}(\omega) P(d\omega), \quad A \in \mathfrak{F}_{\lambda'} \quad . \tag{2}$$

On the other hand

$$\int_A X_{\lambda''}(\omega) P(d\omega) = \int_A E\left(X_{\lambda''} | \mathfrak{G}_{\lambda'}\right)(\omega) P(d\omega), \quad A \in \mathfrak{G}_{\lambda'} . \tag{3}$$

Since $\mathfrak{G}_{\lambda'} \subset \mathfrak{F}_{\lambda'}$ we have by (2) and (3)

$$\int_A E\left(X_{\lambda''} | \mathfrak{G}_{\lambda'}\right)(\omega) P(d\omega) \geq \int_A X_{\lambda'}(\omega) P(d\omega), \quad A \in \mathfrak{G}_{\lambda'}$$

which proves (1). □

Remark 9.5 Given a probability space $(\Omega, \mathfrak{B}, P)$, a monotone increasing system of sub-σ-fields of $\mathfrak{B}$, $\{\mathfrak{F}_\lambda, \lambda \in \Lambda\}$, and two systems of random variables $\{X_\lambda, \lambda \in \Lambda\}$ and $\{Y_\lambda, \lambda \in \Lambda\}$ both adapted to $\{\mathfrak{F}_\lambda, \lambda \in \Lambda\}$ where $X_\lambda, Y_\lambda \in L_1(\Omega)$ for every $\lambda \in \Lambda$. The following statements are immediate consequences of Definition 9.2:

(1) If $\{X_\lambda, \lambda \in \Lambda\}$ and $\{Y_\lambda, \lambda \in \Lambda\}$ are martingales with respect to $\{\mathfrak{F}_\lambda, \lambda \in \Lambda\}$ so is $\{aX_\lambda + bY_\lambda, \lambda \in \Lambda\}$ for $a, b \in R^1$.

(2) If $\{X_\lambda, \lambda \in \Lambda\}$ and $\{Y_\lambda, \lambda \in \Lambda\}$ are submartingales with respect to $\{\mathfrak{F}_\lambda, \lambda \in \Lambda\}$ so is $\{aX_\lambda + bY_\lambda, \lambda \in \Lambda\}$ for $a, b \geq 0$.

(3) If $\{X_\lambda, \lambda \in \Lambda\}$ is a submartingale and $\{Y_\lambda, \lambda \in \Lambda\}$ is a martingale with respect to $\{\mathfrak{F}_\lambda, \lambda \in \Lambda\}$ then $\{aX_\lambda + bY_\lambda, \lambda \in \Lambda\}$ is a submartingale with respect to $\{\mathfrak{F}_\lambda, \lambda \in \Lambda\}$ for $a \geq 0$ and $b \in R^1$.

Example Given a probability space $(\Omega, \mathfrak{B}, P)$ and a random variable $X \in L_1(\Omega)$. Let $\{\mathfrak{F}_\lambda, \lambda \in \Lambda\}$ be a monotone increasing system of sub-σ-fields of $\mathfrak{B}$. The measure defined on $\mathfrak{B}$ by

$$\mu(A) = \int_A X(\omega)\, P(d\omega), \qquad A \in \mathfrak{B} \tag{1}$$

is absolutely continuous with respect to P. Restricted to $\mathfrak{F}_\lambda$, P is absolutely continuous with respect to P on $\mathfrak{F}_\lambda$ so that according to the Radon-Nikodym theorem there exists an $\mathfrak{F}_\lambda$-measurable and P-integrable random variable Y_λ on $(\Omega, \mathfrak{B}, P)$ such that

$$\mu(A) = \int_A Y_\lambda(\omega)\, P(d\omega), \qquad A \in \mathfrak{F}_\lambda. \tag{2}$$

To show that $\{Y_\lambda, \mathfrak{F}_\lambda, \lambda \in \Lambda\}$ is a martingale it remains to show that for $\lambda', \lambda'' \in \Lambda$, $\lambda' \leq \lambda''$,

$$E\left(Y_{\lambda''} \mid \mathfrak{F}_{\lambda'}\right)(\omega) = Y_{\lambda'}(\omega)$$

for a.e. ω with respect to $(\mathfrak{F}_{\lambda'}, P)$. (3)

But from the definition of conditional expectation and (2) we have

$$\int_A E\left(Y_{\lambda''} \mid \mathfrak{F}_{\lambda'}\right)(\omega)\, P(d\omega) = \int_A Y_{\lambda''}(\omega) P(d\omega) = \mu(A) = \int_A Y_{\lambda'}(\omega) P(d\omega), \quad A \in \mathfrak{F}_{\lambda'}$$

which implies (3) .

We shall confine our discussion to $\{X_\lambda, \mathfrak{F}_\lambda, \lambda \in \Lambda\}$ where $\Lambda = \{1, 2, \cdots\}$. For this case we have the following necessary and sufficient condition for $\{X_\lambda, \mathfrak{F}_\lambda, \lambda \in \Lambda\}$ to be a martingale, submartingale, or supermartingale, respectively.

Theorem 9.6 Given a probability space $(\Omega, \mathfrak{B}, P)$, a monotone increasing sequence of sub-σ-fields of $\mathfrak{B}$, $\{\mathfrak{F}_n, n=1,2, \cdots\}$, and a sequence of random variables $\{X_n, n=1, 2, \cdots\}$, adapted to $\{\mathfrak{F}_n, n=1, 2, \cdots\}$, with $X_n \in L_1(\Omega)$ for $n = 1, 2, \cdots$. Then $\{X_n, \mathfrak{F}_n, n=1, 2, \cdots\}$ is a martingale, submartingale, or supermartingale if and only if

$$\int_A X_{n+1}(\omega)P(d\omega) = , \geq \text{ or } \leq \int_A X_n(\omega)P(d\omega) \text{ for } A \in \mathfrak{F}_n , \ n=1, 2, \cdots .$$

Proof Consider the case of submartingale for example. Thus we are to show that

$$\int_A X_{n+1}(\omega)\, P(d\omega) \geq \int_A X_n(\omega)\, P(d\omega),$$

$$\text{for } A \in \mathfrak{F}_n, \ n = 1,2, \cdots \tag{1}$$

if and only if

$$E\left(X_{n+p} \mid \mathfrak{F}_n\right)(\omega) \geq X_n(\omega) \text{ for a.e. } \omega \text{ with respect to } (\mathfrak{F}_n, P)$$

$$\text{for } n = 1,2, \cdots ; p = 1,2, \cdots . \tag{2}$$

for $n = 1, 2, \cdots$; $p = 1, 2, \cdots$.

Assume (2) . Then

$$\int_A X_{n+p}(\omega)P(d\omega) = \int_A E\left(X_{n+p} | \mathfrak{F}_n\right)(\omega)P(d\omega) \geq \int_A X_n(\omega)P(d\omega) \text{ for } A \in \mathfrak{F}_n$$

and, in particular for $p = 1$, we have (1) . Conversely assume (1) . Then

$$\int_A X_n(\omega)P(d\omega) \le \int_A X_{n+1}(\omega)P(d\omega) \le \cdots \le \int_A X_{n+p}(\omega)P(d\omega)$$

$$= \int_A E\left(X_{n+p}|\mathfrak{F}_n\right)(\omega)P(d\omega) \quad \text{for } A \in \mathfrak{F}_n .$$

Since X_n and $E\left(X_{n+p}|\mathfrak{F}_n\right)$ are both $\mathfrak{F}_n$-measurable, the above inequality implies (2) . □

<u>Corollary 9.7</u> If $\{X_n, \mathfrak{F}_n, n=1,2,\cdots\}$ is a martingale, submartingale, or supermartingale on a probability space $(\Omega, \mathfrak{B}, P)$ then we have respectively

$$E(X_n) = \text{const for } n = 1, 2, \cdots, \ E(X_n) \uparrow \text{ or } E(X_n) \downarrow \text{ as } n \to \infty .$$

If $\{X_n, \mathfrak{F}_n, n=1,2,\cdots\}$ is a submartingale or a supermartingale then it is a martingale if and only if $E(X_n) = \text{const}$ for $n=1,2,\cdots$.

<u>Proof</u> The first part of the corollary is immediate from Theorem 9.6 by choosing $A = \Omega$. To prove the sufficiency in the second part let us consider the case where $\{X_n, \mathfrak{F}_n, n=1,2,\cdots\}$ is a submartingale satisfying the condition that $E(X_n) = \text{const}$ for $n = 1, 2, \cdots$. Then by Theorem 9.6

$$\int_A X_{n+1}(\omega)P(d\omega) \ge \int_A X_n(\omega)P(d\omega) \qquad \text{for } A \in \mathfrak{F}_n , \ n = 1, 2, \cdots \tag{1}$$

$$\int_{A^c} X_{n+1}(\omega)P(d\omega) \ge \int_{A^c} X_n(\omega)P(d\omega) \qquad \text{for } A^c \in \mathfrak{F}_n , \ n = 1, 2, \cdots \tag{2}$$

The condition $E(X_{n+1}) = E(X_n)$, for $n = 1, 2, \cdots$, implies then that the equality holds in both (1) and (2) . This, according to

Theorem 9.6, proves that $\{X_n, \mathfrak{F}_n, n=1,2,\cdots\}$ is a martingale.

[II] Domination of a Martingale

Theorem 9.8 Let $\{X_n, \mathfrak{F}_n, n=1,2,\cdots\}$ be a submartingale on a probability space $(\Omega, \mathfrak{B}, P)$. Let $X_n^+(\omega) = \max\{X_n(\omega), 0\}$. Then $\{X_n^+, \mathfrak{F}_n, n=1,2,\cdots\}$ is a submartingale. If $\{X_n, \mathfrak{F}_n, n=1,2,\cdots\}$ is a supermartingale and $X_n^-(\omega) = -\min\{X_n(\omega), 0\}$ then $\{X_n^-, \mathfrak{F}_n, n=1,2,\cdots\}$ is a submartingale.

Proof Let $\{X_n, \mathfrak{F}_n, n=1,2,\cdots\}$ be a submartingale. The $\mathfrak{F}_n$-measurability of X_n implies that of X_n^+ and the P-integrability of X_n implies that of X_n^+. According to Theorem 9.6, to show that $\{X_n^+, \mathfrak{F}_n, n=1,2,\cdots\}$ is a submartingale it suffices to show

$$\int_A X_{n+1}{}^+(\omega)\,P(d\omega) \geq \int_A X_n^+(\omega)\,P(d\omega)$$

for $A \in \mathfrak{F}_n$, $n=1,2,\cdots$.

Now for $A \in \mathfrak{F}_n$, let $A^+ = \{\omega \in A\,;\, X_n(\omega) \geq 0\} \in \mathfrak{F}_n$. By Theorem 9.6

$$\int_A X_n^+(\omega)\,P(d\omega) = \int_{A^+} X_n(\omega)\,P(d\omega) \leq \int_{A^+} X_{n+1}(\omega)\,P(d\omega)$$

$$\leq \int_{A^+} X_{n+1}{}^+(\omega)\,P(d\omega) \leq \int_A X_{n+1}{}^+(\omega)\,P(d\omega) \quad ,$$

Thus $\{X_n^+, \mathfrak{F}_n, n=1,2,\cdots\}$ is a submartingale.

If $\{X_n, \mathfrak{F}_n, n=1,2,\cdots\}$ is a supermartingale then $\{-X_n, \mathfrak{F}_n, n=1,2,\cdots\}$ is a submartingale so that by the above result and the fact that $(-X_n)^+ = X_n^-$, we conclude that $\{X_n^-, \mathfrak{F}_n, n = 1, 2, \cdots\}$ is a submartingale. □

Corollary 9.9 If $\{X_n, \mathfrak{F}_n, n = 1, 2, \cdots\}$ is a martingale on a probability space $(\Omega, \mathfrak{B}, P)$ then $\{X_n^+, \mathfrak{F}_n, n = 1, 2, \cdots\}$, $\{X_n^-, \mathfrak{F}_n, n = 1, 2, \cdots\}$, and $\left\{|X_n|, \mathfrak{F}_n, n = 1, 2, \cdots\right\}$ are all submartingales. The last is a martingale if and only if both the first and the second are.

Proof The fact that both $\{X_n^+, \mathfrak{F}_n, n = 1, 2, \cdots\}$ and $\{X_n^-, \mathfrak{F}_n, n = 1, 2, \cdots\}$ are submartingales is from Theorem 9.8. From the fact that $|X_n| = X_n^+ + X_n^-$, $\left\{|X_n|, \mathfrak{F}_n, n = 1, 2, \cdots\right\}$ is a submartingale by (2) , Remark 9.5. Now that $\{X_n^+, \mathfrak{F}_n, n=1, 2, \cdots\}$, $\{X_n^-, \mathfrak{F}_n, n =1, 2, \cdots\}$, and $\left\{|X|, \mathfrak{F}_n, n = 1, 2, \cdots\right\}$ are all submartingales, $E(X_n^+)$, $E(X_n^-)$, and $E\left(|X_n|\right)$ are all monotone increasing according to Corollary 9.7. According to the same corollary, $\left\{|X_n|, \mathfrak{F}_n, n = 1, 2, \cdots\right\}$ is a martingale if and only if $E\left(|X_n|\right) =$ const for $n = 1, 2, \cdots$, i.e., if and only if $E(X_n^+) =$ const and $E(X_n^-) =$ const for $n = 1, 2, \cdots$, in other words, if and only if both $\{X_n^+, \mathfrak{F}_n, n = 1, 2, \cdots\}$ and $\{X_n^-, \mathfrak{F}_n, n = 1, 2, \cdots\}$ are martingales. □

Theorem 9.10 Let $\{X_n, \mathfrak{F}_n, n = 1, 2, \cdots\}$ be a submartingale on a probability space $(\Omega, \mathfrak{B}, P)$ for which $\sup_n E\left(|X_n|\right) < \infty$. Let $C = \sup_n E(X_n^+)$. Then there exists a martingale $\{Y_n, \mathfrak{F}_n, n = 1, 2, \cdots\}$ on $(\Omega, \mathfrak{B}, P)$ such that

$$X_n^+(\omega) \le Y_n(\omega) , \qquad \omega \in \Omega, \quad n = 1, 2, \cdots$$

$$E(Y_n) = C, \qquad n = 1, 2, \cdots .$$

Proof For each n define a measure μ_n on $\mathfrak{B}$ by

$$\mu_n(A) = \int_A X_n^+(\omega)\, P(d\omega), \qquad A \in \mathfrak{B} \tag{1}$$

Then

$$0 \le \mu_n(A) \le \mu_n(\Omega) \le C, \qquad A \in \mathfrak{B} \tag{2}$$

According to Theorem 9.8, $\{X_n^+, \mathfrak{F}_n, n = 1, 2, \cdots\}$ is a submartingale and hence by Theorem 9.6

$$\mu_n(A) \le \mu_{n+1}(A) \le \mu_{n+2}(A) \le \cdots \qquad A \in \mathfrak{F}_n . \tag{3}$$

Define a set function μ on the field $\mathfrak{F} = \bigcup_{n=1}^{\infty} \mathfrak{F}_n \subset \mathfrak{B}$ by

$$\mu(A) = \lim_{\nu \to \infty} \mu_\nu(A), \qquad A \in \mathfrak{F} . \tag{4}$$

For every $A \in \mathfrak{F}$, we have $A \in \mathfrak{F}_n$ for some n so that by (3) the limit in (4) exists and by (2)

$$0 \le \mu(A) \le C, \qquad A \in \mathfrak{F} . \tag{5}$$

We show next that μ is a measure on the σ-field $\mathfrak{F}_n$ for each n. From (1) and (4), $\mu(\emptyset) = 0$. The additivity of μ on $\mathfrak{F}_n$ follows also from (4) and (1). To show the countability additivity of μ on $\mathfrak{F}_n$ we show that if $\{A_k, k=1, 2, \cdots\} \subset \mathfrak{F}_n$, $A_k \uparrow$ and $A = \lim_{k\to\infty} A_k$ then $\mu(A) = \lim_{k\to\infty}\mu(A_k)$. From $A_k \subset A$ and the finite additivity of μ on $\mathfrak{F}_n$ we have $\mu(A_k) \le \mu(A)$ for every k and hence $\lim_{k\to\infty}\mu(A_k) \le \mu(A)$. We prove the reverse inequality as follows. By (4), for every $\varepsilon > 0$ there exists ν_0 such that

$$\mu(A) \le \mu_{\nu_0}(A) + \varepsilon .$$

Since μ_{ν_0} as defined by (1) is a measure on $\mathfrak{F}_n$ we have $\mu_{\nu_0}(A) = \lim_{k\to\infty}\mu_{\nu_0}(A_k)$ and hence there exists k_0 such that

$$\mu_{\nu_0}(A) \le \mu_{\nu_0}(A_k) + \varepsilon \qquad \text{for } k \ge k_0 .$$

Then for $k \ge k_0$

$$\mu(A) \le \mu_{\nu_0}(A_k) + 2\varepsilon \le \mu(A_k) + 2\varepsilon \le \lim_{k\to\infty}\mu(A_k) + 2\varepsilon .$$

From the arbitrariness of $\varepsilon > 0$ we have $\mu(A) \le \lim_{k\to\infty}\mu(A_k)$. Thus $\mu(A) = \lim_{k\to\infty}\mu(A_k)$ and μ is countably additive on $\mathfrak{F}_n$. This completes the proof that μ is a measure on $\mathfrak{F}_n$.

The measure μ is absolutely continuous with respect to P on $\mathfrak{F}_n$, for if $A \in \mathfrak{F}_n$ and $P(A) = 0$ then by (1) $\mu_\nu(A) = 0$ for $\nu \ge n$ and hence $\mu(A) = 0$ by (4). By the Radon-Nikodym theorem there exists a non-negative $\mathfrak{F}_n$-measurable P-integrable random variable Y_n on Ω such that

$$\mu(A) = \int_A Y_n(\omega)\, P(d\omega) , \qquad A \in \mathfrak{F}_n . \tag{6}$$

From the fact $\mu_n(A) \le \mu(A)$ for $A \in \mathfrak{F}_n$ we have by (1) and (6)

$$\int_A X_n^+(\omega)\, P(d\omega) \le \int_A Y_n(\omega)\, P(d\omega) , \qquad A \in \mathfrak{F}_n . \tag{7}$$

Since X_n^+ and Y_n are both $\mathfrak{F}_n$-measurable, (7) implies that

$$X_n^+(\omega) \le Y_n(\omega) \quad \text{for a.e. } \omega \text{ with respect to } (\mathfrak{F}_n, P) .$$

Redefine $Y_n(\omega)$ to be $\max\{X_n^+(\omega), Y_n(\omega)\}$. Then

$$X_n^+(\omega) \le Y_n(\omega) \qquad \text{for every } \omega \in \Omega$$

and (7) still holds. Now with $A = \Omega$ in (6) we have

$$E(X_n^+) \le E(Y_n) = \mu(\Omega) \le C = \sup_n E(X_n^+) .$$

Since this is valid for every n we have $\mu(\Omega) = C$ and subsequently $E(Y_n) = C$ for all n.

Finally to show that $\{Y_n, \mathfrak{F}_n, n = 1, 2, \cdots\}$ is a martingale it suffices to note that by (6)

$$\int_A Y_{n+1}(\omega)\, P(d\omega) = \mu(A) = \int_A Y_n(\omega) P(d\omega) , \qquad A \in \mathfrak{F}_n . \qquad \square$$

Corollary 9.11 (1) Let $\{X_n, \mathfrak{F}_n, n = 1, 2, \cdots\}$ be a martingale on a probability space $(\Omega, \mathfrak{B}, P)$ with $\sup_n E(|X_n|) < \infty$. There exist two martingales $\{Y_n, \mathfrak{F}_n, n = 1, 2, \cdots\}$ and $\{Z_n, \mathfrak{F}_n, n = 1, 2, \cdots\}$ on $(\Omega, \mathfrak{B}, P)$ such that $X_n = Y_n - Z_n$, $Y_n, Z_n \ge 0$ on Ω for every n and $\sup_n E(Y_n)$, $\sup_n Z(Y_n) < \infty$.

(2) If $\{X_n, \mathfrak{F}_n, n = 1, 2, \cdots\}$ is a submartingale on $(\Omega, \mathfrak{B}, P)$ with $\sup_n E(|X_n|) < \infty$ then there exist a submartingale $\{U_n, \mathfrak{F}_n, n = 1, 2, \cdots\}$ and a martingale $\{V_n, \mathfrak{F}_n, n = 1, 2, \cdots\}$ on $(\Omega, \mathfrak{B}, P)$ such that $X_n = U_n - V_n$, $U_n, V_n \le 0$ on Ω for every n and $\inf_n E(U_n)$, $\inf_n E(V_n) > -\infty$.

Proof (1) Let $\{Y_n, \mathfrak{F}_n, n = 1, 2, \cdots\}$ be the martingale in Theorem 9.10 which satisfies the condition that $Y_n \ge X_n^+ \ge 0$ on Ω for every n. Let $Z_n = Y_n - X_n$. By Remark 9.5 $\{Z_n, \mathfrak{F}_n, n = 1, 2, \cdots\}$ is a martingale. From $Y_n \ge X_n^+ \ge X_n$ we have $Z_n \geq 0$ on Ω for $n = 1, 2, \cdots$. From $0 \leq E(Z_n) = E(Y_n) - E(X_n)$ and from the boundedness of $E(X_n)$, $n = 1, 2, \cdots$ and of $E(Y_n)$, $n = 1, 2, \cdots$ we have the boundedness of $E(Z_n)$, $n = 1, 2, \cdots$.

(2) When $\{X_n, \mathfrak{F}_n, n = 1, 2, \cdots\}$ is a submartingale we use the same Y_n as in (1) and write $X_n = (X_n - Y_n) - (-Y_n)$ and let $U_n = X_n - Y_n$ and $V_n = -Y_n$. By Remark 9.5 , $\{U_n, \mathfrak{F}_n, n=1, 2, \cdots\}$ is a submartingale and $\{V_n, \mathfrak{F}_n, n = 1, 2, \cdots\}$ is a martingale.

[III] Martingale Convergence Theorem

We are now in a position to prove J. L. Doob's Martingale Convergence Theorem which states that if $\{X_n, \mathfrak{F}_n, n=1, 2, \cdots\}$ is a submartingale with $\sup_n E\left(|X_n|\right) < \infty$ then X_n converges a.e. and the limit is integrable. For this we need some lemmas.

Lemma 9.12 Given a finite measure space $(X, \mathfrak{F}, \mu)$. Let $\mathfrak{F}_0 \subset \mathfrak{F}$ be a field which generates $\mathfrak{F}$, i.e., $\sigma(\mathfrak{F}_0) = \mathfrak{F}$. Then for every $A \in \mathfrak{F}$ and $\epsilon > 0$ there exists $E \in \mathfrak{F}_0$ such that $\mu(A \Delta E) < \epsilon$.

Proof Let $\mathfrak{A}$ be the collection of members $A \in \mathfrak{F}$ such that for every $\epsilon > 0$ there exists $E \in \mathfrak{F}_0$ satisfying the condition that $\mu(A \Delta E) < \epsilon$. Clearly $\mathfrak{F}_0 \subset \mathfrak{A}$. Thus if we show that $\mathfrak{A}$ is a σ-field then we have $\mathfrak{F} = \sigma(\mathfrak{F}_0) \subset \mathfrak{A}$ and hence $\mathfrak{F} = \mathfrak{A}$ and we have a proof for the lemma. We show below that $\mathfrak{A}$ is indeed a σ-field.

First of all $\emptyset \in \mathfrak{F}_0 \subset \mathfrak{A}$. We show next that if $A \in \mathfrak{A}$ then $A^c \in \mathfrak{A}$. In general for any two sets M_1 and M_2 we have $M_1 \Delta M_2 = M_1^c \Delta M_2^c$. Now if $A \in \mathfrak{A}$ and $\epsilon > 0$ then there exists $E \in \mathfrak{F}_0$ such that $\mu(A \Delta E) < \epsilon$. Then $\mu(A^c \Delta E^c) = \mu(A \Delta E) < \epsilon$.

Since $E^c \in \mathfrak{Z}_0$, A^c is a member of $\mathfrak{A}$. To show that $A_1, A_2 \in \mathfrak{A}$ implies $A_1 \cup A_2 \in \mathfrak{A}$ let us remark that in general for any four sets F_1, F_2, G_1, G_2

$$(F_1 \cup F_2) \Delta (G_1 \cup G_2) \subset (F_1 \Delta G_1) \cup (F_2 \Delta G_2) \tag{1}$$

holds since $(F_1 \cup F_2) \Delta (G_1 \cup G_2)$ consists of those points which are in at least one of F_1 and F_2 and in none of G_1 and G_2 or in at least one of G_1 and G_2 and in none of F_1 and F_2. Now if $A_1, A_2 \in \mathfrak{A}$ then for $\epsilon > 0$ there exist $E_1, E_2 \in \mathfrak{Z}_0$ such that $\mu(A_1 \Delta E_1), \mu(A_2 \Delta E_2) < \epsilon/2$. By (1)

$$\mu\Big((A_1 \cup A_2) \Delta (E_1 \cup E_2)\Big) \le \mu(A_1 \Delta E_1) + \mu(A_2 \Delta E_2) < \epsilon .$$

But $E_1 \cup E_2 \in \mathfrak{Z}_0$. Thus $A_1 \cup A_2 \in \mathfrak{A}$. So far we have shown that $\mathfrak{A}$ is a field. To show that $\mathfrak{A}$ is a σ-field let $\{A_n, n=1,2,\cdots\} \subset \mathfrak{A}$ and $A = \bigcup_{n=1}^{\infty} A_n$. Since $\mathfrak{A}$ is a field there exists a disjoint collection $\{B_n, n=1,2,\cdots\} \subset \mathfrak{A}$ such that $\bigcup_{n=1}^{\infty} B_n = A$. Since $\mu(A) = \sum_{n=1}^{\infty} \mu(B_n) < \infty$ for $\epsilon > 0$ there exists N such that $\sum_{n=N+1}^{\infty} \mu(B_n) < \epsilon/2$. From $B_n \in \mathfrak{A}$ there exists $E_n \in \mathfrak{Z}_0$ such that $\mu(B_n \Delta E_n) < \epsilon/2^{n+2}$. Then by (1)

$$A \Delta \bigcup_{n=1}^{N} E_n = \Big(\bigcup_{n=1}^{\infty} B_n\Big) \Delta \Big(\bigcup_{n=1}^{N} E_n\Big) \subset \bigcup_{n=1}^{N} \Big(B_n \Delta E_n\Big) \cup \bigcup_{n=N+1}^{\infty} B_n$$

and hence

$$\mu\Big(A \Delta \bigcup_{n=1}^{N} E_n\Big) \le \sum_{n=1}^{N} \mu(B_n \Delta E_n) + \sum_{n=N+1}^{\infty} \mu(B_n) \le \sum_{n=1}^{N} \frac{\epsilon}{2^{n+2}} + \frac{\epsilon}{2} < \epsilon .$$

But $\bigcup_{n=1}^{N} E_n \in \mathfrak{F}_0$. Thus $A \in \mathfrak{A}$ and $\mathfrak{A}$ is a σ-field. □

Lemma 9.13 Given a submartingale $\{X_n, \mathfrak{F}_n, n=1, 2, \cdots\}$ on a probability space $(\Omega, \mathfrak{B}, P)$. Let n_0 and p be positive integers, $M \in \mathfrak{F}_{n_0}$, $\gamma \in R^1$ and

$$A = \{\omega \in M; X_n(\omega) > \gamma \text{ for some } n, n_0 \le n \le n_0 + p\}$$

$$B = \{\omega \in M; X_n(\omega) < \gamma \text{ for some } n, n_0 \le n \le n_0 + p\} .$$

Then

$$\int_A X_{n_0+p}(\omega) P(d\omega) > \gamma P(A) \tag{1}$$

$$\int_M X_{n_0}(\omega) P(d\omega) - \int_{M-B} X_{n_0+p}(\omega) P(d\omega) < \gamma P(B) . \tag{2}$$

Proof (1) Let

$$A_0 = \{\omega \in M ; X_{n_0}(\omega) > \gamma\}$$

$$A_j = \{\omega \in M; X_{n_0}(\omega) \le \gamma, \cdots, X_{n_0+j-1}(\omega) \le \gamma, X_{n_0+j}(\omega) > \gamma\} ,$$

for $j = 1, 2, \cdots, p$.

Then $\{A_j, j = 0, 1, \cdots, p\}$ is a disjoint collection, $A_j \in \mathfrak{F}_{n_0+j}$ for $j = 0, 1, \cdots, p$, and $\bigcup_{j=0}^{p} A_j = A$, so that by Theorem 9.6

$$\int_A X_{n_0+p}(\omega) P(d\omega) = \sum_{j=0}^{p} \int_{A_j} X_{n_0+p}(\omega) P(d\omega)$$

$$\geq \sum_{j=0}^{p} \int_{A_j} X_{n_0+j}(\omega) P(d\omega) > \sum_{j=0}^{p} \gamma P(A_j) = \gamma P(A)$$

which proves (1) .

(2) To prove (2) let

$$B_0 = \{\omega \in M ;\ X_{n_0}(\omega) < \gamma\}$$

$$B_j = \{\omega \in M; X_{n_0}(\omega) \geq \gamma, \cdots, X_{n_0+j-1}(\omega) \geq \gamma, X_{n_0+j}(\omega) < \gamma\}$$

for $j = 1, 2, \cdots, p$.

Then $\{B_j, j = 0, 1, \cdots, p\}$ is a disjoint collection, $B_j \in \mathfrak{F}_{n_0+j}$, $j = 0, 1, \cdots, p$ and $\bigcup_{j=0}^{p} B_j = B$ so that

$$\gamma P(B) = \sum_{j=0}^{p} \gamma P(B_j) > \sum_{j=0}^{p} \int_{B_j} X_{n_0+j}(\omega)\, P(d\omega) \tag{3}$$

Let

$$C_j = \{\omega \in M; X_{n_0}(\omega) \geq \gamma, \cdots, X_{n_0+j}(\omega) \geq \gamma\} ,$$

for $j = 0, 1, \cdots, p$,

then $C_j \in \mathfrak{F}_{n_0+j}$, $B_j \cap C_j = \emptyset$, $B_j \cup C_j = C_{j-1}$ for $j = 0, 1, \cdots, p$ where $C_{-1} \equiv M$ and $C_p = M - B$. From $C_{-1} \in \mathfrak{F}_{n_0}$, $C_{j-1} \in \mathfrak{F}_{n_0+j-1} \subset \mathfrak{F}_{n_0+j}$ for $j = 1, 2, \cdots, p$ and the $\mathfrak{F}_{n_0+j}$-measurability of X_{n_0+j}, $j = 0, 1, \cdots, p$,

$$\int_{B_j} X_{n_0+j}(\omega)\, P(d\omega) \ge \int_{C_{j-1}} X_{n_0+j}(\omega)\, P(d\omega)$$

$$- \int_{C_j} X_{n_0+j}(\omega)\, P(d\omega)\ , \quad j=0, 1, \cdots, p\ . \tag{4}$$

By Theorem 9.6

$$\int_{B_j} X_{n_0+j}(\omega)\, P(d\omega) \ge \int_{C_{j-1}} X_{n_0+j}(\omega)\, P(d\omega)$$

$$- \int_{C_j} X_{n_0+j+1}(\omega) P(d\omega)\ , \quad j=0, 1, \cdots, p\ . \tag{5}$$

Adding the first p inequalities in (4) and the last equality in (5), we have

$$\sum_{j=0}^{p} \int_{B_j} X_{n_0+j}(\omega)\, P(d\omega) \ge \int_M X_{n_0}(\omega) P(d\omega) - \int_{M-B} X_{n_0+p}(\omega) P(d\omega)\ .$$

This combined with (3) gives (2) . □

<u>Theorem 9.14</u> Martingale Convergence Theorem (J. L. Doob). Given a submartingale $\{X_n, \mathfrak{F}_n, n=1, 2, \cdots\}$ on a probability space $(\Omega, \mathfrak{B}, P)$ with $\sup_n E\left(|X_n|\right) < \infty$. Then $X(\omega) = \lim_{n\to\infty} X_n(\omega)$ exists as a finite number for a.e. ω with respect to $(\mathfrak{F}_\infty, P)$ where $\mathfrak{F}_\infty = \sigma\left(\bigcup_{n=1}^{\infty} \mathfrak{F}_n\right)$ and $E\left(|X|\right) < \infty$.

<u>Proof</u> Our submartingale satisfies the conditions of Corollary 9.11 and hence there exist submartingales $\{U_n, \mathfrak{F}_n, n=1, 2, \cdots\}$ and $\{V_n, \mathfrak{F}_n, n=1, 2, \cdots\}$ on $(\Omega, \mathfrak{B}, P)$ such

that $X_n = U_n - V_n$, U_n, $V_n \le 0$ on Ω for every n and $\inf_n E(U_n)$, $\inf_n E(V_n) > -\infty$. Thus it suffices to prove the theorem for a submartingale $\{X_n, \mathfrak{F}_n, n = 1, 2, \cdots\}$ in which $X_n \le 0$ on Ω for every n and $\inf_n E(X_n) > -\infty$.

Let

$$X'(\omega) = \liminf_{n\to\infty} X_n(\omega) \quad \text{and} \quad X''(\omega) = \limsup_{n\to\infty} X_n(\omega) .$$

Then X' and X'' are $\mathfrak{F}_\infty$-measurable and

$$-\infty \le X'(\omega) \le X''(\omega) \le 0 \qquad \text{for } \omega \in \Omega .$$

To show that $\{X_n(\omega), n=1, 2, \cdots\}$ converges for a.e. ω with respect to $(\mathfrak{F}_\infty, P)$ we show first that the $\mathfrak{F}_\infty$-measurable set $\{\omega \in \Omega; X'(\omega) < X''(\omega)\}$ has P-measure 0 by contradiction argument and then show that $X'(\omega)$ is finite for a.e. ω with respect to $(\mathfrak{F}_\infty, P)$. Let ρ and σ run through the countable collection of positive rational numbers. Then

$$\{\omega \in \Omega; X'(\omega) < X''(\omega)\} = \bigcup_{\rho,\sigma} \{\omega \in \Omega; X'(\omega) < -(\rho+\sigma) < -\rho < X''(\omega)\},$$

a countable union of members of $\mathfrak{F}_\infty$. Now if $P\{\omega\in\Omega; X'(\omega)<X''(\omega)\} > 0$ then for some ρ and σ we have

$$P(A) > 0 \qquad \text{where} \qquad A = \{\omega \in \Omega; X'(\omega) < -(\rho+\sigma) < -\rho < X''(\omega)\} ,$$

Let ρ and σ be fixed from now on. According to Lemma 9.12 for every $\varepsilon > 0$ there exists $B \in \bigcup_{n=1}^\infty \mathfrak{F}_n$, say $B \in \mathfrak{F}_{n_0}$, such that $P(A \Delta B) < \varepsilon$ and hence

$$P(A \cap B) \ge P(A) - P(A \Delta B) > P(A) - \varepsilon \tag{1}$$

$$P(A^c \cap B) \le P(A \Delta B) < \epsilon \quad . \tag{2}$$

Let n_1 and n_2 be arbitrary positive integers such that $n_0 < n_1 < n_2$ and let

$$C_{n_1} = \{\omega \in B; X_n(\omega) > -\rho \text{ for some } n, n_0 \le n \le n_1\} \in \mathfrak{F}_{n_1} \tag{3}$$

$$D_{n_1,n_2} = \{\omega \in C_{n_1}; X_n(\omega) < -(\rho+\sigma) \text{ for some } n, n_1 \le n \le n_2\} \in \mathfrak{F}_{n_2} . \tag{4}$$

Then since $X''(\omega) > -\rho$ for $\omega \in A$ we have

$$A \cap C_{n_1} \uparrow A \cap B \qquad \text{as} \qquad n_1 \to \infty$$

and similarly since $X'(\omega) < -(\rho+\sigma)$ for $\omega \in A$ we have

$$A \cap D_{n_1,n_2} \uparrow A \cap C_{n_1} \qquad \text{as} \qquad n_2 \to \infty \quad \text{with fixed } n_1 .$$

Thus

$$P(A \cap B) = \lim_{n_1 \to \infty} P(A \cap C_{n_1}) = \lim_{n_1 \to \infty} \{ \lim_{n_2 \to \infty} P(A \cap C_{n_1,n_2}) \} . \tag{5}$$

From (1) of Lemma 9.13

$$\int_{C_{n_1}} X_{n_1}(\omega)\, P(d\omega) \ge -\rho P(C_{n_1}) \tag{6}$$

and from (2) of Lemma 9.13 and the fact that $X_{n_2} \le 0$

$$\int_{C_{n_1}} X_{n_1}(\omega)\, P(d\omega) \le \int_{C_{n_1} - D_{n_1,n_2}} X_{n_2}(\omega)\, P(d\omega)$$

$$- (\rho+\sigma) P(D_{n_1,n_2}) \le -(\rho+\gamma) P(D_{n_1,n_2}) . \tag{7}$$

Combining (6) and (7) we have

$$P(D_{n_1,n_2}) \le \frac{\rho}{\rho+\sigma} P(C_{n_1}) \quad . \tag{8}$$

From (8) and (2)

$$P(A \cap D_{n_1,n_2}) \le P(D_{n_1,n_2}) \le \frac{\rho}{\rho+\sigma} P(C_{n_1}) = \frac{\rho}{\rho+\sigma}\left\{P(A\cap C_{n_1}) + P(A^c \cap C_{n_1})\right\}$$

$$\le \frac{\rho}{\rho+\sigma}\left\{P(A\cap C_{n_1}) + P(A^c \cap B)\right\} < \frac{\rho}{\rho+\sigma}\left\{P(A\cap C_{n_1}) + \varepsilon\right\} . \tag{9}$$

Applying (5) to (9) in letting $n_2 \to \infty$ with fixed n_1 first and then letting $n_1 \to \infty$ we obtain

$$P(A \cap B) \le \frac{\rho}{\rho+\sigma}\left\{P(A \cap B) + \varepsilon\right\} \quad .$$

Solving for $P(A \cap B)$ we obtain

$$P(A \cap B) \le \frac{\rho}{\sigma}\,\varepsilon \quad . \tag{10}$$

From (10) and (1)

$$P(A) - \varepsilon < \frac{\rho}{\sigma}\,\varepsilon, \qquad \text{i.e.,} \qquad P(A) < \left(1 + \frac{\rho}{\sigma}\right)\varepsilon \ .$$

If we choose $\varepsilon > 0$ so that $(1 + \rho/\sigma)\,\varepsilon \le P(A)$ then we have a contradiction. Thus

$$P\left\{\omega \in \Omega \,;\, X'(\omega) < X''(\omega)\right\} = 0 \,, \qquad \text{i.e.,} \qquad \liminf_{n\to\infty} X_n(\omega) = \limsup_{n\to\infty} X_n(\omega)$$

for a.e. ω with respect to $(\mathfrak{F}_\infty, P)$.

To complete the proof we show that $|\liminf_{n\to\infty} X_n(\omega)| < \infty$ for a.e. ω with respect to $(\mathfrak{F}_\infty, P)$ by showing that

$\lim_{n\to\infty} \inf |X_n(\omega)| < \infty$ for a.e. ω. But by Fatou's lemma and by $\sup_n E(|X_n|) < \infty$

$$\int_\Omega \liminf_{n\to\infty} |X_n(\omega)| P(d\omega) \le \liminf_{n\to\infty} \int_\Omega |X_n(\omega)| P(d\omega) < \infty ,$$

and this implies that $\lim_{n\to\infty} \inf |X_n(\omega)| < \infty$ for a.e. ω with respect to $(\mathfrak{F}_\infty, P)$. □

§10. UNIFORM INTEGRABILITY

[I] Uniform Integrability

Definition 10.1 A sequence of random variables $\{X_n, n = 1, 2, \cdots\} \subset L_1(\Omega)$ on a probability space $(\Omega, \mathfrak{B}, P)$ is said to be uniformly integrable if for every $\epsilon > 0$ there exists $M \ge 0$ such that

$$\int_{\{\omega\in\Omega;\, |X_n(\omega)|>M\}} |X_n(\omega)| P(d\omega) < \epsilon \qquad \text{for } n = 1, 2, \cdots .$$

Theorem 10.2 A sequence of random variables $\{X_n, n = 1, 2, \cdots\} \subset L_1(\Omega)$ on a probability space $(\Omega, \mathfrak{B}, P)$ is uniformly integrable if and only if the following two conditions are satisfied:

1° Given $\epsilon > 0$ there exists $\delta > 0$ such that whenever $A \in \mathfrak{B}$ and $P(A) < \delta$

$$\int_A |X_n(\omega)| P(d\omega) < \epsilon \qquad \text{for } n = 1, 2, \cdots$$

2° $$\sup_n E\left(|X_n|\right) < \infty \;.$$

Proof (1) Suppose $\{X_n, n = 1, 2, \cdots\}$ is uniformly integrable. Then for every $\varepsilon > 0$ there exists $M > 0$ such that

$$\int_{\{\omega\in\Omega;\, |X_n(\omega)| > M\}} |X_n(\omega)|\, P(d\omega) < \frac{\varepsilon}{2} \quad \text{for } n = 1, 2, \cdots .$$

Let $\delta = \varepsilon/2M$. Then for $A \in \mathfrak{B}$, $P(A) < \delta$, we have

$$\int_A |X_n(\omega)|\, P(d\omega) = \int_{A\cap\{\omega\in\Omega;\, |X_n(\omega)| \le M\}} |X_n(\omega)|\, P(d\omega)$$

$$+ \int_{A\cap\{\omega\in\Omega;\, |X_n(\omega)| > M\}} |X_n(\omega)|\, P(d\omega)$$

$$< M\frac{\varepsilon}{2M} + \frac{\varepsilon}{2} = \varepsilon$$

for $n = 1, 2, \cdots$, which proves 1° . For $\varepsilon > 0$ let $M \ge 0$ be as specified in Definition 10.1 then

$$E\left(|X_n|\right) = \int_{\{\omega\in\Omega;\, |X_n(\omega)| > M\}} |X_n(\omega)|\, P(d\omega)$$

$$+ \int_{\{\omega\in\Omega;\, |X_n(\omega)| \le M\}} |X_n(\omega)|\, P(d\omega) < \varepsilon + M$$

for $n = 1, 2, \cdots$

proving 2°.

(2) Conversely assume 1° and 2°. For any $M > 0$ we have

$$MP\{\omega\in\Omega;\ |X_n(\omega)|>M\} \le \int_{\{\omega\in\Omega;\ |X_n(\omega)|>M\}} |X_n(\omega)|P(d\omega) \le \sup_n E(|X_n|) < \infty$$

so that

$$P\{\omega\in\Omega;\ |X_n(\omega)| > M\} \le \frac{1}{M}\sup_n E(|X_n|) .$$

For $\varepsilon > 0$ let $\delta > 0$ be chosen according to 1°. Let $M > 0$ be such that $M^{-1}\sup_n E(|X_n|) < \delta$. Then $P\{\omega\in\Omega;\ |X_n(\omega)|>M\} < \delta$ so that by 1°

$$\int_{\{\omega\in\Omega;\ |X_n(\omega)|>M\}} |X_n(\omega)|\,P(d\omega) < \varepsilon \qquad \text{for } n = 1, 2, \cdots$$ □

Remark 10.3 The condition 1° in Theorem 10.2 is equivalent to the following condition:

3° $\{A_n, n = 1,2,\cdots\} \subset \mathfrak{B}$ and $\lim_{n\to\infty} P(A_n) = 0$

$$\Rightarrow \lim_{n\to\infty} \int_{A_n} |X_n(\omega)|\ P(d\omega) = 0.$$

Proof (1) Assume 1°. Let $\{A_n, n = 1, 2, \cdots\} \subset \mathfrak{B}$ and $\lim_{n\to\infty} P(A_n) = 0$. To prove 3° we use the fact that a sequence of real numbers converges to a real number if and only if every subsequence has a subsequence which converges to that real number. Thus consider an arbitrary subsequence

$\{n_k, k=1,2,\cdots\}$ of $\{n, n=1,2,\cdots\}$. By 1° for $\varepsilon_\ell = 1/\ell$, $\ell = 1,2,\cdots$, there exists $\delta_\ell > 0$, $\ell = 1,2,\cdots$, such that whenever $A \in \mathfrak{B}$ and $P(A) < \delta_\ell$

$$\int_A |X_n(\omega)|\, P(d\omega) < \frac{1}{\ell} \qquad \text{for } n = 1,2,\cdots .$$

Since $\lim_{k\to\infty} P(A_{n_k}) = 0$ we can select a subsequence $\{n_{k_\ell}, \ell = 1,2,\cdots\}$ of $\{n_k, k=1,2,\cdots\}$ with $P(A_{n_{k_\ell}}) < \delta_\ell$, $\ell = 1,2,\cdots$. Then

$$\int_{A_{n_{k_\ell}}} |X_{n_{k_\ell}}(\omega)|\, P(d\omega) < \frac{1}{\ell} \qquad \text{for } \ell = 1,2,\cdots$$

so that

$$\lim_{\ell\to\infty} \int_{A_{n_{k_\ell}}} |X_{n_{k_\ell}}(\omega)|\, P(d\omega) = 0$$

and this implies

$$\lim_{n\to\infty} \int_{A_n} |X_n(\omega)|\, P(d\omega) = 0 .$$

(2) We show that if 1° does not hold then 3° does not hold either. Suppose 1° does not hold for $\{X_n, n=1,2,\cdots\} \subset L_1(\Omega)$. Then for some $\varepsilon_0 > 0$ and an arbitrary $\delta_1 > 0$ there exist X_{n_1} and $A_{n_1} \in \mathfrak{B}$ with $P(A_{n_1}) < \delta_1$ such that

$$\int_{A_{n_1}} |X_{n_1}(\omega)|\, P(d\omega) \ge \varepsilon_0 .$$

For the same ε_0, 1° can not hold for the subsequence $\{X_{n_1+1}, X_{n_1+2}, \cdots\}$ so that for an arbitrary δ_2, $0 < \delta_2 < \min\{P(A_{n_1}), \frac{1}{2}\}$, there exist X_{n_2} with $n_2 > n_1$ and $A_{n_2} \in \mathfrak{B}$ with $P(A_{n_2}) < \delta_2$ such that

$$\int_{A_{n_2}} |X_{n_2}(\omega)| P(d\omega) \geq \varepsilon_0 ,$$

and so on. Thus we have a subsequence $\{X_{n_k}, k = 1, 2, \cdots\}$ of $\{X_n, n = 1, 2, \cdots\}$ and a sequence $\{A_{n_k}, k = 1, 2, \cdots\} \subset \mathfrak{B}$ with $P(A_{n_{k+1}}) \leq \min\{P(A_{n_k}), 1/k\}$ and $\lim_{k\to\infty} P(A_{n_k}) = 0$ such that $\int_{A_{n_k}} |X_{n_k}(\omega)| P(d\omega) \geq \varepsilon_0$ for $k = 1, 2, \cdots$ so that $\left\{\int_{A_{n_k}} |X_{n_k}(\omega)| P(d\omega), k = 1, 2, \cdots\right\}$ does not converge to 0. Then certainly 3° cannot hold. □

<u>Theorem 10.4</u> Given a probability space $(\Omega, \mathfrak{B}, P)$. Each of the following conditions is a sufficient condition for the uniform integrability of a sequence of random variables $\{X_n, n = 1, 2, \cdots\} \subset L_1(\Omega)$:

(i) There exists $X \in L_1(\Omega)$ such that $|X_n(\omega)| \leq X(\omega)$ on Ω for $n = 1, 2, \cdots$.

(ii) There exists $X \in L_1(\Omega)$ such that

$$\lim_{n\to\infty} E\left(|X_n - X|\right) = 0 \ .$$

(iii) For some $p > 1$, $\sup_n E\left(|X_n|^p\right) < \infty$.

Proof (1) Assume (i). Since $X \in L_1(\Omega)$, for every $\varepsilon > 0$ there exists $M \geq 0$ such that

$$\int_{\{\omega\in\Omega;\, X(\omega)>M\}} X(\omega)\, P(d\omega) < \varepsilon \ .$$

Since $|X_n(\omega)| \leq X(\omega)$ on Ω we have $\{\omega \in \Omega; |X_n(\omega)| > M\} \subset \{\omega \in \Omega; X(\omega) > M\}$ and

$$\int_{\{\omega\in\Omega;\, |X_n(\omega)|>M\}} |X_n(\omega)|\, P(d\omega) \leq \int_{\{\omega\in\Omega;\, X(\omega)>M\}} X(\omega)\, P(d\omega) < \varepsilon \ ,$$

for $n = 1, 2, \cdots$.

This proves the uniform integrability according to Definition 10.1.

(2) Assume (ii). To show the uniform integrability of the sequence we show that it satisfies the conditions 1° and 2° of Theorem 10.2. Now 2° is immediate since

$$\sup_n E\left(|X_n|\right) \leq \sup_n E\left(|X_n - X|\right) + E\left(|X|\right) < \infty \ .$$

To prove 1° let $\varepsilon > 0$ be given. Then there exists N such that $E\left(|X_n - X|\right) < \varepsilon$ for $n \geq N$. Now for every $Y \in L_1(\Omega)$ there exists $\delta > 0$ such that $\int_A |Y(\omega)|\, P(d\omega) < \varepsilon$ whenever $A \in \mathfrak{B}$ and $P(A) < \delta$. Applying this to the finite collection $\{X, X_1, \cdots, X_N\}$ we can find $\delta > 0$ such that

$$\int_A |X(\omega)|\,P(d\omega)\,,\ \int_A |X_n(\omega)|\,P(d\omega) < \epsilon$$

for $n = 1, 2, \cdots, N$ when $A \in \mathfrak{B}$ and $P(A) < \delta$. (1)

Then for $A \in \mathfrak{B}$ with $P(A) < \delta$ and $n \geq N$

$$\int_A |X_n(\omega)|P(d\omega) \leq \int_\Omega |X_n(\omega) - X(\omega)|P(d\omega) + \int_A |X(\omega)|P(d\omega) < 2\epsilon\ . \tag{2}$$

From (1) and (2) we have

$$\int_A |X_n(\omega)|P(d\omega) < \epsilon \qquad \text{for } n = 1, 2, \cdots$$

when $A \in \mathfrak{B}$ and $P(A) < \delta$

proving 1° .

(3) Assume (iii) . To show the uniform integrability of the sequence we verify the conditions 1° and 2° of Theorem 10.2. Let q be defined by $1/p + 1/q = 1$. For any $A \in \mathfrak{B}$ we have, by Hölder's inequality,

$$\begin{aligned} \int_A |X_n(\omega)|\,P(d\omega) &= \int_\Omega |X_n(\omega)|\,\chi_A(\omega)\,P(d\omega) \\ &\leq \left\{\int_\Omega |X_n(\omega)|^p\,P(d\omega)\right\}^{\frac{1}{p}} \left\{\int_\Omega \chi_A(\omega)\,P(d\omega)\right\}^{\frac{1}{q}} \\ &\leq \left\{\sup_n E\left(|X_n|^p\right)\right\}^{\frac{1}{p}} P(A)\ . \end{aligned}$$

From this follows 1° . By taking $A = \Omega$ in the above inequality we obtain 2° . □

We say that a sequence of random variables $\{X_n, n = 1, 2, \cdots\}$ on a probability space $(\Omega, \mathfrak{B}, P)$ is a Cauchy sequence with respect to convergence in probability if for every $\epsilon > 0$ there exists N such that

$$P\{\omega \in \Omega; |X_m(\omega) - X_n(\omega)| \geq \epsilon\} < \epsilon \qquad \text{for } m, n \geq N$$

or equivalently if for every $\epsilon, \eta > 0$ there exists N such that

$$P\{\omega \in \Omega; |X_m(\omega) - X_n(\omega)| \geq \epsilon\} < \eta \qquad \text{for } m, n \geq N .$$

If a sequence converges in probability to a random variable then it is a Cauchy sequence with respect to convergence in probability. Conversely if a sequence is a Cauchy sequence with respect to probability then there exists a random variable to which the sequence converges in probability. This fact is well known.

In the Banach space $L_p(\Omega)$, $p \geq 1$, we call the convergence with respect to the L_p norm strong convergence and write $s - \lim_{n\to\infty}$ for the limit of this convergence, i.e., we write $X = s - \lim_{n\to\infty} X_n$ if $\{X, X_n, n = 1, 2, \cdots\} \subset L_p(\Omega)$ and $\lim_{n\to\infty} E(|X_n - X|^p) = 0$. If $X = s - \lim_{n\to\infty} X_n$, then $\{X_n, n = 1, 2, \cdots\}$ is a Cauchy sequence with respect to the metric associated with the L_p norm. Conversely, according to the Riesz-Fischer theorem if $\{X_n, n = 1, 2, \cdots\} \subset L_p(\Omega)$ is a Cauchy sequence with respect to the metric associated with the L_p norm then there exists a unique $X \in L_p(\Omega)$ such that $X = s - \lim_{n\to\infty} X_n$, and furthermore there exists a subsequence of $\{X_n, n = 1, 2, \cdots\}$ which converges a.e. on Ω to X. It is well known that if $X = s - \lim_{n\to\infty} X_n$ then $X = P - \lim_{n\to\infty} X_n$, i.e., $\{X_n, n = 1, 2, \cdots\}$ converges in probability to X.

Remark 10.5 A sequence of random variables $\{X_n, n = 1, 2, \cdots\}$ on a probability space $(\Omega, \mathfrak{B}, P)$ converges in probability to a random variable X if and only if every subsequence has a subsequence which converges a.e. to X.

Proof (1) If the sequence $\{X_n, n = 1, 2, \cdots\}$ converges in probability to X then so does every subsequence and has a further subsequence which converges a.e. to X.

(2) Conversely suppose that every subsequence of $\{X_n, n = 1, 2, \cdots\}$ has a subsequence which converges a.e. to X. If $\{X_n, n = 1, 2, \cdots\}$ does not converge in probability to X then there exists $\varepsilon_0 > 0$ such that

$$C \equiv \limsup_{n\to\infty} P\left\{\omega\in\Omega; |X_n(\omega) - X(\omega)| \geq \varepsilon_0\right\} > 0 .$$

Then there exists a subsequence $\{n_k, k = 1, 2, \cdots\}$ of $\{n, n = 1, 2, \cdots\}$ such that

$$\lim_{k\to\infty} P\left\{\omega\in\Omega; |X_{n_k}(\omega) - X(\omega)| \geq \varepsilon_0\right\} = C .$$

No subsequence of $\{X_{n_k}, k = 1, 2, \cdots\}$ can converge in probability to X let alone converge a.e. to X. This is a contradiction. □

Theorem 10.6 A sequence of random variables $\{X_n, n = 1, 2, \cdots\} \subset L_1(\Omega)$ on a probability space $(\Omega, \mathfrak{B}, P)$ is a Cauchy sequence if and only if the following two conditions are satisfied:

1° The sequence is uniformly integrable.

2° The sequence is a Cauchy sequence with respect to convergence in probability.

Proof (1) If $\{X_n, n = 1, 2, \cdots\}$ is a Cauchy sequence in $L_1(\Omega)$ then there exists $X \in L_1(\Omega)$ such that $\lim_{n\to\infty} E(|X_n - X|) = 0$. By Theorem 10.4 the sequence is uniformly integrable. The convergence $\lim_{n\to\infty} E(|X_n - X|) = 0$ implies also that $X = P\text{-}\lim_{n\to\infty} X_n$ so that the sequence is a Cauchy sequence with respect to convergence in probability.

(2) Conversely assume 1° and 2°. By 1°, for every $\epsilon > 0$ there exists $\delta > 0$ such that

$$\int_A |X_n(\omega)| P(d\omega) < \epsilon \quad \text{for } n = 1, 2, \cdots \text{ when}$$

$$A \in \mathfrak{B} \text{ and } P(A) < \delta .$$

By 2° for the above ϵ and δ there exists N such that

$$P(A_{m,n}) < \delta \quad \text{for } m, n \geq N \quad \text{where}$$

$$A_{m,n} = \{\omega \in \Omega ; |X_m(\omega) - X_n(\omega)| \geq \epsilon\} .$$

Then for $m, n \geq N$

$$\int_\Omega |X_m(\omega) - X_n(\omega)| P(d\omega)$$

$$\leq \int_{A_{m,n}^c} |X_m(\omega) - X_n(\omega)| P(d\omega) + \int_{A_{m,n}} |X_m(\omega)| P(d\omega) + \int_{A_{m,n}} |X_n(\omega)| P(d\omega) < 3\epsilon.$$

Thus $\{X_n, n = 1, 2, \cdots\}$ is a Cauchy sequence in $L_1(\Omega)$. □

[II] Completeness of $L_1(\Omega)$ with Respect to Weak Convergence

Definition 10.7 Given a probability space $(\Omega, \mathfrak{B}, P)$ and a sequence of random variables $\{X_n, n = 0, 1, 2, \cdots\} \subset L_1(\Omega)$. We say that the sequence converges weakly to X_0 and write $X_0 = w - \lim_{n\to\infty} X_n$ if

1° $$\lim_{n\to\infty} \int_A X_n(\omega)\, P(d\omega) = \int_A X_0(\omega)\, P(d\omega)$$

for every $A \in \mathfrak{B}$

2° $$\sup_n E\left(|X_n|\right) < \infty .$$

From 1° follows that if $X = w - \lim_{n\to\infty} X_n$ and $Y = w - \lim_{n\to\infty} Y_n$ also then $X = Y$ a.e. on Ω.

Definition 10.8 A sequence of random variables $\{X_n, n = 1, 2, \cdots\} \subset L_1(\Omega)$ on a probability space $(\Omega, \mathfrak{B}, P)$ is said to be a Cauchy sequence with respect to weak convergence if

1° $\int_A X_n(\omega)\, P(d\omega)$, $n = 1, 2, \cdots$ converges as $n \to \infty$

2° $$\sup_n E\left(|X_n|\right) < \infty .$$

In order to show that the space $L_1(\Omega)$ is complete with respect to weak convergence we need a few lemmas.

Lemma 10.9 For any three subsets A, B, C of a set the following hold:

$$(A \Delta B) \cup (B \Delta C) = A \cup B \cup C - A \cap B \cap C \tag{1}$$

$$A \Delta C \subset (A \Delta B) \cup (B \Delta C) . \tag{2}$$

Proof Since

$$(A \Delta B) \cup (B \Delta C) = (A \cap B^c) \cup (A^c \cap B) \cup (B \cap C^c) \cup (B^c \cap C)$$

and

$$A \cup B \cup C - A \cap B \cap C = \bigcup_{n=1}^{6} M_n$$

where

$$M_1 = A \cap B^c \cap C^c , \qquad M_4 = A \cap B \cap C^c$$

$$M_2 = A^c \cap B \cap C^c , \qquad M_5 = A^c \cap B \cap C$$

$$M_3 = A^c \cap B^c \cap C , \qquad M_6 = A \cap B^c \cap C$$

and

$$A \cap B^c = M_1 \cup M_6 , \qquad B \cap C^c = M_2 \cup M_4$$

$$A^c \cap B = M_2 \cup M_5 , \qquad B^c \cap C = M_3 \cup M_6$$

(1) holds. Using (1) we have

$$A \Delta C = A \cup C - A \cap C \subset A \cup B \cup C - A \cap B \cap C = (A \Delta B) \cup (B \Delta C) . \qquad \square$$

Lemma 10.10 Given a probability space $(\Omega, \mathfrak{B}, P)$. We say that two members A_1 and A_2 of $\mathfrak{B}$ are equivalent and write $A_1 \sim A_2$ if $P(A_1 \Delta A_2) = 0$. [Note that $A_1 \sim A_2$ implies $P(A_1) = P(A_2)$.] The relation $\sim$ is indeed an equivalence relation, i.e., for any $A, B, C \in \mathfrak{B}$:

1° $A \sim A$

2° $A \sim B \Rightarrow B \sim A$

3° $A \sim B$, $B \sim C \Rightarrow A \sim C$.

Proof 1° and 2° are obvious. From Lemma 10.9, $A \Delta C \subset (A \Delta B) \cup (B \Delta C)$ so that $P(A \Delta C) \leq P(A \Delta B) + P(B \Delta C)$. The sum is equal to 0 if $A \sim B$ and $B \sim C$. This proves 3°. □

Lemma 10.11 Let $[A]$ be the equivalence class with respect to the equivalence relation $\sim$ of Lemma 10.10 to which $A \in \mathfrak{B}$ belongs and let $[\mathfrak{B}]$ be the collection of the equivalence classes. The nonnegative function d defined on $[\mathfrak{B}] \times [\mathfrak{B}]$ by

$$d([A_1], [A_2]) = P(A_1 \Delta A_2)$$

is a metric and $[\mathfrak{B}]$ is complete with respect to this metric.

Proof (1) We show first that d is well defined, i.e., it does not depend on the representations of the equivalence classes by the members of the classes. Let $A_1 \sim B_1$ and $A_2 \sim B_2$. By repeated application of (2) of Lemma 10.9 we have

$$B_1 \Delta B_2 \subset (B_1 \Delta A_1) \cup (A_1 \Delta A_2) \cup (A_2 \cup B_2)$$

so that

$$d([B_1],[B_2]) = P(B_1 \Delta B_2) \le P(B_1 \Delta A_1) + P(A_1 \Delta A_2)$$
$$+ P(A_2 \Delta B_2) = P(A_1 \Delta A_2) = d([A_1],[A_2]) .$$

Similarly $d([A_1],[A_2]) \le d([B_1],[B_2])$ so that $d([A_1],[A_2]) = d([B_1],[B_2])$.

(2) To show that d is a metric observe that $d([A_1],[A_2]) \ge 0$ for $[A_1],[A_2] \in [\mathfrak{B}]$ from the definition of d , $d([A],[A]) = P(A \Delta A) = 0$ for $[A] \in [\mathfrak{B}]$ while $d([A_1],[A_2]) = 0$ implies $P(A_1 \Delta A_2) = 0$, i.e., $A_1 \sim A_2$ and $[A_1] = [A_2]$. Finally by (2) of Lemma 10.9

$$d([A_1],[A_2]) = P(A_1 \Delta A_2) \le P(A_1 \Delta A_3) + P(A_3 \Delta A_2)$$
$$= d([A_1],[A_3]) + d([A_3],[A_2])$$

for $[A_1],[A_2],[A_3] \in [\mathfrak{B}]$, establishing the triangle inequality for d .

(3) To prove the completeness of $[\mathfrak{B}]$ with respect to the metric d let us transform $[\mathfrak{B}]$ into $L_1(\Omega)$ by transforming every $[A] \in \mathfrak{B}$ into the characteristic function χ_A of an arbitrarily fixed representative A of $[A]$. This transformation is isometric. In fact

$$d([A_1],[A_2]) = P(A_1 \Delta A_2) = \int_{A_1 \Delta A_2} P(d\omega)$$

$$= \int_\Omega |\chi_{A_1}(\omega) - \chi_{A_2}(\omega)| P(d\omega) = \|\chi_{A_1} - \chi_{A_2}\|$$

where $\|\cdot\|$ is the L_1 norm. Thus, if $\{[A_n], n = 1, 2, \cdots\} \subset [\mathfrak{B}]$ is a Cauchy sequence with respect to d then $\{\chi_{A_n}, n = 1, 2, \cdots\}$ is a Cauchy sequence with respect to the metric associated with the L_1 norm of $L_1(\Omega)$, so that from the completeness of $L_1(\Omega)$ there exists $X \in L_1(\Omega)$ such that $\lim_{n\to\infty} \|\chi_{A_n} - X\| = 0$ and there exists a subsequence $\{\chi_{A_{n_k}}, k = 1, 2, \cdots\}$ which converges a.e. to X. Let $A_0 \in \mathfrak{B}$ be such that $P(A_0) = 0$ and $\lim_{k\to\infty} \chi_{A_{n_k}}(\omega) = X(\omega)$ for $\omega \in \Omega - A_0$. Let $B_{n_k} = A_{n_k} - A_0$. Then $\lim_{k\to\infty} \chi_{B_{n_k}}(\omega)$ exists for every $\omega \in \Omega$ while $\lim_{k\to\infty} \chi_{B_{n_k}}(\omega) = X(\omega)$ when $\omega \in \Omega - A_0$. For every $\omega \in \Omega$ we have

$$\lim_{k\to\infty} \chi_{B_{n_k}}(\omega) = \limsup_{k\to\infty} \chi_{B_{n_k}}(\omega)$$

$$= \chi_{\limsup_{k\to\infty} B_{n_k}}(\omega) = \chi_A(\omega)$$

where $A = \limsup_{k\to\infty} B_{n_k}$

and, by the Bounded Convergence Theorem,

$$\lim_{k\to\infty} \|\chi_{B_{n_k}} - \chi_A\| = 0 .$$

Since $\{[A_n], n = 1, 2, \cdots\}$ is a Cauchy sequence with respect to d, for $\epsilon > 0$ there exists N such that

$$d([A_n], [A_m]) = \|\chi_{A_n} - \chi_{A_m}\| < \frac{\epsilon}{2} \qquad \text{for } m, n \geq N .$$

Since $\lim_{k\to\infty}\|\chi_{B_{n_k}} - \chi_A\| = 0$ there exists K such that

$$\|\chi_{B_{n_k}} - \chi_A\| < \frac{\epsilon}{2} \qquad \text{for } k \geq K .$$

Let $n \geq N$. Then for k so large that $k \geq K$ and $n_k \geq N$ we have

$$d([A_n], [A]) = \|\chi_{A_n} - \chi_A\| \leq \|\chi_{A_n} - \chi_{A_{n_k}}\|$$

$$+ \|\chi_{A_{n_k}} - \chi_{B_{n_k}}\| + \|\chi_{B_{n_k}} - \chi_A\| < \epsilon .$$

Thus we have proved that there exists $A \in \mathfrak{B}$ such that $\lim_{n\to\infty} d([A_n], [A]) = 0$. □

Theorem 10.12 The space $L_1(\Omega)$ of random variables on a probability space $(\Omega, \mathfrak{B}, P)$ is complete with respect to weak convergence, i.e., if $\{X_n, n = 1, 2, \cdots\} \subset L_1(\Omega)$ is a Cauchy sequence with respect to weak convergence then there exists $X_0 \in L_1(\Omega)$ such that $X_0 = w - \lim_{n\to\infty} X_n$.

Proof Let

$$\mu_n(A) = \int_A X_n(\omega)\, P(d\omega) \qquad \text{for } A \in \mathfrak{B} . \tag{1}$$

Then μ_n is a finite signed measure on $(\Omega, \mathfrak{B})$. According to 1° of Definition 10.8

$$\mu(A) = \lim_{n\to\infty} \mu_n(A) \qquad \text{for } A \in \mathfrak{B} \tag{2}$$

exists as a real number. To show that μ is a finite signed measure on $(\Omega, \mathfrak{B})$ which is absolutely continuous with respect to P let us show first that for every $\varepsilon > 0$ there exists $\delta > 0$ such that

$$|\mu_n(A)| < \varepsilon \qquad \text{for } n = 1, 2, \cdots \text{ when } A \in \mathfrak{B} \text{ and } P(A) < \delta \tag{3}$$

and hence by (2)

$$|\mu(A)| < \varepsilon \qquad \text{when } A \in \mathfrak{B} \text{ and } P(A) < \delta . \tag{4}$$

Consider $[\mathfrak{B}]$ as defined in Lemma 10.11. For each n define a real-valued function on $[\mathfrak{B}]$ by

$$\mu_n([A]) = \int_A X_n(\omega)\, P(d\omega) \qquad \text{for } [A] \in [\mathfrak{B}] . \tag{5}$$

Clearly $\mu_n([A])$ does not depend on the representative A of $[A]$ since for $A', A'' \in [A]$ we have $P(A' \Delta A'') = 0$. Let us show that μ_n is a continuous function on the metric space $[\mathfrak{B}]$, the metric being $d([A_1], [A_2]) = P(A_1 \Delta A_2)$ for $[A_1], [A_2] \in [\mathfrak{B}]$. Now since $X_n \in L_1(\Omega)$, for every $\varepsilon > 0$ there exists $\eta > 0$ such that $\int_A |X_n(\omega)| P(d\omega) < \varepsilon$ for $A \in \mathfrak{B}$ with $P(A) < \eta$. Then for $[A_1], [A_2] \in [\mathfrak{B}]$ with $P([A_1], [A_2]) < \eta$ we have

$$\left|\mu_n([A_1]) - \mu_n([A_2])\right| \leq \int_{A_1 \Delta A_2} |X_n(\omega)| P(d\omega) < \varepsilon ,$$

which proves the continuity of μ_n on $[\mathfrak{B}]$.

Let $\varepsilon > 0$. For any positive integers m and n , from the continuity of $\mu_m - \mu_n$ on $[\mathfrak{B}]$ the set

$$\left\{ [A] \in \mathfrak{B};\ \left|\mu_m([A]) - \mu_n([A])\right| \leq \varepsilon \right\}$$

as the inverse image of the closed set $[-\varepsilon, \varepsilon] \subset R^1$ is a closed set in $[\mathfrak{B}]$. For each $k = 1, 2, \cdots$, the set

$$S_k = \bigcap_{m, n \geq k} \left\{ [A] \in [\mathfrak{B}];\ \left|\mu_m([A]) - \mu_n([A])\right| \leq \varepsilon \right\}$$

is a closed set in $[\mathfrak{B}]$. By (5) and 1° of Definition 10. 8, $\{\mu_n([A]), n = 1, 2, \cdots\}$ converges for every $[A] \in [\mathfrak{B}]$ and hence $\left|\mu_m([A]) - \mu_n([A])\right| \leq \varepsilon$ for $m, n \geq k_0$ for sufficiently large k_0 so that $[A] \in S_{k_0}$. Thus

$$[\mathfrak{B}] = \bigcup_{k=1}^{\infty} S_k .$$

According to Lemma 10. 11, $[\mathfrak{B}]$ is a complete metric space with respect to the metric d . Thus by the Bair category theorem, $[\mathfrak{B}]$ is not a countable union of a nondense set. (A set is a nondense set if the interior of its closure is empty.) Then for some k_0, S_{k_0} is not nondense. Since S_{k_0} is closed this means that its interior is nonempty. Let $[A_0]$ be a point in the interior of

S_{k_0}. Then there exists $\eta < 0$ such that

$$d\big([A], [A_0]\big) < \eta \text{ and } [A] \in [\mathfrak{B}] \Rightarrow [A] \in S_{k_0}$$

$$\Rightarrow \left|\mu_n\big([A]\big) - \mu_{k_0}\big([A]\big)\right| \le \epsilon \text{ for } n \ge k_0. \tag{6}$$

Let $A \in \mathfrak{B}$ and $P(A) < \eta$. Then from $A = A_0 \cup A - (A_0 - A)$ we have

$$\begin{aligned} \mu_n\big([A]\big) &= \mu_{k_0}\big([A]\big) + \left\{\mu_n\big([A]\big) - \mu_{k_0}\big([A]\big)\right\} \\ &= \mu_{k_0}\big([A]\big) + \left\{\mu_n\big([A_0 \cup A]\big) - \mu_{k_0}\big([A_0 \cup A]\big)\right\} \\ &\quad - \left\{\mu_n\big([A_0 - A]\big) - \mu_{k_0}\big([A_0 - A]\big)\right\}. \end{aligned} \tag{7}$$

Now

$$(A_0 \cup A) \,\Delta\, A_0 = A - A_0,$$

$$P\big((A_0 \cup A) \,\Delta\, A_0\big) = P(A - A_0) \le P(A) < \eta$$

$$(A_0 - A) \,\Delta\, A_0 = A \cap A_0,$$

$$P\big((A_0 - A) \,\Delta\, A_0\big) = P(A \cap A_0) \le P(A) < \eta,$$

so that (6) applies to $[A_0 \cup A]$ and $[A_0 - A]$ and we have from (7) and (6)

$$\left|\mu_n\left([A]\right)\right| \le \left|\mu_{k_0}\left([A]\right)\right| + 2\varepsilon \quad \text{for} \quad n \ge k_0$$

when $A \in \mathfrak{B}$ and $P(A) < \eta$. (8)

On the other hand since $\{X_1, \cdots, X_{k_0}\} \subset L_1(\Omega)$, there exists $\eta' > 0$ such that

$$\left|\mu_n\left([A]\right)\right| < \varepsilon \quad \text{for} \quad n = 1, 2, \cdots, k_0$$

when $A \in \mathfrak{B}$ and $P(A) < \eta'$. (9)

With $\delta = \min\{\eta, \eta'\}$ we have, from (8) and (9) ,

$$\left|\mu_n\left([A]\right)\right| < 3\varepsilon \qquad \text{for} \quad n = 1, 2, \cdots$$

when $A \in \mathfrak{B}$ and $P(A) < \delta$.

This proves (3) and (4) .

Now we are ready to show that μ as defined by (2) is a finite signed measure on $(\Omega, \mathfrak{B})$ which is absolutely continuous with respect to P . The fact that $\mu(A)$ is finite for every $A \in \mathfrak{B}$ and in particular $\mu(\emptyset) = 0$ follows from (1) and (2) . The finite additivity of μ follows from the finite additivity of μ_n for every n and (2) . We show next that μ is countably additive, i.e., if $\{A_i, i = 1, 2, \cdots\} \subset \mathfrak{B}$ is a disjoint collection and $\sum_{i=1}^{\infty} \mu(A_i)$ exists in the extended real-number system then $\mu(\bigcup_{i=1}^{\infty} A_i) = \sum_{i=1}^{\infty} \mu(A_i)$. Actually since $\mu(\bigcup_{i=1}^{\infty} A_i)$ is finite we only have to consider the case where $\sum_{i=1}^{\infty} \mu(A_i)$ exists as a real number. Now since P is a finite measure there exists M such that

$P\left(\bigcup_{i=1}^{\infty} A_i - \bigcup_{i=1}^{m} A_i\right) < \delta$ for $m \geq M$. Then by the finite additivity of μ and (3)

$$\left|\mu\left(\bigcup_{i=1}^{\infty} A_i\right) - \mu\left(\bigcup_{i=1}^{m} A_i\right)\right| = \left|\mu\left(\bigcup_{i=1}^{\infty} A_i - \bigcup_{i=1}^{m} A_i\right)\right| < \epsilon$$

for $m \geq M$.

From the arbitrariness of $\epsilon > 0$ we have $\mu\left(\bigcup_{i=1}^{\infty} A_i\right) = \sum_{i=1}^{\infty} \mu(A_i)$. This proves that μ is countably additive and is a signed measure on $(\Omega, \mathfrak{B})$. The absolute continuity of μ with respect to P follow from (4).

Finally by the Radon-Nikodym theorem there exists $X_0 \in L_1(\Omega)$ such that

$$\mu(A) = \int_A X_0(\omega)\, P(d\omega) \qquad \text{for } A \in \mathfrak{B},$$

in other words

$$\lim_{n\to\infty} \int_A X_n(\omega)\, P(d\omega) = \int_A X_0(\omega)\, P(d\omega) \qquad \text{for } A \in \mathfrak{B}.$$

Then according to Definition 10.7, $X_0 = \text{w} - \lim_{n\to\infty} X_n$. □

Weak convergence in $L_1(\Omega)$ as defined by Definition 10.7 is equivalent to weak convergence defined in the usual way for sequences of elements in a Banach space, i.e., a sequence $\{X_n, n = 0, 1, 2, \cdots\} \subset L_1(\Omega)$ is said to converge weakly to X_0 if $\ell(X_0) = \lim_{n\to\infty} \ell(X_n)$ for every bounded linear functional ℓ defined on $L_1(\Omega)$. Similarly Cauchy sequence with respect to weak convergence as defined by Definition 10.8 is equivalent to the usual definition in a Banach space, i.e., a sequence

$\{X_n, n = 1, 2, \cdots\} \subset L_1(\Omega)$ is called a Cauchy sequence with respect to weak convergence if $\left\{\ell(X_n), n = 1, 2, \cdots\right\} \subset R^1$ converges for every ℓ. For the proof of these statements we refer to Dunford-Schwartz, Linear Operators, Vol. 1. p. 290. In the sequel we make no use of this equivalence.

[III] Relationship between Strong Convergence, Weak Convergence, and Uniform Integrability

Theorem 10.13 Let $\{X_n, n = 1, 2, \cdots\} \subset L_1(\Omega)$ be a sequence of random variables on a probability space $(\Omega, \mathfrak{B}, P)$. Then

(i) $\{X_n, n = 1, 2, \cdots\}$ is a Cauchy sequence in $L_1(\Omega)$

$\Rightarrow$(ii) $\{X_n, n = 1, 2, \cdots\}$ is a Cauchy sequence with respect to weak convergence,

$\Rightarrow$(iii) $\{X_n, n = 1, 2, \cdots\}$ is uniformly integrable.

Proof (1) If $\{X_n, n = 1, 2, \cdots\}$ is a Cauchy sequence in $L_1(\Omega)$ then for every $\varepsilon > 0$ there exists N such that $E\left(|X_m - X_n|\right) < \varepsilon$ for $m, n \geq N$. Thus for every $A \in \mathfrak{B}$

$$\left|\int_A X_m(\omega)\, P(d\omega) - \int_A X_n(\omega)\, P(d\omega)\right| \leq E\left(|X_m - X_n|\right) < \varepsilon$$

for $m, n \geq N$

so that 1° of Definition 10.8 is satisfied. From the completeness of $L_1(\Omega)$ with respect to strong convergence there exists $X_0 \in L_1(\Omega)$ such that $X_0 = s - \lim_{n\to\infty} X_n$, i.e., $\lim_{n\to\infty} E\left(|X_n - X_0|\right) = 0$. Then 2° of Definition 10.8 follows from the triangle inequality

$$E(|X_n|) \le E(|X_n - X_0|) + E(|X_0|)$$

(2) Suppose that $\{X_n, n = 1, 2, \cdots\}$ is a Cauchy sequence with respect to weak convergence. To show the uniform integrability of the sequence it suffices to verify 1° of Theorem 10.2. According to (3) in the proof of Theorem 10.12, for every $\varepsilon > 0$ there exists $\delta > 0$ such that

$$\left| \int_A X_n(\omega)\, P(d\omega) \right| < \varepsilon \qquad \text{for } n = 1, 2, \cdots$$

when $A \in \mathfrak{B}$ and $P(A) < \delta$.

Let $A \in \mathfrak{B}$ and $P(A) < \delta$. For each n let

$$A_n^+ = \{\omega \in A; X_n(\omega) \ge 0\} \qquad \text{and}$$

$$A_n^- = \{\omega \in A; X_n(\omega) \le 0\} .$$

Then

$$\int_A |X_n(\omega)|\, P(d\omega) = \int_A X_n^+(\omega) P(d\omega) + \int_A X_n^-(\omega) P(d\omega)$$

$$= \int_{A_n^+} X_n(\omega) P(d\omega) + \int_{A_n^-} X_n(\omega) P(d\omega) < 2\varepsilon$$

since $P(A_n^+)$, $P(A_n^-) < \delta$. Thus 1° of Theorem 10.2 is satisfied. □

According to Theorem 10.13 if $\{X_n, n=1, 2, \cdots\} \subset L_1(\Omega)$ is a Cauchy sequence then it is also a Cauchy sequence with respect to weak convergence. From the completeness of $L_1(\Omega)$ with respect to strong convergence and with respect to weak convergence, there exist $X, Y \in L_1(\Omega)$ such that $X = s - \lim_{n\to\infty} X_n$ and $Y = w - \lim_{n\to\infty} X_n$. The fact that $X = w - \lim_{n\to\infty} X_n$ also can be shown by verifying 1° and 2° of Definition 10.8 as we did in (1) of the proof of Theorem 10.13. Then from the remark following Definition 10.7, $X = Y$ a.e. on Ω.

Theorem 10.14 If a sequence of random variables $\{X_n, n = 1, 2, \cdots\} \subset L_1(\Omega)$ on a probability space $(\Omega, \mathfrak{B}, P)$ is a Cauchy sequence with respect to convergence in probability then the conditions (i), (ii), and (iii) of Theorem 10.13 are all equivalent.

Proof In view of Theorem 10.13 it suffices to show that (iii) and the condition that the sequence is a Cauchy sequence with respect to convergence in probability together imply (i). But this is already contained in Theorem 10.6. □

Theorem 10.15 Given a sequence of random variables $\{X_n, n = 1, 2, \cdots\} \subset L_1(\Omega)$ on a probability space $(\Omega, \mathfrak{B}, P)$. If the sequence converges in probability to a random variable X and if the sequence is uniformly integrable then $X \in L_1(\Omega)$ and $E(X) = \lim_{n\to\infty} E(X_n)$.

Proof Since the sequence is a Cauchy sequence with respect to convergence in probability and is uniformly integrable it is a Cauchy sequence in $L_1(\Omega)$ according to Theorem 10.6. Then there exists $X_0 \in L_1(\Omega)$ such that $\lim_{n\to\infty} E\left(|X_n - X_0|\right) = 0$ and in particular $X_0 = P - \lim_{n\to\infty} X_n$. From the uniqueness of limit in convergence in probability, $X_0 = X$ a.e. on Ω. Then $X \in L_1(\Omega)$ and $\lim_{n\to\infty} E\left(|X_n - X|\right) = 0$. The last convergence implies $E(X) = \lim_{n\to\infty} E(X)$ since $|E(X_n) - E(X)| \le E\left(|X_n - X|\right)$. □

Let $\{X_n, n = 1,2, \cdots\} \subset L_1(\Omega)$ be a sequence of nonnegative random variables on a probability space $(\Omega, \mathfrak{B}, P)$. If the sequence converges in probability to a random variable X and if $\lim_{n\to\infty} E(X_n)$ exists then $E(X) \le \lim_{n\to\infty} E(X_n)$. This follows from the fact that there exists a subsequence $\{X_{n_k}, k = 1,2, \cdots\}$ which converges a.e. on Ω to X and from Fatou's lemma, i.e.,

$$E(X) = E\Big(\liminf_{k\to\infty} X_{n_k}\Big) \le \liminf_{k\to\infty} E(X_{n_k}) = \lim_{n\to\infty} E(X_n).$$

Actually for nonnegative sequences from $L_1(\Omega)$ which converge in probability the converse of Theorem 10.15 holds. Thus we have

<u>Theorem 10.16</u> Given a sequence of nonnegative random variables $\{X_n, n = 1,2, \cdots\} \subset L_1(\Omega)$ on a probability space $(\Omega, \mathfrak{B}, P)$. If the sequence converges in probability to a random variable X then

$$X \in L_1(\Omega) \quad \text{and} \quad E(X) = \lim_{n\to\infty} E(X_n)$$

$$\Leftrightarrow \{X_n, n = 1,2, \cdots\} \text{ is uniformly integrable.}$$

<u>Proof</u> The implication $\Rightarrow$ is contained in Theorem 10.15. To prove the implication $\Rightarrow$ we verify 1° and 2° of Theorem 10.2 which for our nonnegative sequence reduce, respectively, to

1° given $\varepsilon > 0$ there exists $\delta > 0$ such that

$$\int_A X_n(\omega)\, P(d\omega) < \varepsilon \text{ for } n = 1,2, \cdots \text{ when } A \in \mathfrak{B} \text{ and } P(A) < \delta.$$

2° $\sup_n E(X_n) < \infty$.

Now 2° holds since the sequence $\{E(X_n), n = 1,2, \cdots\}$ converges to the finite number $E(X)$. To verify 1° we show that

$\left\{\int_A X_n(\omega)\, P(d\omega),\ n=1,2,\cdots\right\}$ converges for every $A \in \mathfrak{B}$. As we saw in the proof of Theorem 10.12 this convergence implies (3) in that proof which is our 1°. Now a sequence of real numbers converges if and only if every subsequence has a further subsequence which converges to a fixed real number. To show that $\left\{\int_A X_n(\omega)\, P(d\omega),\ n=1,2,\cdots\right\}$ converges we show that for every subsequence $\{n_k,\ k=1,2,\cdots\}$ of $\{n,\ n=1,2,\cdots\}$ there exists a further subsequence $\{n_{k_\ell},\ \ell=1,2,\cdots\}$ such that $\left\{\int_A X_{n_{k_\ell}}(\omega)\, P(d\omega),\ \ell=1,2,\cdots\right\}$ converges to $\int_A X(\omega)\, P(d\omega)$. Take an arbitrary subsequence $\{n_k,\ k=1,2,\cdots\}$ of $\{n,\ n=1,2,\cdots\}$. Since X_{n_k} is nonnegative we have

$$0 \le \int_A X_{n_k}(\omega)\, P(d\omega),\quad \int_{A^c} X_{n_k}(\omega)\, P(d\omega) \le \int_\Omega X_{n_k}(\omega)\, P(d\omega).$$

In view of 2° this implies the boundedness of the two sequences of real numbers

$$\left\{\int_A X_{n_k}(\omega)\, P(d\omega),\ k=1,2,\cdots\right\} \quad\text{and}\quad \left\{\int_{A^c} X_{n_k}(\omega)\, P(d\omega),\ k=1,2,\cdots\right\}.$$

Then we can select a subsequence $\{n_{k_\ell},\ \ell=1,2,\cdots\}$ of $\{n_k,\ k=1,2,\cdots\}$ such that

$$\lim_{\ell\to\infty}\int_A X_{n_{k_\ell}}(\omega)\, P(d\omega) = \alpha \quad\text{and}\quad \lim_{\ell\to\infty}\int_{A^c} X_{n_{k_\ell}}(\omega)\, P(d\omega) = \beta$$

where $\alpha, \beta \in R^1$.

Since $X = P = \lim_{\ell\to\infty} X_{n_{k_\ell}}$ there exists a further subsequence, called $X_{n_{k_\ell}}$ again to avoid introducing a further subscript, which converges a.e. on Ω to X. Then, by Fatou's lemma,

$$\begin{cases} \int_A X(\omega)\, P(d\omega) \le \liminf_{\ell\to\infty} \int_A X_{n_{k_\ell}}(\omega)\, P(d\omega) = \alpha \\ \int_{A^c} X(\omega)\, P(d\omega) \le \liminf_{\ell\to\infty} \int_{A^c} X_{n_{k_\ell}}(\omega)\, P(d\omega) = \beta\,. \end{cases} \tag{1}$$

Thus

$$E(X) = \int_A X(\omega)\, P(d\omega) + \int_{A^c} X(\omega)\, P(d\omega) \le \alpha + \beta$$

$$= \lim_{\ell\to\infty} \int_A X_{n_{k_\ell}}(\omega)\, P(d\omega) = \lim_{n\to\infty} E(X_n) = E(X)\,. \tag{2}$$

From (1) and (2) we conclude that

$$\int_A X(\omega)\, P(d\omega) = \alpha \quad \text{and} \quad \int_{A^c} X(\omega)\, P(d\omega) = \beta$$

and in particular

$$\int_A X(\omega)\, P(d\omega) = \lim_{\ell\to\infty} \int_A X_{n_{k_\ell}}(\omega)\, P(d\omega)\,.$$

Thus every subsequence $\{n_k, k=1,2,\cdots\}$ of $\{n, n=1,2,\cdots\}$ has a further subsequence $\{n_{k_\ell}, \ell=1,2,\cdots\}$ such that $\left\{\int_A X_{n_{k_\ell}}(\omega)\, P(d\omega, \ell=1,2,\cdots\right\}$ converges to $\int_A X(\omega)\, P(d\omega)$. This completes the proof that 1° holds. □

§11. MARTINGALE CLOSING THEOREMS

Let $\{X_n, \mathfrak{F}_n, n=1,2,\cdots\}$ be a martingale on a probability space $(\Omega, \mathfrak{B}, P)$ with $\sup_n E(|X_n|) < \infty$. According to Theorem 9.14, $X_\infty(\omega) = \lim_{n\to\infty} X_n(\omega)$ exists as a finite number for a.e. ω with respect to $(\mathfrak{F}_\infty, P)$ where $\mathfrak{F}_\infty = \sigma\left(\bigcup_{n=1}^\infty \mathfrak{F}_n\right)$ and $X_\infty \in L_1(\Omega)$. According to Corollary 9.9 and Corollary 9.7 $\left\{|X_n|, \mathfrak{F}_n, n=1,2,\cdots\right\}$ is a submartingale so that $\left\{E\left(|X_n|\right), n=1,2,\cdots\right\}$ is a monotone increasing sequence. Then since $\sup_n E\left(|X_n|\right) < \infty$, $\lim_{n\to\infty} E\left(|X_n|\right)$ exists as a finite number. By Fatou's lemma we have $E\left(|X_\infty|\right) \le \lim_{n\to\infty} E\left(|X_n|\right)$. Concerning the equality of the two we have the following theorem:

<u>Theorem 11.1</u> Let $\{X_n, \mathfrak{F}_n, n=1,2,\cdots\}$ be a martingale on a probability space $(\Omega, \mathfrak{B}, P)$ with $\sup_n E\left(|X_n|\right) < \infty$. The following conditions are all equivalent:

(i) $\{X_n, \mathfrak{F}_n, n=1,2,\cdots,\infty\}$ is a martingale.

(ii) $\lim_{n\to\infty} E\left(|X_n - X_\infty|\right) = 0$.

(iii) $\{X_n, n=1,2,\cdots\}$ is uniformly integrable.

(iv) $E\left(|X_\infty|\right) = \lim_{n\to\infty} E\left(|X_n|\right)$.

<u>Proof</u> We remark that since $\{X_n, n=1,2,\cdots,\infty\}$ is adapted to $\{\mathfrak{F}_n, n=1,2,\cdots,\infty\}$ and $\{X_n, \mathfrak{F}_n, n=1,2,\cdots\}$ is already a martingale, (i) is equivalent to

$$E\left(X_\infty | \mathfrak{F}_n\right) = X_n \text{ a.e. on } \Omega \text{ with respect to } (\mathfrak{F}_n, P), \text{ for } n=1,2,\cdots$$

i.e.,

$$\text{(i}'\text{)} \qquad \int_A X_\infty(\omega)\, P(d\omega) = \int_A X_n(\omega)\, P(d\omega)$$

for $A \in \mathfrak{F}_n$ for $n = 1, 2, \cdots$.

We prove the theorem by showing that (ii) ⇔ (iii), (ii) ⇒ (i′), (i) ⇒ (iii), and (iii) ⇔ (iv).

(1) (ii) ⇔ (iii). Since $X_\infty(\omega) = \lim_{n\to\infty} X_n(\omega)$ for a.e. ω with respect to $(\mathfrak{F}_\infty, P)$ we have $X_\infty = P - \lim_{n\to\infty} X_n$. Then by Theorem 10.14, (ii) and (iii) are equivalent.

(2) (ii) ⇒ (i′). By Theorem 10.13, (ii) implies

$$\lim_{n\to\infty} \int_A X_n(\omega)\, P(d\omega) = \int_A X_\infty(\omega)\, P(d\omega) \quad \text{for} \quad A \in \mathfrak{B}.$$

On the other hand since $\{X_n, \mathfrak{F}_n, n = 1, 2, \cdots\}$ is a martingale we have by Theorem 9.6

$$\int_A X_{n+p}(\omega)\, P(d\omega) = \int_A X_n(\omega)\, P(d\omega)$$

for $p = 1, 2, \cdots$, when $A \in \mathfrak{F}_n$.

From the last two equalities follows (i′).

(3) (i) ⇒ (iii). If $\{X_n, \mathfrak{F}_n, n = 1, 2, \cdots, \infty\}$ is a martingale then $\left\{|X_n|, \mathfrak{F}_n, n = 1, 2, \cdots, \infty\right\}$ is a submartingale and $\left\{E\left(|X_n|\right), n = 1, 2, \cdots\right\}$ is a monotone increasing sequence while each term is bounded by $E\left(|X_\infty|\right)$. This can be shown as in Corollary 9.9 and Corollary 9.7. Now since $X_\infty \in L_1(\Omega)$, given $\epsilon > 0$ there exists $\delta > 0$ such that

$$\int_A |X_\infty(\omega)|\, P(d\omega) < \epsilon \quad \text{for} \quad A \in \mathfrak{B} \text{ with } P(A) < \delta.$$

For any $M > 0$ we have

$$MP\left\{\omega \in \Omega;\ |X_n(\omega)| > M\right\} \le E\left(|X_n|\right) \le E\left(|X_\infty|\right),$$

so that if we choose $M > E\left(|X_\infty|\right)\delta^{-1}$ then

$$P\left\{\omega \in \Omega;\ |X_n(\omega)| > M\right\} < \delta.$$

Finally since $\left\{|X_n|, \mathfrak{F}_n, n = 1,2,\cdots,\infty\right\}$ is a submartingale and $\left\{\omega \in \Omega;\ |X_n(\omega)| > M\right\} \in \mathfrak{F}_n$ we have

$$\int_{\{\omega \in \Omega;\ |X_n(\omega)| > M\}} |X_n(\omega)|\, P(d\omega) \le \int_{\{\omega \in \Omega;\ |X_n(\omega)| > M\}} |X_\infty(\omega)|\, P(d\omega) < \varepsilon$$

for $n = 1,2,\cdots$,

which proves the uniform integrability of $\{X_n, n = 1,2,\cdots\}$ according to Definition 10.1.

(4) (iii) $\Leftrightarrow$ (iv). Since $|X_\infty(\omega)| = \lim_{n\to\infty} |X_n(\omega)|$ for a.e. ω with respect to $(\mathfrak{F}_\infty, P)$ we have $|X_\infty| = P\text{-}\lim_{n\to\infty} |X_n|$. Then by Theorem 10.16, $E\left(|X_\infty|\right) = \lim_{n\to\infty} E\left(|X_n|\right)$ if and only if $\left\{|X_n|, n = 1,2,\cdots\right\}$ is uniformly integrable. But by Definition 10.1 the uniform integrability of $\left\{|X_n|, n = 1,2,\cdots\right\}$ is equivalent to that of $\{X_n, n = 1,2,\cdots\}$. □

Theorem 11.2 Given a probability space $(\Omega, \mathfrak{B}, P)$ and a random variable $X \in L_1(\Omega)$. Let $\{\mathfrak{F}_n, n = 1,2,\cdots\}$ be a monotone increasing sequence of sub-σ-fields of $\mathfrak{B}$ and let

$$X_n = E\left(X \mid \mathfrak{F}_n\right) \quad \text{for } n = 1,2,\cdots. \tag{1}$$

Then (1) $\{X_n, \mathfrak{F}_n, n = 1,2,\cdots\}$ is a martingale with $\sup_n E\left(|X_n|\right) < \infty$ so that $X_\infty(\omega) = \lim_{n\to\infty} X_n(\omega)$ exists as a finite number for a.e. ω with respect to $(\mathfrak{F}_\infty, P)$ where $\mathfrak{F}_\infty = \sigma\left(\bigcup_{n=1}^{\infty} \mathfrak{F}_n\right)$ and $X_\infty \in L_1(\Omega)$.

(2) $\{X_n, n = 1,2, \cdots\}$ is uniformly integrable so that $\{X_n, \mathfrak{F}_n, n = 1,2, \cdots, \infty\}$ is a martingale and $\lim_{n\to\infty} E\left(|X_n - X_\infty|\right) = 0$.

(3) $X_\infty = E\left(X \mid \mathfrak{F}_\infty\right)$.

Proof (1) By (1), X_n is $\mathfrak{F}_n$-measurable so that $\{X_n, n=1, 2, \cdots\}$ is adapted to $\{\mathfrak{F}_n, n = 1 ,2, \cdots\}$. From the fact that $X \in L_1(\Omega)$ we have $X_n \in L_1(\Omega)$ for $n = 1,2, \cdots$. Also for each $n = 1,2, \cdots$

$$\int_A X_{n+1}(\omega)\, P(d\omega) = \int_A E\left(X | \mathfrak{F}_{n+1}\right)(\omega)\, P(d\omega) = \int_A X(\omega)\, P(d\omega)$$

$$= \int_A E\left(X | \mathfrak{F}_n\right)(\omega)\, P(d\omega) = \int_A X_n(\omega)\, P(d\omega)$$

for $A \in \mathfrak{F}_n$.

Thus by Theorem 9.6 $\{X_n, \mathfrak{F}_n, n = 1,2, \cdots\}$ is a martingale. By (4) of Theorem 8.3, $|X_n| \le E\left(|X| \mid \mathfrak{F}_n\right)$ a.e. with respect to $(\mathfrak{F}_n, P)$ so that

$$E\left(|X_n|\right) \le E\left(E\left(|X| \mid \mathfrak{F}_n\right)\right) = E\left(|X|\right) < \infty,$$

and hence $\sup_n E\left(|X_n|\right) < \infty$. By Theorem 9.14, $X_\infty(\omega) = \lim_{n\to\infty} X_n(\omega)$ exists as a finite number for a.e. ω with respect to $(\mathfrak{F}_\infty, P)$ and $X_\infty \in L_1(\Omega)$.

(2) The uniform integrability of $\{X_n, n = 1,2, \cdots\}$ can be shown by the argument used in (3) of the proof of Theorem 11.1. In fact since $X \in L_1(\Omega)$, for every $\epsilon > 0$ there exists $\delta > 0$ such that

$\int_A |X(\omega)|\, P(d\omega) < \epsilon$ when $A \in \mathfrak{B}$ and $P(A) < \delta$. For every $M > 0$

$$MP\{\omega \in \Omega;\, |X_n(\omega)| > M\} \le E(|X_n|) < E(|X|)$$

so that

$$P\{\omega \in \Omega;\, |X_n(\omega)| > M\} \le \frac{E(|X|)}{M} < \delta \quad \text{for} \quad M > \frac{E(|X|)}{\delta}.$$

For such M we have

$$\int_{\{\omega\in\Omega;\,|X_n(\omega)|>M\}} |X_n(\omega)|\,P(d\omega) \le \int_{\{\omega\in\Omega;\,|X_n(\omega)|>M\}} E(|X|\,|\mathfrak{F}_n)(\omega)\,P(d\omega)$$

$$= \int_{\{\omega\in\Omega;\,|X_n(\omega)|>M\}} |X(\omega)|\,P(d\omega) < \epsilon$$

which proves the uniform integrability of $\{X_n, n=1,2,\cdots\}$ according to Definition 10.1. From this uniform integrability follow the fact that $\{X_n, \mathfrak{F}_n, n=1,2,\cdots,\infty\}$ is a martingale and the fact that $\lim_{n\to\infty} E(|X_n - X_\infty|) = 0$ according to Theorem 11.1.

(3) Since X_∞ is $\mathfrak{F}_\infty$-measurable, to show $X_\infty = E(X|\mathfrak{F}_\infty)$ we only have to show that

$$\int_A X_\infty(\omega)\, P(d\omega) = \int_A X(\omega)\, P(d\omega) \qquad \text{for } A \in \mathfrak{F}_\infty. \tag{2}$$

Consider first $A_0 \in \bigcup_{n=1}^{\infty} \mathfrak{F}_n$. Then $A_0 \in \mathfrak{F}_{n_0}$ for some n_0 and hence $A_0 \in \mathfrak{F}_n$ for $n \ge n_0$. From (1) we have

$$\int_{A_0} X_n(\omega)\, P(d\omega) = \int_{A_0} X(\omega)\, P(d\omega) \qquad \text{for } n \ge n_0$$

and hence

$$\left|\int_{A_0} X_\infty(\omega)\, P(d\omega - \int_{A_0} X(\omega)\, P(d\omega\right| = \left|\int_{A_0} \{X_\infty(\omega) - X_n(\omega)\}\, P(d\omega)\right|$$
$$\leq E\Big(|X_\infty - X_n| \quad \text{for } n \geq n_0.$$

Since $\lim_{n\to\infty} E\big(|X_\infty - X_n|\big) = 0$ the above estimate implies

$$\int_{A_0} X_\infty(\omega)\, P(d\omega) = \int_{A_0} X(\omega)\, P(d\omega) \qquad \text{for } A_0 \in \bigcup_{n=1}^{\infty} \mathfrak{F}_n .$$

Consider now $A \in \mathfrak{F}_\infty = \sigma\left(\bigcup_{n=1}^{\infty} \mathfrak{F}_n\right)$. Since $|X_\infty| + |X| \in L_1(\Omega)$, for every $\epsilon > 0$ there exists $\delta > 0$ such that

$$\int_B \{|X_\infty(\omega)| + |X(\omega)|\}\, P(d\omega) < \epsilon \quad \text{for} \quad B \in \mathfrak{B} \ \text{with} \ P(B) < \delta .$$

Since $A \in \sigma\left(\bigcup_{n=1}^{\infty} \mathfrak{F}_n\right)$ there exists $A_0 \in \bigcup_{n=1}^{\infty} \mathfrak{F}_n$ such that $P(A \,\Delta\, A_0) < \delta$. Then

$$\int_A X_\infty(\omega)\, P(d\omega) - \int_A X(\omega)\, P(d\omega) = \int_{A_0} \{X_\infty(\omega) - X(\omega)\}\, P(d\omega)$$
$$+ \int_{A - A_0} \{X_\infty(\omega) - X(\omega)\}\, P(d\omega) - \int_{A_0 - A} \{X_\infty(\omega) - X(\omega)\}\, P(d\omega),$$

where the 1st term on the right side vanishes since $A_0 \in \bigcup_{n=1}^{\infty} \mathfrak{F}_n$. Thus

$$\left|\int_A X_\infty(\omega)\, P(d\omega) - \int_A X(\omega)\, P(d\omega)\right|$$
$$\leq \int_{A \Delta A_0} \{|X_\infty(\omega)| + |X(\omega)|\}\, P(d\omega) < \epsilon .$$

From the arbitrariness of $\epsilon > 0$, (2) follows. □

Chapter 3

ADDITIVE PROCESSES

§12. ADDITIVE PROCESSES

Definition 12.1 A stochastic process X on a probability space $(\Omega, \mathfrak{B}, P)$ and an interval $D \subset R^1$ is called an additive process or a process with independent increments if for any $\{t_1, t_2, \cdots, t_n\} \subset D$, $t_1 < t_2 < \cdots < t_n$, the system of random variables $\{X(t_{i+1}, \cdot) - X(t_i, \cdot), i = 1,2, n-1\}$ is independent.

If X is an additive process and $\Phi_{t't''}$ is the 1-dimensional probability distribution determined by the random variable $X(t'', \cdot) - X(t', \cdot)$ where $t', t'' \in D$, $t' < t''$, then for any $t_1, t_2, t_3 \in D$, $t_1 < t_2 < t_3$, the convolution of $\Phi_{t_1 t_2}$ and $\Phi_{t_2 t_3}$ satisfies the condition

$$\Phi_{t_1 t_2} * \Phi_{t_2 t_3} = \Phi_{t_1 t_3}$$

since the two random variables $X(t_2, \cdot) - X(t_1, \cdot)$ and $X(t_3, \cdot) - X(t_2, \cdot)$ constitute an independent system and their sum is equal to $X(t_3, \cdot) - X(t_1, \cdot)$. (cf. Theorem A7.6).

Theorem 12.2 Given $D = (a,b)$, $-\infty \le a < b \le \infty$, and a system of 1-dimensional probability distributions $\{\Phi_{t't''}, t', t'' \in D, t' < t''\}$ satisfying the condition that

$$t_1, t_2, t_3 \in D, \quad t_1 < t_2 < t_3 \Rightarrow \Phi_{t_1 t_2} * \Phi_{t_2 t_3} = \Phi_{t_1 t_3}.$$

There exists an additive process X on a probability space $(\Omega, \mathfrak{B}, P)$ and D such that $\Phi_{t't''}$ is the probability distribution determined by the random variable $X(t'', \cdot) - X(t', \cdot)$ for any $t', t'' \in D$, $t' < t''$.

Proof (1) Let $c \in (a, b)$ be arbitrarily fixed. Consider $R^{(c,b)}$, i.e., the collection of all real-valued functions $x(t)$, $t \in (c,b)$. For every finite sequence of distinct elements $\{t_1, \cdots, t_n\} \subset (c,b)$ let $p_{t_1 \cdots t_n}$ be the projection of $R^{(c,b)}$ onto R^n defined by

$$p_{t_1 \cdots t_n}(x) = \left(x(t_1), \cdots, x(t_n)\right) \in R^n \quad \text{for} \quad x \in R^{(c,b)}$$

and $\mathfrak{F}_{t_1 \cdots t_n}$ be the σ-field of subsets of $R^{(c,b)}$ consisting of sets of the type

$$E = p_{t_1 \cdots t_n}^{-1}(B) = \left\{ x \in R^{(c,b)};\ \left(x(t_1), \cdots, x(t_n)\right) \in B \right\},$$

where $B \in \mathfrak{B}^n$. (1)

If $\Pi = \{\Pi_1, \cdots, \Pi_n\}$ is a permutation of $\{1, \cdots, n\}$ then $\mathfrak{F}_{t_{\Pi_1} \cdots t_{\Pi_n}} = \mathfrak{F}_{t_1 \cdots t_n}$ as we noted in 3°, Remark 2.2. Thus in considering $\mathfrak{F}_{t_1 \cdots t_n}$ we may assume that $t_1 < t_2 < \cdots < t_n$. Let $\mathfrak{F}$ be the field of subsets of $R^{(c,b)}$ which is the union of all the σ-fields $\mathfrak{F}_{t_1 \cdots t_n}$. We define a set function λ on $\mathfrak{F}$ as follows. For $E \in \mathfrak{F}$ given by (1) let

$$\lambda(E) = \int_{R^n} \chi_B(\xi_1, \cdots, \xi_n)(\Phi_{ct_1} \times \Phi_{t_1 t_2} \times \cdots \times \Phi_{t_{n-1} t_n})\left(d(\eta_1, \cdots, \eta_n)\right)$$

$$= \int_{R^n} \chi_B(\eta_1, \eta_1 + \eta_2, \cdots, \eta_1 + \cdots + \eta_n)$$

$$(\Phi_{ct_1} \times \Phi_{t_1 t_2} \times \cdots \times \Phi_{t_{n-1} t_n})\bigl(d(\eta_1, \cdots, \eta_n)\bigr) \tag{2}$$

where $(\xi_1, \cdots, \xi_n)$ and $(\eta_1, \cdots, \eta_n)$ are related by

$$\xi_1 = \eta_1, \quad \xi_2 = \eta_1 + \eta_2, \quad \cdots, \quad \xi_n = \eta_1 + \cdots + \eta_n, \tag{3}$$

i.e.,

$$\eta_1 = \xi_1, \quad \eta_2 = \xi_2 - \xi_1, \quad \cdots, \quad \eta_n = \xi_n - \xi_{n-1}. \tag{4}$$

By Fubini's theorem, (2) can be written as

$$\lambda(E) = \int_{R^1} {}^{(n)} \int_{R^1} \chi_B(\eta_1, \eta_1 + \eta_2, \cdots, \eta_1 + \cdots + \eta_n)$$

$$\Phi_{ct_1}(d\eta_1)\, \Phi_{t_1 t_2}(d\eta_2) \cdots \Phi_{t_{n-1} t_n}(d\eta_n). \tag{5}$$

In particular, for $E \in \mathfrak{J}$ of the type

$$E = \left\{x \in R^{(c,b)};\, x(t_1) \in B_1, x(t_2) - x(t_1) \in B_2, \cdots, x(t_n) - x(t_{n-1}) \in B_n\right\},$$

where $B_1, \cdots, B_n \in \mathfrak{B}^1$, (6)

(5) reduces to

$$\lambda(E) = \int_{R^1} {}^{(n)} \int_{R^1} \chi_{B_1}(\eta_1)\, \chi_{B_2}(\eta_2) \cdots \chi_{B_n}(\eta_n)$$

$$\Phi_{ct_1}(d\eta_1)\, \Phi_{t_1 t_2}(d\eta_2) \cdots \Phi_{t_{n-1} t_n}(d\eta_n). \tag{7}$$

(2) Let us show that λ is well defined on $\mathfrak{J}$, i.e., it is

independent of the representation of $E \in \mathfrak{F}$. Let $E \in \mathfrak{F}$ be given by (1) and let $t_0 \in (c,b)$ $t_0 \neq t_1, \cdots, t_n$. Then E can also be given as

$$E = \left\{ x \in R^{(c,b)} ; \left(x(t_1), \cdots, x(t_n) \right) \in B, \ x(t_0) \in R^1 \right\}.$$

Let us consider the three possible situations: $t_0 < t_1$ or $t_i < t_0 < t_{i+1}$ for some $i = 1, 2, \cdots, n-1$, or $t_n < t_0$.

For the case $t_n < t_0$, applying (5) we have

$$\lambda(E) = \int (n+1) \int \chi_B(\eta_1, \cdots, \eta_1 + \cdots + \eta_n)\, \chi_{R^1}(\eta_1 + \cdots + \eta_n + \eta_0)$$

$$\Phi_{ct_1}(d\eta_1) \cdots \Phi_{t_{n-1}t_n}(d\eta_n)\, \Phi_{t_n t_0}(d\eta_0)$$

$$= \int (n) \int \chi_B(\eta_1, \cdots, \eta_1 + \cdots + \eta_n) \left\{ \int \chi_{R^1}(\eta_1 + \cdots + \eta_n + \eta_0) \Phi_{t_n t_0}(d\eta_0) \right\}$$

$$\Phi_{ct_1}(d\eta_1) \cdots \Phi_{t_{n-1}t_n}(d\eta_n)$$

$$= \int (n) \int \chi_B(\eta_1, \cdots, \eta_1 + \cdots + \eta_n)\, \Phi_{ct_1}(d\eta_1) \cdots \Phi_{t_{n-1}t_n}(d\eta_n)$$

which is (5) itself.

Next consider the case $t_i < t_0 < t_{i+1}$ for some $i = 1, 2, \cdots, n-1$. Take as an example the case $i = n-1$. Applying (5) we have

$$\lambda(E) = \int (n+1) \int \chi_B(\eta_1, \cdots, \eta_1 + \cdots + \eta_{n-1}, \eta_1 + \cdots + \eta_{n-1} + \eta_0 + \eta_n)$$

$$\chi_{R^1}(\eta_1 + \cdots + \eta_{n-1} + \eta_0)$$

$$\times \Phi_{ct_1}(d\eta_1) \cdots \Phi_{t_{n-2}t_{n-1}}(d\eta_{n-1})\, \Phi_{t_{n-1}t_0}(d\eta_0)\, \Phi_{t_0 t_n}(d\eta_n).$$

By Theorem A7.3 and the fact that $\Phi_{t_{n-1}t_0} * \Phi_{t_0 t_n} = \Phi_{t_{n-1}t_n}$ and

$\chi_{R^1}(\eta_1 + \cdots + \eta_{n-1} + \eta_0) \equiv 1$, the above expression for $\lambda(E)$ reduces to

$$\lambda(E) = \int^{(n)}\int \chi_B(\eta_1, \cdots, \eta_1 + \cdots + \eta_{n-1}, \eta_1 + \cdots + \eta_{n-1} + \zeta)$$

$$\Phi_{ct_1}(d\eta_1) \cdots \Phi_{t_{n-2}t_{n-1}}(d\eta_{n-1})\, \Phi_{t_{n-1}t_n}(d\zeta_n),$$

which is (5).

Finally consider the case $t_0 < t_1$. Applying (5),

$$\lambda(E) = \int^{(n+1)}\int \chi_{R^1}(\eta_0)\, \chi_B(\eta_0 + \eta_1, \cdots, \eta_0 + \cdots + \eta_n)$$

$$\Phi_{ct_0}(d\eta_0)\, \Phi_{t_0t_1}(d\eta_1) \cdots \Phi_{t_{n-1}t_n}(d\eta_n).$$

Again by Theorem A7.3 and the fact that $\Phi_{ct_0} * \Phi_{t_0t_1} = \Phi_{ct_1}$ and $\chi_{R^1}(\eta_0) \equiv 1$ the above reduces to

$$\lambda(E) = \int^{(n)}\int \chi_B(\zeta, \zeta + \eta_2, \cdots, \zeta + \eta_2 + \cdots + \eta_n)$$

$$\Phi_{ct_1}(d\zeta)\, \Phi_{t_1t_2}(d\eta_2) \cdots \Phi_{t_{n-1}t_n}(d\eta_n),$$

which is (5). This completes the proof that λ is well defined on $\mathfrak{Z}$.

It is obvious that for each $\{t_1, \cdots, t_n\} \subset D$, λ is a probability measure on $\mathfrak{Z}_{t_1 \cdots t_n}$. Thus according to Theorem 2.1, λ can be extended to be a probability measure on the σ-field $\sigma(\mathfrak{Z})$ generated by $\mathfrak{Z}$.

(3) On the probability space $\left(R^{(c,b)}, \sigma(\mathfrak{Z}), \lambda\right)$ and the interval (c,b) we define a stochastic process X by

$$X(t,x) = x(t) \quad \text{for} \quad t \in (c,b),\ x \in R^{(c,b)}. \tag{8}$$

Then for any $t \in (c,b)$ and $B \in \mathfrak{B}^1$ we have, by (7),

$$\lambda\{x \in R^{(c,b)}; X(t,x) \in B\} = \lambda\{x \in R^{(c,b)}; x(t) \in B\}$$
$$= \int \chi_B(\eta)\, \Phi_{ct}(d\eta) \tag{9}$$

so that the random variable $X(t,\cdot)$ has Φ_{ct} as its probability distribution. For $t', t'' \in (c,b)$, $t' < t''$, and $B \in \mathfrak{B}^1$, again by (7),

$$\lambda\{x \in R^{(c,b)}; X(t'',x) - X(t',x) \in B\} = \lambda\{x \in R^{(c,b)}; x(t'')-x(t') \in B\}$$
$$= \int \chi_B(\eta)\, \Phi_{t't''}(d\eta) \tag{10}$$

so that $X(t'',\cdot) - X(t',\cdot)$ has $\Phi_{t't''}$ as its probability distribution.

The fact that for $c < t_1 < \cdots t_n < b$, the system of random variables $\{X(t_1,\cdot),\ X(t_2,\cdot) - X(t_1,\cdot), \cdots, X(t_n,\cdot) - X(t_{n-1},\cdot)\}$ is independent, i.e., the equality

$$\lambda\{x \in R^{(c,b)}; X(t_1,x) \in B_1,$$
$$X(t_2,x) - X(t_1,x) \in B_2, \cdots, X(t_n,x) - X(t_{n-1},x) \in B_n\}$$
$$= \lambda\{x \in R^{(c,b)}; X(t_1,x) \in B_1\}\ \lambda\{x \in R^{(c,b)}; X(t_2,x) - X(t_1,x) \in B_2\} \cdots$$
$$\lambda\{x \in R^{(c,b)}; X(t_n,x) - X(t_{n-1},x) \in B_n\}$$
$$\text{for } B_1, \cdots, B_n \in \mathfrak{B}^1 \tag{11}$$

follows from the fact that, by (7), the left side of (11) is equal to

$$\left\{\int_{R^1} \chi_{B_1}(\eta_1)\Phi_{ct_1}(d\eta_1)\right\}\left\{\int_{R^1} \chi_{B_2}(\eta_2)\Phi_{t_1t_2}(d\eta_2)\right\}\cdots\left\{\int_{R^1} \chi_{B_n}(\eta_n)\Phi_{t_{n-1}t_n}(d\eta_n)\right\},$$

which according to (9) and (10) is equal to the right side of (11).

(4) Now consider $R^{(a,c)}$, the collection of all real-valued functions $y(t)$, $t \in (a,c)$. For $a < t_1 < \cdots < t_n < c$ let $\mathfrak{G}_{t_1 \cdots t_n}$ be the σ-field of subsets of $R^{(a,c)}$ of the type

$$E = p_{t_1 \cdots t_n}^{-1}(B) = \left\{y \in R^{(a,c)};\ \left(y(t_1), \cdots, y(t_n)\right) \in B\right\},$$

$$\text{where } B \in \mathfrak{B}^n. \tag{12}$$

On the union $\mathfrak{G}$ of all the σ-fields $\mathfrak{G}_{t_1 \cdots t_n}$ we define a set function μ by setting $\mu(E)$ for $E \in \mathfrak{G}$ given by (12):

$$\begin{aligned}\mu(E) &= \int_{R^n} \chi_B(\xi_1, \cdots, \xi_n)(\Phi_{t_1t_2} \times \Phi_{t_2t_3} \times \cdots \times \Phi_{t_nc})\left(d(\eta_1, \cdots, \eta_n)\right) \\ &= \int_{R^n} \chi_B(\eta_1 + \cdots + \eta_n, \cdots, \eta_{n-1} + \eta_n, \eta_n) \\ &\qquad (\Phi_{t_1t_2} \times \Phi_{t_2t_3} \times \cdots \times \Phi_{t_nc})\left(d(\eta_1, \cdots, \eta_n)\right)\end{aligned} \tag{13}$$

where $(\xi_1, \cdots, \xi_n)$ and $(\eta_1, \cdots, \eta_n)$ are related by

$$\xi_1 = \eta_1 + \cdots + \eta_n, \cdots, \xi_{n-1} = \eta_{n-1} + \eta_n,\ \xi_n = \eta_n,$$

i.e.,

$$\eta_1 = \xi_1 - \xi_2, \cdots, \eta_{n-1} = \xi_{n-1} - \xi_n,\ \eta_n = \xi_n.$$

The fact that μ is well defined on $\mathfrak{G}$ can be shown as we did for λ on $\mathfrak{Z}$ in (2). Since μ is a probability measure on $\mathfrak{G}_{t_1 \cdots t_n}$ for each $\{t_1, \cdots, t_n\} \subset (a,c)$, it can be extended to be a probability measure on the σ-field $\sigma(\mathfrak{G})$ generated by $\mathfrak{G}$.

On the probability space $\left(R^{(a,c)}, \sigma(\mathfrak{G}), \mu\right)$ and the interval (a,c) we define a stochastic process Y by

$$Y(t,y) = -y(t) \qquad \text{for} \qquad t \in (a,c),\ y \in R^{(a,c)}.$$

Proceeding as in (3) we can show that for any $t \in (a,c)$, the random variable $-Y(t,y) = y(t)$ has Φ_{tc} as its probability distribution; for any $t', t'' \in (a,c)$, $t' < t''$, the random variable $Y(t'',y) - Y(t',y) = y(t') - y(t'')$ has $\Phi_{t',t''}$ as its probability distribution, and finally for any $a < t_1 < \cdots < t_n < c$, the system of random variables $\left\{Y(t_2, \cdot) - Y(t_1, \cdot), \cdots, Y(t_n, \cdot) - Y(t_{n-1}, \cdot), -Y(t_n, \cdot)\right\}$ is an independent system.

(5) Now let $\Omega = R^{(a,c)} \times \{0\} \times R^{(c,b)}$, i.e., the collection of all real-valued functions $z(t)$, $t \in (a,b)$, with $z(c) = 0$. Let $\mathfrak{H}$ be the σ-field of subsets of the space $\{0\}$ consisting of $\emptyset$ and $\{0\}$ and let ν be the probability measure on $\mathfrak{H}$ defined by $\nu\left(\{0\}\right) = 1$. Consider the σ-field $\mathfrak{B}$ of subsets of Ω defined by $\mathfrak{B} = \sigma(\mathfrak{G} \times \mathfrak{H} \times \mathfrak{J})$ and the probability measure P on $\mathfrak{B}$ defined by $P = \mu \times \nu \times \lambda$. Let us define a stochastic process Z on the probability space $(\Omega, \mathfrak{B}, P)$ and the interval (a,b) by

$$Z(t,z) = \begin{cases} -z(t) & \text{for } t \in (a,c) \\ 0 & \text{for } t = c \\ z(t) & \text{for } t \in (c,b) \end{cases}$$

where $z \in \Omega$.

To show that Z is a process with independent increments let $a < t_1 < \cdots < t_n < b$. There are two possible situations, namely, the case where $c = t_i$ for some $i = 1,2,\cdots,n$ and the case where $c \neq t_i$ for every $i = 1,2,\cdots,n$. Consider the first case. Take for example the situation $a < t_1 < \cdots < t_5 < b$ with $t_3 = c$. Then

$$Z(t_2,z) - Z(t_1,z) = z(t_1) - z(t_2) \qquad Z(t_3,z) - Z(t_2,z) = z(t_2)$$

$$Z(t_4,z) - Z(t_3,z) = z(t_4), \qquad Z(t_5,z) - Z(t_4,z) = z(t_5) - z(t_4).$$

Now for $B_1, B_2, B_3, B_4 \in \mathfrak{B}^1$,

$$\begin{aligned}
&P\{z \in \Omega\,;\, Z(t_2,z) - Z(t_1,z) \in B_1,\ Z(t_3,z) - Z(t_2,z) \in B_2,\\
&\quad Z(t_4,z) - Z(t_3,z) \in B_3,\ Z(t_5,z) - Z(t_4,z) \in B_4\}\\
&= P\{z \in \Omega\,;\, z(t_1) - z(t_2) \in B_1,\ z(t_2) \in B_2,\ z(t_4) \in B_3,\ z(t_5) - z(t_4) \in B_4\}\\
&= \mu\{y \in R^{(a,c)}\,;\, y(t_1) - y(t_2) \in B_1,\ y(t_2) \in B_2\}\\
&\quad \lambda\{x \in R^{(c,b)}\,;\, x(t_4) \in B_3,\ x(t_5) - x(t_4) \in B_4\}\\
&= \mu\{y \in R^{(a,c)}\,;\, y(t_1) - y(t_2) \in B_1\}\ \mu\{y \in R^{(a,c)}\,;\, y(t_2) \in B_2\}\\
&\quad \lambda\{x \in R^{(c,b)}\,;\, x(t_4) \in B_3\}\ \lambda\{x \in R^{(c,b)}\,;\, x(t_5) - x(t_4) \in B_4\}\\
&= P\{z \in \Omega\,;\, z(t_1) - z(t_2) \in B_1\}\ P\{z \in \Omega\,;\, z(t_2) \in B_2\}\\
&\quad P\{z \in \Omega\,;\, z(t_4) \in B_3\}\ P\{z \in \Omega\,;\, z(t_5) - z(t_4) \in B_4\},
\end{aligned}$$

which proves the independence of the system of random variables

$$\{Z(t_2,\cdot) - Z(t_1,\cdot),\ Z(t_3,\cdot) - Z(t_2,\cdot),\ Z(t_4,\cdot) - Z(t_3,\cdot),\ Z(t_5,\cdot) - Z(t_4,\cdot)\}.$$

Next consider the case where $c \neq t_i$ for $i = 1,2,\cdots,n$.

Again for brevity take as an example the case where $a < t_1 < t_2 < c < t_3 < b$. According to the result above, for the case where $c = t_i$ for some i, the system of random variables $\{Z_1, Z_2, Z_3\}$ where

$$Z_1(\cdot) = Z(t_2,\cdot) - Z(t_1,\cdot),\ Z_2(\cdot) = Z(c,\cdot) - Z(t_2,\cdot),\ Z_3(\cdot) = Z(t_3,\cdot) - Z(c,\cdot)$$

is an independent system. Then the system of random vectors consisting of Z_1 and (Z_2, Z_3) is an independent system according to (1), Theorem A6.5 so that the system of random variables $\{Z_1, Z_2 + Z_3\}$ is an independent system by Theorem A6.6. This proves the independence of the system of random variables $\{Z(t_2,\cdot) - Z(t_1,\cdot),\ Z(t_3,\cdot) - Z(t_2,\cdot)\}$.

Finally to show that for any $t', t'' \in (a,b)$, $t' < t''$, the random variable $Z(t'',\cdot) - Z(t',\cdot)$ has $\Phi_{t't''}$ as its probability distribution we need only to consider the case where $t' < c < t''$ since the case where $t' < t'' < c$ and the case where $c < t' < t''$ have already been treated in the discussion of $Y(t,y)$ and $X(t,x)$. Now for $t' < c < t''$ we have

$$Z(t'',z) - Z(t',z) = z(t'') + z(t') = x(t'') + y(t').$$

As we pointed out earlier, $x(t'')$ and $y(t')$ have $\Phi_{ct''}$ and $\Phi_{t'c}$, respectively, as their probability distributions. Also from our proof of independence of increments for the stochastic process Z, $\{z(t'), z(t'')\}$ is an independent system of random variables. (Identify t' and t'' with t_2 and t_4 in the case $a < t_1 < t_2 < t_3 = c < t_4 < t_5 < b$ which we considered above.) Then the sum of $z(t')$ and $z(t'')$ has $\Phi_{t'c} * \Phi_{ct''}$ as its probability distribution according to Theorem A7.6. But $\Phi_{t'c} * \Phi_{ct''} = \Phi_{t't''}$. □

Theorem 12.3 Let $D = [a,b)$, $-\infty < a < b \leq \infty$ (or $D = (a,b]$, $-\infty \leq a < b < \infty$). Let $\{\Phi_{t',t''}, t', t'' \in D, t' < t''\}$ be a system of 1-dimensional probability distributions satisfying the condition

$$t_1, t_2, t_3 \in D, \qquad t_1 < t_2 < t_3 \Rightarrow \Phi_{t_1 t_2} * \Phi_{t_2 t_3} = \Phi_{t_1 t_3}$$

and let Φ_a (or Φ_b) be a 1-dimensional probability distribution. There exists an additive process X on a probability space $(\Omega, \mathfrak{B}, P)$ and D in which $\Phi_{t't''}$ is the probability distribution of the random variable $X(t'', \cdot) - X(t', \cdot)$ for any $t', t'' \in D$, $t' < t''$, and Φ_a (or Φ_b) is the initial (or final) probability distribution of the process, i.e., the probability distribution or $X(a, \cdot)$ [or $X(b, \cdot)$].

Proof (1) When $D = [a,b)$, consider $R^{[a,b)}$, the collection of all real-valued functions $x(t)$, $t \in [a,b)$, For $a = t_0 < t_1 < \cdots < t_n < b$ let $\mathfrak{Z}_{t_0 t_1 \cdots t_n}$ be the σ-field of subsets of $R^{[a,b)}$ of the type

$$E = p_{t_0 t_1 \cdots t_n}^{-1}(B) = \left\{x \in R^{[a,b)}; \left(x(t_0), x(t_1), \cdots, x(t_n)\right) \in B\right\},$$

$$\text{where } B \in \mathfrak{B}^{n+1} \tag{1}$$

and let $\mathfrak{Z}$ be the field of subsets of $R^{[a,b)}$ which is the union of all $\mathfrak{Z}_{t_0 t_1 \cdots t_n}$. Define a set function μ on $\mathfrak{Z}$ by setting $\mu(E)$ for $E \in \mathfrak{Z}$ given by (1):

$$\mu(E) = \int_{(n+1)} \int \chi_B(\eta_0, \eta_0 + \eta_1, \cdots, \eta_0 + \eta_1 + \cdots + \eta_n)$$
$$\Phi_a(d\eta_0)\, \Phi_{at_1}(d\eta_1) \cdots \Phi_{t_{n-1} t_n}(d\eta_n). \tag{2}$$

The fact that μ is well defined on $\mathfrak{Z}$ and is a probability measure on each $\mathfrak{J}_{t_0 t_1 \cdots t_n}$ can be verified in the same way as in the proof of Theorem 12.2. Then μ can be extended to be a probability measure on the σ-field $\sigma(\mathfrak{J})$ generated by $\mathfrak{J}$ according to Theorem 2.1.

Define a stochastic process X on the probability space $\left(R^{[a,b)}, \sigma(\mathfrak{J}), \mu\right)$ and the interval $[a,b)$ by

$$X(t,x) = x(t) \qquad \text{for} \qquad t \in [a,b), \quad x \in R^{[a,b)}.$$

The fact that X is an additive process in which $\Phi_{t't''}$ is the probability distribution of the random variable $X(t'', \cdot) - X(t', \cdot)$ for any $t', t'' \in D, t' < t''$, can be shown as in Theorem 12.1. For $X(a, \cdot)$ we have, by (2),

$$\begin{aligned}\mu\left\{x \in R^{[a,b)}; X(a,x) \in B\right\} &= \mu\left\{x \in R^{[a,b)}; x(a) \in B\right\} \\ &= \int \chi_B(\eta_0)\, \Phi_a(d\eta_0) \\ &= \Phi_a(B) \quad \text{for} \quad B \in \mathfrak{B}^1,\end{aligned}$$

So that Φ_a is the probability distribution of $X(a,\cdot)$.

(2) The case $D = (a,b]$ can be handled similarly. Let $R^{(a,b]}$ be the collection of all real-valued functions $x(t)$, $t \in (a,b]$. For $a < t_1 < \cdots < t_n < t_0 = b$ let $\mathfrak{J}_{t_1 \cdots t_n t_0}$ be the σ-field of subsets of $R^{(a,b]}$ of the type

$$\begin{aligned}E &= p_{t_1 \cdots t_n t_0}^{-1}(B) \\ &= \left\{x \in R^{(a,b]}; \left(x(t_1), \cdots, x(t_n), x(t_0)\right) \in B\right\}, \quad \text{where } B \in \mathfrak{B}^n\end{aligned}$$

and define a set function μ on $\mathfrak{J}$ by

$$\mu(E) = \int (n+1) \int \chi_B(\eta_1 + \cdots + \eta_n + \eta_0, \cdots, \eta_{n-1} + \eta_n + \eta_0, \eta_n + \eta_0, \eta_0)$$

$$\times \Phi_{t_1 t_2}(d\eta_1) \cdots \Phi_{t_{n-1} t_n}(d\eta_{n-1}) \Phi_{t_n b}(d\eta_n) \Phi_b(d\eta_0)$$

and finally define a stochastic process on the probability space $\left(R^{(a,b]} \sigma(\mathfrak{Z}), \mu\right)$ and the interval $(a,b]$ by

$$X(t,x) = -x(t) \qquad \text{for} \qquad t \in (a,b],\ x \in R^{(a,b]}. \qquad \square$$

Remark 12.4 When the initial probability distribution Φ_a in Theorem 12.3 is a translated unit distribution, say $\Phi_a(\{\alpha\}) = 1$ for some $\alpha \in R^1$, i.e., $X(a,x) = \alpha$ for a.e. $x \in R^{[a,b)}$, then the system of random variables $\{X(a,\cdot),\ X(t,\cdot) - X(a,\cdot)\}$ is an independent system so that $X(t,\cdot)$, being equal to the sum of the two random variables, has $\Phi_a * \Phi_{at}$ as its probability distribution. Also, in this case (2) in the proof of Theorem 12.3 reduces to

$$\mu(E) = \int (n) \int \chi_B(\alpha, \alpha + \eta_1, \cdots, \alpha + \eta_1 + \cdots + \eta_n)$$

$$\Phi_{at_1}(d\eta_1) \cdots \Phi_{t_{n-1} t_n}(d\eta_n),$$

so that if C is the section of B at $\eta_0 = \alpha$ then

$$\mu(E) = \int (n) \int \chi_C(\alpha + \eta_1, \cdots, \alpha + \eta_1 + \cdots + \eta_n)$$

$$\Phi_{at_1}(d\eta_1) \cdots \Phi_{t_{n-1} t_n}(d\eta_n).$$

[II] Continuity and Measurability of an Additive Process

If an additive process X on a probability space $(\Omega, \mathfrak{B}, P)$

and an interval $D \subset R^1$ is separable and is stochastically continuous at $t_0 \in D$ then almost every sample function is continuous at t_0. If X is separable and is stochastically continuous on D then it is a measurable process. To prove these statements we require the following lemma.

Lemma 12.5 Ottaviani inequality. Let $\{X_i, i = 1,2,\cdots,n\}$ be an independent system of random variables on a probability space $(\Omega, \mathfrak{B}, P)$. Let $S_k = X_1 + \cdots + X_k$ for $k = 1,2,\cdots,n$, and $S_0 = 0$ and

$$T_k = \max\{|S_1|, \cdots, |S_k|\} \quad \text{for} \quad k = 1,2,\cdots,n.$$

If $c > 0$ is such that

$$P\{\omega \in \Omega; |S_n(\omega) - S_k(\omega)| > c\} \le \tfrac{1}{2} \quad \text{for} \quad k = 0,1,2,\cdots,n \tag{1}$$

then

$$P\{\omega \in \Omega; T_n(\omega) > 2c\} \le 2P\{\omega \in \Omega; |S_n(\omega)| > c\}. \tag{2}$$

Proof Let

$$A_1 = \{\omega \in \Omega; T_1(\omega) > 2c\} = \{\omega \in \Omega; |S_1(\omega)| > 2c\},$$

$$A_k = \{\omega \in \Omega; T_{k-1}(\omega) \le 2c, T_k(\omega) > 2c\}$$

$$= \{\omega \in \Omega; T_{k-1}(\omega) \le 2c, |S_k(\omega)| > 2c\}, \quad k = 2,3,\cdots,n,$$

$$A = \{\omega \in \Omega; T_n(\omega) > 2c\}.$$

Then $\{A_1, \cdots, A_n\}$ is a disjoint collection and $\bigcup_{i=1}^n A_i = A$. Let

$B_k = \{\omega \in \Omega; |S_n(\omega) - S_k(\omega)| \le c\}$, $k = 1,2,\cdots,n$, and in particular, $B_n = \Omega$,

$$B = \{\omega \in \Omega; |S_n(\omega)| > c\}.$$

We have then

$$A_k \cap B_k \subset \{\omega \in \Omega; |S_k(\omega)| > 2c, |S_n(\omega) - S_k(\omega)| \le c\}$$

$$\subset \{\omega \in \Omega; |S_k(\omega)| > 2c, |S_k(\omega)| - |S_n(\omega)| \le c\}$$

$$\subset \{\omega \in \Omega; |S_n(\omega)| > c\} = B$$

for $k = 1, 2, \cdots, n$, so that $B \supset \bigcup_{k=1}^{n} (A_k \cup B_k)$ and from the disjointness of the collection $\{A_k \cap B_k, k = 1, 2, \cdots\}$:

$$P(B) \ge P\Big(\bigcup_{k=1}^{n} (A_k \cap B_k)\Big) = \sum_{k=1}^{n} P(A_k \cap B_k).$$

Since the two random vectors $(X_1, \cdots, X_k)$ and $(X_{k+1}, \cdots, X_n)$ constitute an independent system according to (1) of Theorem A6.5 and since the characteristic functions χ_{A_k} and χ_{B_k} are Baire functions of the random vectors $(X_1, \cdots, X_k)$ and $(X_{k+1}, \cdots, X_n)$, respectively, $\{\chi_{A_k}, \chi_{B_k}\}$ is an independent system of random variables according to Theorem A6.6. Thus $\{A_k, B_k\}$ is an independent system of measurable events. Then, using (1),

$$P(B) \ge \sum_{k=1}^{n} P(A_k \cap B_k) = \sum_{k=1}^{n} P(A_k)\, P(B_k) \ge \tfrac{1}{2} \sum_{k=1}^{n} P(A_k) = \tfrac{1}{2} P(A)$$

which is (2). □

<u>Theorem 12.6</u> Let X be an additive process on a probability space $(\Omega, \mathfrak{B}, P)$ and an interval $D \subset R^1$. If X is stochastically continuous at $t_0 \in D$ then for every sequence $\{s_n, n = 1, 2, \cdots\} \subset D$ such that $\lim_{n\to\infty} s_n = t$ we have

$$P\left\{\omega \in \Omega ; \lim_{n\to\infty} X(s_n, \omega) = X(t_0, \omega)\right\} = 1. \tag{1}$$

If in addition X is separable then

$$P\left\{\omega \in \Omega ; \lim_{t\to t_0} X(t, \omega) = X(t_0, \omega)\right\} = 1. \tag{2}$$

<u>Proof</u> (1) If X is stochastically continuous at $t_0 \in D$, then for every $\epsilon > 0$ there exists $\delta > 0$ such that

$$|t - t_0| < \delta, \quad t \in D \Rightarrow P\left\{\omega \in \Omega ; |X(t,\omega) - X(t_0,\omega)| \geq \frac{\epsilon}{2}\right\} < \frac{\epsilon}{2}$$

and hence

$$\begin{aligned} t_0 \leq t', t'' < t_0 + \delta \Rightarrow P\left\{\omega \in \Omega ; |X(t',\omega) - X(t'',\omega)| \geq \epsilon\right\} \\ \leq P\left\{\omega \in \Omega ; |X(t',\omega) - X(t_0,\omega)| \geq \frac{\epsilon}{2}\right\} \\ + P\left\{\omega \in \Omega ; |X(t'',\omega) - X(t_0,\omega)| \geq \frac{\epsilon}{2}\right\} < \epsilon . \end{aligned}$$

Let $t_0 < t_1 < \cdots < t_n < t_0 + \delta$ and

$$Y_k(\omega) = X(t_k,\omega) - X(t_{k-1}, \omega) \quad \text{for} \quad \omega \in \Omega, k = 1,2, \cdots, n,$$

$$S_k(\omega) = Y_1(\omega) + \cdots + Y_k(\omega) \quad \text{for} \quad \omega \in \Omega, k = 1,2, \cdots, n,$$

$$S_0(\omega) = 0 \quad \text{for} \quad \omega \in \Omega.$$

Since X is an additive process $\{Y_k, k = 1, 2, \cdots, n\}$ is an independent system. Also, if we choose $\epsilon \in (0, \frac{1}{2})$ then, by (3),

$$\begin{aligned} P\left\{\omega \in \Omega ; |S_n(\omega) - S_k(\omega)| \geq \epsilon\right\} = P\left\{\omega \in \Omega ; |X(t_n,\omega) - X(t_k,\omega)| \geq \epsilon\right\} \\ < \epsilon < \tfrac{1}{2} \ \text{for} \ k = 0,1,2, \cdots, n. \end{aligned}$$

Thus, according to Lemma 12.5 and (3),

$$P\left\{\omega \in \Omega;\ \max_{k=1,2,\cdots,n} |X(t_k, \omega) - X(t_0, \omega)| > 2\epsilon\right\}$$

$$\leq 2P\left\{\omega \in \Omega;\ |X(t_n, \omega) - X(t_0, \omega)| > \epsilon\right\} < 2\epsilon . \tag{4}$$

Let S be a countable dense subset of D. Let the elements of $S \cap [t_0, t_0 + \delta)$ be arbitrarily numbered and let the result be $\{s_n, n = 1,2, \cdots\}$. For any positive integer n we have, by (4),

$$P\left\{\omega \in \Omega;\ \max_{k=1,2,\cdots,n} |X(s_k, \omega) - X(t_0, \omega)| > 2\epsilon\right\} < 2\epsilon. \tag{5}$$

Now

$$\left\{\omega \in \Omega;\ \sup_{S\cap[t_0, t_0+\delta)} |X(s, \omega) - X(t_0, \omega)| > 2\epsilon\right\}$$

$$\subset \left\{\omega \in \Omega;\ \max_{k=1,2,\cdots,n} |X(s_k, \omega) - X(t_0, \omega)| > 2\epsilon \right.$$

$$\left. \text{for some } n \text{ depending on } \omega\right\}$$

$$= \bigcup_{n=1}^{\infty} \left\{\omega \in \Omega;\ \max_{k=1,2,\cdots,n} |X(s_k, \omega) - X(t_0, \omega)| > 2\epsilon\right\}$$

$$= \lim_{n\to\infty} \left\{\omega \in \Omega;\ \max_{k=1,2,\cdots,n} |X(s_k, \omega) - X(t_0, \omega)| > 2\epsilon\right\}.$$

From this and from (5) we have

$$P\left\{\omega \in \Omega;\ \sup_{S\cap[t_0, t_0+\delta)} |X(s, \omega) - X(t_0, \omega)| > 2\epsilon\right\} \leq 2\epsilon .$$

and consequently

$$P\left\{\omega \in \Omega;\ \lim_{\delta\downarrow 0} \sup_{S\cap[t_0, t_0+\delta)} |X(s, \omega) - X(t_0, \omega)| > 2\epsilon\right\} \leq 2\epsilon . \tag{6}$$

From the arbitrariness of $\epsilon \in (0, \frac{1}{2})$ in (6), we have

$$P\left\{\omega \in \Omega;\ \lim_{\delta\downarrow 0} \sup_{S\cap[t_0, t_0+\delta)} |X(s, \omega) - X(t_0, \omega)| > 0\right\} = 0 . \tag{7}$$

Similarly we have

$$P\left\{\omega \in \Omega;\ \lim_{\delta \downarrow 0}\ \sup_{(t_0-\delta,\, t_0] \cap S} |X(s,\omega) - X(t_0,\omega)| > 0\right\} = 0. \tag{8}$$

Combining (7) and (8) we have

$$P\left\{\omega \in \Omega;\ \lim_{\delta \downarrow 0}\ \sup_{S \cap (t_0-\delta,\, t_0+\delta)} |X(s,\omega) - X(t_0,\omega)| = 0\right\} = 1. \tag{9}$$

To obtain (1) from (9) let $\{s_n, n = 1, 2, \cdots\} \subset D$ be such that $\lim_{n\to\infty} s_n = t_0$. Let S be a countable dense subset of D which contains the range of the sequence. Then

$$\left\{\omega \in \Omega;\ \lim_{\delta \downarrow 0}\ \sup_{S \cap (t_0-\delta,\, t_0+\delta)} |X(s,\omega) - X(t_0,\omega)| = 0\right\}$$

$$\subset \left\{\omega \in \Omega;\ \lim_{n\to\infty} \sup |X(s_n,\omega) - X(t_0,\omega)| = 0\right\}$$

$$= \left\{\omega \in \Omega;\ \lim_{n\to\infty} |X(s_n,\omega) - X(t_0,\omega)| = 0\right\},$$

so that (1) follows from (9).

(2) If X is a separable process then according to condition (S_4) of Theorem 4.2 there exists a countable dense subset S of D such that, for every $t_0 \in D$ and $\omega \in \Omega$,

$$\operatorname*{upp\ env}_{t \to t_0} |X(t,\omega) - X(t_0,\omega)| = \operatorname*{upp\ env}_{s \to t_0} |X(s,\omega) - X(t_0,\omega)|. \tag{10}$$

If X is stochastically continuous at t_0 then, by (9) and (10),

$$P\left\{\omega \in \Omega;\ \operatorname*{upp\ env}_{t \to t_0} |X(t,\omega) - X(t_0,\omega)| = 0\right\} = 1$$

and hence

$$P\left\{\omega \in \Omega;\ \lim_{t \to t_0} |X(t,\omega) - X(t_0,\omega)| = 0\right\} = 1,$$

which is (2). □

Theorem 12.7 Let X be an additive process on a probability space $(\Omega, \mathfrak{B}, P)$ and an interval $D \subset R^1$. If X is separable and is stochastically continuous at every $t_0 \in D - D_0$ where $D_0 \in \mathfrak{M}_D$ (i.e., the σ-field of Lebesgue measurable sets contained in D) with $m_L(D_0) = 0$ then there exists $E \in \sigma(\mathfrak{M}_D \times \mathfrak{B})$ such that $(m_L \times P)(E) = 0$ and X is measurable with respect to $\sigma(\mathfrak{M}_D \times \mathfrak{B})$ on $D \times \Omega - E$.

Proof This theorem is just a combination of (2) of Theorem 12.6 and Theorem 5.4.

§13. BROWNIAN MOTION PROCESSES

[I] Existence Theorem

Definition 13.1 By a Brownian motion process we mean an additive process X on a probability space $(\Omega, \mathfrak{B}, P)$ and an interval $D \subset R^1$ in which the probability distribution of the random variable $X(t'', \cdot) - X(t', \cdot)$, $t', t'' \in D$, $t' < t''$, is the normal distribution $N\big(0, c(t'' - t')\big)$ where c is a fixed positive number for the process.

Let us recall that a normal distribution $N(m,v)(E)$, $E \in \mathfrak{B}^1$, $m \in R^1$, $v > 0$, is a 1-dimensional probability distribution which is absolutely continuous with respect to the Lebesgue measure m_L on $(R^1, \mathfrak{B}^1)$ with the density function (i.e., the Radon-Nikodym derivative with respect to m_L) given by

$$N'(m,v)(x) = \frac{dN(m,v)}{dm_L}(x) = \frac{1}{\sqrt{2\pi v}} \exp\left\{-\frac{1}{2}\frac{(x-m)^2}{v}\right\} \qquad \text{for } x \in R^1.$$

We list some of the well-known facts of normal distributions in the following lemmas.

Lemma 13.2 Let Φ be the normal distribution $N(m,v)$, $m \in R^1$, $v > 0$, then the following hold:

(1) The characteristic function φ of Φ is given by

$$\varphi(y) = \exp\left\{im\ y - \frac{v}{2} y^2\right\} \quad \text{for } y \in R^1. \tag{1}$$

(2) All moments of Φ, i.e., $M^p(\Phi)$ where

$$M^p(\Phi) = \int_{R^1} x^p\ \Phi(dx) \quad \text{for } p = 1, 2, \cdots$$

exist and are finite. In particular for the 1st moment $M^1(\Phi)$ and the variance $V(\Phi)$ we have

$$M^1(\Phi) = m \quad \text{and} \quad V(\Phi) = v. \tag{2}$$

(3) All the central moments of Φ, i.e., $M_0^{\ p}(\Phi)$ where

$$M_0^{\ p}(\Phi) = \int_{R^1} \left\{x - M^1(\Phi)\right\}^p \Phi(dx) \quad \text{for } p = 1, 2, \cdots$$

exist as finite numbers and are given by

$$M_0^{\ p}(\Phi) = \begin{cases} 0 & \text{for odd } p \\ \left(\dfrac{2^p v^p}{\pi}\right)^{\frac{1}{2}} \Gamma\left(\dfrac{p}{2} + \dfrac{1}{2}\right) & \text{for even } p, \end{cases} \tag{3}$$

where $\Gamma(t)$ is gamma function

$$\Gamma(t) = \int_0^\infty x^{t-1} e^{-x}\, dx$$

and

$$\Gamma(t) = (t-1)\ \Gamma(t-1) \quad \text{with} \quad \Gamma(\tfrac{1}{2}) = \sqrt{\pi}\,.$$

Proof From the equality

$$\int_{-\infty}^{\infty} e^{-u^2}\, du = \sqrt{\pi} \tag{4}$$

we obtain the equality

$$\int_{-\infty}^{\infty} \exp\left\{-(\alpha u^2+\beta u)\right\} du = \sqrt{\frac{\pi}{\alpha}}\ \exp\left\{\frac{\beta^2}{4\alpha}\right\}$$

where $\alpha > 0$ and β is real or imaginary (5)

by completing square for $\alpha u^2+\beta u$ and, in case β is imaginary, using contour integration. Now

$$\varphi(y) = \int_{R^1} e^{iyx}\, \Phi(dx) = \int_{R^1} e^{iyx} \frac{1}{\sqrt{2\pi v}} \exp\left\{-\frac{1}{2}\frac{(x-m)^2}{v}\right\} m_L(dx).$$

Letting $u = (x-m)v^{-\frac{1}{2}}$ and using (5) we obtain (1). Since

$$M^p(\Phi) = \frac{1}{\sqrt{2\pi v}} \int_{R^1} x^p \exp -\frac{1}{2}\frac{(x-m)^2}{v}\quad m_L(dx),$$

it is obvious that $M^p(\Phi)$ exists and is finite for $p = 1, 2, \cdots$. In particular

$$M^1(\Phi) = m,\quad M^2(\Phi) = m^2+v,\quad V(\Phi) = M^2(\Phi) - \left\{M^1(\Phi)\right\}^2 = v.$$

We can also obtain $M^p(\Phi)$ by differentiating φ (cf. Theorem A3.2). As for (3) we have, setting $u = (x-m)v^{-\frac{1}{2}}$,

$$M_0^{\,p}(\Phi) = \int_{-\infty}^{\infty} \frac{1}{\sqrt{2\pi v}} (x-m)^2 \exp\left\{-\frac{1}{2}\frac{(x-m)^2}{v}\right\} dx = \int_{-\infty}^{\infty} \frac{1}{\sqrt{2\pi}} v^{p/2} u^p e^{-u^2/2}\, du$$

which is equal to 0 when p is odd. When p is even we set $w = u^2/2$ to obtain

$$M_0^{\,p}(\Phi) = \frac{1}{\sqrt{\pi}}(2v)^{p/2}\int_0^{\infty} w^{p/2-\frac{1}{2}}\, e^{-w}\, dw = \frac{1}{\sqrt{\pi}}(2v)^{p/2}\,\Gamma\left(\frac{p}{2}+\frac{1}{2}\right). \qquad \square$$

The characteristic function φ of the translated unit distribution with the unit mass concentrated at $m \in R^1$ (i.e., the 1-dimensional probability distribution Φ with $\Phi(\{m\}) = 1$ and $\Phi(R^1 - \{m\}) = 0$) is given by $\varphi(y) = \exp\{im\, y\}$, $y \in R^1$. In view of (1) of Lemma 13.2 it is convenient to treat this probability distribution as a degenerate normal distribution $N(m,v)$ with $v = 0$ for which the density function does not exist. Let us agree to mean by a normal distribution a 1-dimension probability distribution whose characteristic function φ is given by $\varphi(y) = \exp\left\{im\, y - \frac{1}{2} vy^2\right\}$, $y \in R^1$, $m \in R^1$, $v \geq 0$, and say that the normal distribution is nondegenerate or degenerate according as $v > 0$ or $v = 0$.

Lemma 13.3 The convolution of two normal distributions $N(m_1, v_1)$ and $N(m_2, v_2)$, $m_1, m_2 \in R^1$, $v_1, v_2 \geq 0$, is a normal distribution and in fact

$$N(m_1, v_1) * N(m_1, v_2) = N(m_1 + m_2, v_1 + v_2).$$

Proof Let φ_1, φ_2, and φ be the characteristic functions of the normal distributions $N(m_1, v_1)$, $N(m_2, v_2)$, and $N(m_1 + m_2,\ v_1 + v_2)$, respectively. Then

$$\varphi_1(y)\, \varphi_2(y) = \exp\left\{i(m_1 + m_2)y - \frac{v_1 + v_2}{2}\, y^2\right\} = \varphi(y) \quad \text{for} \quad y \in R^1.$$

According to Theorem A7.4, this proves our lemma. $\square$

Definition 13.4 Let $D \subset R^1$ be an interval and let $\alpha \in \overline{D}$

where $\alpha = \infty$ or $-\infty$ is admissible in case D is an infinite interval. Let $\{\varphi_n, n = 0,1,2,\cdots\}$ be a sequence of real-valued analytic functions on D satisfying the condition

$$\varphi_{n+1}(x) = 0\left(\varphi_n(x)\right) \quad \text{as} \quad x \to \alpha \quad \text{for} \quad n = 0,1,2,\cdots .$$

We say that a function J on D has the series $\sum_{n=0}^{\infty} \varphi_n(x)$ (which may or may not converge) as its asymptotic expansion as $x \to \alpha$ and write

$$J(x) \sim \sum_{n=0}^{\infty} \varphi_n(x) \qquad \text{as} \qquad x \to \alpha$$

if

$$J(x) - \sum_{k=0}^{n} \varphi_k(x) = O\left(\varphi_{n+1}(x)\right) \quad \text{as} \quad x \to \alpha \quad \text{for} \quad n = 0,1,2,\cdots .$$

Lemma 13.5 Let f and F be the density function and the distribution function of the normal distribution N(0,1), i.e.,

$$f(x) = \frac{1}{\sqrt{2\pi}} \exp\left\{-\frac{x^2}{2}\right\} \qquad \text{for} \qquad x \in R^1$$

$$F(x) = \int_{-\infty}^{x} f(u)\, du \qquad \text{for} \qquad x \in R^1 .$$

Then on $(0, \infty)$,

$$1 - F(x) \sim f(x)\left\{\frac{1}{x} - \frac{1}{x^3} + \frac{1\cdot 3}{x^5} - \frac{1\cdot 3\cdot 5}{x^7} + \cdots\right\} \quad \text{as} \quad x \to \infty, \tag{1}$$

and for every $x \in (0, \infty)$,

$$1 - F(x) < f(x)\frac{1}{x},\ f(x)\left\{\frac{1}{x} - \frac{1}{x^3} + \frac{1\cdot 3}{x^5}\right\}, \cdots \tag{2}$$

$$1 - F(x) > f(x)\left\{\frac{1}{x} - \frac{1}{x^3}\right\},\ f(x)\left\{\frac{1}{x} - \frac{1}{x^3} + \frac{1\cdot 3}{x^5} - \frac{1\cdot 3\cdot 5}{x^7}\right\}, \cdots . \tag{3}$$

Proof Let $x \in (0, \infty)$. Then

$$\sqrt{2\pi}\left\{1 - F(x)\right\} = \int_x^\infty e^{-u^2/2}\, du = \int_x^\infty -\frac{1}{u}\frac{d}{du}\left\{e^{-u^2/2}\right\} du.$$

By repetition of integration by parts we obtain

$$\begin{aligned}\sqrt{2\pi}\left\{1 - F(x)\right\} &= \frac{1}{x}e^{-x^2/2} - \int_x^\infty \frac{1}{u^2} e^{-u^2/2}\, du \\ &= \frac{1}{x}e^{-x^2/2} - \frac{1}{x^3}e^{-x^2/2} + 3\int_x^\infty \frac{1}{u^4}e^{-u^2/2}\, du \\ &= \frac{1}{x}e^{-x^2/2} - \frac{1}{x^3}e^{-x^2/2} + \frac{1\cdot 3}{x^5}e^{-x^2/2} - 1\cdot 3\cdot 5\int_x^\infty \frac{1}{u^6}e^{-u^2/2}\, du \\ &= \frac{1}{x}e^{-x^2/2} - \frac{1}{x^3}e^{-x^2/2} + \frac{1\cdot 3}{x^5}e^{-x^2/2} - \frac{1\cdot 3\cdot 5}{x^7}e^{-x^2/2} \\ &\quad + 1\cdot 3\cdot 5\cdot 7\int_x^\infty \frac{1}{u^8}e^{-u^2/2}\, du \end{aligned} \tag{4}$$

and so forth. Let

$$\varphi_0(x) = \frac{1}{\sqrt{2\pi}}e^{-x^2/2}\frac{1}{x} \quad \text{and}$$

$$\varphi_n(x) = \frac{1}{\sqrt{2\pi}}e^{-x^2/2}(-1)^n\frac{1\cdot 3\cdot \cdots \cdot(2n-1)}{x^{2n+1}} \quad \text{for } n = 1, 2, \cdots.$$

Then clearly $\lim_{x\to\infty}\varphi_{n+1}(x)\left\{\varphi_n(x)\right\}^{-1} = 0$ for $n = 0, 1, \cdots$, i.e., $\varphi_{n+1}(x) = 0\left(\varphi_n(x)\right)$ as $x \to \infty$ for $n = 0, 1, 2, \cdots$. From (4),

$$1 - F(x) = \sum_{k=0}^n \varphi_k(x) + \frac{(-1)^{n+1}}{\sqrt{2\pi}}\, 1\cdot 3\cdot \cdots \cdot(2n+1)\int_x^\infty \frac{1}{u^{2n+2}}e^{-u^2/2}\, du,$$

so that

$$\left| \frac{1 - F(x) - \sum_{k=0}^{n} \varphi_k(x)}{\varphi_{n+1}(x)} \right| = x^{2n+3} e^{x^2/2} \int_x^\infty \frac{1}{u^{2n+2}} e^{-u^2/2} du$$

$$\leq e^{x^2/2} \int_x^\infty u e^{-u^2/2} du = 1,$$

which implies in particular that $1 - F(x) - \sum_{k=0}^{n} \varphi_k(x) = O\left(\varphi_{n+1}(x)\right)$ as $x \to \infty$ for $n = 0, 1, 2, \cdots$. This completes the proof of (1). Finally, (2) and (3) are apparent from (4). □

Theorem 13.6 Given an interval $D \subset R^1$ and a system of 1-dimensional probability distributions $\{\Phi_{t't''}, t', t'' \in D, t' < t''\}$ where $\Phi_{t't''} = N\left(0, c(t''-t')\right)$ with fixed $c > 0$. There exists a Brownian motion process X on a probability space $(\Omega, \mathfrak{B}, P)$ and the interval D in which $\Phi_{t't''}$ is the probability distribution for the random variable $X(t'', \cdot) - X(t', \cdot)$ for any $t', t'' \in D, t' < t''$. If D contains its left (or right) endpoint and Φ_a (or Φ_b) is an arbitrary 1-dimensional probability distribution then there exists a Brownian motion process X with the additional property that Φ_a (or Φ_b) is the initial (or final) probability distribution of X.

Proof According to Lemma 13.3, for $t_1, t_2, t_3 \in D$, $t_1 < t_2 < t_3$,

$$\Phi_{t_1 t_2} * \Phi_{t_2 t_3} = N\left(0, c(t_2 - t_1)\right) * N\left(0, c(t_3 - t_2)\right)$$
$$= N\left(0, (t_3 - t_1)\right) = \Phi_{t_1 t_3}.$$

Then according to Theorem 12.2, there exists an additive process X on a probability space $(\Omega, \mathfrak{B}, P)$ and the interval D in which $\Phi_{t't''}$ is the probability distribution of the random variable $X(t'', \cdot) - X(t', \cdot)$ for any $t', t'' \in D$, $t' < t''$, and this process is our

Brownian motion process. The last part of the theorem is from Theorem 12.3. □

[II] Continuity of a Brownian Motion Process

Theorem 13.7 Let X be Brownian motion process on a probability space $(\Omega, \mathfrak{B}, P)$ and an interval D in which the probability distribution of the random variable $X(t'', \cdot) - X(t', \cdot)$, $t', t'' \in D$, $t' < t''$, is given by $N(0, c(t'' - t'))$, $c > 0$. Then X is stochastically continuous at every $t_0 \in D$ and in fact, for every $\epsilon > 0$,

$$P\{\omega \in \Omega ; |X(t_0 + h, \omega) - X(t_0, \omega)| \geq \epsilon\}$$

$$\leq \frac{1}{\epsilon}\sqrt{\frac{2c|h|}{\pi}} \exp\left\{-\frac{\epsilon^2}{2c|h|}\right\}. \tag{1}$$

If X is separable, then at every $t_0 \in D$

$$P\left\{\omega \in \Omega ; \lim_{t \to t_0} X(t, \omega) = X(t_0, \omega)\right\} = 1. \tag{2}$$

Proof Clearly $X(t_0 + h, \cdot) - X(t_0, \cdot)$ has $N(0, c|h|)$ as its probability distribution. Writing f and F for the density function and the distribution function of N(0,1) we have, by (2) of Lemma 13.5,

$$P\{\omega \in \Omega ; |X(t_0 + h, \omega) - X(t_0, \omega)| \geq \epsilon\}$$

$$= \frac{2}{\sqrt{2\pi c|h|}} \int_{\epsilon}^{\infty} \exp\left\{-\frac{u^2}{2c|h|}\right\} du$$

$$= \sqrt{\frac{2}{\pi}} \int_{\epsilon\{c|h|\}^{-\frac{1}{2}}}^{\infty} \exp\left\{-\frac{v^2}{2}\right\} dv =$$

$$= 2\left\{1 - F\left(\frac{\epsilon}{\sqrt{c\,|h|}}\right)\right\} < 2f\left(\frac{\epsilon}{\sqrt{c\,|h|}}\right)\frac{\sqrt{c\,|h|}}{\epsilon}$$

$$= \frac{1}{\epsilon}\sqrt{\frac{2c\,|h|}{\pi}}\ \exp\left\{-\frac{\epsilon^2}{2c\,|h|}\right\},$$

which proves (1). (2) is a particular case of Theorem 12.6. □

Theorem 13.8 Let X be a Brownian motion process on a probability space $(\Omega, \mathfrak{B}, P)$ and an interval $D \subset R^1$. Then there exists a continuous process Y on $(\Omega, \mathfrak{B}, P)$ and D which is equivalent to X (and is hence a Brownian motion).

Proof To prove the existence of Y we show that X satisfies the condition of Theorem 6.2. (Theorem 6.2 was proved for the case $D = [0,1]$, but it can be extended to the case of an arbitrary interval D in an obvious way.) If we take $\epsilon = |h|^a$ where $0 < a < \frac{1}{2}$ in (1) of Theorem 13.7, then

$$P\left\{\omega \in \Omega\,;\, |X(t+h,\omega) - X(t,\omega)| \geq |h|^a\right\}$$

$$\leq \sqrt{\frac{2c}{\pi}}\ |h|^{\frac{1}{2}-a} \exp\left\{-\frac{|h|^{2a-1}}{2c}\right\}.$$

Let

$$g(h) = |h|^a \quad \text{and} \quad q(h) = \sqrt{\frac{2c}{\pi}}\ |h|^{\frac{1}{2}-a} \exp\left\{-\frac{|h|^{2a-1}}{2c}\right\}.$$

For $h > 0$, $g(h)$ is monotone increasing, and

$$q'(h) = \sqrt{\frac{2c}{\pi}}\ \exp\left\{-\frac{h^{2a-1}}{2c}\right\}\left\{(\tfrac{1}{2} - a)\, h^{-\frac{1}{2}-a} - \frac{1}{2c}(2a-1)\, h^{-\frac{3}{2}+a}\right\} > 0$$

since $\frac{1}{2} - a > 0$ and $2a - 1 < 0$, so that $q(h)$ is also monotone increasing. Now

$$\sum_{n=1}^{\infty} g\left(\frac{1}{2^n}\right) = \sum_{n=1}^{\infty}\left(\frac{1}{2^a}\right)^n < \infty$$

and

$$\sum_{n=1}^{\infty} 2^n q\left(\frac{1}{2^n}\right) = \sqrt{\frac{2c}{\pi}} \sum_{n=1}^{\infty} \left(2^{\frac{1}{2}+a}\right)^n \exp\left\{-\frac{1}{2c}\left(2^{1-2a}\right)^n\right\}.$$

By applying the logarithmic ratio test we see that this series converges. Thus the conditions of Theorem 6.2 are satisfied by X, and Y exists. □

Theorem 13.9 A separable Brownian motion process is almost surely continuous.

Proof This theorem is a consequence of Theorem 13.8 and Theorem 6.5. □

[III] Reflexion Principle

Definition 13.10 A random variable X on a probability space $(\Omega, \mathfrak{B}, P)$ is said to be symmetrically distributed if

$$P\{\omega \in \Omega; X(\omega) \le x\} = P\{\omega \in \Omega; X(\omega) \ge -x\} \quad \text{for every } x \in R^1. \quad (1)$$

The condition (1) is equivalent to

$$P\{\omega \in \Omega; X(\omega) < x\} = P\{\omega \in \Omega; X(\omega) > -x\} \quad \text{for every } x \in R^1. \quad (2)$$

To obtain (2) from (1) we take the complements of the two sets in (1) and use the fact that x is an arbitrary real number. We obtain (1) from (2) likewise. From (1) and (2) we have

$$P\{\omega \in \Omega; X(\omega) = x\} = P\{\omega \in \Omega; X(\omega) = -x\} \quad \text{for every } x \in R^1.$$

However this condition does not imply that X is symmetrically distributed since an arbitrarily distributed random variable satisfies this condition as soon as it satisfies the condition that $P\{\omega \in \Omega; X(\omega) = x\} = 0$ for every $x \in R^1$.

Let Φ and F be the 1-dimensional probability distribution determined by X and its distribution function, respectively, i.e.,

$$\Phi(E) = P\left(X^{-1}(E)\right) = P\{\omega \in \Omega ; X(\omega) \in E\} \quad \text{for} \quad E \in \mathfrak{B}^1,$$

$$F(x) = \Phi\left((-\infty, x]\right) = P\{\omega \in \Omega ; X(\omega) \leq x\} \quad \text{for} \quad x \in R^1.$$

Then (1) is equivalent to

$$F(x) = 1 - F(-x-0), \text{ i.e., } F(x+0) + F(-x-0) = 1$$
$$\text{for every } x \in R^1 \tag{3}$$

in view of the right-continuity of F. It is also equivalent to

$$\Phi(E) = \Phi(-E) \text{ for every } E \in \mathfrak{B}^1 \text{ where}$$
$$-E = \{x \in R^1 ; -x \in E\} \tag{4}$$

since Φ is uniquely determined on $\mathfrak{B}^1$ by its values for intervals of the type $(-\infty, x]$, $x \in R^1$.

Lemma 13.11 A random variable X on a probability space $(\Omega, \mathfrak{B}, P)$ is symmetrically distributed if and only if its characteristic function φ is real valued.

Proof Let Φ be the 1-dimensional probability distribution determined by X. If X is symmetrically distributed then, by (4) of Definition 13.10,

$$\varphi(y) = \int_{R^1} e^{iyx}\,\Phi(dx) = \int_{R^1} e^{-iyu}\,\Phi\left(d(-u)\right) = \int_{R^1} e^{-iyu}\,\Phi(du) = \overline{\varphi(y)},$$

so that φ is real valued. Conversely, if φ is real valued then $\varphi(y) = \overline{\varphi(y)}$ for every $y \in R^1$, i.e.,

$$\int_{R^1} e^{iyx}\,\Phi(dx) = \int_{R^1} e^{-yx}\,\Phi(dx)$$

or

$$\int_{R^1} e^{iyx}\,\Phi(dx) = \int_{R^1} e^{iyu}\,\Phi\big(d(-u)\big).$$

From the one-to-one correspondence between characteristic functions and probability distributions (cf. Theorem A2.3) we conclude that (4) holds so that X is symmetrically distributed.

□

<u>Lemma 13.12</u> Let $\{X_j,\ j=1,2,\cdots,n\}$ be an independent system of symmetrically distributed random variables on a probability space $(\Omega, \mathfrak{B}, P)$ and let

$$S_j = X_1 + \cdots + X_j \quad \text{for } j=1,2,\cdots,n \text{ and } S_0 = 0.$$

Then for every $\lambda,\ \epsilon > 0$,

$$\begin{aligned} 2P\{\omega\in\Omega; S_n(\omega) \ge \lambda\} &\ge P\{\omega\in\Omega; \max_{1\le j\le n} S_j(\omega) \ge \lambda\} \\ &\ge 2P\{\omega\in\Omega; S_n(\omega) \ge \lambda + 2\epsilon\} \\ &\quad - 2\sum_{j=1}^{n} P\{\omega\in\Omega; X_j(\omega) \ge \epsilon\}. \end{aligned}$$

<u>Proof</u> The sum S_j is symmetrically distributed. This follows from Lemma 13.11 and from the fact that the characteristic function of S_j is the product of the characteristic functions of $X_1, \cdots, X_j$ on account of the independence of the system $\{X_1, \cdots, X_j\}$ (cf. Theorem A7.6).

We proceed to prove the first equality in the lemma. Let

$$N(\omega) = \min\{j; S_j(\omega) \ge \lambda\} \quad \text{for} \quad \omega\in\Omega.$$

$N(\omega)$, $\omega \in \Omega$, thus defined is a random variable since, for every positive integer k,

$$\{\omega \in \Omega ; N(\omega) = k\} = \{\omega \in \Omega ; S_j(\omega) < \lambda,\ j = 0, 1, \cdots, k-1, S_k(\omega) \geq \lambda\}.$$

Now

$$P\{\omega \in \Omega ;\ \max_{1 \leq j \leq n} S_j(\omega) \geq \lambda, S_n(\omega) \geq \lambda\} = P\{\omega \in \Omega ; S_n(\omega) \geq \lambda\}, \tag{1}$$

$$P\{\omega \in \Omega ;\ \max_{1 \leq j \leq n} S_j(\omega) \geq \lambda,\ S_n(\omega) < \lambda\}$$

$$= \sum_{k=1}^{n-1} P\{\omega \in \Omega ; N(\omega) = k,\ S_n(\omega) < \lambda\} \leq \sum_{k=1}^{n-1} P\{\omega \in \Omega ; N(\omega) = k, S_n(\omega) - S_k(\omega) < 0\}$$

$$= \sum_{k=1}^{n-1} P\{\omega \in \Omega ; N(\omega) = k\}\ P\{\omega \in \Omega ; S_n(\omega) - S_k(\omega) < 0\}$$

$$= \sum_{k=1}^{n-1} P\{\omega \in \Omega ; N(\omega) = k\}\ P\{\omega \in \Omega ; S_n(\omega) - S_k(\omega) > 0\}$$

$$= \sum_{k=1}^{n-1} P\{\omega \in \Omega ; N(\omega) = k, S_n(\omega) - S_k(\omega) > 0\}$$

$$\leq \sum_{k=1}^{n-1} P\{\omega \in \Omega ; N(\omega) = k, S_n(\omega) \geq \lambda\} \leq P\{\omega \in \Omega ; S_n(\omega) \geq \lambda\}, \tag{2}$$

where we used the independence of the two events $\{\omega \in \Omega ; N(\omega) = k\}$ and $\{\omega \in \Omega ; S_n(\omega) - S_k(\omega) < 0\}$ which is a consequence of the independence of the system of random vectors $\{(X_1, \cdots, X_k), (X_{k+1}, \cdots, X_n)\}$. Adding (1) and (2) sides by side, we obtain the first inequality of the lemma.

To prove the second inequality of the lemma consider the first equality in (2). We have

$$\{\omega \in \Omega ; N(\omega) = k, S_n(\omega) < \lambda\}$$

$$\supset \{\omega \in \Omega ; N(\omega) = k, S_n(\omega) < S_{k-1}(\omega), S_{k-1}(\omega) < \lambda\}$$

$$\supset \{\omega \in \Omega ; N(\omega) = k, S_n(\omega) < S_{k-1}(\omega) + X_k(\omega) - \epsilon, X_k(\omega) - \epsilon < 0, S_{k-1}(\omega) < \lambda\}$$

$$= \{\omega \in \Omega ; N(\omega) = k, S_n(\omega) < S_k(\omega) - \epsilon, X_k(\omega) < \epsilon, S_{k-1}(\omega) < \lambda\}$$

$$= \{\omega \in \Omega ; N(\omega) = k, S_n(\omega) - S_k(\omega) < -\epsilon, X_k(\omega) < \epsilon\}$$

$$= \{\omega \in \Omega ; N(\omega) = k, S_n(\omega) - S_k(\omega) < -\epsilon\} \cap \{\omega \in \Omega ; X_k(\omega) \geq \epsilon\}^c$$

and hence

$$P\{\omega \in \Omega ; N(\omega) = k, S_n(\omega) < \lambda\} \geq P\{\omega \in \Omega ; N(\omega) = k, S_n(\omega) - S_k(\omega) < -\epsilon\}$$
$$- P\{\omega \in \Omega ; X_k(\omega) \geq \epsilon\}.$$

Thus

$$P\{\omega \in \Omega ; \max_{1 \leq j \leq n} S_j(\omega) \geq \lambda, S_n(\omega) < \lambda\}$$
$$\geq \sum_{k=1}^{n-1} P\{\omega \in \Omega ; N(\omega) = k, S_n(\omega) - S_k(\omega) < -\epsilon\}$$
$$- \sum_{k=1}^{n-1} P\{\omega \in \Omega ; X_k(\omega) \geq \epsilon\} \tag{3}$$

Now

$$P\{\omega \in \Omega ; N(\omega) = k, S_n(\omega) - S_k(\omega) < -\epsilon\}$$
$$= P\{\omega \in \Omega ; N(\omega) = k\} \, P\{\omega \in \Omega ; S_n(\omega) - S_k(\omega) < -\epsilon\}$$
$$= P\{\omega \in \Omega ; N(\omega) = k\} \, P\{\omega \in \Omega ; S_n(\omega) - S_k(\omega) > \epsilon\}$$
$$= P\{\omega \in \Omega ; N(\omega) = k, S_n(\omega) - S_k(\omega) > \epsilon\}. \tag{4}$$

Furthermore

$$\left\{\omega \in \Omega ; N(\omega) = k, S_n(\omega) - S_k(\omega) > \epsilon\right\}$$

$$\supset \left\{\omega \in \Omega ; N(\omega) = k, S_n(\omega) \geq \lambda + 2\epsilon, S_k(\omega) < \lambda + \epsilon\right\}$$

$$\supset \left\{\omega \in \Omega ; N(\omega) = k, S_n(\omega) \geq \lambda + 2\epsilon, X_k(\omega) < \epsilon, S_{k-1}(\omega) < \lambda\right\}$$

$$= \left\{\omega \in \Omega ; N(\omega) = k, S_n(\omega) \geq \lambda + 2\epsilon, X_k(\omega) < \epsilon\right\}$$

$$= \left\{\omega \in \Omega ; N(\omega) = k, S_n(\omega) \geq \lambda + 2\epsilon\right\} - \left\{\omega \in \Omega ; X_k(\omega) \geq \epsilon\right\},$$

so that

$$P\left\{\omega \in \Omega ; N(\omega) = k, S_n(\omega) - S_k(\omega) > \epsilon\right\}$$

$$\geq P\left\{\omega \in \Omega ; N(\omega) = k, S_n(\omega) \geq \lambda + 2\epsilon\right\}$$

$$- P\left\{\omega \in \Omega ; X_k(\omega) \geq \epsilon\right\}. \tag{5}$$

Using (4) and (5) in (3) we obtain

$$P\left\{\omega \in \Omega ; \max_{1 \leq j \leq n} S_j(\omega) \geq \lambda, S_n(\omega) < \lambda\right\}$$

$$\geq \sum_{k=1}^{n-1} P\left\{\omega \in \Omega ; N(\omega) = k, S_n(\omega) \geq \lambda + 2\epsilon\right\}$$

$$- 2 \sum_{k=1}^{n-1} P\left\{\omega \in \Omega ; X_k(\omega) \geq \epsilon\right\}. \tag{6}$$

From (6) and

$$\bigcup_{k=1}^{n-1} \left\{\omega \in \Omega ; N(\omega) = k, S_n(\omega) \geq \lambda + 2\epsilon\right\}$$

$$\supset \left\{\omega \in \Omega ; S_n(\omega) \geq \lambda + 2\epsilon, S_{n-1}(\omega) \geq \lambda + \epsilon\right\}$$

$$\supset \left\{\omega \in \Omega ; S_n(\omega) \geq \lambda + 2\epsilon, X_n(\omega) < \epsilon\right\}$$

$$= \{\omega \in \Omega ; S_n(\omega) \geq \lambda + 2\epsilon\} - \{\omega \in \Omega ; X_n(\omega) \geq \epsilon\}$$

we have

$$P\left\{\omega \in \Omega ; \max_{1 \leq j \leq n} S_j(\omega) \geq \lambda, S_n(\omega) < \lambda\right\}$$

$$\geq P\{\omega \in \Omega ; S_n(\omega) \geq \lambda + 2\epsilon\} - 2\sum_{k=1}^{n} P\{\omega \in \Omega ; X_k(\omega) \geq \epsilon\} . \tag{7}$$

On the other hand

$$P\left\{\omega \in \Omega; \max_{1 \leq j \leq n} S_j(\omega) \geq \lambda, S_n(\omega) \geq \lambda\right\}$$

$$= P\{\omega \in \Omega ; S_n(\omega) \geq \lambda\} \geq P\{\omega \in \Omega ; S_n(\omega) \geq \lambda + 2\epsilon\} . \tag{8}$$

Adding (7) and (8) side by side we have the second inequality of the lemma. □

Theorem 13.13 Reflexion Principle. Let X be a separable Brownian motion process on a probability space $(\Omega, \mathfrak{B}, P)$ and an interval $D \subset R^1$ in which the probability distribution of the random variable $X(t'', \cdot) - X(t', \cdot)$, $t', t'' \in D$, $t' < t''$, is given by $N\big(0, c(t'' - t')\big)$, $c > 0$. Then for any $\alpha, \beta \in D$, $\alpha < \beta$, and $\lambda > 0$

$$P\left\{\omega \in \Omega; \sup_{[\alpha, \beta]} \{X(t, \omega) - X(\alpha, \omega)\} \geq \lambda\right\}$$

$$= 2P\{\omega \in \Omega ; X(\beta, \omega) - X(\alpha, \omega) \geq \lambda\} \leq \sqrt{\frac{2c(\beta - \alpha)}{\pi}} \frac{1}{\lambda} \exp\left\{-\frac{\lambda^2}{2c(\beta - \alpha)}\right\}.$$

Proof Since X is separable there exists a countable dense subset $S \subset D$ such, that, for every open interval $I \subset R^1$,

$$\sup_{D \cap I} X(t, \omega) = \sup_{S \cap I} X(s, \omega) .$$

Let $\alpha, \beta \in D$, $\alpha < \beta$. Adjoin α and β to S if they are not already in S. With $I = (\alpha, \beta)$, the above equality implies

$$\sup_{[\alpha,\beta]} X(t,\omega) = \sup_{S\cap[\alpha,\beta]} X(s,\omega). \tag{1}$$

Let $S \cap (\alpha, \beta) = \{s_n, n = 1, 2, \cdots\}$. For any n, let the rearrangement of $\{\alpha, s_1, \cdots, s_n, \beta\}$ in the ascending order of magnitude be $\{t_{n,k}, k = 0, 1, 2, \cdots, n+1\}$, or simply, $\{t_k, k = 0, 1, 2, \cdots, n+1\}$ for brevity. For arbitrary λ, $\epsilon > 0$, we have

$$\left\{\omega \in \Omega;\ \sup_{S\cap[\alpha,\beta]} \{X(s,\omega) - X(\alpha,\omega)\} \geq \lambda\right\}$$

$$\subset \bigcup_{n=1}^{\infty} \left\{\omega \in \Omega;\ \max_{1\leq k\leq n+1} \{X(t_k,\omega) - X(t_0,\omega)\} \geq \lambda - \epsilon\right\}. \tag{2}$$

By (1) and the fact that the sequence of sets in (2) is a monotone increasing sequence we have

$$P\left\{\omega \in \Omega;\ \sup_{[\alpha,\beta]} \{X(t,\omega) - X(\alpha,\omega)\} \geq \lambda\right\}$$

$$\leq \lim_{n\to\infty} P\left\{\omega \in \Omega;\ \max_{1\leq k\leq n+1} \{X(t_k,\omega) - X(t_0,\omega)\} \geq \lambda - \epsilon\right\}. \tag{3}$$

Now $\{X(t_k, \cdot) - X(t_{k-1}, \cdot), k = 1, 2, \cdots, n+1\}$ is an independent system of random variables, each of which is normally and hence symmetrically distributed. By the first inequality in Lemma 13.12,

$$P\left\{\omega \in \Omega;\ \max_{1\leq k\leq n+1} \{X(t_k,\omega) - X(t_0,\omega)\} \geq \lambda - \epsilon\right\}$$

$$\leq 2P\{\omega \in \Omega; X(\beta,\omega) - X(\alpha,\omega) \geq \lambda - \epsilon\} \tag{4}$$

From (3) and (4) we have

$$P\left\{\omega \in \Omega;\ \sup_{[\alpha,\beta]} \left\{X(t,\omega) - X(\alpha,\omega) \geq \lambda\right\}\right.$$

$$\leq 2P\left\{\omega \in \Omega; X(\beta,\omega) - X(\alpha,\omega)\right\} \geq \lambda\Big\} \tag{5}$$

Since $X(\beta,\omega) - X(\alpha,\omega)$ is normally distributed its distribution function is continuous. Then letting $\epsilon \downarrow 0$ in (5) we obtain

$$P\left\{\omega \in \Omega;\ \sup_{[\alpha,\beta]} \left\{X(t,\omega) - X(\alpha,\omega)\right\} \geq \lambda\right\}$$

$$\leq 2P\left\{\omega \in \Omega; X(\beta,\omega) - X(\alpha,\omega) \geq \lambda\right\}. \tag{6}$$

To obtain the reverse inequality to (6), let $t_k = \alpha + k(\beta-\alpha)/n$, $k = 0,1,2,\cdots,n$. For any λ, $\epsilon > 0$, according to the second inequality in Lemma 13.12,

$$P\left\{\omega \in \Omega;\ \sup_{[\alpha,\beta]} \left\{X(t,\omega) - X(\alpha,\omega)\right\} \geq \lambda\right\}$$

$$\geq P\left\{\omega \in \Omega;\ \sup_{1\leq k\leq n} \left\{X(t_k,\omega) - X(\alpha,\omega)\right\} \geq \lambda\right\}$$

$$\geq 2P\left\{\omega \in \Omega; X(\beta,\omega) - X(\alpha,\omega) \geq \lambda + 2\epsilon\right\}$$

$$-2\sum_{k=1}^{n} P\left\{\omega \in \Omega; X(t_k,\omega) - X(t_{k-1},\omega) \geq \epsilon\right\}.$$

Writing f and F for the density function and the distribution function of $N(0,1)$, we have by (2) of Lemma 13.5,

$$P\left\{\omega \in \Omega; X(t_k,\omega) - X(t_{k-1},\omega) \geq \epsilon\right\}$$

$$= \frac{1}{\sqrt{2\pi n^{-1} c(\beta-\alpha)}} \int_{\epsilon}^{\infty} \exp\left\{-\frac{u^2}{2n^{-1}c(\beta-\alpha)}\right\} du$$

$$= 1 - F\left(\sqrt{\frac{n}{c(\beta-\alpha)}}\,\epsilon\right) \le f\left(\sqrt{\frac{n}{c(\beta-\alpha)}}\,\epsilon\right)\sqrt{\frac{c(\beta-\alpha)}{n}}\,\frac{1}{\epsilon}$$

$$= \sqrt{\frac{c(\beta-\alpha)}{2\pi n}}\,\frac{1}{\epsilon}\,\exp\left\{-\frac{n\epsilon^2}{2c(\beta-\alpha)}\right\}. \tag{7}$$

Thus

$$\lim_{n\to\infty}\sum_{k=1}^{n} P\{\omega\in\Omega;\, X(t_k,\omega) - X(t_{k-1},\omega) \ge \epsilon\}$$

$$\le \lim_{n\to\infty}\sqrt{\frac{c(\beta-\alpha)n}{2\pi}}\,\frac{1}{\epsilon}\,\exp\left\{-\frac{n\epsilon^2}{2c(\beta-\alpha)}\right\} = 0\,,$$

and hence

$$P\left\{\omega\in\Omega;\, \sup_{[\alpha,\beta]}\{X(t,\omega) - X(\alpha,\omega)\} \ge \lambda\right\}$$

$$\ge 2P\{\omega\in\Omega;\, X(\beta,\omega) - X(\alpha,\omega) \ge \lambda + 2\epsilon\}\,.$$

Again letting $\epsilon \downarrow 0$ and using the continuity of the distribution function of $X(\beta,\cdot) - X(\alpha,\cdot)$ we obtain the reverse inequality to (6). This proves the equality in the theorem. The inequality in the theorem is obtained by taking $n = 1$ and $\epsilon = \lambda$ in (7). □

Remark 13.14 The Reflexion Principle can be used to give another proof that a separable Brownian motion process is almost surely continuous. Let X be a Brownian motion process on a probability space $(\Omega, \mathfrak{B}, P)$ and $D = R^1$. We shall show that for a.e. $\omega\in\Omega$ there exists a positive integer $N(\omega)$ such that

$$\left|X(t,\omega) - X\left(\frac{j}{n},\omega\right)\right| \le \frac{1}{n^{\frac{1}{4}}} \quad \text{for}$$

$$t\in\left[\frac{j}{n}, \frac{j+1}{n}\right],\ j = -n^2, -n^2+1, \cdots, n^2-1 \ \text{ when } n \ge N(\omega) \tag{1}$$

so that $X(\cdot,\omega)$ is uniformly continuous on $[-n,n]$ for $n \geq N(\omega)$ and in particular continuous on $(-\infty,\infty)$.

According to the Reflexion Principle,

$$P\left\{\omega\in\Omega;\ \sup_{t\in\left[\frac{j}{n},\frac{j+1}{n}\right],\ j=-n^2,\cdots,n^2-1}\left|X(t,\omega)-X\left(\frac{j}{n},\omega\right)\right| \geq \frac{1}{n^{\frac{1}{4}}}\right\}$$

$$\leq \sum_{j=-n^2}^{n^2-1} P\left\{\omega\in\Omega;\ \sup_{t\in\left[\frac{j}{n},\frac{j+1}{n}\right]}\left|X(t,\omega)-X\left(\frac{j}{n},\omega\right)\right| \geq \frac{1}{n^{\frac{1}{4}}}\right\}$$

$$\leq 2n^2\sqrt{\frac{2c}{\pi n}}\ n^{\frac{1}{4}}\exp\left\{-\frac{n^{\frac{1}{2}}}{2c}\right\} = 2\sqrt{\frac{2c}{\pi}}\ n^{\frac{7}{4}}\exp\left\{-\frac{n^{\frac{1}{2}}}{2c}\right\}.$$

Now $\sum_{n=1}^{\infty} n^{\frac{7}{4}}\exp\left\{-(2c)^{-1}n^{\frac{1}{2}}\right\} < \infty$, so that, by the Borel-Cantelli theorem (cf. Theorem A1.3),

$$P\left(\liminf_{n\to\infty} A_n^c\right) = 1 \quad \text{where}$$

$$A_n = \left\{\omega\in\Omega;\ \sup_{t\in\left[\frac{j}{n},\frac{j+1}{n}\right],\ j=-n^2,\cdots,n^2-1}\left|X(t,\omega)-X\left(\frac{j}{n},\omega\right)\right| \geq \frac{1}{n^{\frac{1}{4}}}\right\},$$

i.e., except for ω in a set of probability measure 0, every $\omega\in\Omega$ is in A_n^c for all but finitely many n, i.e., there exists $N(\omega)$ such that for $n \geq N(\omega)$

$$\sup_{t\in\left[\frac{j}{n},\frac{j+1}{n}\right],\ j=-n^2,\cdots,n^2-1}\left|X(t,\omega)-X\left(\frac{j}{n},\omega\right)\right| < \frac{1}{n^{\frac{1}{4}}}$$

proving (1).

[IV] Differentiability of Sample Functions in a Brownian Motion Process

As we have seen, almost every sample function of a separable Brownian motion process is continuous. However almost every sample function of the process is almost everywhere nondifferentiable. To prove this we need the following lemma.

Lemma 13.15 Let X be a separable Brownian motion process on a probability space $(\Omega, \mathfrak{B}, P)$ and an interval $D \subset R^1$. Then for every $t_0 \in D$,

$$P\left\{\omega \in \Omega ; \limsup_{t \to t_0} \frac{X(t,\omega) - X(t_0,\omega)}{t-t_0} = \infty\right\} = 1.$$

Proof The limit superior in question is $\mathfrak{B}$-measurable. This is a consequence of the separability of X. In fact if S is a countable dense subset of D relative to which X is separable then

$$\limsup_{t \to t_0} \frac{X(t,\omega) - X(t_0,\omega)}{t-t_0} = \lim_{n\to\infty} \sup_{0<|t-t_0|<\frac{1}{n}} \frac{X(t,\omega) - X(t_0,\omega)}{t-t_0}$$

$$= \lim_{n\to\infty} \sup_{0<|s-t_0|<\frac{1}{n}} \frac{X(s,\omega) - X(t_0,\omega)}{s-t_0}$$

which is $\mathfrak{B}$-measurable since S is a countable set.

Let us show that

$$P\left\{\omega \in \Omega ; \limsup_{t \downarrow t_0} \frac{X(t,\omega) - X(t_0,\omega)}{t-t_0} = \infty\right\} = 1 \tag{1}$$

by showing that, for any $\lambda > 0$,

$$P\left\{\omega \in \Omega ; \limsup_{t \downarrow t_0} \frac{X(t,\omega) - X(t_0,\omega)}{t - t_0} \geq \lambda \right\} = 1 . \tag{2}$$

Now

$$\left\{\omega \in \Omega ; \limsup_{t \downarrow t_0} \frac{X(t,\omega) - X(t_0,\omega)}{t - t_0} \geq \lambda \right\}$$

$$= \left\{\omega \in \Omega ; \lim_{n \to \infty} \sup_{\left(t_0, t_0 + \frac{1}{n}\right]} \frac{X(t,\omega) - X(t_0,\omega)}{t - t_0} \geq \lambda \right\}$$

$$= \bigcap_{n=1}^{\infty} \left\{\omega \in \Omega ; \sup_{\left(t_0, t_0 + \frac{1}{n}\right]} \frac{X(t,\omega) - X(t_0,\omega)}{t - t_0} \geq \lambda \right\},$$

so that

$$P\left\{\omega \in \Omega ; \limsup_{t \downarrow t_0} \frac{X(t,\omega) - X(t_0,\omega)}{t - t_0} \geq \lambda \right\}$$

$$= \lim_{n \to \infty} P\left\{\omega \in \Omega ; \sup_{\left(t_0, t_0 + \frac{1}{n}\right]} \frac{X(t,\omega) - X(t_0,\omega)}{t - t_0} \geq \lambda \right\}. \tag{3}$$

By the Reflexion Principle,

$$P\left\{\omega \in \Omega ; \sup_{\left(t_0, t_0 + \frac{1}{n}\right]} \frac{X(t,\omega) - X(t_0,\omega)}{t - t_0} \geq \lambda \right\}$$

$$\geq P\left\{\omega \in \Omega ; \sup_{\left[t_0, t_0 + \frac{1}{n}\right]} \left\{X(t,\omega) - X(t_0,\omega)\right\} \geq \frac{\lambda}{n} \right\}$$

$$= 2P\left\{\omega \in \Omega ; X\left(t_0 + \frac{1}{n}, \omega\right) - X(t_0,\omega) \geq \frac{\lambda}{n} \right\}$$

$$= 2P\left\{\omega \in \Omega ; \sqrt{n} \left\{X\left(t_0 + \frac{1}{n}, \omega\right) - X(t_0,\omega)\right\} \geq \frac{\lambda}{\sqrt{n}} \right\}. \tag{4}$$

Since the probability distribution of $X(t_0+1/n, \cdot) - X(t_0, \cdot)$ is $N(0, c/n)$ (where c is the constant in Definition 13.1), the probability distribution of $\sqrt{n}\left\{X(t_0+1/n, \cdot) - X(t_0, \cdot)\right\}$ is $N(0,c)$ irrespective of n. Therefore, from the continuity of the distribution function F of $N(0,c)$, we have

$$\lim_{n\to\infty} 2P\left\{\omega \in \Omega ; \sqrt{n}\left\{X\left(t_0+\frac{1}{n}, \omega\right) - X(t_0, \omega)\right\} \geq \frac{\lambda}{\sqrt{n}}\right\}$$
$$= 2\left\{1 - F(0)\right\} = 1 . \tag{5}$$

Combining (3), (4), and (5) we obtain (2), which implies (1). We can show similarly that

$$P\left\{\omega \in \Omega ; \limsup_{t\uparrow t_0} \frac{X(t,\omega) - X(t_0,\omega)}{t-t_0} = \infty\right\} = 1 , \tag{6}$$

which together with (1) yields our lemma. □

Theorem 13.16 Let X be a separable Brownian motion process on a probability space $(\Omega, \mathfrak{B}, P)$ and an interval $D \subset R^1$. Then for a.e. $\omega \in \Omega$ the sample function $X(\cdot, \omega)$ is a.e. non-differentiable on D, the exceptional subset of D with Lebesgue measure 0 depending on ω.

Proof According to Theorem 13.9, $X(\cdot, \omega)$ is continuous on D for a.e. $\omega \in \Omega$. We may assume without loss of generality that $X(\cdot, \omega)$ is continuous on D for every $\omega \in \Omega$. Then by Theorem 5.5, X is measurable with respect to $\sigma(\mathfrak{B}_D \times \mathfrak{B})$ where $\mathfrak{B}_D$ is the σ-field of Borel sets contained in D.

According to Lemma 13.15, for every $t \in D$,

$$P\left\{\omega \in \Omega ; \limsup_{\tau\to t} \left|\frac{X(\tau, \omega) - X(t, \omega)}{\tau - t}\right| = \infty\right\} = 1 .$$

Let

$$D(t,\omega) = \limsup_{\tau \to t} \left| \frac{X(\tau,\omega) - X(t,\omega)}{\tau - t} \right| \quad \text{for} \quad (t,\omega) \in D \times \Omega .$$

The fact that D is measurable with respect to $\sigma(\mathfrak{B}_D \times \mathfrak{B})$ follows from the measurability of X with respect to $\sigma(\mathfrak{B}_D \times \mathfrak{B})$ and the separability of X. In fact if S is a countable dense subset of D relative to which X is separable, then

$$\begin{aligned} D(t,\omega) &= \lim_{n\to\infty} \sup_{\tau \in D,\, 0<|\tau - t|<\frac{1}{n}} \left| \frac{X(\tau,\omega) - X(t,\omega)}{\tau - t} \right| \\ &= \lim_{n\to\infty} \sup_{0<|s-t|<\frac{1}{n}} \left| \frac{X(s,\omega) - X(t,\omega)}{s - t} \right| , \end{aligned}$$

which is measurable with respect to $\sigma(\mathfrak{B}_D \times \mathfrak{B})$. By the Fubini theorem,

$$\int_\Omega \left\{ \int_D \frac{1}{D(t,\omega)} m_L(dt) \right\} P(d\omega) = \int_D \left\{ \int_\Omega \frac{1}{D(t,\omega)} P(d\omega) \right\} m_L(dt) = 0.$$

Since $\left[D(t,\omega)\right]^{-1} \geq 0$ on $D \times \Omega$ and $\int_D \left[D(t,\omega)\right]^{-1} m_L(dt) \geq 0$ on Ω, the above implies that $\int_D \left[D(t,\omega)\right]^{-1} m_L(dt) = 0$ for a.e. $\omega \in \Omega$. Then for a.e. $\omega \in \Omega$, $\left[D(t,\omega)\right]^{-1} = 0$ for a.e. $t \in D$, i.e., $D(t,\omega) = \infty$ for a.e. $t \in D$. Therefore for a.e. $\omega \in \Omega$, $X(\cdot,\omega)$ is a.e. non-differentiable on D. □

§14. CONTINUOUS ADDITIVE PROCESSES

[I] Existence of a Continuous Additive Process with Preassigned Normal Distributions for the Increments

Given a real-valued continuous function m and a continuous monotone increasing function v on an interval $D \subset R^1$, there exists a continuous additive process X on a probability space $(\Omega, \mathfrak{B}, P)$ and D in which the probability distribution of $X(t'', \cdot) - X(t', \cdot)$, $t', t'' \in D$, $t' < t''$, is given by $N\big(m(t'') - m(t'), v(t'') - v(t')\big)$. [According to our convention $N(m, 0)$ is the translated unit distribution with unit mass at $m \in R^1$.] To prove this statement we need the following lemma.

<u>Lemma 14.1</u> Let X be a stochastically continuous additive process on a probability space $(\Omega, \mathfrak{B}, P)$ and an interval $D \subset R^1$. Let S be the collection of rational numbers contained in D. If, for every $\alpha, \beta \in S$, $\alpha < \beta$, $\alpha_{n,k} = \alpha + k(\beta - \alpha)/n$, $k = 0, 1, 2, \cdots, n$, and $\epsilon > 0$,

$$\lim_{n \to \infty} \sum_{k=1}^{n} P\left\{\omega \in \Omega;\ |X(\alpha_{n,k}, \omega) - X(\alpha_{n,k-1}, \omega)| > \epsilon\right\} = 0 \tag{1}$$

holds, then there exists an equivalent process Y of X on $(\Omega, \mathfrak{B}, P)$ and D which is continuous.

<u>Proof</u> For $\alpha, \beta \in S$, $\alpha < \beta$, let $S_{\alpha,\beta} = S \cap [\alpha, \beta]$ and

$$\Omega_{\alpha,\beta} = \left\{\omega \in \Omega;\ X(s, \omega),\ s \in S, \text{ is uniformly continuous on } S_{\alpha,\beta}\right\}.$$

To show that $\Omega_{\alpha,\beta} \in \mathfrak{B}$ and $P(\Omega_{\alpha,\beta}) = 1$, define

$$Z_n(\omega) = \sup_{s', s'' \in S_{\alpha,\beta}\ |s' - s''| \le n^{-1}(\beta - \alpha)} |X(s', \omega) - X(s'', \omega)| \quad \text{for} \quad \omega \in \Omega,$$

which is a random variable since $S_{\alpha,\beta}$ is a countable set. In terms of $\{Z_n, n = 1, 2, \cdots\}$ we have

$$\Omega_{\alpha,\beta} = \left\{\omega \in \Omega;\ \lim_{n \to \infty} Z_n(\omega) = 0\right\} \in \mathfrak{B}.$$

To show that $P(\Omega_{\alpha,\beta}) = 1$ let us show that

$P\{\omega \in \Omega ; \lim_{n\to\infty} Z_n(\omega) > 0\} = 0$ by showing that for every $\epsilon > 0$, $P\{\omega \in \Omega ; \lim_{n\to\infty} Z_n(\omega) > \epsilon\} = 0$. This is done by means of the Ottaviani inequality (Lemma 12.5). Since X is stochastically continuous on D it is uniformly stochastically continuous on $[\alpha, \beta]$ according to Theorem 3.5. Then for every $\epsilon > 0$ there exists N such that

$$P\{\omega \in \Omega ; |X(\alpha_{n,k}, \omega) - X(t,\omega)| > \epsilon\} \le \tfrac{1}{2} \quad \text{for}$$
$$t \in [\alpha_{n,k-1}, \alpha_{n,k}], \; k = 1,2, \cdots, n ; n \ge N. \tag{2}$$

Let $S \cap [\alpha_{n,k-1}, \alpha_{n,k}) = \{s_\mu, \mu = 0,1,2, \cdots\}$ with $s_0 = \alpha_{n,k-1}$. For every positive integer m let $\{t_0, t_1, \cdots, t_m\}$ be the rearrangement of $\{s_0, s_1, \cdots, s_{m-1}, \alpha_{n,k}\}$ in ascending order of magnitude. Then

$$X_\mu(\omega) = X(t_\mu, \omega) - X(t_{\mu-1}, \omega), \qquad \omega \in \Omega, \; \mu = 1,2, \cdots, m$$

is an independent system of random variables and furthermore, by (2),

$$P\{\omega \in \Omega ; |X_\mu(\omega) + \cdots + X_m(\omega)| > \epsilon\}$$
$$= P\{\omega \in \Omega ; |X(\alpha_{n,k}, \omega) - X(t_{\mu-1}, \omega)| > \epsilon\} \le \tfrac{1}{2}$$

for $\mu = 1,2, \cdots, m ; k = 1,2, \cdots, n ; n \ge N$. The Ottaviani inequality is applicable now and we have

$$P\left\{\omega \in \Omega ; \max_{\mu=1,2,\cdots,m} |X(t_\mu, \omega) - X(t_0, \omega)| > 2\epsilon\right\}$$
$$\le 2P\{\omega \in \Omega ; |X(\alpha_{n,k}, \omega) - X(\alpha_{n,k-1}, \omega)| > \epsilon\} \tag{3}$$

for $k = 1,2, \cdots, n$, $n \ge N$. Let

$$Y_{n,k}(\omega) = \sup_{S_{\alpha_{n,k-1},\alpha_{n,k}}} |X(s,\omega) - X(\alpha_{n,k-1},\omega)|.$$

Then

$$\{\omega \in \Omega; Y_{n,k}(\omega) > 2\epsilon\} \subset \bigcup_{m=1}^{\infty} \left\{\omega \in \Omega; \max_{\mu=1,2,\cdots,m} |X(t_\mu,\omega) - X(t_0,\omega)| > 2\epsilon\right\}.$$

Since the sequence of the sets is monotone decreasing we have, by (3),

$$\begin{aligned} &P\{\omega \in \Omega; Y_{n,k}(\omega) > 2\epsilon\} \\ &\le \lim_{m\to\infty} P\left\{\omega \in \Omega; \max_{\mu=1,2,\cdots,m} |X(t_\mu,\omega) - X(t_0,\omega)| > 2\epsilon\right\} \\ &\le 2P\{\omega \in \Omega; |X(\alpha_{n,k},\omega) - X(\alpha_{n,k-1},\omega)| > \epsilon\} \end{aligned} \tag{4}$$

for $k = 1,2,\cdots,n; n \ge N$. Consider Z_n. For $s', s'' \in S_{\alpha,\beta}$, $|s'-s''| \le n^{-1}(\beta-\alpha)$, let $s' \le s''$. Then $s' \in [\alpha_{n,k_0-1}, \alpha_{n,k_0}]$ for some k_0, $1 \le k_0 \le n$, and either $s'' \in [\alpha_{n,k_0-1}, \alpha_{n,k_0}]$ also or $s'' \in [\alpha_{n,k_0}, \alpha_{n,k_0+1}]$. In the latter case

$$\begin{aligned} |X(s',\omega) - X(s'',\omega)| &\le \left|X(s',\omega) - X\left(\alpha_{n,k_0-1},\omega\right)\right| \\ &+ \left|X\left(\alpha_{n,k_0-1},\omega\right) - X\left(\alpha_{n,k_0},\omega\right)\right| \\ &+ \left|X\left(\alpha_{n,k_0},\omega\right) - X(s'',\omega)\right| \\ &\le 3\max_{k=1,2,\cdots,n} Y_{n,k}(\omega). \end{aligned}$$

In the former case $2\max_{k=1,2,\cdots,n} Y_{n,k}(\omega)$ will do as an upper bound. In any case

$$Z_n(\omega) \le 3\max_{k=1,2,\cdots,n} Y_{n,k}(\omega),$$

and, by (4),

$$P\{\omega \in \Omega ; Z_n(\omega) > 6\epsilon\} \le P\left\{\omega \in \Omega ; \max_{k=1,2,\cdots,n} Y_{n,k}(\omega) > 2\epsilon\right\}$$

$$\le \sum_{k=1}^{n} P\{\omega \in \Omega ; Y_{n,k}(\omega) > 2\epsilon\}$$

$$\le 2\sum_{k=1}^{n} P\{\omega \in \Omega ; |X(\alpha_{n,k}, \omega) - X(\alpha_{n,k-1}, \omega)| > \epsilon\}. \quad (5)$$

Since Z_n is monotone decreasing we have

$$\left\{\omega \in \Omega ; \lim_{n\to\infty} Z_n(\omega) > 6\epsilon\right\} \subset \bigcap_{n=1}^{\infty} \{\omega \in \Omega ; Z_n(\omega) > 6\epsilon\},$$

and, by (5) and (1),

$$P\left\{\omega \in \Omega ; \lim_{n\to\infty} Z_n(\omega) > 6\epsilon\right\} \le \lim_{n\to\infty} P\{\omega \in \Omega ; Z_n(\omega) > 6\epsilon\} = 0.$$

This completes the proof that $P(\Omega_{\alpha,\beta}) = 1$.

Let a and b be the endpoints of D, $\{\alpha_n, n = 1,2, \cdots\}$ and $\{\beta_n, n = 1,2, \cdots\}$ be sequences from S so chosen that $\alpha_n \downarrow a$ and $\beta_n \uparrow b$ and let $\Omega_0 = \bigcap_{n=1}^{\infty} \Omega_{\alpha_n, \beta_n}$. From $P(\Omega_{\alpha_n, \beta_n}) = 1$ for $n = 1,2, \cdots$ follows $P(\Omega_0) = 1$. By the definition of $\Omega_{\alpha_n, \beta_n}$, $X(s,\omega)$, $s \in S$, is uniformly continuous on S_{α_n, β_n} and consequently has a unique continuous extension to $[\alpha_n, \beta_n]$ when $\omega \in \Omega_{\alpha_n, \beta_n}$. Thus for every $\omega \in \Omega_0$, $X(s,\omega)$, $s \in S$, has a unique continuous extension to D. Let $Y(t,\omega)$, $t \in D$, be this continuous extension for $\omega \in \Omega_0$. For $\omega \in \Omega - \Omega_0$ let $Y(t,\omega) = 0$, $t \in D$.

To show that Y is a stochastic process on $(\Omega, \mathfrak{B}, P)$ and D let $t \in D$ and take a sequence $\{s_n, n = 1,2, \cdots\} \subset S$ which converges to t. From the continuity of Y,

$$Y(t,\omega) = \lim_{n\to\infty} Y(s_n, \omega) = \lim_{n\to\infty} X(s_n, \omega) \quad \text{for} \quad \omega \in \Omega_0 . \tag{6}$$

On the other hand, $Y(t, \omega) = 0$ for $\omega \in \Omega - \Omega_0$. Thus $Y(t, \cdot)$ is $\mathfrak{B}$-measurable and Y is a stochastic process, in fact a continuous process on $(\Omega, \mathfrak{B}, P)$ and D. Since X is additive and stochastically continuous, we have, according to (1) of Theorem 12.6,

$$X(t, \omega) = \lim_{n\to\infty} X(s_n, \omega) \quad \text{for} \quad \text{a.e.} \quad \omega \in \Omega . \tag{7}$$

(6) and (7) give $X(t, \omega) = Y(t, \omega)$ for a.e. $\omega \in \Omega$ for every $t \in D$, i.e., the equivalence of X and Y. □

<u>Theorem 14.2</u> (K. Itô) Given a real-valued continuous function m and a continuous monotone increasing function v on an interval $D \subset R^1$. There exists a continuous additive process Z on a probability space $(\Omega, \mathfrak{B}, P)$ and D in which the probability distribution of $Z(t'', \cdot) - Z(t', \cdot)$, $t', t'' \in D$, $t' < t''$, is given by $N\left(m(t'') - m(t'), v(t'') - v(t')\right)$.

<u>Proof</u> Let us consider first the case where $m = 0$ on D. For $t', t'' \in D$, $t' < t''$, let $\Phi_{t't''} = N\left(0, v(t'') - v(t')\right)$. Then for $t_1, t_2, t_3 \in D$, $t_1 < t_2 < t_3$, $\Phi_{t_1 t_2} * \Phi_{t_2 t_3} = \Phi_{t_1 t_3}$ by Lemma 13.3, so that according to Theorem 12.2 there exists an additive process X on a probability space $(\Omega, \mathfrak{B}, P)$ and D in which the probability distribution of $X(t'', \cdot) - X(t', \cdot)$, $t', t'' \in D$, $t' < t''$, is given by $\Phi_{t't''}$. We will verify that X satisfies the conditions of Lemma 14.1 and consequently has an equivalent process Y which is continuous.

The stochastic continuity of X follows from the continuity of v and the Chebyshev inequality (c.f. §A3). Indeed, for $t_0 \in D$ and $\epsilon > 0$,

$$\lim_{t\to t_0} \left\{\omega \in \Omega;\ |X(t,\omega) - X(t_0,\omega)| \geq \epsilon\right\} \leq \lim_{t\to t_0} \frac{1}{\epsilon^2} V\left[X(t,\cdot) - X(t_0,\cdot)\right]$$
$$= \lim_{t\to t_0} \frac{1}{\epsilon^2} |v(t) - v(t_0)| = 0.$$

Next we verify the condition that, for every pair of rational numbers $\alpha, \beta \in D$, $\alpha < \beta$, $\alpha_{n,k} = \alpha + k/n(\beta - \alpha)$, $k = 0,1,2,\cdots,n$, and $\epsilon > 0$,

$$\lim_{n\to\infty} \sum_{k=1}^{n} P\left\{\omega \in \Omega;\ |X(\alpha_{n,k},\omega) - X(\alpha_{n,k-1},\omega)| > \epsilon\right\} = 0. \tag{1}$$

Now for any k such that $v(\alpha_{n,k}) - v(\alpha_{n,k-1}) = 0$, the corresponding term in the sum is 0. Thus it suffices to consider the case where v is strictly increasing on D. For such v we have

$$P\left\{\omega \in \Omega;\ |X(\alpha_{n,k},\omega) - X(\alpha_{n,k-1},\omega)| > \epsilon\right\}$$
$$= \frac{2}{\left\{2\pi\left[v(\alpha_{n,k}) - v(\alpha_{n,k-1})\right]\right\}^{\frac{1}{2}}} \int_{\epsilon}^{\infty} \exp\left\{-\frac{u^2}{2\left[v(\alpha_{n,k}) - v(\alpha_{n,k-1})\right]}\right\} du$$
$$= \sqrt{\frac{2}{\pi}} \int_{\epsilon\left[v(\alpha_{n,k}) - v(\alpha_{n,k-1})\right]^{-\frac{1}{2}}}^{\infty} \exp\left\{-\frac{u^2}{2}\right\} du$$
$$\leq \sqrt{\frac{2}{\pi}} \exp\left\{-\frac{\epsilon^2}{2\left[v(\alpha_{n,k}) - v(\alpha_{n,k-1})\right]}\right\} \frac{\left[v(\alpha_{n,k}) - v(\alpha_{n,k-1})\right]^{\frac{1}{2}}}{\epsilon}$$

by (2) of Lemma 13.5. Since $\lim_{x\to\infty} xe^{-x^2/2} = 0$, for every $p > 0$ there exists $M_p > 0$ such that $xe^{-x^2/2} < p^{-1}$, i.e., $x^{-1}e^{-x^2/2} < p^{-1}x^{-2}$ for $x > M_p$. From the uniform continuity of v on $[\alpha, \beta]$ there exists N such that

$$\frac{\epsilon}{\left[v(\alpha_{n,k}) - v(\alpha_{n,k-1})\right]^{\frac{1}{2}}} > M_p \quad \text{for } k = 1,2,\cdots,n \text{ whenever } n > N.$$

Then for $k = 1,2,\cdots,n$ and $n > N$ we have

$$\exp\left\{-\frac{\epsilon^2}{2\left[v(\alpha_{n,k}) - v(\alpha_{n,k-1})\right]}\right\}\frac{\left[v(\alpha_{n,k}) - v(\alpha_{n,k-1})\right]^{\frac{1}{2}}}{\epsilon}$$

$$< \frac{1}{p}\,\frac{v(\alpha_{n,k}) - v(\alpha_{n,k-1})}{\epsilon^2},$$

and hence

$$\lim_{n\to\infty}\sum_{k=1}^{n} P\left\{\omega \in \Omega;\ |X(\alpha_{n,k},\omega) - X(\alpha_{n,k-1},\omega)| > \epsilon\right\}$$

$$\leq \lim_{n\to\infty}\sqrt{\frac{2}{\pi}}\sum_{k=1}^{n}\frac{1}{p}\,\frac{v(\alpha_{n,k}) - v(\alpha_{n,k-1})}{\epsilon^2} = \sqrt{\frac{2}{\pi}}\,\frac{v(\beta) - v(\alpha)}{p\epsilon^2}.$$

Since this holds for $p > 0$, (1) holds. This completes the proof of the theorem for the case where $m = 0$ on D.

For the general case where m is a real-valued continuous function on D, let us define a stochastic process Z on $(\Omega, \mathfrak{B}, P)$ and D by

$$Z(t,\omega) = Y(t,\omega) + m(t) \qquad \text{for} \qquad t \in D,\ \omega \in \Omega,$$

where Y is the stochastic process discussed above. The continuity of Z follows from that of Y. Since the probability distribution of $Y(t'',\cdot) - Y(t',\cdot)$, $t', t'' \in D$, $t' < t''$, is given by $N\left(0, v(t'') - v(t')\right)$, the probability distribution of $Z(t'',\cdot) - Z(t',\cdot)$ is given by $N\left(m(t'') - m(t'),\ v(t'') - v(t')\right)$. Since $\left\{Y(t_k,\cdot) - Y(t_{k-1},\cdot),\ k = 1,2,\cdots,n\right\}$ for $t_0, t_1, \cdots, t_n \in D$, $t_0 < t_1 < \cdots < t_n$, is an independence system of random variables, so is the system $\{Y(t_k, \cdot) - Y(t_{k-1}, \cdot),\ m(t_k) - m(t_{k-1}),\ k = 1,2,\cdots,n\}$. Then $\{Z(t_k, \cdot) - Z(t_{k-1}, \cdot),\ k = 1,2,\cdots,n\}$ being a Baire transformation of the last system is an independent system (c.f. Theorem A6.6).

□

[II] Central Limit Theorems

If an additive process is almost surely continuous then every increment of the process is normally distributed. This will be proved in [III]. In preparation for this we prove here the central limit theorem under the Lindeberg condition and its corollaries.

Theorem 14.3 Central Limit Theorem. Given a system of random variables $\{X_{n,k},\ k = 1,2,\cdots,p(n),\ n = 1,2,\cdots\}$ on a probability space $(\Omega, \mathfrak{B}, P)$ with finite $E(X_{n,k}^2)$ where $\{X_{n,k},\ k = 1,2,\cdots,p(n)\}$ is an independent system for each n. Let

$$a_{n,k} = E(X_{n,k}),\quad k = 1,2,\cdots,p(n)$$

$$S_n = \sum_{k=1}^{p(n)} X_{n,k},\qquad B_n = V(S_n) = \sum_{k=1}^{p(n)} V(X_{n,k}),$$

$$Z_n = \frac{S_n - E(S_n)}{V(S_n)^{\frac{1}{2}}}\qquad \text{for } n = 1,2,\cdots,$$

where we assume that $B_n > 0$ for some n on. If the system of random variables satisfies the Lindeberg condition

$$\lim_{n\to\infty} \frac{1}{B_n} \sum_{k=1}^{p(n)} \int_{|x-a_{n,k}|>\tau\sqrt{B_n}} (x-a_{n,k})^2\, \Phi_{X_{n,k}}(dx) = 0$$

for every $\tau > 0$,

then

$$\lim_{n\to\infty} \Phi_{Z_n} = N(0,1)$$

where $\Phi_{X_{n,k}}$ and Φ_{Z_n} are the probability distributions of $X_{n,k}$ and Z_n, respectively.

In proving this theorem we need the following lemma.

Lemma 14.4 For $\alpha \in R^1$,

$$|e^{i\alpha}-1| \le |\alpha|, \tag{1}$$

$$|e^{i\alpha}-1-i\alpha| \le \frac{\alpha^2}{2}, \tag{2}$$

$$\left|e^{i\alpha}-1-i\alpha-\frac{(i\alpha)^2}{2}\right| \le \frac{|\alpha|^3}{6}. \tag{3}$$

Proof We have

$$|e^{i\alpha}-1| = \left|\int_0^{\alpha} e^{ix}\,dx\right| \le \int_0^{|\alpha|} |e^{ix}|\,dx = |\alpha|,$$

which proves (1). Using (1) we have

$$|e^{i\alpha}-1-i\alpha| = \left|\frac{e^{i\alpha}-1}{i}-\alpha\right| \le \int_0^{|\alpha|} |e^{ix}-1|\,dx$$

$$\le \int_0^{|\alpha|} |x|\,dx = \frac{\alpha^2}{2},$$

which proves (2). Finally, using (2), we have

$$\left|e^{i\alpha}-1-i\alpha-\frac{(i\alpha)^2}{2}\right| = \left|\frac{e^{i\alpha}-1}{i}-\alpha-\frac{i\alpha^2}{2}\right|$$

$$\le \int_0^{|\alpha|} |e^{ix}-1-ix|\,dx \le \int_0^{|\alpha|} \frac{x^2}{2}\,dx = \frac{|\alpha|^3}{6}. \qquad \square$$

Proof of Theorem 14.3 From the definition of Z_n we have $E(Z_n) = 0$ and $V(Z_n) = 1$. Let

$$Z_{n,k} = \frac{X_{n,k} - E(X_{n,k})}{V(S_n)^{\frac{1}{2}}} = \frac{X_{n,k} - a_{n,k}}{B_n^{\frac{1}{2}}}. \tag{1}$$

Since the sum of the members of the independent system $\{Z_{n,k}, k = 1,2,\cdots,p(n)\}$ is equal to Z_n,

$$\sum_{k=1}^{p(n)} V(Z_{n,k}) = V(Z_n) = 1. \tag{2}$$

In terms of $Z_{n,k}$, the Lindeberg condition can be written as

$$\lim_{n\to\infty} \sum_{k=1}^{p(n)} \int_{|x|>\tau} x^2 \, \Phi_{Z_{n,k}}(dx) = 0. \tag{3}$$

Let φ_n be the characteristic function of Φ_{Z_n}. To show that $\lim_{n\to\infty} \Phi_{Z_n} = N(0,1)$ we show that $\lim_{n\to\infty} \varphi_n(y) = \exp\left\{-\frac{1}{2}y^2\right\}$, $y \in R^1$ [c.f. (2) of Theorem A4.3]. For this we show that $\lim_{n\to\infty} \log \varphi_n(y) = -\frac{1}{2}y^2$, $y \in R^1$.

Let $\varphi_{n,k}$ be the characteristic function of $\Phi_{Z_{n,k}}$. Let us show that, for every $B \geq 0$, $\lim_{n\to\infty} \varphi_{n,k}(y) = 1$ uniformly for $k = 1,2,\cdots,p(n)$ and $|y| \leq B$. Let $\varepsilon > 0$ be given. Since $E(Z_{n,k}) = 0$,

$$\varphi_{n,k}(y) - 1 = \varphi_{n,k}(y) - 1 - iy\,E(Z_{n,k})$$

$$= \int_{R^1} (e^{iyx} - 1 - iyx)\, \Phi_{Z_{n,k}}(dx),$$

so that, by (2) of Lemma 14.4,

$$
\begin{aligned}
|\varphi_{n,k}(y) - 1| &\le \int_{R^1} \frac{y^2 x^2}{2} \Phi_{Z_{n,k}}(dx) \\
&= \frac{y^2}{2} \left\{ \int_{|x| \le \epsilon} x^2 \Phi_{Z_{n,k}}(dx) + \int_{|x| > \epsilon} x^2 \Phi_{Z_{n,k}}(dx) \right\} \\
&\le \frac{y^2}{2} \left\{ \epsilon^2 + \int_{|x| > \epsilon} x^2 \Phi_{Z_{n,k}}(dx) \right\}. \qquad (4)
\end{aligned}
$$

By (3) there exist N such that

$$\sum_{k=1}^{p(n)} \int_{|x| > \epsilon} x^2 \Phi_{Z_{n,k}}(dx) < \epsilon \qquad \text{for } n \ge N.$$

Then for $n \ge N$ we have assuming $\epsilon < 1$

$$|\varphi_{n,k}(y) - 1| \le \frac{y^2}{2} \{\epsilon^2 + \epsilon\} \le \epsilon B^2$$

for $k = 1, 2, \cdots, p(n)$ and $|y| \le B$.

This establishes the uniform convergence. In particular there exists N_0 such that

$$|\varphi_{n,k}(y) - 1| < \tfrac{1}{2} \text{ for } k = 1, 2, \cdots, p(n)$$

$$\text{and } |y| \le B \text{ when } n \ge N_0. \qquad (5)$$

Since $\{Z_{n,k}, k = 1, 2, \cdots, p(n)\}$ is an independent system and $\sum_{k=1}^{p(n)} Z_{n,k} = Z_n$ we have $\Phi_{Z_n} = \Phi_{Z_{n,1}} * \cdots * \Phi_{Z_{n,p(n)}}$ and $\varphi_n(y) = \varphi_{n,1}(y) \cdots \varphi_{n,p(n)}(y)$ for $y \in R^1$ (c.f. Theorems A7.6 and A7.4). Thus

$$\log \varphi_n(y) = \sum_{k=1}^{p(n)} \operatorname{Log} \varphi_{n,k}(y) \tag{6}$$

where by Log we mean the principal branch of logarithm, and the left side of (6) is the branch which is equal to the right side of (6). From (5),

$$\operatorname{Log} \varphi_{n,k}(y) = \operatorname{Log}\left[1 + \left\{\varphi_{n,k}(y) - 1\right\}\right] = \sum_{m-1}^{\infty} \frac{(-1)^{m+1}}{m} \left\{\varphi_{n,k}(y) - 1\right\},$$

and consequently

$$\log \varphi_n(y) = \sum_{k=1}^{p(n)} \left\{\varphi_{n,k}(y) - 1\right\} + R_n(y) \tag{7}$$

with

$$R_n(y) = \sum_{k=1}^{p(n)} \sum_{m=2}^{\infty} \frac{(-1)^{m+1}}{m} \left[\varphi_{n,k}(y) - 1\right]^m$$

for $k = 1,2,\cdots, p(n)$ and $|y| \le B$ when $n \ge N_0$. Now, by (5),

$$|R_n(y)| \le \sum_{k=1}^{p(n)} \sum_{m=2}^{\infty} \tfrac{1}{2} |\varphi_{n,k}(y) - 1|^m = \sum_{k=1}^{p(n)} \tfrac{1}{2} \frac{|\varphi_{n,k}(y) - 1|^2}{1 - |\varphi_{n,k}(y) - 1|}$$

$$\le \sum_{k=1}^{p(n)} |\varphi_{n,k}(y) - 1|^2$$

$$\le \max_{k=1,2,\cdots, p(n)} |\varphi_{n,k}(y) - 1| \sum_{k=1}^{p(n)} |\varphi_{n,k}(y) - 1|.$$

By the first inequality in (4),

$$\sum_{k=1}^{p(n)} |\varphi_{n,k}(y) - 1| \le \frac{y^2}{2} \sum_{k=1}^{p(n)} V(Z_{n,k}) = \frac{y^2}{2},$$

and hence

$$|R_n(y)| \le \frac{B^2}{2} \max_{k=1,2,\cdots,p(n)} |\varphi_{n,k}(y) - 1| \quad \text{for} \quad |y| \le B \quad \text{when} \quad n \ge N_0.$$

Then since $\lim_{n\to\infty} \varphi_{n,k}(y) = 1$ uniformly for $k = 1,2,\cdots, p(n)$ and $|y| \le B$ we have $\lim_{n\to\infty} R_n(y) = 0$ uniformly for $|y| \le B$.

Finally we show that $\lim_{n\to\infty} \sum_{k=1}^{p(n)} \left[\varphi_{n,k}(y) - 1\right] = -y^2/2$ uniformly for $|y| \le B$. This together with the uniform convergence of $R_n(y)$ to 0 for $|y| \le B$ will complete the proof that $\lim_{n\to\infty} \log \varphi_n(y) = -y^2/2$ uniformly for $|y| \le B$ in view of (7). Now

$$\rho_n(y) \equiv \sum_{k=1}^{p(n)} \left\{\varphi_{n,k}(y) - 1\right\} + \frac{y^2}{2}$$

$$= \sum_{k=1}^{p(n)} \left\{\varphi_{n,k}(y) - 1 - iyE(Z_{n,k})\right\} + \frac{y^2}{2} \sum_{k=1}^{p(n)} V(Z_{n,k})$$

$$= \sum_{k=1}^{p(n)} \int_{R^1} \left\{e^{iyx} - 1 - iyx - \frac{(iyx)^2}{2}\right\} \Phi_{Z_{n,k}}(dx) .$$

Applying (3) and (2) of Lemma 14.4 we have

$$|\rho_n(y)| \le \sum_{k=1}^{p(n)} \left\{ \int_{|x|\le\epsilon} \frac{|yx|^3}{6} \Phi_{Z_{n,k}}(dx) + \int_{|x|>\epsilon} |yx|^2 \Phi_{Z_{n,k}}(dx) \right\}$$

$$\le \sum_{k=1}^{p(n)} \left\{ \frac{|y|^3}{6} \epsilon \int_{|x|\le\epsilon} x^2 \Phi_{Z_{n,k}}(dx) + y^2 \int_{|x|>\epsilon} x^2 \Phi_{Z_{n,k}}(dx) \right\}$$

$$\le \frac{|y|^3}{6} \epsilon \sum_{k=1}^{p(n)} V(Z_{n,k}) + y^2 \sum_{k=1}^{p(n)} \int_{|x|>\epsilon} x^2 \Phi_{Z_{n,k}}(dx)$$

$$\le \frac{B^3}{6}\epsilon + B^2 \sum_{k=1}^{p(n)} \int_{|x|>\epsilon} x^2 \Phi_{Z_{n,k}}(dx) \quad \text{for } |y| \le B.$$

According to (3) there exists N such that

$$|\rho_n(y)| \le \frac{B^3}{6}\epsilon + B^2\epsilon \quad \text{for } |y| \le B \text{ when } n \ge N.$$

Thus $\lim_{n\to\infty} \rho_n(y) = 0$ uniformly for $|y| \le B$. □

Corollary 14.5 Let $X_{n,k}$, $a_{n,k}$, S_n, and Z_n be as defined in Theorem 14.3. If

1° for each n, $\{X_{n,k},\ k = 1,2,\cdots,p(n)\}$ is an independent system,

2° for each n, $|X_{n,k}(\omega)| \le \epsilon_n$ for a.e. ω for $k = 1,2,\cdots,p(n)$ where $\epsilon_n > 0$ and $\lim_{n\to\infty} \epsilon_n = 0$,

3° $V(S_n) \ge c$ for $n = 1,2,\cdots$ for some $c > 0$,

then $\lim_{n\to\infty} \Phi_{Z_n} = N(0,1)$.

Proof Let $Z_{n,k}$ be as defined by (1) in the proof Theorem 14.3. To prove the corollary we show that (3) is satisfied. Now from 2°, $|a_{n,k}| \le E\left(|X_{n,k}|\right) \le \epsilon_n$ so that $|X_{n,k}(\omega) - a_{n,k}| \le 2\epsilon_n$ for a.e. ω for $k = 1,2,\cdots,p(n)$ and hence

$$P\left\{\omega \in \Omega;\ |Z_{n,k}(\omega)| \le \frac{2\epsilon_n}{V(S_n)^{\frac{1}{2}}}\right\} = 1 \quad \text{for } k = 1,2,\cdots,p(n).$$

Let $\tau > 0$ be given. Since $V(S_n) \ge c > 0$ for $n = 1,2,\cdots$ and $\lim_{n\to\infty} \epsilon_n = 0$, there exists N such that $2\epsilon_n V(S_n)^{-\frac{1}{2}} < \tau$ for $n \ge N$. Then

$$P\{\omega \in \Omega ; |Z_{n,k}(\omega)| > \tau\} = 0 \qquad \text{for } k = 1,2,\cdots,p(n) \text{ for } n \geq N,$$

and (3) in the proof of Theorem 14.3 holds. □

Lemma 14.6 Let $\{S_n, n = 1,2,\cdots\}$ be a sequence of random variables on a probability space $(\Omega, \mathfrak{B}, P)$ with finite $E(S_n^2)$, $n = 1,2,\cdots$. Suppose that

$$S(\omega) = \lim_{n\to\infty} S_n(\omega) \text{ exists for a.e. } \omega \in \Omega, \tag{1}$$

If $\{V(S_n), n = 1,2,\cdots\}$ has a subsequence which converges to 0 then $S(\omega) = a$ for a.e. $\omega \in \Omega$ where $a \in R^1$. If no such subsequence exists, then under the assumption that

$$\lim_{n\to\infty} \Phi_{Z_n} = N(0,1), \qquad \text{where } Z_n = \frac{S_n - E(S_n)}{V(S_n)^{\frac{1}{2}}} \tag{2}$$

S is distributed $N(a,v)$ where $a, v \in R^1$, $v > 0$, and $\lim_{n\to\infty} E(S_n) = a$ and $\lim_{n\to\infty} V(S_n) = v$.

Proof (1) Suppose $\lim_{n\to\infty} V(S_{n_m}) = 0$ for some subsequence $\{n_m, m = 1,2,\cdots\}$. Then for every $\epsilon > 0$, according to the Chebyshev inequality,

$$\lim_{m\to\infty} P\{\omega \in \Omega ; |S_{n_m}(\omega) - E(S_{n_m})| \geq \epsilon\} \leq \lim_{m\to\infty} \frac{1}{\epsilon^2} V(S_{n_m}) = 0,$$

so that $\{S_{n_m} - E(S_{n_m}), m = 1,2,\cdots\}$ converges to 0 in probability and hence there exists a subsequence $\{n_{m_\ell}, \ell = 1,2,\cdots\}$ such that

$$\lim_{\ell\to\infty} \left\{ S_{n_{m_\ell}}(\omega) - E(S_{n_{m_\ell}}) \right\} = 0 \qquad \text{for a.e. } \omega \in \Omega. \tag{3}$$

Let $\omega_0 \in \Omega$ be a point where both (1) and (3) hold and let $a = \lim_{n\to\infty} S_n(\omega_0)$. Then from (3), $\lim_{\ell\to\infty} E(S_{n_{m_\ell}}) = a$ and $\lim_{\ell\to\infty} S_{n_{m_\ell}}(\omega) = a$ for a.e. $\omega \in \Omega$. From (1), $S(\omega) = a$ for a.e. $\omega \in \Omega$.

(2) Suppose no subsequence of $\{V(S_n),\ n = 1,2,\cdots\}$ converges to 0. Then $V(S_n) \geq c$ for $n = 1,2,\cdots$ for some $c > 0$. Let us show that this fact together with (2) implies the boundedness of $\{E(S_n),\ n = 1,2,\cdots\}$ and $\{V(S_n),\ n = 1,2,\cdots\}$. For this purpose let us recall that (2) implies

$$\lim_{n\to\infty} P\{\omega \in \Omega\,;\, Z_n(\omega) \leq x\} = F_{N(0,1)}(x) \quad \text{for } x \in R^1,$$

where $F_{N(0,1)}$ is the distribution function of $N(0,1)$; in other words

$$\lim_{n\to\infty} P\{\omega \in \Omega\,;\, S_n(\omega) \leq E(S_n) + xV(S_n)^{\frac{1}{2}}\} = \frac{1}{\sqrt{2\pi}} \int_{-\infty}^{x} e^{-u^2/2}\, du. \tag{4}$$

If $\{V(S_n),\ n = 1,2,\cdots\}$ is not bounded then $\lim_{m\to\infty} V(S_{n_m}) = \infty$ for some subsequence $\{n_m,\ m = 1,2,\cdots\}$. Consider the case where $E(S_{n_m}) \geq 0$ for infinitely many values of m. In this case $E\left(S_{n_{m_\ell}}\right) \geq 0$ for $\ell = 1,2,\cdots$ for some subsequence $\{n_{m_\ell}, \ell = 1,2,\cdots\}$. Then for any $B \geq 0$ there exists L such that

$$E\left(S_{n_{m_\ell}}\right) + V\left(S_{n_{m_\ell}}\right)^{\frac{1}{2}} \geq B \quad \text{when } \ell \geq L. \tag{5}$$

Let $\Omega_0 \in \mathfrak{B}$ be such that $P(\Omega_0) = 1$ and $\lim_{n\to\infty} S_n(\omega) = S(\omega)$ for

$\omega \in \Omega_0$. Then

$$\left\{\omega \in \Omega_0 ; S(\omega) \le \frac{B}{2}\right\} \subset \liminf_{\ell\to\infty} \left\{\omega \in \Omega_0 ; S_{n_{m_\ell}}(\omega) \le B\right\},$$

so that, by Fatou's lemma,

$$P\left\{\omega \in \Omega_0 ; S(\omega) \le \frac{B}{2}\right\} \le \liminf_{n\to\infty} P\left\{\omega \in \Omega_0 ; S_{n_{m_\ell}}(\omega) \le B\right\}. \qquad (6)$$

From (6), (5), and (4) with $x = 1$ we have

$$P\left\{\omega \in \Omega ; S(\omega) \le \frac{B}{2}\right\}$$

$$\le \liminf_{\ell\to\infty} P\left\{\omega \in \Omega ; S_{n_{m_\ell}}(\omega) \le E\left(S_{n_{m_\ell}}\right) + V\left(S_{n_{m_\ell}}\right)^{\frac{1}{2}}\right\}$$

$$\le \frac{1}{\sqrt{2\pi}} \int_{-\infty}^{1} e^{-u^2/2}\, du < 1 .$$

Letting $B \to \infty$ we obtain $P(\Omega) < 1$, a contradiction. In the case where $E(S_{n_m}) \ge 0$ for at most finitely many values of m and hence $E(S_{n_m}) \le 0$ for infinitely many values of m, we get a contradiction as above by considering $\{-S_n, n = 1,2, \cdots\}$ and $-S$. Thus in any case $\left\{V(S_n), n = 1,2, \cdots\right\}$ must be bounded.

To show the boundedness of $\left\{E(S_n), n = 1,2, \cdots\right\}$ let us assume first that it is not bounded above. Then $\lim_{m\to\infty} E(S_{n_m}) = \infty$ for some subsequence $\{n_m, m = 1,2, \cdots\}$, and for every $B \ge 0$ there exists M such that $E(S_{n_m}) \ge B$ for $m \ge M$. With $x = 0$ in (4) we obtain, by the same argument used above,

$$P\left\{\omega \in \Omega ; S(\omega) \le \frac{B}{2}\right\} \le \liminf_{m\to\infty} P\left\{\omega \in \Omega ; S_{n_m}(\omega) \le E(S_{n_m})\right\}$$

$$\leq \frac{1}{\sqrt{2\pi}} \int_{-\infty}^{0} e^{-u^2/2}\, du = \tfrac{1}{2}.$$

Letting $B \to \infty$ we have $P(\Omega) \leq \frac{1}{2}$, a contradiction. Thus $\{E(S_n), n = 1,2,\cdots\}$ must be bounded above. The fact that it is also bounded below can be shown likewise.

From the boundedness of $\{E(S_n), n = 1,2,\cdots\}$ and $\{V(S_n), n = 1,2,\cdots\}$ and from the fact that $V(S_n) \geq c > 0$ for $n = 1,2,\cdots$, there exists a subsequence $\{n_m, m = 1,2,\cdots\}$ such that $a = \lim_{m\to\infty} E(S_{n_m})$ and $v = \lim_{m\to\infty} V(S_{n_m})$ exist and $a, v \in R^1$, $v > 0$. By (1),

$$\lim_{m\to\infty} Z_{n_m}(\omega) = \frac{S(\omega) - a}{\sqrt{v}} \quad \text{for a.e. } \omega \in \Omega, \tag{7}$$

and in particular $\lim_{m\to\infty} \Phi_{Z_{n_m}} = \Phi$ where Φ is the probability distribution of $(S - a)/\sqrt{v}$. But $\lim_{m\to\infty} \Phi_{Z_{n_m}} = N(0,1)$ according to (2), so that by the uniqueness of limit in the convergence of a a sequence of probability distributions $\Phi = N(0,1)$ and consequently S is distributed $N(a,v)$.

It remains to show that $\lim_{n\to\infty} E(S_n) = a$ and $\lim_{n\to\infty} V(S_n) = v$. If $\{E(S_n), n = 1,2,\cdots\}$ does not converge to a then from the boundedness of $\{E(S_n), n = 1,2,\cdots\}$ and $\{V(S_n), n = 1,2,\cdots\}$ we can select a subsequence $\{n_k, k = 1,2,\cdots\}$ such that $\lim_{k\to\infty} E(S_{n_k}) = a'$ and $\lim_{k\to\infty} V(S_{n_k}) = v'$ where $a', v' \in R^1$, $v' > 0$, and $a' \neq a$. Then by the argument used in obtaining (7) we have

$$\lim_{k\to\infty} Z_{n_k}(\omega) = \frac{S(\omega) - a'}{\sqrt{v'}} \quad \text{for a.e. } \omega \in \Omega,$$

and in particular $\lim_{k\to\infty} \Phi_{Z_{n_k}} = \Phi'$ where Φ' is the probability distribution of $(S - a')/\sqrt{v'}$. But $\lim_{k\to\infty} \Phi_{Z_{n_k}} = N(0,1)$ by (2), so that $\Phi' = N(0,1)$ and S is distributed $N(a', v')$. This is a contradiction since $a' \neq a$. Thus $\lim_{n\to\infty} E(S_n) = a$. Similarly $\lim_{n\to\infty} V(S_n) = v$. □

Corollary 14.7 Let $X_{n,k}$, $a_{n,k}$, S_n, and Z_n be as defined in Theorem 14.3 and assume that 1° and 2° of Corollary 14.5 are satisfied. Suppose $S(\omega) = \lim_{n\to\infty} S_n(\omega)$ exists for a.e. $\omega \in \Omega$. If $\{V(S_n), n = 1,2,\cdots\}$ has a subsequence which converges to 0 then $S(\omega) = a$ for a.e. $\omega \in \Omega$ for some $a \in R^1$. If no such subsequence exists then S is distributed $N(a,v)$ where $a, v \in R^1$, and $v > 0$.

Proof If $\{V(S_n), n = 1,2,\cdots\}$ has a subsequence which converges to 0 then $S(\omega) = a$ for a.e. $\omega \in \Omega$ for some $a \in R^1$ according to the first part of Lemma 14.6. If $\{V(S_n), n = 1,2,\cdots\}$ has no such subsequence then 3° of Corollary 14.5 is satisfied so that $\lim_{n\to\infty} \Phi_{Z_n} = N(0,1)$. Then by the second part of Lemma 14.6, S is distributed $N(a,v)$ where $a, v \in R^1$ and $v > 0$. □

[III] Probability Distributions of Increments in a Continuous Additive Process

Definition 14.8 An additive process X on a probability space $(\Omega, \mathfrak{B}, P)$ and an interval $D \subset R^1$ is said to have stationary increments if for every $t', t'' \in D$, $h \geq 0$, such that $t'+h, t''+h \in D$, the probability distributions of $X(t'+h, \cdot) - X(t', \cdot)$ and $X(t''+h, \cdot) - X(t'', \cdot)$ are identical.

Theorem 14.9 If X is an almost surely continuous additive process on a probability space $(\Omega, \mathfrak{B}, P)$ and an interval $D \subset R^1$ then for every $t', t'' \in D$, $t' < t''$, $X(t'', \cdot) - X(t', \cdot)$ is normally distributed and furthermore there exist a real-valued continuous function m and a continuous monotone increasing function v on D such that $N\big(m(t'') - m(t'), v(t'') - v(t')\big)$ is the probability distribution of $X(t'', \cdot) - X(t', \cdot)$. If in addition X has stationary increments then m and v necessarily satisfy the conditions

$$m(t'') - m(t') = c_1(t'' - t') \quad \text{and}$$

$$v(t'') - v(t') = c_2(t'' - t') \quad \text{where } c_1, c_2 \in R^1,\ c_2 \geq 0,$$

respectively.

Proof (1) Let $\alpha, \beta \in D$, $\alpha < \beta$. We use Corollary 14.7 to show that $X(\beta, \cdot) - X(\alpha, \cdot)$ is normally distributed.

Let $t_{n,k} = \alpha + k(\beta - \alpha)/n$, $k = 0, 1, 2, \cdots, n$; $n = 1, 2, \cdots$ and for $\epsilon > 0$ let

$$A_{n,\epsilon} = \left\{ \omega \in \Omega;\ \max_{k=1,2,\cdots,n} |X(t_{n,k}, \omega) - X(t_{n,k-1}, \omega)| \geq \epsilon \right\}.$$

For every $\omega \in \Omega$ for which $X(\cdot, \omega)$ is continuous on D, $X(\cdot, \omega)$ is uniformly continuous on $[\alpha, \beta]$ so that there exists $N(\omega)$ such that

$$\max_{k=1,2,\cdots,n} |X(t_{n,k}, \omega) - X(t_{n,k-1}, \omega)| < \epsilon \quad \text{for } n \geq N(\omega),$$

i.e. $\omega \in \liminf_{n\to\infty} A_{n,\epsilon}^c$. Since $X(\cdot, \omega)$ is continuous on D for a.e. $\omega \in \Omega$, we have $P\left(\lim_{n\to\infty} \inf A_{n,\epsilon}{}^c\right) = 1$, or equivalently $P\left(\lim_{n\to\infty} \sup A_{n,\epsilon}\right) = 0$. Then, by Fatou's Lemma, $\lim_{n\to\infty} \sup P(A_{n,\epsilon}) \leq P\left(\lim_{n\to\infty} \sup A_{n,\epsilon}\right) = 0$ so that $\lim_{n\to\infty} P(A_{n,\epsilon}) = 0$ for every $\epsilon > 0$. Thus, corresponding to an arbitrary monotone decreasing sequence of positive numbers $\{\epsilon_m, m = 1,2,\cdots\}$ which converges to 0, we can select a subsequence $\{n_m, m = 1,2,\cdots\}$ such that

$$P\left\{\omega \in \Omega;\ \max_{k=1,2,\cdots,n_m} \left|X\left(t_{n_m,k},\omega\right) - X\left(t_{n_m,k-1},\omega\right)\right| \geq \epsilon_m\right\} < \epsilon_m. \qquad (1)$$

For $k = 1,2,\cdots,n_m$ and $m = 1,2,\cdots$, let

$$X_{m,k}(\omega) = \left\{X\left(t_{n_m,k},\omega\right) - X\left(t_{n_m,k-1},\omega\right)\right\}\chi_{(-\epsilon_m,\epsilon_m)}\left[X\left(t_{n_m,k},\omega\right) - X\left(t_{n_m,k-1},\omega\right)\right] \qquad (2)$$

and

$$S_m(\omega) = \sum_{k=1}^{n_m} X_{m,k}(\omega).$$

Then

$$\left|X(\beta,\omega) - X(\alpha,\omega) - S_m(\omega)\right| \leq \sum_{k=1}^{n_m} \left|X\left(t_{n_m,k},\omega\right) - X\left(t_{n_m,k-1},\omega\right)\right| \left\{1 - \chi_{(-\epsilon_m,\epsilon_m)}\left[X\left(t_{n_m,k},\omega\right) - X\left(t_{n_m,k-1},\omega\right)\right]\right\},$$

from which we have

$$\{\omega \in \Omega\,;\, |X(\beta,\omega) - X(\alpha,\omega) - S_m(\omega)| > 0\}$$

$$\subset \left\{\omega \in \Omega\,;\, \chi_{(-\epsilon_m,\epsilon_m)}\left[X\left(t_{n_m,k},\omega\right) - X\left(t_{n_m,k-1},\omega\right)\right] = 0 \right.$$
$$\left. \text{for at least one } k,\ 1 \le k \le n_m \right\}$$

$$= \left\{\omega \in \Omega\,;\, \max_{k=1,2,\cdots,n_m} \left|X\left(t_{n_m,k},\omega\right) - X\left(t_{n_m,k-1},\omega\right)\right| \ge \epsilon_m \right\}$$

$$= A_{n_m,\epsilon_m},$$

and then, by (1),

$$\limsup_{m\to\infty} P\{\omega \in \Omega\,;\, |X(\beta,\omega) - X(\alpha,\omega) - S_m(\omega)| > 0\}$$

$$\le \limsup_{m\to\infty} P\left(A_{n_m,\epsilon_m}\right) \le \lim_{m\to\infty} \epsilon_m = 0.$$

This implies that $\{S_m, m = 1,2,\cdots\}$ converges to $X(\beta,\cdot) - X(\alpha,\cdot)$ in probability. Thus there exists a subsequence $\{S_{m_\ell}, \ell = 1,2,\cdots\}$ which converges to $X(\beta,\cdot) - X(\alpha,\cdot)$ a.e. on Ω. For each ℓ, $\{X_{m_\ell,k}, k = 1,2,\cdots,n_{m_\ell}\}$ is an independent system from the additivity of the process X. Also by (2), $\left|X_{m_\ell,k}(\omega)\right| \le \epsilon_{m_\ell}$ for $\omega \in \Omega$, $k = 1,2,\cdots,n_{m_\ell}$. Thus the conditions in Corollary 14.7 are satisfied by the system $\{X_{m_\ell}, k = 1,2,\cdots,n_{m_\ell}, \ell = 1,2,\cdots\}$, and consequently $X(\beta,\cdot) - X(\alpha,\cdot)$ is normally distributed.

(2) We define two real-valued functions m and v on D as follows. For $c \in D$ fixed arbitrarily, let

$$m(t) = E\left[X(t,\cdot) - X(c,\cdot)\right] \qquad \text{for } t \in D$$

$$v(t) = \begin{cases} V\left[X(t, \cdot) - X(c, \cdot)\right] & \text{for } t \in D,\ t \geq c \\ -V\left[X(t, \cdot) - X(c, \cdot)\right] & \text{for } t \in D,\ t < c \ . \end{cases}$$

Then m and v satisfy

$$m(t'') - m(t') = E\left[X(t'', \cdot) - X(t', \cdot)\right] \tag{3}$$

$$v(t'') - v(t') = V\left[X(t'', \cdot) - X(t', \cdot)\right] \tag{4}$$

whenever $t', t'' \in D$, $t' < t''$. (3) is immediate from the definition of m and the linearity of E. (4) can be verified by considering the three possible cases $c \leq t'$, $t' < c \leq t''$, and $t'' < c$ one by one using the fact that X is an additive process and the fact that the variance of the sum of two independent random variables is the sum of the variances of the two. Note also that (4) implies that v is monotone increasing. Let us show that m and v are continuous on D.

To prove the continuity of v at $t_0 \in D$ take an arbitrary sequence $\{t_n, n = 1, 2, \cdots\} \subset D$ which converges to t_0. Let $c_0 \in D$ and $c_0 \neq t_0$, say $c_0 < t_0$. We may assume without loss of generality that $c_0 < t_n$ for $n = 1, 2, \cdots$. Since X is stochastically continuous on D,

$$X(t_0, \cdot) - X(c_0, \cdot) = P - \lim_{n\to\infty} \left\{X(t_n, \cdot) - X(c_0, \cdot)\right\},$$

and hence

$$\lim_{n\to\infty} \varphi_n(u) = \varphi_0(u) \qquad \text{for} \quad u \in R^1, \tag{5}$$

where φ_n is the characteristic function of $X(t_n, \cdot) - X(c_0, \cdot)$ and is given by

$$\varphi_n(u) = \exp\left\{iu\left[m(t_n) - m(c_0)\right] - \frac{u^2}{2}\left[v(t_n) - v(c_0)\right]\right\} \quad \text{for} \quad n = 0,1,2,\cdots \tag{6}$$

since $X(t_n, \cdot) - X(c_0, \cdot)$ is distributed $N\left(m(t_n) - m(c_0),\ v(t_n) - v(t_0)\right)$ for $n = 0,1,2,\cdots$. From (5) and (6) it follows that

$$\lim_{n\to\infty}\left\{-2 \log |\varphi_n(1)|\right\} = -2 \log |\varphi_0(1)|,$$

i.e.,

$$\lim_{n\to\infty}\left\{v(t_n) - v(c_0)\right\} = v(t_0) - v(c_0).$$

Thus $\lim_{n\to\infty} v(t_n) = v(t_0)$. This proves the continuity of v at $t_0 \in D$.

The continuity of m at $t_0 \in D$ follows from the continuity of v at t_0 and the Chebyshev inequality. Indeed we have, for every $\epsilon > 0$,

$$\lim_{t\to t_0} P\left\{\omega \in \Omega;\ \left|X(t, \cdot) - X(t_0, \cdot) - \left[m(t) - m(t_0)\right]\right| \geq \epsilon\right\}$$

$$\leq \lim_{t\to t_0} \frac{1}{\epsilon^2} V\left[X(t, \cdot) - X(t_0, \cdot)\right] = \lim_{t\to t_0} \frac{1}{\epsilon^2} |v(t) - v(t_0)| = 0,$$

so that

$$P - \lim_{t\to t_0}\left\{X(t, \cdot) - X(t_0, \cdot) - \left[m(t) - m(t_0)\right]\right\} = 0.$$

But the fact that X is almost surely continuous implies $P - \lim_{t\to t_0}\left\{X(t, \cdot) - X(t_0, \cdot)\right\} = 0$. Thus $\lim_{t\to t_0}\left\{m(t) - m(t_0)\right\} = 0$ and m is continuous at $t_0 \in D$.

(3) When X has stationary increments then, for $t \in D$

and $h \geq 0$ such that $t+h \in D$, the probability distribution of $X(t+h, \cdot) - X(t, \cdot)$ is completely determined by h. But $X(t+h, \cdot) - X(t, \cdot)$ is normally distributed. Thus there exist a real-valued function $f(h)$ and a nonnegative function $g(h)$ for $h \in [0, L)$ where L is the length of D such that $X(t+h, \cdot) - X(t, \cdot)$ is distributed $N\big(f(h), g(h)\big)$. But $X(t+h, \cdot) - X(t, \cdot)$ is known to be distributed $N\big(m(t+h) - m(t),\ v(t+h) - v(t)\big)$. Thus

$$\left.\begin{aligned} f(h) &= m(t+h) - m(t) \\ g(h) &= v(t+h) - v(t) \end{aligned}\right\} \quad \text{for } h \in [0, L) \quad .$$

Now for $h_1, h_2 \geq 0$ such that $h_1 + h_2 \in [0, L)$ if we choose $t \in D$ so that $t + h_1 + h_2 \in D$ then

$$f(h_1 + h_2) = m(t+h_1+h_2) - m(t+h_1) + m(t+h_1) - m(t) = f(h_2) + f(h_1).$$

From this it follows that, for fixed $h_0 \in (0, L)$ and arbitrary natural numbers p and q, we have

$$f(h_0) = f\left(2^p \frac{h_0}{2^p}\right) = 2^p f\left(\frac{h_0}{2^p}\right) \quad \text{i.e.,} \quad f\left(\frac{h_0}{2^p}\right) = \frac{1}{2^p} f(h_0),$$

and hence

$$f\left(\frac{q}{2^p} h_0\right) = \frac{q}{2^p} f(h_0) \quad \text{as long as} \quad \frac{q}{2^p} h_0 \in [0, L).$$

Now for any $h \in [0, L)$ we can select a sequence of nonnegative binary rationals $\{r_n, n = 1, 2, \cdots\}$ such that $r_n h_0 \in [0, L)$, $n = 1, 2, \cdots$, and $\lim_{n\to\infty} r_n h_0 = h$. Then, by the continuity of f,

$$f(h) = f\left(\lim_{n\to\infty} r_n h_0\right) = \lim_{n\to\infty} f(r_n h_0) = \lim_{n\to\infty} r_n f(h_0) = \frac{h}{h_0} f(h_0) = c_1 h$$

where $c_1 = f(h_0) / h_0$. Thus

$$m(t+h) - m(t) = f(h) = c_1 h .$$

Similarly

$$v(t+h) - v(t) = g(h) = c_2 h$$

where $c_2 \geq 0$ since $g(h)$ is nonnegative and $h \geq 0$. □

§15. POISSON PROCESSES

[I] Convergence to Poisson Distributions

A Poisson distribution $\Phi_{P,\lambda}$ where $\lambda > 0$ is a 1-dimensional probability distribution given by

$$\Phi_{P,\lambda}\left(\{x\}\right) = e^{-\lambda} \frac{\lambda^x}{x!} \qquad \text{for } x = 0,1,2, \cdots .$$

Note that

$$\sum_{x=0}^{\infty} \Phi_{P,\lambda}\left(\{x\}\right) = e^{-\lambda} \sum_{k=0}^{\infty} \frac{\lambda^x}{x!} = 1 ,$$

so that, in particular,

$$\Phi_{P,\lambda}(E) = 0$$

for every $E \in \mathfrak{B}^1$ which is disjoint from $\{0,1,2, \cdots\}$.

Lemma 15.1 For the Poisson distribution $\Phi_{P,\lambda}$ the characteristic function φ is given by

$$\varphi(y) = e^{\lambda(e^{iy}-1)} .$$

In particular the first moment and the variance are both equal to λ.

Proof From the definition of a characteristic function,

$$\varphi(y) = \int_{R^1} e^{iyx}\, \Phi_{P,\lambda}(dx) = \sum_{x=0}^{\infty} e^{iyx} e^{-\lambda} \frac{\lambda^x}{x!}$$

$$= e^{-\lambda} \sum_{x=0}^{\infty} \frac{(\lambda e^{iy})^x}{x!} = e^{-\lambda} e^{\lambda e^{iy}} = e^{\lambda(e^{iy}-1)}.$$

According to Theorem A3.2, the pth moment $M^p(\Phi_{P,\lambda})$ is given by

$$M^p(\Phi_{P,\lambda}) = \frac{1}{i^p}\, \varphi^{(p)}(0),$$

so that, in particular, $M^1(\Phi_{P,\lambda}) = \lambda$, $M^2(\Phi_{P,\lambda}) = \lambda^2 + \lambda$ and

$$V(\Phi_{P,\lambda}) = M^2(\Phi_{P,\lambda}) - \left[M^1(\Phi_{P,\lambda})\right]^2 = \lambda.$$ □

<u>Lemma 15.2</u> The convolution of two Poisson distributions is again a Poisson distribution. Indeed

$$\Phi_{P,\lambda_1} * \Phi_{P,\lambda_2} = \Phi_{P,\lambda_1+\lambda_2}.$$

<u>Proof</u> Let φ_1, φ_2, and φ be the characteristic functions of Φ_{P,λ_1}, Φ_{P,λ_2}, and $\Phi_{P,\lambda_1} * \Phi_{P,\lambda_2}$, respectively. Then, by Theorem A7.4 and Lemma 15.1,

$$\varphi(y) = \varphi_1(y)\, \varphi_2(y) = e^{(\lambda_1+\lambda_2)(e^{iy}-1)}.$$

Thus $\Phi_{P,\lambda_1} * \Phi_{P,\lambda_2} = \Phi_{P,\lambda_1+\lambda_2}$ according to Theorem A2.3. □

<u>Lemma 15.3</u> If a system of complex numbers $\left\{\alpha_{n,k},\ k = 1,2,\cdots, p(n)\,;\ n = 1,2,\cdots\right\}$ satisfies

$$\lim_{n\to\infty} \sum_{k=1}^{p(n)} |\alpha_{n,k}|^2 = 0, \tag{1}$$

$$\lim_{n\to\infty} \sum_{k=1}^{p(n)} \alpha_{n,k} = \alpha, \tag{2}$$

then

$$\lim_{n\to\infty} \prod_{k=1}^{p(n)} (1+\alpha_{n,k}) = e^{\alpha}. \tag{3}$$

Proof For $z \in C$ with $|z| \le \frac{1}{2}$ we have

$$\mathrm{Log}\,(1+z) = z - \frac{z^2}{2} + \frac{z^3}{3} - \frac{z^4}{4} + \cdots .$$

Now

$$\left| -\frac{z^2}{2} + \frac{z^3}{3} - \frac{z^4}{4} + \cdots \right| \le \frac{|z|^2}{2} \left\{1 + |z| + |z|^2 + \cdots\right\}$$

$$= \frac{|z|^2}{2} \frac{1}{1-|z|} \le |z|^2 \quad \text{for} \quad |z| \le \tfrac{1}{2},$$

so that

$$\mathrm{Log}(1+z) = z + \theta\,|z|^2, \quad \text{where } \theta \in C \text{ with } |\theta| \le 1 \text{ when } |z| \le \tfrac{1}{2}. \tag{4}$$

Since (1) implies

$$\lim_{n\to\infty} \max_{k=1,2,\cdots,p(n)} |\alpha_{n,k}| = 0,$$

we may assume that $|\alpha_{n,k}| \le \frac{1}{2}$ for $k = 1,2,\cdots,p(n)$; $n = 1,2,\cdots$.
Then, by (4),

$$\mathrm{Log}(1+\alpha_{n,k}) = \alpha_{n,k} + \theta_{n,k}|\alpha_{n,k}|^2, \quad \text{where } \theta_{n,k} \in C \text{ with } |\theta_{n,k}| \le 1,$$

and for the branch of the logarithm of $\prod_{k=1}^{p(n)} (1+\alpha_{n,k})$ given by $\sum_{k=1}^{p(n)} \mathrm{Log}(1+\alpha_{n,k})$, we have

$$\log \prod_{k=1}^{p(n)} (1+\alpha_{n,k}) = \sum_{k=1}^{p(n)} \mathrm{Log}\,(1+\alpha_{n,k}) = \sum_{k=1}^{p(n)} \alpha_{n,k} + \sum_{k=1}^{p(n)} \theta_{n,k} |\alpha_{n,k}|^2 . \tag{5}$$

Now applying (1) we have

$$\lim_{n\to\infty} \left| \sum_{k=1}^{p(n)} \theta_{n,k} |\alpha_{n,k}|^2 \right| \le \lim_{n\to\infty} \sum_{k=1}^{p(n)} |\alpha_{n,k}|^2 = 0 .$$

Using this and (2) in (5), we obtain

$$\lim_{n\to\infty} \log \prod_{k=1}^{p(n)} (1+\alpha_{n,k}) = \alpha ,$$

and hence (3). □

Theorem 15.4 Let $\{X_{n,k},\ k=1,2,\cdots,p(n)\,;\ n=1,2,\cdots\}$ be a system of random variables on a probability space $(\Omega, \mathfrak{B}, P)$ which satisfies the following conditions:

1° $\{X_{n,k}\ k=1,2,\cdots,p(n)\}$ is an independent system for each n.

2° Each $X_{n,k}$ can assume at most two values, namely, 0 and 1.

3° For $\lambda_{n,k} \equiv P\{\omega \in \Omega\,;\, X_{n,k}(\omega) = 1\}$,

$\lim_{n\to\infty} \max_{k=1,2,\cdots,p(n)} \lambda_{n,k} = 0$ holds.

4° $\lim_{n\to\infty} \sum_{k=1}^{p(n)} \lambda_{n,k} = \lambda$ where $\lambda \in [0,\infty)$.

Then the probability distribution of $S_n = \sum_{k=1}^{p(n)} X_{n,k}$, $n=1,2,\cdots,$

converges to the Poisson distribution $\Phi_{P,\lambda}$, $\lambda \in [0,\infty)$ as $n \to \infty$ where, by $\Phi_{P,0}$, we understand the unit distribution which has the constant 1 as its characteristic function and may be treated as a degenerate Poisson distribution in view of Lemma 15.1.

Proof Let $\varphi_{n,k}$ and φ_n be the characteristic functions of $X_{n,k}$ and S_n, respectively. According to Theorem A4.3, to prove our theorem it suffices to show that φ_n converges to the characteristic function of $\Phi_{P,\lambda}$, $\lambda \in [0,\infty)$, as $n \to \infty$, i.e.,

$$\lim_{n\to\infty} \varphi_n(y) = e^{\lambda(e^{iy}-1)} .$$

Now

$$\varphi_{n,k}(y) = \int_{R^1} e^{iyx} \Phi_{X_{n,k}}(dx) = e^{iy\cdot 0}(1-\lambda_{n,k}) + e^{iy\cdot 1}\lambda_{n,k} = 1 + \lambda_{n,k}(e^{iy}-1)$$

and

$$\varphi_n(y) = \prod_{k=1}^{p(n)} \varphi_{n,k}(y) = \prod_{k=1}^{p(n)} \left\{1 + \lambda_{n,k}(e^{iy}-1)\right\} .$$

To apply Lemma 15.3 let

$$\alpha_{n,k} = \lambda_{n,k}(e^{iy}-1) .$$

This implies in particular

$$|\alpha_{n,k}| \le 2\lambda_{n,k} .$$

Then

$$\lim_{n\to\infty} \sum_{k=1}^{p(n)} |\alpha_{n,k}|^2 \le \lim_{n\to\infty} \max_{k=1,2,\cdots,p(n)} |\alpha_{n,k}| \sum_{k=1}^{p(n)} |\alpha_{n,k}|$$

$$\le 4 \lim_{n\to\infty} \max_{k=1,2,\cdots,p(n)} \lambda_{n,k} \sum_{k=1}^{p(n)} \lambda_{n,k} = 0$$

and

$$\lim_{n\to\infty} \sum_{k=1}^{p(n)} \alpha_{n,k} = \lim_{k\to\infty} \sum_{k=1}^{p(n)} \lambda_{n,k}(e^{iy} - 1) = \lambda(e^{iy} - 1).$$

Thus (1) and (2) of Lemma 15.3 are satisfied, and consequently

$$\lim_{n\to\infty} \varphi_n(y) = \lim_{n\to\infty} \prod_{k=1}^{p(n)} (1 + \alpha_{n,k}) = e^{\lambda(e^{iy} - 1)}.$$

This completes the proof of the theorem. □

Corollary 15.5 If a system of random variables $\{X_{n,k}, k = 1,2,\cdots, p(n); n = 1,2,\cdots\}$ on a probability space $(\Omega, \mathfrak{B}, P)$ satisfies the conditions 1°, 2°, 3° of Theorem 15.4 and if $S_n = \sum_{k=1}^{p(n)} X_{n,k}$, $n = 1,2,\cdots$, converges a.e. then the limit function S has a Poisson distribution $\Phi_{P,\lambda}$, $\lambda \in [0, \infty)$, as its probability distribution.

Proof Let $\lambda_n = \sum_{k=1}^{p(n)} \lambda_{n,k}$, $n = 1,2,\cdots$. We show that, under the conditions 1°, 2°, 3° of Theorem 15.4, $\{\lambda_n, n = 1,2,\cdots\}$ is a bounded sequence and hence has a subsequence $\{\lambda_{n_m}, m = 1,2,\cdots\}$ which converges to some $\lambda \in [0, \infty)$. Then according to Theorem 15.4 the probability distribution of S_{n_m}, $m = 1,2,\cdots$, converges to $\Phi_{P,\lambda}$ as $m \to \infty$. But S_{n_m} converges a.e. to S as $m \to \infty$. Thus S must have $\Phi_{P,\lambda}$ as its probability distribution.

We show the boundedness of the sequence $\{\lambda_n, n = 1,2,\cdots\}$ by contradiction. Suppose the sequence is not bounded. Then there exists a subsequence $\{\lambda_{n_m}, m = 1,2,\cdots\}$ with $\lim_{m\to\infty} \lambda_{n_m} = \infty$. Since $\lim_{m\to\infty} \max_{k=1,2,\cdots,p(n)} \lambda_{n_m,k} = 0$, for every fixed $\lambda > 0$ we can select a subsequence $\{n_{m_\ell}, \ell = 1,2,\cdots\}$ and a nonnegative integer $q(n_{m_\ell})$, $0 \le q(n_{m_\ell}) \le p(n_{m_\ell})$, $\ell = 1,2,\cdots$, such that

$$\lim_{\ell\to\infty} \sum_{k=1}^{q(n_{m_\ell})} \lambda_{n_{m_\ell},k} = \lambda .$$

According to Theorem 15.4, the probability distribution of

$$T_{n_{m_\ell}} = \sum_{k=1}^{q(n_{m_\ell})} X_{n_{m_\ell},k}, \quad \ell = 1,2,\cdots$$

converges to $\Phi_{P,\lambda}$ as $\ell\to\infty$. From the fact that $\{S_{n_{m_\ell}}, \ell = 1,2,\cdots\}$ converges a.e. to S as $\ell\to\infty$ and the fact that $T_{n_{m_\ell}} \le S_{n_{m_\ell}}$, we have, for every nonnegative integer j,

$$\begin{aligned} P\left\{\omega\in\Omega\,;S(\omega)\le j\right\} &\le P\left\{\liminf_{\ell\to\infty}\left\{\omega\in\Omega\,;S_{n_{m_\ell}}(\omega)\le j+\tfrac{1}{2}\right\}\right\} \\ &\le \liminf_{\ell\to\infty} P\left\{\omega\in\Omega\,;S_{n_{m_\ell}}(\omega)\le j+\tfrac{1}{2}\right\} \\ &\le \liminf_{\ell\to\infty} P\left\{\omega\in\Omega\,;T_{n_{m_\ell}}(\omega)\le j+\tfrac{1}{2}\right\} . \end{aligned}$$

Since the probability distribution of $T_{n_{m_\ell}}$, $\ell = 1,2,\cdots$, converges to $\Phi_{P,\lambda}$ as $\ell\to\infty$, the distribution function of $T_{n_{m_\ell}}$, $\ell = 1,2,\cdots$, converges to the distribution function of $\Phi_{P,\lambda}$ at its points of continuity according to Theorem A4.2. Thus

$$\lim_{\ell\to\infty} P\left\{\omega\in\Omega\,;T_{n_{m_\ell}}(\omega)\le j+\tfrac{1}{2}\right\} \le \sum_{x=0}^{j+1} e^{-\lambda}\frac{\lambda^x}{x!} \le e^{-\lambda}(j+2)\lambda^{j+1} \quad \text{for } \lambda \ge 1,$$

and hence

$$P\{\omega \in \Omega ; S(\omega) \le j\} \le e^{-\lambda}(j+2)\lambda^{j+1} \quad \text{for } j = 0,1,2,\cdots \text{ and } \lambda \ge 1 .$$

Letting $\lambda \to \infty$ we have

$$P\{\omega \in \Omega ; S(\omega) \le j\} \le 0 .$$

Finally letting $j \to \infty$ we have $1 \le 0$, a contradiction. □

[II] Poisson Processes

Lemma 15.6 Let X be a stochastic process on a probability space $(\Omega, \mathfrak{B}, P)$ and an interval $D \subset R^1$. If X is stochastically continuous and in addition satisfies the condition that for every pair of rational numbers $\alpha, \beta \in D$, $\alpha < \beta$, and $t_{n,k} = \alpha + k(\beta - \alpha)/2^n$, $k = 0,1,2,\cdots,2^n$,

$$\lim_{n\to\infty} \sum_{k=1}^{2^n} P\{\omega \in \Omega ; X(t_{n,k}, \omega) - X(t_{n,k-1}, \omega) \neq 0, 1\} = 0$$

holds then there exists an equivalent process Y of X on $(\Omega, \mathfrak{B}, P)$ and D in which almost every sample function is a monotone increasing right-continuous step function having at most finitely many jumps of magnitude 1 in any finite subinterval of D as the only possible discontinuities.

Proof Let α, β and $t_{n,k}$ be as stated in the lemma and let

$$A_{n,k} = \{\omega \in \Omega ; X(t_{n,k}, \omega) - X(t_{n,k-1}, \omega) \neq 0, 1\} \quad \text{and} \quad A_n = \bigcup_{k=1}^{2^n} A_{n,k}.$$

By (1), $\lim_{n\to\infty} P(A_n) \le \lim_{n\to\infty} \sum_{k=1}^{2^n} P(A_{n,k}) = 0$ so that we can select a subsequence $\{A_{n_m}, m = 1,2,\cdots\}$ with $\sum_{m=1}^{\infty} P(A_{n_m}) < \infty$. Then, by the Borel-Cantelli theorem,

$$P\left(\liminf_{m\to\infty} A_{n_m}{}^c\right) = 1.$$

Now if $\omega \in \liminf_{m\to\infty} A_{n_m}{}^c$ there exists a positive integer $M(\omega)$ such that

$$\omega \in A_{n_m}{}^c = \bigcap_{k=1}^{2^{n_m}} A_{n_m, k}{}^c \qquad \text{for} \quad m \geq M(\omega),$$

in other words

$$X(t_{n_m, k}, \omega) - X(t_{n_m, k-1}, \omega) = 0 \quad \text{or} \quad 1$$

$$\text{for} \quad k = 1,2,\cdots, 2^{n_m} \quad \text{when} \quad m \geq M(\omega). \tag{2}$$

Since

$$X(\beta, \omega) - X(\alpha, \omega) = \sum_{k=1}^{2^{n_m}} \left\{X(t_{n_m, k}, \omega) - X(t_{n_m, k-1}, \omega)\right\}$$

and $P\left(\liminf_{m\to\infty} A_{n_m}{}^c\right) = 1$ we have

$$P\left\{\omega \in \Omega ; X(\beta, \omega) - X(\alpha, \omega) = 0,1,2,\cdots\right\} = 1.$$

Let Ω_0 be the collection of $\omega \in \Omega$ such that $X(\beta, \omega) - X(\alpha, \omega) = 0,1,2,\cdots$ for every pair of rational numbers $\alpha, \beta \in D$, $\alpha < \beta$. Then Ω_0 is the intersection of countably many measurable events each having a probability measure equal to 1 so that it too has a probability measure equal to 1.

Let

$$\psi_n(t) = \frac{[2^n t] + 1}{2^n} \qquad \text{for } n = 1, 2, \cdots .$$

Each ψ_n is a monotone increasing right-continuous step function on R^1 with jumps of magnitude $1/2^n$ at $t = k/2^n$, $k = 0, \pm 1, \pm 2, \cdots$, and $\psi_n(0) = 1/2^n$. Also $\psi_n(t) \geq t$ and $\psi_n(t) \downarrow t$ on R^1 as $n \to \infty$. If $\omega \in \Omega_0$ then $X(\psi_n(t), \omega)$, $t \in D$, is a monotone increasing right-continuous step function whose only possible jumps take place at $t = k/2^n$, $k = 0, \pm 1, \pm 2, \cdots$, and have magnitude equal to $1, 2, \cdots$, and furthermore, for each $t \in D$, $X(\psi_n(t), \omega) \downarrow$ as $n \to \infty$ and $X(\psi_n(t), \omega)$ = const from some n onward. Let

$$Y(t, \omega) = \begin{cases} \lim_{n\to\infty} X(\psi_n(t), \omega) & \text{for } \omega \in \Omega_0 \\ 0 & \text{for } \omega \in \Omega_0^c . \end{cases}$$

Then for $\omega \in \Omega_0$, $Y(t, \omega)$, $t \in D$, is a monotone increasing right-continuous step function with at most finitely many jumps of magnitude equal to $1, 2, \cdots$ in any finite subinterval of D as the only possible discontinuities.

Y as defined by (3) is a stochastic process on $(\Omega, \mathfrak{B}, P)$ and D. Its equivalence to X can be seen as follows. Since X is stochastically continuous on D and $\lim_{n\to\infty} \psi_n(t) = t$ for $t \in D$, we have P - $\lim_{n\to\infty} X(\psi_n(t), \cdot) = X(t, \cdot)$ and hence there exists a subsequence $\{n_m, m = 1, 2, \cdots\}$ such that $\lim_{m\to\infty} X(\psi_{n_m}(t), \omega) = X(t, \omega)$ for a.e $\omega \in \Omega$. But according to (3), $\lim_{n\to\infty} X(\psi_n(t), \omega) = Y(t, \omega)$ for a.e. $\omega \in \Omega$. Thus $X(t, \omega) = Y(t, \omega)$ for a.e. $\omega \in \Omega$ establishing the equivalence of X and Y.

Now that Y is an equivalent process of X, (1) holds for

Y as well and consequently so does (2). Thus there exists $\Omega_0' \in \mathfrak{B}$ with $P(\Omega_0') = 1$ such that for every $\omega \in \Omega_0'$ there exists $M(\omega)$ for which

$$Y\left(t_{n_m, k}, \omega\right) - Y\left(t_{n_m, k-1}, \omega\right) = 0 \text{ or } 1 \text{ for}$$

$$\text{for } k = 1, 2, \cdots, 2^{n_m} \text{ when } m \geq M(\omega).$$

Thus 1 is the only possible magnitude of jump for $Y(t, \omega)$ for $\omega \in \Omega_0'$. □

<u>Theorem 15.7</u> Let λ be a continuous monotone increasing function defined on an interval $D \subset R^1$. Then there exists an additive process X on a probability space $(\Omega, \mathfrak{B}, P)$ and D such that:

(1) For every $t', t'' \in D$, $t' < t''$, $X(t'', \cdot) - X(t', \cdot)$ has the Poisson distribution $\Phi_{P, \lambda(t'') - \lambda(t')}$ as its probability distribution:

(2) Almost every sample function is a monotone increasing right-continuous step function having at most finitely many jumps of magnitude 1 in any finite subinterval of D as the only possible discontinuities.

<u>Proof</u> For $t', t'' \in D, t' < t''$, let $\Phi_{t't''} = \Phi_{P, \lambda(t'') - \lambda(t')}$. Then according to Lemma 15.2, for $t_1, t_2, t_3 \in D$, $t_1 < t_2 < t_3$, we have $\Phi_{t_1 t_2} * \Phi_{t_2 t_3} = \Phi_{t_1 t_3}$, so that by Theorem 12.2 there exists an additive process X on a probability space $(\Omega, \mathfrak{B}, P)$ and D such that for every $t', t'' \in D, t' < t''$, $X(t'', \cdot) - X(t', \cdot)$ has $\Phi_{P, \lambda(t'') - \lambda(t')}$ as its probability distribution.

To prove (2) of the theorem we show that our X satisfies the conditions of Lemma 15.6. Let us verify the stochastic continuity of X first. Let $t_0 \in D$. To show that $P - \lim_{t\to t_0} X(t,\cdot) = X(t_0,\cdot)$, i.e., $P - \lim_{t\to t_0} \{X(t,\cdot) - X(t_0,\cdot)\} = 0$, it suffices to show $\lim_{t\to t_0} E\left[\{X(t,\cdot) - X(t_0,\cdot)\}^2\right] = 0$ since convergence in moment implies convergence in probability. Let $\{t_n, n = 1,2,\cdots\} \subset D$ with $\lim_{n\to\infty} t_n = t_0$. If $t_0 \le t_n$ then $X(t_n,\cdot) - X(t_0,\cdot)$ has $\Phi_{P,\lambda(t_n)-\lambda(t_0)}$ as its probability distribution so that both the mean and the variance are equal to $\lambda(t_n) - \lambda(t_0)$. If $t_0 \ge t_n$ then $X(t_0,\cdot) - X(t_n,\cdot)$ has $\Phi_{P,\lambda(t_0)-\lambda(t_n)}$ as its probability distribution, so that $X(t_n,\cdot) - X(t_0,\cdot)$ has $\lambda(t_n) - \lambda(t_0)$ as its mean and $\lambda(t_0) - \lambda(t_n)$ as its variamce. Thus

$$\lim_{n\to\infty} E\left[\{X(t_n,\cdot) - X(t_0,\cdot)\}^2\right]$$

$$= \lim_{n\to\infty} \left\{V\left[X(t_n,\cdot) - X(t_0,\cdot)\right] + \left\{E\left[X(t_n,\cdot) - X(t_0,\cdot)\right]\right\}^2\right\}$$

$$= \lim_{n\to\infty} \left\{\pm\{\lambda(t_n) - \lambda(t_0)\} + \{\lambda(t_n) - \lambda(t_0)\}^2\right\} = 0$$

from the continuity of $\lambda(t)$.

It remains to verify (1) of Lemma 15.6. Let $\alpha, \beta \in D$, $\alpha < \beta$, be rational numbers and let $t_{n,k} = \alpha + k(\beta-\alpha)/2^n$, $k = 0,1,2,\cdots,2^n$. Since $X(t_{n,k},\cdot) - X(t_{n,k-1},\cdot)$ has $\Phi_{P,\lambda(t_{n,k})-\lambda(t_{n,k-1})}$ as its probability distribution

$$P\{\omega \in \Omega\,;\, X(t_{n,k},\omega) - X(t_{n,k-1},\omega) = \ell\}$$

$$= \exp\left\{-\left[\lambda(t_{n,k}) - \lambda(t_{n,k-1})\right]\right\} \frac{\left[\lambda(t_{n,k}) - \lambda(t_{n,k-1})\right]^{\ell}}{\ell!} \quad \text{for } \ell = 0,1,2,\cdots.$$

Note that, for $\lambda \le \frac{1}{2}$,

$$\sum_{\ell=2}^{\infty} e^{-\lambda} \frac{\lambda^{\ell}}{\ell!} \le \sum_{\ell=2}^{\infty} \frac{\lambda^{\ell}}{\ell!} \le \frac{\lambda^2}{2} \sum_{\ell=0}^{\infty} \lambda^{\ell} \le \lambda^2 ,$$

and that from the uniform continuity of λ on $[\alpha, \beta]$ we have, for sufficiently large n ,

$$\lambda(t_{n,k}) - \lambda(t_{n,k-1}) \le \tfrac{1}{2} \qquad \text{for } k = 1,2,\cdots,2^n .$$

Thus

$$\sum_{k=1}^{2^n} P\left\{\omega \in \Omega ; X(t_{n,k}, \omega) - X(t_{n,k-1}, \omega) \neq 0, 1\right\}$$

$$= \sum_{k=1}^{2^n} \sum_{\ell=2}^{\infty} \exp\left\{-\left[\lambda(t_{n,k}) - \lambda(t_{n,k-1})\right]\right\} \frac{\left[\lambda(t_{n,k}) - \lambda(t_{n,k-1})\right]^{\ell}}{\ell!}$$

$$\le \sum_{k=1}^{2^n} \left[\lambda(t_{n,k}) - \lambda(t_{n,k-1})\right]^2$$

$$\le \max_{k=1,2,\cdots,2^n} \left[\lambda(t_{n,k}) - \lambda(t_{n,k-1})\right] \sum_{k=1}^{2^n} \left[\lambda(t_{n,k}) - \lambda(t_{n,k-1})\right]$$

$$= \max_{k=1,2,\cdots,2^n} \left[\lambda(t_{n,k}) - \lambda(t_{n,k-1})\right]\left[\lambda(\beta) - \lambda(\alpha)\right] ,$$

which converges to 0 as $n \to \infty$ since λ is uniformly continuous on $[\alpha, \beta]$. This completes the proof of the theorem. □

<u>Definition 15.8</u> An additive process X on a probability space $(\Omega, \mathfrak{B}, P)$ and an interval $D \subset R^1$ is called a Poisson process if for every $t', t'' \in D$, $t' < t''$, the probability distribution of $X(t'', \cdot) - X(t', \cdot)$ is given by the Poisson distribution $\Phi_{P, c(t''-t')}$

where $c \geq 0$ is a fixed constant.

Theorem 15.9 Let X be a stochastic process on a probability space $(\Omega, \mathfrak{B}, P)$ and an interval $D \subset R^1$. If X is stochastically continuous and almost every sample function of X is a monotone increasing right-continuous stepfunction having at most finitely many jumps of magnitude 1 in any finite subinterval of D as the only possible discontinuities, then for every $t', t'' \in D, t' < t''$, the probability distribution of $X(t'', \cdot) - X(t', \cdot)$ is given by the Poisson distribution $\Phi_{P, \lambda(t'') - \lambda(t')}$ where λ is a continuous monotone increasing function on D. If X has stationary increments then λ satisfies the condition $\lambda(t'') - \lambda(t') = c(t'' - t')$ where $c \geq 0$, so that X is a Poisson process.

Proof Let $\alpha, \beta \in D$, $\alpha < \beta$, $t_{n,k} = \alpha + k(\beta - \alpha)/n$, $k = 1, 2, \cdots, n$, and let

$$X_{n,k}(\omega) = X(t_{n,k}, \omega) - X(t_{n,k-1}, \omega) \qquad \text{for } k = 1, 2, \cdots, n$$

and

$$Y_{n,k}(\omega) = \begin{cases} 0 & \text{when } X_{n,k}(\omega) = 0 \\ 1 & \text{when } X_{n,k}(\omega) = 1, 2, \cdots . \end{cases}$$

Let us verify that $\{Y_{n,k}, k = 1, 2, \cdots, n; n = 1, 2, \cdots\}$ satisfies the conditions of Corollary 15.5.

First of all, since X is an additive process, $\{X_{n,k}, k = 1, 2, \cdots, n\}$ is an independent system for each n. Then $\{Y_{n,k}, k = 1, 2, \cdots, n\}$, which is obtained by a Baire transformation of $\{X_{n,k}, k = 1, 2, \cdots, n\}$, is an independent system (c.f. Theorem A6.6).

Secondly, $Y_{n,k}$ can assume at most two values, namely,

0 and 1.

Thirdly, $\lim_{n\to\infty} \max_{k=1,2,\cdots,n} \lambda_{n,k} = 0$ where $\lambda_{n,k} = P\{\omega \in \Omega; Y_{n,k}(\omega) = 1\}$. This can be verified as follows. Since X is uniformly stochastically continuous on $[\alpha, \beta]$ by Theorem 3.5, for every $\epsilon > 0$ and $\eta > 0$ there exists $\delta > 0$ such that

$$P\{\omega \in \Omega; |X(t', \omega) - X(t'', \omega)| \geq \epsilon\} < \eta \quad \text{whenever}$$

whenever $t', t'' \in [\alpha, \beta]$ and $|t' - t''| < \delta$.

Thus for every $\eta > 0$ we have, for sufficiently large n,

$$P\{\omega \in \Omega; |X(t_{n,k}, \omega) - X(t_{n,k-1}, \omega)| \geq 1\} < \eta \quad \text{for} \quad k=1,2,\cdots,n,$$

and hence

$$\max_{k=1,2,\cdots,n} P\{\omega \in \Omega; |X(t_{n,k}, \omega) - X(t_{n,k-1}, \omega)| \geq 1\} < \eta.$$

Therefore, from the arbitrariness of $\eta > 0$,

$$\lim_{n\to\infty} \max_{k=1,2,\cdots,n} \lambda_{n,k} = 0.$$

To apply Corollary 15.5 it remains to show that $\lim_{n\to\infty} \sum_{k=1}^{n} Y_{n,k}(\omega) = X(\beta, \omega) - X(\alpha, \omega)$ for a.e. $\omega \in \Omega$. By the hypothesis of the theorem, there exists $\Omega_0 \in \mathfrak{B}$ with $P(\Omega_0) = 1$ such that, for every $\omega \in \Omega_0$, $X(\cdot, \omega)$ is a monotone increasing step function having at most finitely many jumps of magnitude 1 in any finite subinterval of D as the only possible discontinuities. Then, for every $\omega \in \Omega_0$, there exists $N(\omega)$ such that

$$X(t_{n,k}, \omega) - X(t_{n,k-1}, \omega) = 0 \quad \text{or} \quad 1$$

for $k = 1,2,\cdots,n$ when $n \geq N(\omega)$.

Thus

$$X(\beta, \omega) - X(\alpha, \omega) = \sum_{k=1}^{n} X_{n,k}(\omega) = \sum_{k=1}^{n} Y_{n,k}(\omega) \quad \text{for } n \geq N(\omega)$$

and consequently

$$P\left\{\omega \in \Omega ; \lim_{n\to\infty} \sum_{k=1}^{n} Y_{n,k}(\omega) = X(\beta, \omega) - X(\alpha, \omega)\right\} = 1.$$

Now all the conditions in Corollary 15.5 are verified and $X(\beta, \cdot) - X(\alpha, \cdot)$ has a Poisson distribution as its probability distribution.

Let $c \in D$ be arbitrarily fixed. Let us define a real-valued function λ on D by

$$\lambda(t) = E\left[X(t, \cdot)\right] - E\left[X(c, \cdot)\right] \quad \text{for } t \in D.$$

Then

$$\lambda(t'') - \lambda(t') = E\left[X(t'', \cdot) - X(t', \cdot)\right] \quad \text{for } t', t'' \in D, \quad t' < t''.$$

But $X(t'', \cdot) - X(t', \cdot)$ has a Poisson distribution $\Phi_{P,\mu}$ as its probability distribution, and the mean of $\Phi_{P,\mu}$ is equal to μ. Thus the probability distribution of $X(t'', \cdot) - X(t', \cdot)$ is given by $\Phi_{P,\lambda(t'')-\lambda(t')}$. This also implies that $\lambda(t'') - \lambda(t') \geq 0$, i.e., λ is monotone increasing.

The continuity of λ on D can be shown by showing that, for $t', t'' \in D$, $t' < t''$,

$$\lim_{t' \uparrow t''} \left\{\lambda(t'') - \lambda(t')\right\} = 0 \quad \text{and} \quad \lim_{t'' \downarrow t'} \left\{\lambda(t'') - \lambda(t')\right\} = 0.$$

Let us show the former as an example. Now, by the stochastic continuity of X at t''

$$\lim_{t' \uparrow t''} P\{\omega \in \Omega;\, X(t'', \omega) - X(t', \omega) = 0\}$$

$$= \lim_{t' \uparrow t''} \left[1 - P\{\omega \in \Omega;\, X(t'', \omega) - X(t', \omega) \geq 1\}\right] = 1,$$

so that

$$\lim_{t' \uparrow t''} \exp\{-[\lambda(t'') - \lambda(t')]\} \frac{[\lambda(t'') - \lambda(t')]^0}{0!} = 1,$$

i.e.,

$$\lim_{t' \uparrow t''} \exp\{-[\lambda(t'') - \lambda(t')]\} = 1,$$

implying $\lim_{t' \uparrow t''} [\lambda(t'') - \lambda(t')] = 0.$

Finally, the fact that the stationarity of increments of X implies $\lambda(t'') - \lambda(t') = c(t'' - t')$ with $c \geq 0$ for $t', t'' \in D$, $t' < t''$, can be shown as in Theorem 14.9. □

Chapter 4
GAUSSIAN PROCESSES

§16. GAUSSIAN SYSTEMS OF RANDOM VARIABLES

[I] Multidimensional Normal Distributions

Let us begin by summarizing facts about matrices which are relevant to our discussion of multidimensional normal distributions. Let $A = [a_{ij},\ i, j = 1, 2, \cdots, k]$ and $x = [x_i,\ i = 1, 2, \cdots, k]$ where a_{ij} and x_i are real numbers and x is a column vector. If A is symmetric then it has k not necessarily distinct real eigenvalues λ_i, $i = 1, 2, \cdots, k$, and

$$\det A = \prod_{i=1}^{k} \lambda_i .$$

Let $'$ denote the transpose. Consider the quadratic form

$$x'Ax = (Ax, x) = \sum_{i=1}^{k} \sum_{j=1}^{k} a_{ij} x_i x_j .$$

A is said to be nonnegative definite if $(Ax, x) \ge 0$ for every x. If in addition, $(Ax, x) = 0$ if and only if $x = 0$ then A is said to be positive definite. A symmetric matrix A is nonnegative definite if and only if $\lambda_i \ge 0$, $i = 1, 2, \cdots, k$, and it is positive definite if and only if $\lambda_i > 0$, $i = 1, 2, \cdots, k$. Also a symmetric matrix A is positive definite if and only if there exists a nonsingular matrix C such that $C'C = A$.

A k-dimensional normal distribution is a k-dimensional

probability distribution Φ which is absolutely continuous with respect to the Lebesgue measure with the density function given by

$$\Phi'(x) = \frac{d\Phi}{dm_L}(x) = \left[\frac{\det A}{(2\pi)^k}\right]^{\frac{1}{2}} \exp\left\{-\tfrac{1}{2}\Big(A[x-m], x-m\Big)\right\}$$

$$\text{for } x \in R^k \tag{1}$$

where $m \in R^k$ and A is a $k \times k$ positive definite symmetric matrix. As we shall see, the characteristic function of our Φ is given by

$$\varphi(y) = \exp\left\{i(m, y) - \tfrac{1}{2}(Vy, y)\right\} \quad \text{for } y \in R^k \tag{2}$$

where V is the inverse of A and is a $k \times k$ positive definite symmetric matrix. On account of this a k-dimensional probability distribution determined by a characteristic function of the form (2) in which V is a $k \times k$ nonnegative definite but not positive definite symmetric matrix will be called a degenerate k-dimensional normal distribution. Thus by a k-dimensional normal distribution we will mean a k-dimensional probability distribution whose characteristic function is given by (2) in which V is a $k \times k$ nonnegative definite symmetric matrix.

Returning to (1), let us verify that $\int_{R^k} \Phi'(x)\, m_L(dx) = 1$.

Now since A is symmetric and positive definite, there exists a $k \times k$ nonsingular matrix C with $C'C = A$. Then

$$\Big(A[x-m], x-m\Big) = \Big(C'C[x-m], x-m\Big) = \Big(C[x-m], C[x-m]\Big). \tag{3}$$

Consider a one-to-one linear transformation of R^k onto R^k

given by

$$y = C[x-m]$$

whose inverse is given by

$$x = C^{-1}y + m. \tag{4}$$

The Jacobian of this last transformation is given by

$$|\det C^{-1}| = |\det C|^{-1} = (\det A)^{-\frac{1}{2}}. \tag{5}$$

Thus from (1), (3), (4), and (5)

$$\int_{R^k} \Phi'(x)\, m_L(dx) \tag{6}$$

$$= \left[\frac{\det A}{(2\pi)^k}\right]^{\frac{1}{2}} \int_{R^k} \exp\left\{-\tfrac{1}{2}(y, y)\right\} (\det A)^{-\frac{1}{2}} m_L(dy)$$

$$= \frac{1}{(2\pi)^{k/2}} \int_{-\infty}^{\infty} (k) \int_{-\infty}^{\infty} \exp\left\{-\tfrac{1}{2}\sum_{j=1}^{k} y_j^2\right\} dy_1 \cdots dy_k$$

$$= \left\{\frac{1}{\sqrt{2\pi}} \int_{-\infty}^{\infty} \exp\left\{-\tfrac{1}{2}y^2\right\} dy\right\}^k = 1.$$

The mean vector $E(\Phi)$ of a k-dimensional probability distribution Φ is defined by

$$E(\Phi) = \left[E(\Phi)_j,\ j = 1, 2, \cdots, k\right], \tag{7}$$

where

$$E(\Phi)_j = \int_{R^k} x_j\, \Phi(dx) \qquad \text{for } j=1, 2, \cdots, k \tag{8}$$

provided all the k integrals exist and are finite. The covariance matrix $V(\Phi)$ of Φ is then defined by

$$V(\Phi) = \left[V(\Phi)_{j\ell},\ j,\ell = 1,2,\cdots,k\right], \tag{9}$$

where

$$V(\Phi)_{j\ell} = \int_{R^k} \left\{x_j - E(\Phi)_j\right\}\left\{x_\ell - E(\Phi)_\ell\right\} \Phi(dx)$$

$$\text{for } j,\ell = 1,2,\cdots,k \tag{10}$$

provided all the k^2 integrals exist and are finite. A covariance matrix $V(\Phi)$ is always symmetric and nonnegative definite since, for every $y = (y_1,\cdots,y_k) \in R^k$,

$$(Vy, y) = \sum_{j=1}^{k}\sum_{\ell=1}^{k} V(\Phi)_{j\ell}\, y_j\, y_\ell = \int_{R^k}\left[\sum_{j=1}^{k}\left\{x_j - E(\Phi)_j\right\} y_j\right]^2 \Phi(dx) \geq 0 .$$

<u>Theorem 16.1</u> The characteristic function φ of a k-dimensional normal distribution Φ with the density function (1) is given by (2), and the mean vector and the covariance matrix of Φ are given by

$$E(\Phi) = m \quad \text{and} \quad V(\Phi) = V,$$

where $V = A^{-1}$.

<u>Proof</u> Since $V = A^{-1}$ is symmetric and positive definite there exists a $k \times k$ nonsingular matrix B such that $BB' = V$. Then

$$\Phi'(x) = \frac{1}{\left\{(2\pi)^k \det V\right\}^{\frac{1}{2}}} \exp\left\{-\tfrac{1}{2}\left(B^{-1}[x-m],\ B^{-1}[x-m]\right)\right\},$$

and for the characteristic function φ of Φ we have

$$\varphi(y) = \int_{R^k} e^{i(y,x)}\, \Phi'(x)\, m_L(dx) \quad \text{for } y \in R^k.$$

Let $z = B^{-1}[x-m]$, i.e., $x = Bz + m$ with the Jacobian $|\det B| = \sqrt{\det V}$. Then

$$\varphi(y) = e^{i(y,m)} (2\pi)^{-k/2} \int_{R^k} e^{-\frac{1}{2}(z,z)+i(B'y,z)} m_L(dz).$$

For simplicity write $B'y = (w_1, \cdots, w_k)$. Then

$$\varphi(y) = e^{i(y,m)}(2\pi)^{-k/2} \prod_{j=1}^{k} \int_{R^1} \exp\left\{-\tfrac{1}{2} z_j^2 + i w_j z_j\right\} m_L(dz_j)$$

$$= e^{i(y,m)}(2\pi)^{-k/2} \prod_{j=1}^{k} \sqrt{2\pi}\, \exp\left\{-\frac{w_j^2}{2}\right\},$$

$$= e^{i(y,m)}\, e^{-\frac{1}{2}(B'y, B'y)} = e^{i(y,m) - \frac{1}{2}(Vy,y)},$$

which proves (2).

To show that $E(\Phi) = m$, we apply Theorem A3.4 to (8). Thus

$$E(\Phi)_j = \int_{R^k} x_j \Phi(dx) = \frac{1}{i}\frac{\partial \varphi}{\partial y_j}(0) = \frac{1}{i}\frac{\partial}{\partial y_j} e^{i(m,y)-\frac{1}{2}(Vy,y)}\Big|_{y=0} = m_j ,$$

where m_j is the jth component of m.

As for $V(\Phi)$, using $E(\Phi) = m$ in (10) we have

$$V(\Phi)_{j\ell} = \int_{R^k} (x_j - m_j)(x_\ell - m_\ell) \frac{1}{\left\{(2\pi)^k \det V\right\}^{\frac{1}{2}}}$$

$$\exp\left\{-\tfrac{1}{2}\left(V^{-1}[x-m], x-m\right)\right\} m_L(dx).$$

With $z = x - m$, we see that

$$V(\Phi)_{j\ell} = V(\Psi)_{j\ell},$$

where Ψ is the k-dimensional normal distribution with the density function

$$\Psi'(z) = \frac{1}{\{(2\pi)^k \det V\}^{\frac{1}{2}}} \exp\left\{-\tfrac{1}{2}(V^{-1}z, z)\right\}.$$

According to (2), the characteristic function ψ of Ψ is given by

$$\psi(y) = e^{-\frac{1}{2}(Vy, y)}.$$

Applying Theorem A3.4 to Ψ we have

$$V(\Psi)_{j\ell} = \int_{R^k} z_j z_\ell \, \Psi(dz) = \frac{1}{i^2} \frac{\partial^2 \psi}{\partial y_j \partial y_\ell}(0) = \frac{1}{i^2} \frac{\partial^2}{\partial y_j \partial y_\ell} e^{-\frac{1}{2}(Vy, y)}\bigg|_{y=0} = v_{j\ell}$$

where $v_{j\ell}$ is the $j\ell$ entry of V. Thus

$$V(\Phi) = V(\Psi) = V.$$

This completes the proof of the theorem. □

With (2) we can now enlarge the class of multidimensional normal distributions as announced earlier. Let V be a $k \times k$ nonnegative definite symmetric matrix. For each positive integer n let $V_n = V + (1/n)I$. Clearly V_n is symmetric and nonnegative definite. To show that it is actually positive definite, suppose $(V_n y, y) = 0$ for some $y \in R^k$. Then $(Vy, y) + (1/n)(y, y) = 0$. Since V is nonnegative definite, we have $(1/n)(y, y) = 0$ and hence $y = 0$. Now that V_n is positive definite, consider the k-dimensional normal distribution Φ_n whose characteristic function φ_n is given by

$$\varphi_n(y) = \exp\left\{i(m, y) - \tfrac{1}{2}(V_n y, y)\right\}$$

$$= \exp\left\{i(m, y) - \tfrac{1}{2}(Vy, y) - \frac{1}{2n}(y, y)\right\} \quad \text{for} \quad y \in R^k,$$

where $m \in R^k$. Now

$$\varphi(y) \equiv \lim_{n\to\infty} \varphi_n(y) = \exp\left\{i(m, y) - \tfrac{1}{2}(Vy, y)\right\} \quad \text{for} \quad y \in R^k. \tag{11}$$

φ is also continuous on R^k. Thus according to (3) of Theorem A4.3, φ is the characteristic function of a k-dimensional distribution Φ. By a k-dimensional normal distribution we shall mean a k-dimensional probability distribution whose characteristic function is given by the right side of (11). We use the notation $N(m,V)$ for such a probability distribution.

[II] Gaussian Systems of Random Variables

Definition 16.2 A collection $\mathfrak{X} = \left\{X(\alpha, \cdot), \alpha \in A\right\}$ of random variables on a probability space $(\Omega, \mathfrak{B}, P)$ where A is an arbitrary index set is called a Gaussian system if for every finite subcollection $\{\alpha_1, \cdots, \alpha_n\} \subset A$ the probability distribution of the n-dimensional random vector $\left(X(\alpha_1, \cdot), \cdots, X(\alpha_n, \cdot)\right)$ is an n-dimensional normal distribution. A Gaussian system in which the index set A is a subset of R^1 is called a Gaussian process.

Let $X_1, \cdots, X_n$ be random variables on a probability space $(\Omega, \mathfrak{B}, P)$. The mean vector $E(X)$ of the n-dimensional random vector $X = (X_1, \cdots, X_n)$ is defined by

$$E(X) = \left(E(X_1), \cdots, E(X_n)\right)$$

provided $E(X_j)$, $j = 1, 2, \cdots, n$, exist and are finite. The covariance matrix $V(X)$ of X is defined by

$$V(X) = \left\{C(X_j, X_\ell), j, \ell = 1,2, \cdots, n\right\}$$

provided the covariances $C(X_j, X_\ell), j, \ell = 1,2, \cdots, n$, exist and are finite, $C(X_j, X_\ell)$ being defined by

$$C(X_j, X_\ell) = E\left[\left\{X_j - E(X_j)\right\}\left\{X_\ell - E(X_\ell)\right\}\right].$$

Let Φ_X be the n-dimensional probability distribution determined by X. Then from (7), (8), (9), and (10) of [I],

$$E(X_j) = \int_{R^n} x_j \, \Phi_X(dx) = E(\Phi_X)_j ,$$

$$C(X_j, X_\ell) = \int_{R^n} \left\{x_j - E(X_j)\right\} \left\{x_\ell - E(X_\ell)\right\} \Phi_X(dx) = V(X)_{j\ell} ,$$

so that

$$E(X) = E(\Phi_X)$$

$$V(X) = V(\Phi_X).$$

In particular when Φ_X is an n-dimensional normal distribution, i.e., the characteristic function φ_X of Φ_X is given by

$$\varphi_X(y) = \exp\left\{i(m, y) - \tfrac{1}{2}(Vy, y)\right\} \quad \text{for} \quad y \in R^n$$

where $m \in R^n$ and V is an $n \times n$ nonnegative definite symmetric matrix, then for the components of m and V we have, Theorem 16.1,

$$m_j = E(\Phi_X)_j = E(X_j) ,$$

$$v_{j\ell} = V(\Phi_X)_{j\ell} = V(X)_{j\ell} = C(X_j, X_\ell).$$

Theorem 16.3 Given a finite collection of random

variables $\{X_1, \cdots, X_n\}$ on a probability space $(\Omega, \mathfrak{B}, P)$.

(1) If the probability distribution of the n-dimensional random vector $X = (X_1, \cdots, X_n)$ is an n-dimensional normal distribution $N(m, V)$, then an arbitrary linear combination of $X_1, \cdots, X_n$, $Z = \sum_{j=1}^{n} \gamma_j X_j$ where $\gamma_j \in R^1$, $j = 1, 2, \cdots, n$, has a normal distribution $N(m_0, v_0)$ as its probability distribution, with m_0 and v_0 given by

$$m_0 = \sum_{j=1}^{n} \gamma_j m_j \quad \text{and} \quad v_0 = \sum_{j=1}^{n} \sum_{\ell=1}^{n} \gamma_j \gamma_\ell v_{j\ell} \geq 0, \tag{1}$$

where m_j and $v_{j\ell}$ are the components of m and V, i.e.,

$$\begin{aligned} m_j &= E(X_j) \quad \text{for } j = 1, 2, \cdots, n \text{ and} \\ v_{j\ell} &= C(X_j, X_\ell) \quad \text{for } j, \ell = 1, 2, \cdots, n. \end{aligned} \tag{2}$$

(2) Conversely if every linear combination of $X_1, \cdots, X_n$ is normally distributed then the probability distribution of the n-dimensional random vector $X = (X_1, \cdots, X_n)$ is an n-dimensional normal distribution $N(m, V)$ where the components of m and V are given by (2).

(3) If every linear combination of $X_1, \cdots, X_n$ is normally distributed then $\{X_1, \cdots, X_n\}$ is a Gaussian system in the sense of Definition 16.2. Thus if the probability distribution of the n-dimensional random vector $X = (X_1, \cdots, X_n)$ is an n-dimensional normal distribution then $\{X_1, \cdots, X_n\}$ is a Gaussian system.

<u>Proof</u> (1) If the probability distribution Φ_X of $X = (X_1, \cdots, X_n)$ is an n-dimensional normal distribution $N(m, V)$ then the characteristic function of X is given by

$$E\left[e^{i(X,y)}\right] = \int_{R^n} e^{i(x,y)} \Phi_X(dx) = e^{i(m,y)-\frac{1}{2}(Vy,y)}$$

for $y \in R^n$.

In other words,

$$E\left[\exp\left\{i\sum_{j=1}^{n} X_j y_j\right\}\right] = \exp\left\{i\sum_{j=1}^{n} m_j y_j - \frac{1}{2}\sum_{j=1}^{n}\sum_{\ell=1}^{n} v_{j\ell} y_j y_\ell\right\}$$

for $y = (y_1, \cdots, y_n) \in R^n$. (3)

Consider the linear combination $Z = \sum_{j=1}^{n} \gamma_j X_j$, $\gamma_j \in R^1$, $n = 1, 2, \cdots, n$. With the transformation $y_j = t\gamma_j$, $t \in R^1$, $j = 1, 2, \cdots, n$, (3) becomes

$$E\left[e^{itZ}\right] = \exp\left\{it\sum_{j=1}^{n} \gamma_j m_j - \frac{1}{2}t^2 \sum_{j=1}^{n}\sum_{\ell=1}^{n} \gamma_j \gamma_\ell v_{j\ell}\right\} = e^{itm_0 - \frac{1}{2}t^2 v_0}, \quad (4)$$

where m_0 and v_0 are as defined by (1). Thus the characteristic function of Z is given by the right side of (4) and the probability distribution of Z is the normal distribution $N(m_0, v_0)$.

(2) Suppose an arbitrary linear combination $Y = \sum_{j=1}^{n} y_j X_j$ is normally distributed. Then the characteristic function of Y is given by

$$E\left[e^{iYt}\right] = e^{itE(Y) - \frac{1}{2}t^2 V(Y)} \quad \text{for } t \in R^1. \quad (5)$$

On the other hand the characteristic function of the n-dimensional random vector $X = (X_1, \cdots, X_n)$ is given by

$$E\left[e^{i(X,y)}\right] = E\left[e^{i\sum_{j=1}^{n} X_j y_j}\right] \quad \text{for } y = (y_1, \cdots, y_n) \in R^n. \quad (6)$$

Since $(X, y) = Y$, we have, from (5)

$$E\left[e^{i(X,y)}\right] = E\left[e^{iY\cdot 1}\right] = e^{iE(Y)-\frac{1}{2}V(Y)} .$$

But

$$E(Y) = E\left(\sum_{j=1}^{n} y_j X_j\right) = \sum_{j=1}^{n} y_j E(X_j)$$

and

$$V(Y) = E\left[\left\{\sum_{j=1}^{n} y_j X_j - E\left(\sum_{j=1}^{n} y_j X_j\right)\right\}^2\right] = E\left[\left\{\sum_{j=1}^{n} y_j\left[X_j - E(X_j)\right]\right\}^2\right]$$

$$= \sum_{j=1}^{n}\sum_{\ell=1}^{n} y_j y_\ell\, C(X_j, X_\ell).$$

Thus

$$E\left[e^{i(X,y)}\right] = \exp\left\{i\sum_{j=1}^{n} y_j E(X_j) - \frac{1}{2}\sum_{j=1}^{n}\sum_{\ell=1}^{n} y_j y_\ell\, C(X_j, X_\ell)\right\}$$

$$= e^{i(m,y) - \frac{1}{2}(Vy,y)}, \tag{7}$$

where the components of m and V are given by (2). Now that the characteristic function of X is given by the right side of (7), the probability distribution of X is $N(m, V)$.

(3) Suppose every linear combination of $X_1, \cdots, X_n$ is normally distributed. Take an arbitrary subset $\{X_{j_1}, \cdots, X_{j_k}\}$ of $\{X_1, \cdots, X_n\}$. Then every linear combination of $X_{j_1}, \cdots, X_{j_k}$ is normally distributed so that by (2) the probability distribution of the k-dimensional random vector $(X_{j_1}, \cdots, X_{j_k})$ is a k-dimensional normal distribution. According to Definition 16.2, $\{X_1, \cdots, X_n\}$ is a Gaussian system. □

From Definition 16.2 and (3) of Theorem 16.3 we have

Theorem 16.4 A collection of random variables on a probability space is a Gaussian system if and only if every linear combination of members of the collection is normally distributed.

Definition 16.5 Let $\mathfrak{X} = \{X(\alpha, \cdot), \alpha \in A\}$ be a system of random variables on a probability space each having a finite second moment, i.e., $E[X(\alpha, \cdot)^2] < \infty, \alpha \in A$. The real-valued functions

$$m(\alpha) = E[X(\alpha, \cdot)] \quad \text{for } \alpha \in A \quad \text{and}$$

$$v(\alpha, \beta) = C(X(\alpha, \cdot), X(\beta, \cdot)) \quad \text{for } \alpha, \beta \in A$$

are called, respectively, the mean and the covariance functions of $\mathfrak{X}$.

Remark 16.6 The covariance function v of a system of random variables $\mathfrak{X} = \{X(\alpha, \cdot), \alpha \in A\}$ is symmetric and non-negative definite, i.e.,

$$v(\alpha, \beta) = v(\beta, \alpha) \quad \text{for } \alpha, \beta \in A, \tag{1}$$

$$\sum_{j=1}^{n} \sum_{\ell=1}^{n} v(\alpha_j, \alpha_\ell)\, \xi_j \xi_\ell \geq 0 \quad \text{whenever}$$

$$\{\alpha_1, \cdots, \alpha_n\} \subset A \text{ and } \{\xi_1, \cdots, \xi_n\} \subset R^1. \tag{2}$$

Proof (1) is obvious. To prove (2) we observe that

$$\sum_{j=1}^{n} \sum_{\ell=1}^{n} v(\alpha_j, \alpha_\ell)\, \xi_j \xi_\ell = E\left[\left\{\sum_{j=1}^{n} \left[X(\alpha_j, \cdot) - E[X(\alpha_j, \cdot)]\right] \xi_j\right\}^2\right] \geq 0.$$

□

Lemma 16.7 Given $m = [m_1, \cdots, m_n] \in R^n$ and an $n \times n$ nonnegative definite symmetric matrix $V = [v_{j\ell}, j, \ell = 1, 2, \cdots, n]$. Let $\{p_1, \cdots, p_q\}$, $1 \le q \le n$, be a permutation of a subsequence of $\{1, 2, \cdots, n\}$ and let $\tilde{m} = (m_{p_1}, \cdots, m_{p_q})$, $\tilde{V} = (v_{p_j p_\ell}, j, \ell = 1,2, \cdots, q)$, $\Phi = N(m,V)$, and $\tilde{\Phi} = N(\tilde{m}, \tilde{V})$. Then, for any Baire function f on R^q,

$$\int_{R^q} f(y)\, \tilde{\Phi}(dy) = \int_{R^n} f(x_{p_1}, \cdots, x_{p_q})\, \Phi(dx),$$

where $y = (y_1, \cdots, y_q) \in R^q$ and $x = (x_1, \cdots, x_n) \in R^n$, in the sense that if one of the integrals exists so does the other and the two are equal.

Proof Let us interpret the two integrals as expectations of random variables on a probability space. Thus consider the probability space $(\Omega, \mathfrak{B}, P) = (R^n, \mathfrak{B}^n, \Phi)$ where $\Phi = N(m,V)$ and n random variables X_j, $j = 1,2, \cdots, n$, on this probability space defined by $X_j(x) = x_j$, $x = (x_1, \cdots, x_n) \in R^n$. Then the probability distribution of the n-dimensional random vector $X = (X_1, \cdots, X_n)$ is just Φ. By (3) of Theorem 16.3, $\{X_1, \cdots, X_n\}$ is a Gaussian system, and consequently the probability distribution of the q-dimensional random vector $\tilde{X} = (X_{p_1}, \cdots, X_{p_q})$ is a q-dimensional normal distribution. The mean vector and the covariance matrix of this normal distribution are given by

$$\left[E(X_{p_j}), j = 1,2, \cdots, q\right] = \left[m_{p_j}, j = 1,2, \cdots, q\right] = \tilde{m},$$

$$\left[C(X_{p_j}, X_{p_\ell}), j, \ell = 1,2,\cdots, q\right] = \left[v_{p_j p_\ell}, j, \ell = 1,2,\cdots, q\right] = \tilde{V},$$

i.e., the q-dimensional normal distribution in question is in fact

$N(\tilde{m}, \tilde{V}) = \tilde{\Phi}$. Now consider the random variable

$$Y(x) = f\left[\tilde{X}(x)\right] = f\left[X_{p_1}(x), \cdots, X_{p_q}(x)\right] \quad \text{for} \quad x \in R^n.$$

Applying Theorem A1.6 to the two expressions of Y, we have

$$\int_{R^q} f(y)\, \tilde{\Phi}(dy) = E(Y) = \int_{R^n} f(x_{p_1}, \cdots, x_{p_q})\, \Phi(dx)$$

in the sense that in each of the two equalities the existence of one side implies that of the other and the equality of the two. □

Theorem 16.8 Given an arbitrary set A, a real-valued function $m(\alpha), \alpha \in A$, and a nonnegative definite symmetric function $v(\alpha, \beta)$, $\alpha, \beta \in A$. There exists a Gaussian system of random variables $\mathfrak{X} = \{X(\alpha, \cdot), \alpha \in A\}$ on a probability space which has m and v as its mean and covariance functions respectively.

Proof Consider R^A, the collection of all real-valued functions $\omega(\alpha)$, $\alpha \in A$. Let $p_{\alpha_1 \cdots \alpha_n}$ be the projection of R^A onto R^n corresponding to a finite sequence $\{\alpha_1, \cdots, \alpha_n\}$ of distinct elements of A defined by

$$p_{\alpha_1 \cdots \alpha_n}(\omega) = \left[\omega(\alpha_1), \cdots, \omega(\alpha_n)\right] \in R^n,$$

and let

$$\mathfrak{F}_{\alpha_1 \cdots \alpha_n} = \left\{p_{\alpha_1 \cdots \alpha_n}^{-1}(B),\ B \in \mathfrak{B}^n\right\},$$

which is a σ-field of subsets of R^A. On the field $\mathfrak{F} = \bigcup \mathfrak{F}_{\alpha_1 \cdots \alpha_n}$ we define a set function μ as follows. If $E \in \mathfrak{F}$ and $E \in \mathfrak{F}_{\alpha_1 \cdots \alpha_n}$ and is given by

$$E = p_{\alpha_1 \cdots \alpha_n}^{-1}(B), \quad \text{where } B \in \mathfrak{B}^n, \tag{1}$$

we let

$$\mu(E) = \int_{R^n} \chi_B(x)\, \Phi_{\alpha_1 \cdots \alpha_n}(dx), \tag{2}$$

where

$$\Phi_{\alpha_1 \cdots \alpha_n} = N(m_{\alpha_1 \cdots \alpha_n}, v_{\alpha_1 \cdots \alpha_n})$$

with

$$m_{\alpha_1 \cdots \alpha_n} = \left[m(\alpha_1), \cdots, m(\alpha_n) \right] \quad \text{and}$$

$$v_{\alpha_1 \cdots \alpha_n} = \left[v(\alpha_j, \alpha_\ell), j, \ell = 1,2, \cdots, n \right].$$

Let us show first that μ is well defined on $\mathfrak{F}$, i.e., $\mu(E)$ as defined by (2) does not depend on the representation (1) of E. In 4°, Remark 2.2 we defined that a representation (1) of E is a minimal representation if B is not the Cartesian product of R^1 and a member of $\mathfrak{B}^{n-1}$. R^A is the only member of $\mathfrak{F}$ which does not have a minimal representation. For any $E \in \mathfrak{F}$, $E \neq R^A$, if (1) is not already a minimal representation then there exists a permutation $\Pi = \{\Pi_1, \cdots, \Pi_n\}$ of $\{1, \cdots, n\}$ such that $E = p_{\alpha_{\Pi_1} \cdots \alpha_{\Pi_n}}^{-1}\left(\Pi(B)\right)$ where $\Pi(B) = B' \times R^1$, $B' \in \mathfrak{B}^{n-1}$. Then

$$E = p_{\alpha_{\Pi_1} \cdots \alpha_{\Pi_{n-1}}}^{-1}(B'). \tag{3}$$

If (3) is not a minimal representation yet, repeat the process until we arrive at a minimal representation. The fact that at each stage the two values of $\mu(E)$ corresponding to the two representations of E are actually equal can be seen as follows. Applying (2) to (3) we have

$$\mu(E) = \int_{R^{n-1}} \chi_{B'}(y)\, \tilde{\Phi}(dy) \tag{4}$$

where

$$\tilde{\Phi} = N\left(\left[m(\alpha_{\Pi_1}), \cdots, m(\alpha_{\Pi_{n-1}})\right], \left[v(\alpha_{\Pi_j}, \alpha_{\Pi_\ell}),\ j, \ell = 1, 2, \cdots, n-1\right]\right).$$

On the other hand, applying (2) to (1) we have

$$\mu(E) = \int_{R^n} \chi_B(x)\, \Phi(dx) = \int_{R^n} \chi_{B'}(x_{\Pi_1}, \cdots, x_{\Pi_{n-1}})\, \Phi(dx), \tag{5}$$

where

$$\Phi = N\left(\left[m(\alpha_1), \cdots, m(\alpha_n)\right], \left[v(\alpha_j, \alpha_\ell),\ j, \ell = 1, 2, \cdots, n\right]\right).$$

The fact that the two integrals (4) and (5) are equal is guaranteed by Lemma 16.7. Now consider two minimal representations of E given by

$$E = p_{\alpha_1 \cdots \alpha_n}^{-1}(B_1) \quad \text{where} \quad B_1 \in \mathfrak{B}^n \quad \text{and}$$

$$E = p_{\beta_1 \cdots \beta_m}^{-1}(B_2) \quad \text{where} \quad B_2 \in \mathfrak{B}^m.$$

According to 5° of Remark 2.2, $m = n$, $\{\beta_1, \cdots, \beta_n\} = \{\alpha_{\Pi_1}, \cdots, \alpha_{\Pi_n}\}$, and $B_2 = \Pi(B_1)$ for some permutation $\Pi = \{\Pi_1, \cdots, \Pi_n\}$ of $\{1, \cdots, n\}$. Again by Lemma 16.7, $\mu(E)$ has the same value for these two representations. This completes the proof of the well definedness of μ on $\mathfrak{Z}$.

For each fixed $\{\alpha_1, \cdots, \alpha_n\}$, μ defined by (1) is clearly a probability measure on $\mathfrak{Z}_{\alpha_1 \cdots \alpha_n}$. Thus according to the Kolmogorov Extension Theorem (Theorem 2.1), μ can be extended uniquely to be a probability measure on the σ-field $\sigma(\mathfrak{Z})$ generated by $\mathfrak{Z}$.

On the probability space $\left(R^A, \sigma(\mathfrak{Z}), \mu\right)$ thus constructed define a system of random variables $\mathfrak{X} = \left\{X(\alpha, \cdot),\ \alpha \in A\right\}$ by

$$X(\alpha, \omega) = \omega(\alpha) \quad \text{for } \omega \in R^A.$$

Then, for $\{\alpha_1, \cdots, \alpha_n\} \subset A$ and $B \in \mathfrak{B}^n$,

$$\mu\left\{\omega \in R^A;\ \left[X(\alpha_1, \omega), \cdots, X(\alpha_n, \omega)\right] \in B\right\}$$
$$= \mu\left\{\omega \in R^A;\ \left[\omega(\alpha_1), \cdots, \omega(\alpha_n)\right] \in B\right\}$$
$$= \mu\left(p_{\alpha_1 \cdots \alpha_n}^{-1}(B)\right) = \int_{R^n} \chi_B(x)\, \Phi_{\alpha_1 \cdots \alpha_n}(dx),$$

so that $\mathfrak{X}$ is a Gaussian system and in particular the mean and the covariance functions of $\mathfrak{X}$ are given by m and v, respectively.□

[III] Enlarging a Given Gaussian System

From the definition of a Gaussian system it is obvious that any subcollection of a Gaussian system is itself a Gaussian system. Let us consider ways of enlarging a given Gaussian system.

Theorem 16.9 The collection of all linear combinations of members of a Gaussian system is a Gaussian system. Furthermore if $X_1, \cdots, X_n$ are n random variables from a Gaussian system then the mean vector and the covariance matrix of the k-dimensional normal distribution of the random vector $(Y_1, \cdots, Y_k)$ where

$Y_p = \sum_{j=1}^{n} a_{pj} X_j$, $p = 1,2,\cdots,k$, and $\{a_{pj}, p = 1,2,\cdots,k; j = 1,2,\cdots,n\} \subset R^1$, are given by

$$\left[\sum_{j=1}^{n} a_{pj} E(X_j),\ p = 1,2,\cdots,k\right]$$

and

$$\left[\sum_{j=1}^{n} \sum_{\ell=1}^{n} a_{pj} a_{q\ell} C(X_j, X_\ell),\ p, q = 1,2,\cdots,k\right],$$

respectively.

Proof The first statement of the theorem is obvious from Theorem 16.4. Thus, in particular, the probability distribution of our $(Y_1, \cdots, Y_k)$ is a k-dimensional normal distribution $N(m, V)$ where the components of m and V are found as follows:

$$m_p = E(Y_p) = \sum_{j=1}^{n} a_{pj} E(X_j) \quad \text{for } p = 1,2,\cdots,k$$

$$\begin{aligned} v_{pq} &= C(Y_p, Y_q) = E\left[\{Y_p - E(Y_p)\}\{Y_q - E(Y_q)\}\right] \\ &= E\left[\sum_{j=1}^{n} a_{pj} \{X_j - E(X_j)\} \cdot \sum_{\ell=1}^{n} a_{q\ell} \{X_\ell - E(X_\ell)\}\right] \\ &= \sum_{j=1}^{n} \sum_{\ell=1}^{n} a_{pj} a_{q\ell} C(X_j, X_\ell) \quad \text{for } p, q = 1,2,\cdots,k. \end{aligned}$$

This completes the proof of the theorem. □

Lemma 16.10 If a sequence of n-dimensional normal distributions $\{\Phi_k, k = 1,2,\cdots\}$ converges to an n-dimensional distribution Φ_0 then Φ_0 is an n-dimensional normal distribution.

Furthermore if $\Phi_k = N\left(m^{(k)}, V^{(k)}\right)$, $k = 0,1,2,\cdots$, then $\left\{m^{(k)}, k = 1,2,\cdots\right\}$ and $\left\{V^{(k)}, k = 1,2,\cdots\right\}$ converge componentwise to $m^{(0)}$ and $V^{(0)}$, respectively.

Proof Let φ_k be the characteristic function of Φ_k for $k = 0,1,2,\cdots$. Then

$$\varphi_k(y) = \exp\left\{i\left(m^{(k)}, y\right) - \tfrac{1}{2}\left(V^{(k)}y, y\right)\right\} \quad \text{for } k = 1,2,\cdots, \tag{1}$$

and, according to (1) of Theorem A4.3,

$$\lim_{k\to\infty} \varphi_k(y) = \varphi_0(y) \text{ uniformly on every compact subset of } R^n. \tag{2}$$

Taking the absolute values in (2) and using (1) we have

$$\lim_{k\to\infty} \exp\left\{-\tfrac{1}{2}\left(V^{(k)}y, y\right)\right\} = |\varphi_0(y)|. \tag{3}$$

Since φ_0 is a characteristic function it is continuous on R^n and $\varphi_0(0) = 1$. Thus there exists $\delta > 0$ such that $\varphi(y) \neq 0$ for y in a cube of side 2δ and centered at $0 \in R^n$. To show the convergence of $\left\{v_{j\ell}^{(k)}, k = 1,2,\cdots\right\}$, $1 \le j, \ell \le n$, take the vector $a \in R^n$ whose z^{th} and ℓ^{th} components are equal to δ and other components are equal to 0. Then from the symmetry of $V^{(k)}$, $\left(V^{(k)}a, a\right) = 2\delta^2 v_{j\ell}$, so that (3) reduces to

$$\lim_{k\to\infty} \exp\left\{-\delta^2 v_{j\ell}^{(k)}\right\} = |\varphi_0(a)|.$$

Taking the logarithm in the sense of real variable, we have

$$\lim_{k\to\infty} -\delta^2 v_{j\ell}^{(k)} = \operatorname{Log} |\varphi_0(a)|,$$

and hence

$$\lim_{\ell\to\infty} v_{j\ell}^{(k)} = -\frac{1}{\delta^2} \operatorname{Log} |\varphi_0(a)|.$$

This proves the componentwise convergence of $\{V^{(k)}, k = 1,2, \cdots\}$. Let $V^{(0)}$ be the matrix whose components are the limits of the components of $V^{(k)}, k = 1,2, \cdots$.

Now let

$$\psi_k(y) = \varphi_k(y) \exp\left\{\tfrac{1}{2}(V^{(k)}y, y)\right\} = \exp\left\{i\,(m^{(k)}, y)\right\} \quad \text{for } k = 1,2, \cdots,$$

$$\psi_0(y) = \varphi_0(y) \exp\left\{\tfrac{1}{2}(V^{(0)}y, y)\right\}.$$

From the convergence of $\varphi_k(y)$ and $\exp\left\{\tfrac{1}{2}(V^{(k)}y, y)\right\}$, $k = 1,2, \cdots$, we have the convergence of $\exp\left\{i\,(m^{(k)}, y)\right\}$, $k = 1,2, \cdots$. In letting y be the vector whose only nonvanishing component is the jth component which is equal to 1, we have the convergence of $\exp\left\{i\, m_j^{(k)}\right\}$, $k = 1,2, \cdots$. However, this does not yet imply the convergence of $m_j^{(k)}, k = 1,2, \cdots$. Let S be the set consisting of those points $y \in R^n$ for which $y_j \in [0, 1]$ and $y_\ell = 0$ for $\ell \neq j$. Then

$$\psi_k(y) = \varphi_k(y) \exp\left\{\tfrac{1}{2} v_{jj}^{(k)} y_j^2\right\} = \exp\left\{i\, m_j^{(k)} y_j\right\} \quad \text{for } y_j \in [0, 1],\ k = 1,2, \cdots$$

$$\psi_0(y) = \varphi_0(y) \exp\left\{\tfrac{1}{2} v_{jj}^{(0)} y_j^2\right\} \quad \text{for } y_j \in [0, 1].$$

According to (2), $\lim_{k\to\infty} \varphi_k(y) = \varphi_0(y)$ uniformly for $y \in S$. To show the uniform convergence of the exponential factors, observe that

$$\left| \exp\left\{\tfrac{1}{2} v_{jj}^{(k)} y_j^2\right\} - \exp\left\{\tfrac{1}{2} v_{jj}^{(0)} y_j^2\right\} \right|$$

$$= \begin{cases} \exp\left\{\tfrac{1}{2} v_{jj}^{(0)} y_j^2\right\} \left[\exp\left\{\tfrac{1}{2}\left(v_{jj}^{(k)} - v_{jj}^{(0)}\right) y_j^2\right\} - 1\right] & \text{if } v_{jj}^{(k)} \ge v_{jj}^{(0)} \\ \exp\left\{\tfrac{1}{2} v_{jj}^{(k)} y_j^2\right\} \left[\exp\left\{\tfrac{1}{2}\left(v_{jj}^{(0)} - v_{jj}^{(k)}\right) y_j^2\right\} - 1\right] & \text{if } v_{jj}^{(k)} \le v_{jj}^{(0)}, \end{cases}$$

so that in any case the maximum over S is attained when $y_j = 1$. But for $y_j = 1$ we have, from $\lim_{k\to\infty} v_{jj}^{(k)} = v_{jj}^{(0)}$,

$$\lim_{k\to\infty} \left| \exp\left\{\tfrac{1}{2} v_{jj}^{(k)}\right\} - \exp\left\{\tfrac{1}{2} v_{jj}^{(0)}\right\} \right| = 0\,.$$

Thus

$$\lim_{k\to\infty} \exp\left\{\tfrac{1}{2} v_{jj}^{(k)} y_j^2\right\} = \exp\left\{\tfrac{1}{2} v_{jj}^{(0)} y_j^2\right\} \quad \text{uniformly for } y_j \in [0,1].$$

Therefore we have shown that $\psi_k(y) = \exp\left\{i\, m_j^{(k)} y_j\right\}, k = 1,2,\cdots,$ converges uniformly for $y \in S$, so that for every $\varepsilon > 0$ there exists K such that

$$|\psi_{k'}(y) - \psi_{k''}(y)| < \varepsilon \quad \text{for all } y \in S \text{ whenever } k', k'' \ge K. \tag{4}$$

Consider the path C_k on the complex plane defined by

$$C_k : z(y) = \psi_k(y) = \exp\left\{i\, m_j^{(k)} y_j\right\} \quad \text{for } y \in S, \text{ i.e., } y_j \in [0,1].$$

C_k starts at $z = 1$, winds around the unit circle in the direction determined by the sign of $m_j^{(k)}$, and ends at $z = \exp\{i\, m_j^{(k)}\}$. From (4), for every $\epsilon > 0$, there exists K such that

$$\left| \int_{C_{k'}} \frac{1}{z}\, dz - \int_{C_{k''}} \frac{1}{z}\, dz \right| < \epsilon \quad \text{for } k', k'' \geq K .$$

But

$$\int_{C_k} \frac{1}{z}\, dz = \int_0^1 i\, m_j^{(k)}\, dy_j = i\, m_j^{(k)} .$$

Thus

$$|m_j^{(k')} - m_j^{(k'')}| < \epsilon \qquad \text{for } k', k'' \geq K .$$

This proves the convergence of $m_j^{(k)}, k = 1, 2, \cdots$. Let $m_j^{(0)} = \lim_{k\to\infty} m_j^{(k)}$, $j = 1, 2, \cdots, n$. Then

$$\begin{aligned} \varphi_0(y) &= \lim_{k\to\infty} \varphi_k(y) \\ &= \lim_{k\to\infty} \exp\left\{ i\left(m^{(k)}y, y\right) - \tfrac{1}{2}\left(V^{(k)}y, y\right) \right\} \\ &= \exp\left\{ i\left(m^{(0)}y, y\right) - \tfrac{1}{2}\left(V^{(0)}y, y\right) \right\} . \end{aligned}$$

This completes the proof of the lemma. □

Theorem 16.11 The collection $\mathfrak{Y}$ of all limits of convergence in probability of sequences of members in a Gaussian system $\mathfrak{X}$ is again a Gaussian system.

Proof To show that $\mathfrak{Y}$ is a Gaussian system we show that, for any $\{Y_j, j = 1, 2, \cdots n\} \subset \mathfrak{Y}$, the probability distribution of the random vector $Y = (Y_1, \cdots, Y_n)$ is an n-dimensional normal distribution. Let $Y_j = P - \lim_{k\to\infty} X_{jk}$ where $X_{jk} \in \mathfrak{X}$ for $k = 1,2,\cdots$, and $j = 1,2,\cdots,n$, and let $X_k = (X_{1,k},\cdots,X_{n,k})$ for $k = 1,2,\cdots$. From the contrapositive of the statement that if the lengths of all the n adjacent sides of an n-dimensional rectangle are less than $\epsilon n^{-\frac{1}{2}}$ then the length of the diagonal is less than ϵ, we have

$$P\{\omega \in \Omega ; \; |X_k(\omega) - Y(\omega)| \geq \epsilon\} \leq \sum_{j=1}^{n} P\left\{\omega \in \Omega ; |X_{jk}(\omega) - Y_j(\omega)| \geq \frac{\epsilon}{\sqrt{n}}\right\} .$$

The sum of the right side can be made as small as we wish for sufficiently large k since $Y_j = P - \lim_{k\to\infty} X_{jk}$ for $j = 1,2,\cdots,n$. Thus $Y = P - \lim_{k\to\infty} X_k$. Since $\mathfrak{X}$ is a Gaussian system the probability distributions of $X_k, k = 1,2,\cdots$, are n-dimensional normal distributions, and these converge to the probability distribution of Y according to (3) of Theorem A5.4. Then by Lemma 16.10, the probability distribution of Y is an n-dimensional normal distribution. □

[IV] Independence and Gaussian System

<u>Theorem 16.12</u> If $\{X_1,\cdots,X_n\}$ is an independent system of random variables and the probability distribution of X_j is given by $N(m_j, v_j)$ for $j = 1,2,\cdots,n$, then the probability distribution of the random vector $(X_1,\cdots,X_n)$ is given by $N(m, V)$ where $m = (m_1,\cdots,m_n)$ and V is a diagonal matrix whose diagonal entries are $v_1,\cdots,v_n$. Consequently if $\mathfrak{X}$ is an independent system of random variables each of which is normally distributed then $\mathfrak{X}$ is a Gaussian system.

<u>Proof</u> Let $\varphi_j(y_j)$, $y_j \in R^1, j = 1,2,\cdots,n$, and $\varphi(y), y \in R^n$,

be the characteristic functions of $X_j, j = 1,2,\cdots,n$, and $(X_1,\cdots,X_n)$, respectively. Since $\{X_1,\cdots,X_n\}$ is an independent system, we have, by Theorem A6.4,

$$\varphi(y) = \prod_{j=1}^{n} \varphi_j(y_j) = \prod_{j=1}^{n} \exp\left\{i\, m_j y_j - \tfrac{1}{2} v_j y_j^2\right\} = \exp\left\{i\,(m,y) - \tfrac{1}{2}(Vy,y)\right\}.$$

Thus the probability distribution of $(X_1,\cdots,X_n)$ is given by $N(m,V)$. □

<u>Theorem 16.13</u> Let $\{X_1,\cdots,X_n\}$ be a Gaussian system of random variables. Then the system is independent if and only if $C(X_j,X_\ell) = 0$ for $j \neq \ell$.

<u>Proof</u> In general if $\{X_1,\cdots,X_n\}$ is an independent system of random variables each having a finite second moment, then, for $j \neq \ell$,

$$C(X_j,X_\ell) = E\left[X_j - E(X_j)\right] E\left[X_\ell - E(X_\ell)\right] = 0.$$

On the other hand if $\{X_1,\cdots,X_n\}$ is a Gaussian system, then the probability distribution of the random vector $(X_1,\cdots,X_n)$ is an n-dimensional normal distribution $N(m,V)$ with the characteristic function

$$\varphi(y) = \exp\left\{i(m,y) - \tfrac{1}{2}(Vy,y)\right\} \quad \text{for } y \in R^n,$$

where

$$m = \left[E(X_j), j = 1,2,\cdots,n\right] \quad \text{and} \quad V = \left\{C(X_j,X_\ell), j,\ell = 1,2,\cdots,n\right\}.$$

If $C(X_j,X_\ell) = 0$ for $j \neq \ell$ then, with the variance of X_j, $V(X_j) = C(X_j,X_j)$, φ reduces to

$$\varphi(y) = \prod_{j=1}^{n} \exp\left\{i\, m_j y_j - \tfrac{1}{2} V(X_j)\, y_j^{\,2}\right\} = \prod_{j=1}^{n} \varphi_j(y_j),$$

where φ_j is the characteristic function of X_j for $j = 1, 2, \cdots, n$. According to Theorem A6.4, this proves the independence of the system $\{X_1, \cdots, X_n\}$.

[V] Expectations of Quadratic Forms in Normally Distributed Random Vectors

For an n-dimensional random vector $(X_1, \cdots, X_n)$ on a probability space whose probability distribution is an n-dimensional normal distribution with mean vector m and covariance matrix V, all the moments exist and in fact can be calculated according to Theorem A3.4 by

$$E\left(X_1^{p_1} \cdots X_n^{p_n}\right) = \frac{1}{i^{p_1 + \cdots + p_n}} \left. \frac{\partial^{p_1 + \cdots + p_n}}{\partial y_1^{p_1} \cdots \partial y_n^{p_n}} e^{i(m,y) - \frac{1}{2}(Vy,y)} \right|_{y=0} .$$

From this the expectation of any polynomial in the variables $X_1, \cdots, X_n$ can be obtained. For quadratic forms and powers of quadratic forms in $X_1, \cdots, X_n$ there is an alternate way of calculation.

Lemma 16.14 Let A and C be $n \times n$ symmetric matrices of real numbers and let A be positive definite. Then there exists $\varepsilon_0 > 0$ such that, for every real ε with $|\varepsilon| < \varepsilon_0$, the symmetric matrix $A + \varepsilon C$ is positive definite.

Proof Since A is symmetric, an arbitrary orthonormal system of eigenvectors $\{e_1, \cdots, e_n\}$ corresponding to the eigenvalues $\{\lambda_1, \cdots, \lambda_n\}$ of A spans R^n, and for every $x = x_1 e_1 + \cdots + x_n e_n \in R^n$ we have $(Ax, x) = \sum_{k=1}^n \lambda_k x_k^2$. Since A is positive definite every eigenvalue is positive. Let $\lambda_0 = \min\{\lambda_1, \cdots \lambda_n\} > 0$. Then

$$(Ax, x) \geq \lambda_0 \sum_{k=1}^{n} x_k^2 = \lambda_0 \|x\|^2 \quad \text{for every } x \in R^n.$$

On the other hand, writing $\|C\|$ for the norm of C as a bounded linear operator on R^n, we have

$$|(Cx, x)| \leq \|Cx\| \, \|x\| \leq \|C\| \, \|x\|^2 \quad \text{for every } x \in R^n.$$

Thus for real ε we have

$$\big([A + \varepsilon C]x, x\big) = (Ax, x) + \varepsilon(Cx, x) \geq \big\{\lambda_0 - |\varepsilon| \, \|C\|\big\} \, \|x\|^2.$$

Let $\varepsilon_0 > 0$ be so chosen that $\lambda_0 - \varepsilon_0 \|C\| > 0$. Then, for real ε with $|\varepsilon| < \varepsilon_0$, $\big([A + \varepsilon C]x, x\big) \geq 0$ for every $x \in R^n$ and $\big([A + \varepsilon C]x, x\big) = 0$ implies $\|x\| = 0$ so that $A + \varepsilon C$ is positive definite. □

<u>Lemma 16.15</u> Let A and C be $n \times n$ symmetric matrices of real numbers and let A be positive definite. Then

$$\left\{\frac{\det A}{(2\pi)^n}\right\}^{\frac{1}{2}} \int_{R^n} (Cx, x) \exp\left\{-\tfrac{1}{2}(Ax, x)\right\} m_L(dx) = \operatorname{Tr}(CA^{-1}) \tag{1}$$

and

$$\left\{\frac{\det A}{(2\pi)^n}\right\}^{\frac{1}{2}} \int_{R^n} (Cx, x)^2 \exp\left\{-\tfrac{1}{2}(Ax, x)\right\} m_L(dx)$$
$$= 3\sum_{j=1}^{n} b_{jj}^{\,2} + 2\sum_{j=1}^{n} \sum_{j<\ell} \left(b_{jj} b_{\ell\ell} + 2b_{j\ell}^{\,2}\right), \tag{2}$$

where $[b_{j\ell}] = CA^{-1}$ and $\mathrm{Tr}(CA^{-1}) = \sum_{j=1}^{n} b_{jj}$.

<u>Proof</u> Every positive definite symmetric matrix B can be written as $B = M'M$ where M is a nonsingular matrix. By the transformation $y = Mx$, for which the Jacobian is given by $|\det M|$, we have

$$(Bx, x) = (Mx, Mx) = (y, y) = \sum_{j=1}^{n} y_j^2 \quad \text{and} \quad \det B = (\det M)^2.$$

Thus

$$\left\{\frac{\det B}{(2\pi)^n}\right\}^{\frac{1}{2}} \int_{R^n} \exp\left\{-\tfrac{1}{2}(Bx, x)\right\} m_L(dx)$$

$$= \left\{\frac{1}{\sqrt{2\pi}} \int_{R^1} \exp\left\{-\frac{y_j^2}{2}\right\} m_L(dy_j)\right\}^n = 1. \tag{3}$$

According to Lemma 16.14 there exists $\epsilon_0 > 0$ such that, for real ϵ with $|\epsilon| < \epsilon_0$, $A + \epsilon C$ is positive definite. By

$$\det(A + \epsilon C) = \det(I + \epsilon CA^{-1}) \det A$$

and by (3), we have

$$\left\{\frac{\det A}{(2\pi)^n}\right\}^{\frac{1}{2}} \int_{R^n} \exp\left\{-\tfrac{1}{2}\left([A + \epsilon C]x, x\right)\right\} m_L(dx) = \left\{\det(I + \epsilon CA^{-1})\right\}^{-\frac{1}{2}}. \tag{4}$$

Writing $[b_{ij}] = CA^{-1}$ we have

$$\det(I+\epsilon CA^{-1}) = \begin{vmatrix} 1+\epsilon b_{11} & \epsilon b_{12} & \epsilon b_{13} & \cdots & \epsilon b_{1n} \\ \epsilon b_{21} & 1+\epsilon b_{22} & \epsilon b_{23} & & \epsilon b_{2n} \\ \epsilon b_{31} & \epsilon b_{32} & 1+\epsilon b_{33} & & \epsilon b_{3n} \\ \vdots & \vdots & \vdots & & \vdots \\ \epsilon b_{n1} & \epsilon b_{n2} & \epsilon b_{n3} & & 1+\epsilon b_{nn} \end{vmatrix}$$

$$= 1 + \left\{\sum_{j=1}^{n} b_{jj}\right\}\epsilon + \left\{\sum_{j=1}^{n}\sum_{j<\ell}\left(b_{jj}b_{\ell\ell} - b_{j\ell}^{2}\right)\right\}\epsilon^2 + \cdots . \tag{5}$$

The coefficient of ϵ^2 in (5) is obtained by developing the determinant along the first row. In doing so we consider the 2nd, 3rd, $\cdots$, and n^{th} entries in the 1st row times their respective cofactors and finally the 1st entry of the 1st row times its cofactor. This last cofactor is then developed in the same way as above. We repeat this process to obtain

$$-\left\{b_{12}b_{21} + b_{13}b_{31} + b_{14}b_{41} + \cdots + b_{1n}b_{n1}\right\} + b_{11}\left\{b_{22} + b_{33} + b_{44} + \cdots + b_{nn}\right\}$$

$$-\left\{b_{23}b_{32} + b_{24}b_{42} + \cdots + b_{2n}b_{n2}\right\} + b_{22}\left\{b_{33} + b_{44} + \cdots + b_{nn}\right\}$$

$$\vdots$$

$$- b_{n-1,n}b_{n,n-1} + b_{n-1,n-1}b_{nn} = \sum_{j=1}^{n}\sum_{j<\ell}\left\{b_{jj}b_{\ell\ell} - b_{j\ell}^{2}\right\}.$$

Combining

$$(1 + a\epsilon + b\epsilon^2 + \cdots)^{-1} = 1 - a\epsilon + (a^2 - b)\epsilon^2 + \cdots$$

and

$$(1 + \alpha\epsilon + \beta\epsilon^2 + \cdots)^{\frac{1}{2}} = 1 + \frac{\alpha}{2}\epsilon + \tfrac{1}{2}(\beta - \frac{\alpha^2}{4})\epsilon^2 + \cdots ,$$

we have

$$(1+a\varepsilon+b\varepsilon^2+\cdots)^{-\frac{1}{2}} = 1-\frac{a}{2}\varepsilon+\left(\frac{3a^2}{8}-\frac{b}{2}\right)\varepsilon^2+\cdots .$$

Applying this to (5) we obtain

$$\left\{\det(I+\varepsilon CA^{-1})\right\}^{-\frac{1}{2}}$$

$$= 1-\tfrac{1}{2}\operatorname{Tr}(CA^{-1})\varepsilon$$

$$+\left\{\tfrac{3}{8}\left[\operatorname{Tr}(CA^{-1})\right]^2-\tfrac{1}{2}\sum_{j=1}^{n}\sum_{j<\ell}\left(b_{jj}b_{\ell\ell}-b_{j\ell}^{2}\right)\right\}\varepsilon^2+\cdots$$

$$= 1-\tfrac{1}{2}\operatorname{Tr}(CA^{-1})\varepsilon$$

$$+\tfrac{1}{2}\left\{\tfrac{3}{4}\left[\sum_{j=1}^{n}b_{jj}^{2}+2\sum_{j=1}^{n}\sum_{j<\ell}b_{jj}b_{\ell\ell}\right]-\sum_{j=1}^{n}\sum_{j<\ell}\left(b_{jj}b_{\ell\ell}-b_{j\ell}^{2}\right)\right\}\varepsilon^2+\cdots$$

$$= 1-\tfrac{1}{2}\operatorname{Tr}(CA^{-1})\varepsilon$$

$$+\tfrac{1}{2}\left\{\tfrac{3}{4}\sum_{j=1}^{n}b_{jj}^{2}+\tfrac{1}{2}\sum_{j=1}^{n}\sum_{j<\ell}b_{jj}b_{\ell\ell}+\sum_{j=1}^{n}\sum_{j<\ell}b_{j\ell}^{2}\right\}\varepsilon^2+\cdots . \quad (6)$$

On the other hand by (4),

$$\left\{\det(I+\varepsilon CA^{-1})\right\}^{-\frac{1}{2}}$$

$$= \left\{\frac{\det A}{(2\pi)^n}\right\}^{\frac{1}{2}}\int_{R^n}\exp\left\{-\tfrac{1}{2}(Ax,x)\right\}\exp\left\{-\tfrac{1}{2}\varepsilon(Cx,x)\right\}m_L(dx). \quad (7)$$

Equating the right side of (7) to that of (6) and then differentiating both sides with respect to ε and setting $\varepsilon = 0$ we obtain (1). Similarly differentiating with respect to ε twice and setting $\varepsilon = 0$ we obtain (2). □

<u>Theorem 16.16</u> Let $X = (X_1, \cdots, X_n)$ be an n-dimensional

random vector on a probability space whose probability distribution is an n-dimensional normal distribution with zero mean vector and covariance matrix V. Then for an $n \times n$ symmetric matrix C of real numbers we have

$$E\left[(CX, X)\right] = \mathrm{Tr}(CV) \tag{1}$$

and

$$E\left[(CX, X)^2\right] = 3\sum_{j=1}^{n} b_{jj}^{2} + 2\sum_{j=1}^{n}\sum_{j<\ell}(b_{jj}b_{\ell\ell} + 2b_{j\ell}^{2}),$$

$$\text{where } [b_{j\ell}] = CV. \tag{2}$$

Proof When V is positive definite then the n-dimensional normal distribution of X has the density function

$$\frac{1}{\left\{(2\pi)^n \det V\right\}^{\frac{1}{2}}} \exp\left\{-\tfrac{1}{2}(V^{-1}x, x)\right\} \quad \text{for } x \in R^n.$$

In this case (1) and (2) follow from (1) and (2) of Lemma 16.15 by identifying our V^{-1} with A in Lemma 16.15. On the other hand when V is nonnegative definite we can always calculate $E\left[(CX, X)\right]$ and $E\left[(CX, X)^2\right]$ by using

$$E\left(X_1^{p_1} \cdots X_n^{p_n}\right) = \frac{1}{i^{p_1 + \cdots + p_n}} \left. \frac{\partial^{p_1 + \cdots + p_n}}{\partial y_1^{p_1} \cdots \partial y_n^{p_n}} e^{-\frac{1}{2}(Vy, y)} \right|_{y=0},$$

and the results will be a polynomial in the entries of V and C in the same way whether V is positive definite or not. Thus (1) and (2) hold even when V is merely nonnegative definite. □

§17. BROWNIAN MOTION PROCESS AS GAUSSIAN PROCESS

With $D = [0, \infty)$ let $a(t)$, $t \in D$, be a continuous real-valued function and $b(t)$, $t \in D$, be a continuous monotone increasing function. Let

$$\Phi_{t't''} = N\Big(a(t'') - a(t'),\ b(t'') - b(t')\Big) \quad \text{for } t', t'' \in D,\ t' < t'',$$

$$\Phi_0 = \Phi_E(c), \text{ a translated unit distribution with } \Phi_0\Big(\{c\}\Big) = 1.$$

Since $\Phi_{t_1 t_2} * \Phi_{t_2 t_3} = \Phi_{t_1 t_3}$ for $t_1, t_2, t_3 \in D$, $t_1 < t_2 < t_3$, by Lemma 13.2, there exists according to Theorem 12.3 an additive process X on a probability space $(\Omega, \mathfrak{B}, P)$ and D such that the probability distribution of $X(t'', \cdot) - X(t', \cdot)$, $t', t'' \in D$, $t' < t''$, is given by $\Phi_{t't''}$, and the probability distribution of $X(0, \cdot)$ is given by Φ_0, i.e., $X(0, \omega) = c$ for a.e. $\omega \in \Omega$. Let us call this process X a generalized Brownian motion process. When $a(t) = 0$, $b(t) = t$ for $t \in D$ and $c = 0$ we have the standard Brownian motion process. Let us note that we can proceed as in the proof of Theorem 14.2 using Lemma 14.1 to construct a generalized Brownian motion process in which the sample functions are continuous.

<u>Theorem 17.1</u> A generalized Brownian motion process X determined by a continuous real-valued function a, a continuous monotone increasing function b on $D = [0, \infty)$, and a translated unit distribution $\Phi_E(c)$ is a Gaussian process whose mean and covariance functions are given by

$$m(t) = E\Big[X(t, \cdot)\Big] = a(t) - a(0) + c \qquad \text{for } t \in D$$

$$v(s, t) = C\Big[X(s, \cdot),\ X(t, \cdot)\Big] = b\Big(\min\{s, t\}\Big) - b(0) \quad \text{for } s, t \in D.$$

In particular, for the standard Brownian motion process in which $a(t) = 0$, $b(t) = t$, $t \in D$, and $c = 0$, we have

$$m(t) = 0 \qquad \text{for } t \in D$$

$$v(s,t) = \min\{s,t\} \qquad \text{for } s,t \in D.$$

<u>Proof</u> Let us show that, for $0 = t_0 < t_1 < \cdots < t_n$, the probability distribution of the random vector $[X(t_1, \cdot), \cdots, X(t_n, \cdot)]$ is an n-dimensional normal distribution. Once this is done then from the independence of the two random vectors $X(t_0, \cdot) = c$, a.e. on Ω and $[X(t_1, \cdot), \cdots, X(t_n, \cdot)]$ we conclude that the probability distribution of the random vector $[X(t_0, \cdot), X(t_1, \cdot), \cdots, X(t_n, \cdot)]$ is an $n+1$-dimensional normal distribution by considering its characteristic function which is the product of the characteristic functions of the two random vectors.

Now let

$$Y_j = X(t_j, \cdot) - X(t_{j-1}, \cdot) \qquad \text{for } j = 1,2,\cdots,n.$$

Then $\{Y_j, j = 1,2,\cdots,n\}$ is an independent system of random variables each of which is normally distributed so that according to Theorem 16.12 it is a Gaussian system. Let

$$S_j = \sum_{p=1}^{j} Y_p = X(t_j, \cdot) - X(t_0, \cdot) \qquad \text{for } j = 1,2,\cdots,n.$$

By Theorem 16.9, $\{S_j, j = 1,2,\cdots,n\}$ is a Gaussian system and hence the probability distribution of the random vector $(S_1, \cdots, S_n)$ is an n-dimensional normal distribution. Let us find the mean vector and the covariance matrix of this n-dimensional normal distribution. Now

$$E(S_j) = E\left[X(t_j, \cdot) - X(t_0, \cdot)\right] = a(t_j) - a(0) \quad \text{for } j = 1, 2, \cdots, n.$$

To calculate $C(S_j, S_k)$ for $j, k = 1, 2, \cdots, n$, let us note that if $\{Z_1, \cdots, Z_n\}$ is an independent system of random variables and $\{\zeta_1, \cdots, \zeta_n\} \subset R^1$ then $\{Z_1, \cdots, Z_n, \zeta_1, \cdots, \zeta_n\}$ is an independent system of $2n$ random variables, consequently $\{[Z_1, \zeta_1], \cdots, [Z_n, \zeta_n]\}$ is an independent system of n 2-dimensional random vectors by (1) of Theorem A6.5, and finally $\{Z_1 + \zeta_1, \cdots, Z_n + \zeta_n\}$ is an independent system of n random variables by Theorem A6.6. Thus $\left\{Y_j - E(Y_j),\ j = 1, 2, \cdots, n\right\}$ is an independent system of random variables so that, for $j \le k$, we have

$$\begin{aligned} C(S_j, S_k) &= E\left[\left\{S_j - E(S_k)\right\}\left\{S_k - E(S_k)\right\}\right] \\ &= E\left[\sum_{p=1}^{j}\left\{Y_p - E(Y_p)\right\} \cdot \sum_{q=1}^{k}\left\{Y_q - E(Y_q)\right\}\right] \\ &= \sum_{p=1}^{j} E\left[\left\{Y_p - E(Y_p)\right\}^2\right] \\ &= \sum_{p=1}^{j}\left\{b(t_p) - b(t_{p-1})\right\} = b(t_j) - b(0). \end{aligned}$$

This establishes

$$C(S_j, S_k) = b\left(\min\{t_j, t_k\}\right) - b(0) \quad \text{for } j, k = 1, 2, \cdots, n.$$

Let us consider the random vector $\left[X(t_1, \cdot), \cdots, X(t_n, \cdot)\right]$. Recall that $X(t_j, \cdot) = S_j + X(t_0, \cdot)$. Since $X(t_0, \cdot) = c$ a.e., the two random vectors $(S_1, \cdots, S_n)$ and $X(t_0, \cdot)$ are independent. By considering the characteristic functions we conclude that the probability distribution of the random vector

$\left[S_1, \cdots, S_n, X(t_0, \cdot)\right]$ is an $n+1$-dimensional normal distribution. Then $\{S_1, \cdots, S_n, X(t_0, \cdot)\}$ is a Gaussian system and so is $\{S_1 + X(t_0, \cdot), \cdots, S_n + X(t_0, \cdot)\}$ by Theorem 16.9. So the probability distribution of the random vector

$$\left[X(t_1, \cdot), \cdots, X(t_n, \cdot)\right] = \left[S_1 + X(t_0, \cdot), \cdots, S_n + X(t_0, \cdot)\right]$$

is an n-dimensional normal distribution. Furthermore

$$E\left[X(t_j, \cdot)\right] = E\left[S_j + X(t_0, \cdot)\right] = a(t_j) - a(0) + c ,$$

$$C\left[X(t_j, \cdot), X(t_k, \cdot)\right] = C(S_j, S_k) = b\left(\min\{t_j, t_k\}\right) - b(0).$$

This proves the assertions about $m(t)$ and $v(s,t)$. □

<u>Lemma 17.2</u> Let $0 = \beta_0 \le \beta_1 \le \cdots \le \beta_n$ and $B = \left[\min\{\beta_j, \beta_k\}, \ j,k = 1,2,\cdots,n\right]$, i.e.,

$$B = \begin{bmatrix} \beta_1 & \beta_1 & \beta_1 & \cdots & \beta_1 \\ \beta_1 & \beta_2 & \beta_2 & \cdots & \beta_2 \\ \beta_1 & \beta_2 & \beta_3 & \cdots & \beta_3 \\ \vdots & \vdots & \vdots & & \vdots \\ \beta_1 & \beta_2 & \beta_3 & \cdots & \beta_n \end{bmatrix} \tag{1}$$

Then (1) $\det B = \prod_{j=1}^{n} (\beta_j - \beta_{j-1})$. In particular $\det B = 0$ if and only if $\beta_{j-1} = \beta_j$ for some $j = 1,2,\cdots,n$.

(2) B is positive definite if and only if $\beta_{j-1} < \beta_j$ for $j = 1,2,\cdots,n$.

(3) When $\beta_{j-1} < \beta_j$ for $j = 1,2,\cdots,n$, we have

$$
B^{-1} = \begin{bmatrix}
\frac{\beta_2}{\beta_1(\beta_2 - \beta_1)} & \frac{-1}{\beta_2 - \beta_1} & 0 & \cdots & 0 & 0 \\
\frac{-1}{\beta_2 - \beta_1} & \frac{\beta_3 - \beta_1}{(\beta_2 - \beta_1)(\beta_3 - \beta_2)} & \frac{-1}{\beta_3 - \beta_2} & \cdots & 0 & 0 \\
0 & \frac{-1}{\beta_3 - \beta_2} & \frac{\beta_4 - \beta_2}{(\beta_3 - \beta_2)(\beta_4 - \beta_3)} & \cdots & 0 & 0 \\
\cdots & \cdots & \cdots & & \vdots & \cdots \\
0 & 0 & 0 & \cdots & \frac{\beta_n - \beta_{n-2}}{(\beta_{n-1} - \beta_{n-2})(\beta_n - \beta_{n-1})} & \frac{-1}{\beta_n - \beta_{n-1}} \\
0 & 0 & 0 & \cdots & \frac{-1}{\beta_n - \beta_{n-1}} & \frac{1}{\beta_n - \beta_{n-1}}
\end{bmatrix} \qquad (2)
$$

If we write $\gamma_j = (\beta_j - \beta_{j-1})^{-1}$ for $j = 1, 2, \cdots, n$, then

$$B^{-1} = \begin{bmatrix} \gamma_1+\gamma_2 & -\gamma_2 & 0 & & & \\ -\gamma_2 & \gamma_2+\gamma_3 & -\gamma_3 & & & \\ 0 & -\gamma_3 & \gamma_3+\gamma_4 & & & \\ & & \ddots & \gamma_{n-2}+\gamma_{n-1} & -\gamma_{n-1} & 0 \\ & & & -\gamma_{n-1} & \gamma_{n-1}+\gamma_n & -\gamma_n \\ & & & 0 & -\gamma_n & \gamma_n \end{bmatrix} \tag{3}$$

and

$$\det B^{-1} = \begin{vmatrix} \gamma_1 & 0 & 0 & \cdots & 0 & 0 & 0 \\ -\gamma_2 & \gamma_2 & 0 & \cdots & 0 & 0 & 0 \\ 0 & -\gamma_3 & \gamma_3 & \cdots & 0 & 0 & 0 \\ \vdots & \vdots & & & \vdots & \vdots & \vdots \\ 0 & 0 & 0 & \cdots & \gamma_{n-2} & 0 & 0 \\ 0 & 0 & 0 & \cdots & -\gamma_{n-1} & \gamma_{n-1} & 0 \\ 0 & 0 & 0 & \cdots & 0 & -\gamma_n & \gamma_n \end{vmatrix} = \gamma_1 \gamma_2 \cdots \gamma_n. \tag{4}$$

Proof (1) To show that $\det B = \prod_{j=1}^{n} (\beta_j - \beta_{j-1})$, subtract the 1st row from the 2nd, 3rd, $\cdots$, and n^{th} row in the determinant of (1) to reduce it to an $n-1 \times n-1$ determinant and repeat the process of reduction.

(2) It is well known that a matrix $A = [a_{jk}, j, k = 1, 2, \cdots, n]$ is positive definite if and only if $\det A_p > 0$ for $p = 1, 2, \cdots, n$, where

$$A_p = \begin{bmatrix} a_{11} & \cdots & a_{1p} \\ \vdots & & \vdots \\ a_{p1} & \cdots & a_{pp} \end{bmatrix}.$$

From this fact and from (1), B is positive definite if and only if $\beta_j - \beta_{j-1} > 0$ for $j = 1,2,\cdots,n$.

(3) When $\beta_{j-1} < \beta_j$ for $j = 1,2,\cdots,n$, B is positive definite by part (2) so that B^{-1} exists. B^{-1} as given by (2) is obtained by direct inversion. It is easy to verify that B^{-1} as given by (2) indeed satisfies $B^{-1}B = BB^{-1} = I$. The expression (3) is immediate from the definition of $\gamma_j, j = 1,2,\cdots,n$. By adding the nth row to the $(n-1)^{st}$ row in (3) and then adding the resulting $(n-1)^{st}$ row to the $(n-2)^{nd}$ row and so forth, we obtain the first equality in (4). Obviously the equality $\det B^{-1} = \gamma_1\gamma_2\cdots\gamma_3$ holds by the definition of $\gamma_j, j = 1,2,\cdots,n$ and (1) without the aid of the first equality in (4). □

Theorem 17.3 Let X be the generalized Brownian motion process defined in Theorem 17.1. If $0 = t_0 < t_1 < \cdots < t_n$ and $b(t_j) - b(t_{j-1}) > 0$ for $j = 1,2,\cdots,n$, then the n-dimensional normal distribution Φ of the random vector $[X(t_1,\cdot),\cdots,X(t_n,\cdot)]$ has a density function Φ' which is given by

$$\Phi'(\xi) = \left\{(2\pi)^n \prod_{j=1}^{n} \left[b(t_j) - b(t_{j-1})\right]\right\}^{-\frac{1}{2}}$$

$$\exp\left\{-\frac{1}{2}\sum_{j=1}^{n} \frac{\left\{\left[\xi_j - a(t_j)\right] - \left[\xi_{j-1} - a(t_{j-1})\right]\right\}^2}{b(t_j) - b(t_{j-1})}\right\}, \qquad (1)$$

where $\xi_0 \equiv c$ for $\xi = (\xi_1, \cdots, \xi_n) \in R^n$. In particular, when X is the standard Brownian motion process,

$$\Phi'(\xi) = \left\{ (2\pi)^n \prod_{j=1}^{n} (t_j - t_{j-1}) \right\}^{-\frac{1}{2}} \exp\left\{ -\frac{1}{2} \sum_{j=1}^{n} \frac{\left(\xi_j - \xi_{j-1}\right)^2}{t_j - t_{j-1}} \right\}. \quad (2)$$

Proof According to Theorem 17.1 the components of the mean vector m and the covariance matrix V of Φ are given by

$$m_j = m(t_j) = E\left[X(t_j, \cdot)\right] = a(t_j) - a(t_0) + c,$$

$$v_{jk} = C\left[X(t_j, \cdot), X(t_k, \cdot)\right] = b\left(\min\{t_j, t_k\}\right) - b(t_0).$$

Let

$$\beta_j = b(t_j) - b(t_0) \quad \text{for } j = 1, 2, \cdots, n.$$

Then $V = B$ as given by (1) of Lemma 17.2 with our β_j, $j = 1, 2, \cdots, n$. If $b(t_j) - b(t_{j-1}) > 0$, $j = 1, 2, \cdots, n$, then $\beta_j - \beta_{j-1} > 0$, $j = 1, 2, \cdots, n$, so that, by (2) of Lemma 17.2, V is positive definite. Thus our $\Phi = N(m, V)$ has a density function given by

$$\Phi'(\xi) = \left\{(2\pi)^n \det V\right\}^{-\frac{1}{2}} \exp\left\{-\frac{1}{2}\left(V^{-1}[\xi - m], \xi - m\right)\right\}$$

$$\text{for } \xi \in R^n. \quad (3)$$

According to part (1) of Lemma 17.2,

$$\det V = \prod_{j=1}^{n} (\beta_j - \beta_{j-1}) = \prod_{j=1}^{n} \left\{b(t_j) - b(t_{j-1})\right\}.$$

Using (3), Lemma 17.2, and writing $\zeta = \xi - m$ we have

$$\left(V^{-1}[\xi - m], \xi - m\right)$$

$$= (V^{-1}\zeta, \zeta)$$

$$= (\gamma_1 + \gamma_2)\zeta_1^2 + (\gamma_2 + \gamma_3)\zeta_2^2 + \cdots + (\gamma_{n-1} + \gamma_n)\zeta_{n-1}^2 + \gamma_n \zeta_n^2$$

$$- 2\gamma_2 \zeta_1 \zeta_2 - 2\gamma_3 \zeta_2 \zeta_3 - \cdots - 2\gamma_n \zeta_{n-1}\zeta_n$$

$$= \sum_{j=1}^{n} \gamma_j (\zeta_j - \zeta_{j-1})^2 \quad (\text{with } \zeta_0 \equiv 0 \text{ and } \xi_0 \equiv m(t_0) = c)$$

$$= \sum_{j=1}^{n} (\beta_j - \beta_{j-1})^{-1} \left\{[\xi_j - m_j] - [\xi_j - m_{j-1}]\right\}^2$$

$$= \sum_{j=1}^{n} \left\{b(t_j) - b(t_{j-1})\right\}^{-1} \left\{\left[\xi_j - a(t_j)\right] - \left[\xi_{j-1} - a(t_{j-1})\right]\right\}^2 .$$

Using this in (3) we have (1). □

In connection with the covariance function of a generalized Brownian motion process let us consider Gaussian processes with factorable covariance functions. As we saw in Theorem 17.1, the generalized Brownian motion process X determined by a real-valued continuous function a and a continuous monotone increasing function b on $D = [0, \infty)$ and a translated unit distribution $\Phi_E(c)$ is a Gaussian process whose covariance function is given by

$$v(s,t) = C\left[X(s,\cdot),\ X(t,\cdot)\right] = \min\left\{b(s),\ b(t)\right\} - b(0)$$

for $(s,t) \in D \times D$.

If $b(0) = 0$ then b is a monotone increasing nonnegative function on D and

$$v(s,t) = \begin{cases} b(s) & \text{for } s \le t,\ (s,t) \in D \times D \\ b(t) & \text{for } s \ge t,\ (s,t) \in D \times D. \end{cases}$$

Let us ask then the following question: What conditions must two nonnegative valued functions u and v on $D = [0, \infty)$ satisfy in order that $r(s,t)$, $(s,t) \in D \times D$ defined by

$$r(s,t) = \begin{cases} u(s)\,v(t) & \text{for } s \le t,\ (s,t) \in D \times D \\ u(t)\,v(s) & \text{for } s \ge t,\ (s,t) \in D \times D \end{cases}$$

be the covariance function of a Gaussian process on a probability space and the interval D ? As we saw in Remark 16.6 and Theorem 16.8, in order that a real-valued function v on $D \times D$ be the covariance function of a Gaussian process on a probability space and the interval D it is necessary and sufficient that v be symmetric and nonnegative definite. The latter condition means that, for any $\{t_1, \cdots, t_n\} \subset D$, with $t_1 < \cdots < t_n$, the matrix $\left[v(t_i, t_j),\ i, j = 1, 2, \cdots, n\right]$ is nonnegative definite. Recall also that a matrix of real numbers $[c_{i,j}, i, j = 1, 2, \cdots, n]$ is nonnegative definite if and only if $\det[c_{ij}, i, j = 1, 2, \cdots, k] \ge 0$ for $k = 1, 2, \cdots, n$. For our factorable function r these conditions can be specialized as follows.

<u>Lemma 17.4</u> Given real numbers $a_1, \cdots, a_n, b_1, \cdots, b_n$. Let $C = [c_{ij}, i, j = 1, 2, \cdots, n]$ be a symmetric matrix whose entries are given by $c_{ij} = a_i b_j$ for $i \le j$, i.e.,

$$C = \begin{vmatrix} a_1b_1 & a_1b_2 & a_1b_3 & a_1b_4 & \cdots & a_1b_n \\ a_1b_2 & a_2b_2 & a_2b_3 & a_2b_4 & \cdots & a_2b_n \\ a_1b_3 & a_2b_3 & a_3b_3 & a_3b_4 & \cdots & a_3b_n \\ a_1b_4 & a_2b_4 & a_3b_4 & a_4b_4 & \cdots & a_4b_n \\ \vdots & \vdots & \vdots & \vdots & & \vdots \\ a_1b_n & a_2b_n & a_3b_n & a_4b_n & \cdots & a_nb_n \end{vmatrix} .$$

Then

$$\det C = a_1b_n \prod_{i=2}^{n} (a_ib_{i-1} - a_{i-1}b_i) .$$

Proof We prove the lemma by induction on n. The lemma is clearly valid for $n = 2$. Let us show that if it is valid for $n = k$ then it is valid for $n = k+1$ also. For simplicity let us write $C^{(k)}$ for $[c_{ij}, \ i,j = 1,2,\cdots,k]$. In calculating $\det C^{(k+1)}$ let us expand the determinant along the first column. Consider the minors $M_{11}, M_{21}, \cdots, M_{k+1,1}$ corresponding to $c_{11}, c_{21}, \cdots, c_{k+1,1}$. In any of these minors except M_{11} and M_{21}, the first two rows are proportional so that its determinant is 0. Thus

$$\det C^{(k+1)} = a_1b_1 \det M_{11} - a_1b_2 \det M_{21}$$

$$= a_1 b_1 \begin{vmatrix} a_2b_2 & a_2b_3 & a_2b_4 & \cdots & a_2b_{k+1} \\ a_2b_3 & a_3b_3 & a_3b_4 & \cdots & a_3b_{k+1} \\ a_2b_4 & a_3b_4 & a_4b_4 & \cdots & a_4b_{k+1} \\ \vdots & \vdots & \vdots & & \vdots \\ a_2b_{k+1} & a_3b_{k+1} & a_4b_{k+1} & \cdots & a_{k+1}b_{k+1} \end{vmatrix}$$

$$- a_1 b_2 \begin{vmatrix} a_1b_2 & a_1b_3 & a_1b_4 & \cdots & a_1b_{k+1} \\ a_2b_3 & a_3b_3 & a_3b_4 & \cdots & a_3b_{k+1} \\ a_2b_4 & a_3b_4 & a_4b_4 & \cdots & a_4b_{k+1} \\ \vdots & \vdots & \vdots & & \vdots \\ a_2b_{k+1} & a_3b_{k+1} & a_4b_{k+1} & \cdots & a_{k+1}b_{k+1} \end{vmatrix} .$$

Now $\det M_{11}$ as shown is precisely the type under consideration. Thus by the assumption that the lemma is valid for $n = k$, we have

$$\det M_{11} = a_2 b_{k+1} \prod_{i=3}^{k+1} (a_i b_{i-1} - a_{i-1} b_i) .$$

As for $\det M_{21}$, its transpose is identical with $\det M_{11}$ except that the factors a_2 in the first column of $\det M_{11}$ are all replaced by a_1. Thus

$$\det M_{21} = a_1 b_{k+1} \prod_{i=3}^{k+1} (a_i b_{i-1} - a_{i-1} b_i).$$

Therefore

$$\det C^{(k+1)} = (a_1 b_1 a_2 b_{k+1} - a_1 b_2 a_1 b_{k+1}) \prod_{i=3}^{k+1} (a_i b_{i-1} - a_{i-1} b_i)$$

$$= a_1 b_{k+1} \prod_{i=2}^{k+1} (a_i b_{i-1} - a_{i-1} b_i),$$

i.e., the lemma is valid for $n = k + 1$. This proves the lemma by induction. □

Theorem 17.5 Given two nonnegative functions u and v on $D = [0, \infty)$. Let

$$r(s,t) = \begin{cases} u(s)\, v(t) & \text{for} \quad s \le t, \ (s,t) \in D \times D \\ u(t)\, v(s) & \text{for} \quad s \ge t, \ (s,t) \in D \times D \end{cases} . \tag{1}$$

Then r is the covariance function of a Gaussian process on a probability space and the interval D if and only if for every $t', t'' \in D$, $t' < t''$,

$$u(t'')\, v(t') - u(t')\, v(t'') \ge 0. \tag{2}$$

Proof Since r as defined by (1) is symmetric, it suffices to show that r is nonnegative definite if and only if (2) holds. Now if r is nonnegative definite, then for $t', t'' \in D$, $t' < t''$, with $t_1 = t'$ and $t_2 = t''$, we have, from the nonegative definiteness of the matrix $\left[r(t_i, t_j),\ i,j = 1,2 \right]$,

$$0 \le r(t_1, t_1)\, r(t_2, t_2) - r(t_1, t_2)\, r(t_2, t_1)$$

$$= u(t_1)\, v(t_1)\, u(t_2)\, v(t_2) - u(t_1)\, v(t_2)\, u(t_1)\, v(t_2)$$

$$= u(t')\, v(t'') \left\{ u(t'')\, v(t') - u(t')\, v(t'') \right\},$$

which implies (2) in view of the nonnegativity of u and v. Conversely if (2) holds, then for $\{t_1, \cdots, t_n\} \subset D$ where $t_1 < \cdots < t_n$ we have, according to Lemma 17.4,

$$\det\left[r(t_i, t_j),\ i, j = 1, 2, \cdots, k \right]$$

$$= u(t_1)\, v(t_k) \prod_{i=2}^{k} \left\{ u(t_i)\, v(t_{i-1}) - u(t_{i-1})\, v(t_i) \right\} \geq 0$$

for $k = 2, 3, \cdots, n$, while for $k = 1$, $\det r(t_1, t_1) = u(t_1)\, v(t_1) \geq 0$. Thus $\left[r(t_i, t_j),\ i, j = 1, 2, \cdots, n \right]$ is a nonnegative definite matrix and r is nonnegative definite. □

§18. THE INTEGRAL OPERATOR WITH KERNEL min {s, t}

Let $L_2[0, a]$ be the Hilbert space consisting of complex-valued Lebesgue measurable functions on the interval $[0, a]$ with

$$\int_{[0, a]} |f(t)|^2\, m_L(dt) < \infty$$

in which two such functions which are equal almost everywhere on $[0, a]$ are not distinguished and the inner product is defined by

$$(f, g) = \int_{[0, a]} f(t)\, \overline{g(t)}\, m_L(dt) \qquad \text{for } f, g \in L_2[0, a].$$

As we saw in §17 the Brownian motion process is a Gaussian process with a mean function that is identically vanishing on the domain of definition D of the process and a covariance function given by $\min\{s, t\}$ for $s, t \in D$. Here we shall show that the integral operator T on $L_2[0, a]$ into $L_2[0, a]$ defined by

$$(Tf)(t) = \int_{[0,a]} f(s) \min\{s,t\}\, m_L(ds) \quad \text{for } t \in [0,a] \text{ and } f \in L_2[0,a]$$

is a strictly positive compact self-adjoint operator. T being such an operator, a full orthonormal system of eigenvectors of T is a complete orthonormal system in $L_2[0,a]$. We shall convert the integral equation $Tf = \lambda f$ into a differential system and determine all the eigenvalues of T and a corresponding orthonormal system of eigenvectors.

Let A be a linear operator on a Hilbert space $\mathfrak{H}$ into $\mathfrak{H}$. A complex number λ is called an eigenvalue of A if there exists $x \in \mathfrak{H}$, $x \neq 0$, such that $Ax = \lambda x$. x is called an eigenvector of A corresponding to λ. $\lambda = 0$ is an eigenvalue of A if and only if $\mathfrak{N}(A) \neq \{0\}$ where $\mathfrak{N}(A)$ is the null space of A., i.e., $\mathfrak{N}(A) = \{x \in \mathfrak{H}; Ax = 0\}$. Let us agree to call a complex number ρ a characteristic value of A if there exists $x \in \mathfrak{H}$, $x \neq 0$, such that $\rho A x = x$. Thus $\rho = 0$ is never a characteristic value and there exists a one-to-one correspondence between the characteristic values ρ of A and the nonzero eignevalues λ of A by $\rho = 1/\lambda$.

We say that a sequence $\{x_n, n = 1, 2, \cdots\} \subset \mathfrak{H}$ converges weakly to $x_0 \in \mathfrak{H}$ and write $x_0 = w - \lim_{n\to\infty} x_n$ if $(x_0, y) = \lim_{n\to\infty} (x_n, y)$ for every $y \in \mathfrak{H}$. If $\{x_n, n=1,2,\cdots\}$ converges weakly then $\{\|x_n\|, n=1,2,\cdots\}$ is a bounded sequence. If $x_0 = \lim_{n\to\infty} x_n$ then $x_0 = w - \lim_{n\to\infty} x_n$. On the other hand, if $x_0 = w - \lim_{n\to\infty} x_n$ and $\|x_0\| = \lim_{n\to\infty} \|x_n\|$, then $x_0 = \lim_{n\to\infty} x_n$. A linear operator A on $\mathfrak{H}$ into $\mathfrak{H}$ is called a compact operator if $x_0 = w - \lim_{n\to\infty} x_n$ implies $Ax = \lim_{n\to\infty} Ax_n$. A is called a self-adjoint operator if $(Ax, y) = (x, Ay)$ for every $x, y \in \mathfrak{H}$. Concerning the eigenvalues and eigenvectors of a compact self-adjoint operator there is the following well-known theorem, a proof of which can be found for instance in R. Schatten, Norm Ideals of Completely Continuous Operators, Springer Verlag, 1960.

Theorem Let A be a compact self-adjoint operator on a Hilbert space $\mathfrak{H}$ into $\mathfrak{H}$ and $A \neq O$. Then A has at least one and at most countably many nonzero eigenvalues and $\lambda = 0$ is the only possible limit point of the eigenvalues. Every eigenvalue of A is real and every nonzero eigenvalue of A has a finite multiplicity. Let $\{\lambda_n, n = 1, 2, \cdots\}$ be the nonzero eigenvalues of A where an eigenvalue of multiplicity p is repeated p times. Then there exists an orthonormal system of eigenvectors $\{e_n, n = 1, 2, \cdots\}$ corresponding to $\{\lambda_n, n = 1, 2, \cdots\}$. (Such a system is called a full orthonormal system of eigenvectors of A.) An arbitrary full orthonormal system of eigenvectors of A and an orthonormal basis of the null space of A constitute a complete orthonormal system of $\mathfrak{H}$. Finally

$$Ax = \sum_{n=1}^{\infty} \lambda_n (x, e_n) e_n \quad \text{for every } x \in \mathfrak{H}.$$

A linear operator A on a Hilbert space $\mathfrak{H}$ into $\mathfrak{H}$ is called a positive operator if $(Ax, x) \geq 0$ for every $x \in \mathfrak{H}$. It is called a strictly positive operator if in addition $(Ax, x) = 0$ implies $x = 0$. A compact self-adjoint operator $A \neq O$ on $\mathfrak{H}$ into $\mathfrak{H}$ is a positive operator if and only if all the eigenvalues are nonnegative, and it is a strictly positive operator if and only if all the eigenvalues are positive.

Theorem 18.1 Let T be a linear operator on the Hilbert space $L_2[0, a]$ defined by

$$(Tf)(t) = \int_0^a \min\{s, t\}\, f(s)\, m_L(ds) \quad \text{for } t \in [0, a],\ f \in L_2[0, a].$$

Then T is a strictly positive self-adjoint operator on $L_2[0, a]$ into $L_2[0, a]$.

Proof To show that $Tf \in L_2[0, a]$ for every $f \in L_2[0, a]$ we show that Tf is actually continuous on $[0, a]$. This continuity is a consequence of the continuity of $\min\{s, t\}$, $(s, t) \in [0,a] \times [0,a]$. Indeed for $t', t'' \in [0, a]$ we have

$$\begin{aligned} &|(Tf)(t') - (Tf)(t'')| \\ &\leq \int_0^a |\min\{s, t'\} - \min\{s, t''\}|\, |f(s)|\, m_L(ds) \\ &\leq \left\{\int_0^a |\min\{s, t'\} - \min\{s, t''\}|^2\, m_L(ds)\right\}^{\frac{1}{2}} \left\{\int_0^a |f(s)|^2\, m_L(ds)\right\}^{\frac{1}{2}} \\ &\leq |t' - t''|\, \sqrt{a}\, \|f\|, \end{aligned}$$

from which follows the continuity of Tf on $[0, a]$.

The self-adjointness of T is a consequence of the fact that $\min\{s, t\}$ is real valued and symmetric. Thus, for $f, g \in L_2[0, a]$,

$$\begin{aligned} (Tf, g) &= \int_0^a \left\{\int_0^a \min\{s, t\}\, f(s)\, m_L(ds)\right\} \overline{g(t)}\, m_L(dt) \\ &= \int_{[0, a]\times[0, a]} \min\{s, t\}\, f(s)\, \overline{g(t)}\, m_L\big(d(s, t)\big) \end{aligned}$$

$$= \int_0^a f(s) \left\{ \int_0^a \min\{s,t\}\, \overline{g(t)}\, m_L(dt) \right\} m_L(ds)$$

$$= \int_0^a f(s) \overline{\left\{ \int_0^a \min\{s,t\}\, g(t)\, m_L(dt) \right\}} m_L(ds)$$

$$= (f, Tg).$$

The positivity of T is obvious. To prove the strict positivity of T it suffices to consider real-valued $f \in L_2[0, a]$ only. For complex-valued $f \in L_2[0, a]$ we need only to decompose f in real and imaginary parts and use the fact that T is self-adjoint and positive. Thus let f be real-valued. From the symmetry of $\min\{s, t\}$,

$$(Tf, f) = \int_0^a \left\{ \int_0^a \min\{s,t\}\, f(s)\, m_L(ds) \right\} f(t)\, m_L(dt)$$

$$= \int_{[0,a]\times[0,a]} \min\{s,t\}\, f(s)\, f(t)\, m_L\big(d(s,t)\big)$$

$$= 2\int_0^a \left\{ \int_t^a t f(s)\, f(t)\, m_L(ds) \right\} m_L(dt)$$

$$= 2\int_0^a \left\{ t f(t) \int_t^a f(s)\, m_L(ds) \right\} m_L(dt)$$

$$= \int_0^a \left[-t \frac{d}{dt} \left\{ \int_t^a f(s)\, m_L(ds) \right\}^2 \right] m_L(dt),$$

where in obtaining the last equality we used the fact that an indefinite integral is differentiable a.e. and its derivative is equal to the integrand a.e. According to a theorem for integration by parts for Lebesgue integrals, if G_1 and G_2 are indefinite integrals of g_1 and g_2, respectively, then

$$\int_\alpha^\beta G_1(t)\, g_2(t)\, m_L(dt) = \Big[G_1(t)\, G_2(t)\Big]_\alpha^\beta - \int_\alpha^\beta g_1(t)\, G_2(t)\, m_L(dt).$$

Using this theorem we have

$$(Tf, f) = \left[-t\left\{\int_t^a f(s)\, m_L(ds)\right\}^2\right]_0^a + \int_0^a \left\{\int_t^a f(s)\, m_L(ds)\right\}^2 m_L(dt)$$

$$= \int_0^a \left\{\int_t^a f(s)\, m_L(ds)\right\}^2 m_L(dt) \geq 0.$$

For simplicity write

$$\varphi(t) = \int_t^a f(s)\, m_L(ds) \qquad \text{for } t \in [0, a].$$

If $(Tf, f) = 0$, then $\varphi(t) = 0$ for a.e. $t \in [0, a]$, so that from the continuity of $\varphi(t)$ on $[0, a]$, $\varphi(t) = 0$ for $t \in [0, a]$. But

$$f(t) = -\frac{d}{dt}\varphi(t) \qquad \text{for a.e. } t \in [0, a].$$

Thus $f(t) = 0$ for a.e. $t \in [0, a]$, i.e., $f = 0 \in L_2[0, a]$. This completes the proof of the theorem. □

To show that our integral operator with the kernel $\min\{s, t\}$ is a compact operator we prove the following theorem.

Theorem 18.2 Let $K(s, t)$ be a complex-valued Lebesgue measurable function on $[0, a] \times [0, a]$ with

$$\int_{[0,a]\times[0,a]} |K(s, t)|^2\, m_L\big(d(s, t)\big) < \infty .$$

Define a linear operator T on $L_2[0, a]$ by

$$(Tf)(t) = \int_0^a K(s, t)\, f(s)\, m_L(ds) \qquad \text{for } t \in [0, a]$$

for $f \in L_2[0, a]$. Then T is a compact operator on $L_2[0, a]$ into $L_2[0, a]$.

<u>Proof</u> Let us show first that $Tf \in L_2[0, a]$ for every $f \in L_2[0, a]$. Since K and f, regarded as a function on $[0, a] \times [0, a]$ both belong to $L_2\left([0, a] \times [0, a]\right)$, we have $K(s, t)\, f(s) \in L_1\left([0, a] \times [0, a]\right)$ according to the Schwarz inequality. Then for a.e. $t \in [0, a]$, $K(s, t)\, f(s)$ is an integrable function of s, and

$$(Tf)(t) = \int_0^a K(s, t)\, f(s)\, m_L(ds) \qquad \text{for } t \in [0, a]$$

is an integrable function of t. Furthermore, by the Schwarz inequality,

$$\int_0^a |(Tf)(t)|^2\, m_L(dt) = \int_0^a \left| \int_0^a K(s, t)\, f(s)\, m_L(ds) \right|^2 m_L(dt)$$

$$\leq \|f\|^2 \int_{[0, a] \times [0, a]} |K(s, t)|^2 m_L\left(d(s, t)\right) < \infty,$$

so that $Tf \in L_2[0, a]$.

To show that T is a compact operator we show that, whenever $\{f_n, n = 1, 2, \cdots\} \subset L_2[0, a]$ and $w - \lim_{n\to\infty} f_n = f_0 \in L_2[0, a]$, then $Tf_0 = \lim_{n\to\infty} Tf_n$, or equivalently $\|Tf_0\| = \lim_{n\to\infty} \|Tf_n\|$ and $Tf_0 = w - \lim_{n\to\infty} Tf_n$. Now since $K \in L_2\left([0, a] \times [0, a]\right)$, we have $K(\cdot, t) \in L_2[0, a]$ for a.e. $t \in [0, a]$. Then from $f_0 = w - \lim_{n\to\infty} f_n$ we have

$$\lim_{n\to\infty} \left(f_n, \overline{K(\cdot, t)}\right) = \left(f_0, \overline{K(\cdot, t)}\right) \qquad \text{for a.e. } t \in [0, a],$$

i.e.,

$$\lim_{n\to\infty} (Tf_n)(t) = (Tf_0)(t) \qquad \text{for a.e. } t \in [0, a].$$

Since $\{f_n, n = 1, 2, \cdots\}$ converges weakly, we have $\| f_n \| \le M$, $n = 1, 2, \cdots$, for some $M \ge 0$. Then for $t \in [0, a]$,

$$|(Tf)(t)|^2 \le \left\{\int_0^a |K(s, t)|^2 \, m_L(ds)\right\}\left\{\int_0^a |f_n(s)|^2 \, m_L(ds)\right\}$$

$$\le M \int_0^a |K(s, t)|^2 \, m_L(ds),$$

which is an integrable function of $t \in [0, a]$. Thus by the Dominated Convergence Theorem,

$$\lim_{n\to\infty} \int_0^a |(Tf_n)(t)|^2 \, m_L(dt) = \int_0^a |(Tf_0)(t)|^2 \, m_L(dt),$$

i.e.,

$$\lim_{n\to\infty} \| Tf_n \|^2 = \| Tf_0 \|^2.$$

Finally let us show that $Tf_0 = w - \lim_{n\to\infty} Tf_n$, i.e., $(Tf_0, g) = \lim_{n\to\infty} (Tf_n, g)$ for every $g \in L_2[0, a]$. For this observe that

$$(Tf_n, g) = \int_0^a \left\{\int_0^a K(s, t) \, f_n(s) \, m_L(ds)\right\} \overline{g(t)} \, m_L(dt)$$

$$= \int_0^a \left\{\int_0^a K(s, t) \, \overline{g(t)} \, m_L(dt)\right\} f_n(s) \, m_L(ds)$$

$$= (t_n, T^* g),$$

where the operator T^* is defined by

$$(T^* g)(s) = \int_0^a \overline{K(s, t)}\, g(t)\, m_L(dt) \qquad \text{for } s \in [0, a]$$

for $g \in L_2[0,a]$. The fact that $T^* g \in L_2[0, a]$ for every $g \in L_2[0,a]$ can be shown exactly in the same way as we did for T. Thus from $f_0 = w - \lim_{n\to\infty} f_n$,

$$\lim_{n\to\infty} (Tf_n, g) = \lim_{n\to\infty} (f_n, T^* g) = (f_0, T^* g) = (Tf_0, g).$$

This completes the proof of the theorem. □

As we have shown, the integral operator with kernel $\min\{s, t\}$ on the complex Hilbert space $L_2[0, a]$ is a strictly positive compact self-adjoint operator, and hence every eigenvalue of T is positive, and a full orthonormal system of eigenvectors of T is also a complete orthonormal system in $L_2[0, a]$. Let us find a full orthonormal system of eigenvectors of T. Since there is a one-to-one correspondence between the characteristic values ρ and the nonzero eigenvalues λ by $\rho = 1/\lambda$, let us find the characteristic values. We shall show that the integral equation $\rho Tf = f$ is equivalent to a differential system which can be solved by elementary methods.

Lemma 18.3 Let f be complex valued and continuous on $[0, a]$ and let g be defined by

$$g(t) = \rho \int_0^a \min\{s, t\}\, f(s)\, ds \qquad \text{for } t \in [0, a], \tag{1}$$

where ρ is a complex number. Then g satisfies the differential system

$$\left.\begin{aligned} &g''(t) + \rho f(t) = 0 \\ &g(0) = g'(a) = 0 \end{aligned}\right\} \qquad \text{for } t \in [0, a]. \tag{2}$$

Proof The function g as defined is continuous on $[0, a]$, as we saw in the first part of the proof of Theorem 18.1. For each $t \in [0, a]$ we have

$$g(t) = \rho \int_0^t sf(s)\, ds + \rho \int_t^a tf(s)\, ds,$$

$$g'(t) = \rho t f(t) + \rho \int_t^a f(s)\, ds - \rho t f(t) = \rho \int_t^a f(s)\, ds,$$

$$g''(t) = -\rho f(t),$$

so that (2) holds. □

Lemma 18.4 Let f be complex valued and continuous on $[0, a]$. If g is a complex-valued function on $[0, a]$ which satisfies the differential system (2), (3) of Lemma 18.3 then it satisfies the integral equation (1).

Proof Let φ and ψ be complex-valued functions with Riemann integrable φ'' and ψ'' on $[\alpha, \beta]$. Then

$$\frac{d}{dt}\left\{\varphi(t)\,\psi'(t) - \varphi'(t)\,\psi(t)\right\} = \varphi(t)\,\psi''(t) - \varphi''(t)\,\psi(t)$$

from which follows Green's identity:

$$\int_\alpha^\beta \left\{\varphi(t)\,\psi''(t) - \varphi''(t)\,\psi(t)\right\} dt = \Big[\varphi(t)\,\psi'(t) - \varphi'(t)\,\psi(t)\Big]_\alpha^\beta .$$

Let $\varphi = g$. Then φ'' exists and $\varphi'' = g'' = -\rho f$ on $[0, a]$. For fixed s let $\psi(t) = \min\{s, t\}$ for $t \in [0, a]$. Then, with $\delta > 0$,

$$t \in [0, s-\delta]; \quad \psi(t) = t, \quad \psi'(t) = 1, \quad \psi''(t) = 0,$$

$$t \in [s+\delta, a]; \quad \psi(t) = s, \quad \psi'(t) = 0, \quad \psi''(t) = 0,$$

so that, by Green's identity,

$$\int_0^{s-\delta} \rho f(t) \min\{s,t\}dt = \left[g(s-\delta) - g'(s-\delta)(s-\delta)\right] - \left[g(0) - g'(0)\cdot 0\right]$$

$$= g(s-\delta) - g'(s-\delta)(s-\delta)$$

$$\int_{s+\delta}^{a} \rho f(t) \min\{s,t\}dt = \left[g(a)\cdot 0 - g'(a)s\right] - \left[g(s+\delta)\cdot 0 - g'(s+\delta)s\right]$$

$$= g'(s+\delta)s .$$

Adding these two equalities side by side and then letting $\delta \downarrow 0$, we have

$$\int_0^a \rho f(t) \min\{s,t\}dt = g(s)$$

from the existence of the integral on the left side and from the continuity of g and g'. □

Combining the last two lemmas we have the following theorem:

Theorem 18.5 With an arbitrary complex number ρ, $f \in L_2[0,a]$ satisfies the integral equation

$$f(t) = \rho \int_0^a \min\{s,t\}\, f(s)\, m_L(ds) \tag{1}$$

if and only if it satisfies the differential system

$$\begin{aligned} f''(t) + \rho f(t) &= 0 \\ f(0) = f'(a) &= 0 \end{aligned} \qquad \text{for } t \in [0,a]. \tag{2}$$

Note that if f satisfies the integral equation then f is continuous on $[0,a]$ so that Lemma 18.3 is applicable.

The problem of finding the characteristic values of the integral operator with kernel $\min\{s,t\}$ on the complex Hilbert space $L_2[0, a]$ has thus been reduced to that of finding every positive number ρ for which a complex-valued, not identically vanishing continuous function f satisfying the differential system (2) in Theorem 18.5 exists.

As a general solution of the differential system we have

$$f(t) = A \cos \sqrt{\rho}\, t + B \sin \sqrt{\rho}\, t.$$

By $f(0) = 0$ we have $A = 0$ and by $f'(a) = 0$ we have $B\sqrt{\rho} \cos \sqrt{\rho}\, a = 0$, i.e., $\sqrt{\rho}\, a = \frac{1}{2}(2n+1)\pi$ for $n = 0,1,2,\cdots$. Thus the characteristic values ρ_n, $n = 0,1,2,\cdots$, are given by

$$\rho_n = (n+\tfrac{1}{2})^2 \frac{\pi^2}{a^2} \quad \text{for } n = 0,1,2,\cdots,$$

and as a full orthonormal system of the integral operator with kernel $\min\{s,t\}$ on the complex Hilbert space $L_2[0, a]$ we have

$$e_n(t) = \sqrt{\frac{2}{a}} \sin(n+\tfrac{1}{2}) \frac{\pi}{a} t \quad \text{for } t \in [0, a],\ n = 0,1,2,\cdots.$$

§19. ORTHOGONAL EXPANSIONS OF GAUSSIAN PROCESSES

The covariance function v of a Gaussian process X on a probability space $(\Omega, \mathfrak{B}, P)$ and an interval $D = [a,b] \subset R^1$ is a real-valued symmetric nonnegative definite function on $D \times D$. For simplicity in the argument we assume that v is continuous. Then the integral operator T with v as its kernel is a positive compact self-adjoint operator transforming the real Hilbert space $L_2(D)$ into $L_2(D)$ (see Lemma 19.3 below). If we assume that T is strictly positive then an arbitrary full orthonormal system of eigenvectors of T, $\{e_k, k = 1,2,\cdots\}$, corresponding to the non-zero eigenvalues $\{\lambda_k, k = 1,2,\cdots\}$ of T is in fact a complete orthonormal system in $L_2(D)$ (c.f. §18). Here we shall show that the sample functions of X can be expanded orthogonally in terms of $\{e_k, k = 1, 2, \cdots\}$ in such a way that the coefficients in the expansion constitute an independent Gaussian system of random variables on $(\Omega, \mathfrak{B}, P)$.

Lemma 19.1 Let X be a stochastic process on a probability space $(\Omega, \mathfrak{B}, P)$ and an interval $D = [a, b] \subset R^1$ whose mean function $m(t) = E\left[X(t, \cdot)\right] = 0$ for $t \in D$ and covariance function $v(s, t) = E\left[X(s, \cdot)\, X(t, \cdot)\right]$ for $(s, t) \in D \times D$ are continuous. Then X is continuous in the second moment and stochastically continuous on D. Also there exists an extended real-valued measurable stochastic process Y which is equivalent to X. For Y,

$$\int_{D \times \Omega} \left\{Y(t, \omega)\right\}^2 (m_L \times P)\left(d(t, \omega)\right) < \infty \tag{1}$$

and

$$Y(\cdot, \omega) \in L_2(D) \qquad \text{for a.e. } \omega \in \Omega \tag{2}$$

hold.

Proof The continuity of X in the second moment is an immediate consequence of the continuity of v on $D \times D$. In fact, for $t_0 \in D$,

$$\lim_{t \to t_0} E\left[\left\{X(t, \cdot) - X(t_0, \cdot)\right\}^2\right]$$

$$= \lim_{t \to t_0} \left\{v(t, t) - 2v(t, t_0) + v(t_0, t_0)\right\} = 0.$$

Then since convergence in the second moment implies convergence in probability according to Theorem A5.4, X is stochastically continuous. Thus according to Theorem 5.2 there exists an extended real-valued measurable stochastic process Y which is equivalent to X. With the measurability of Y we can apply the Fubini theorem to obtain

$$\int_{D\times\Omega} \{Y(t,\omega)\}^2 (m_L \times P)\big(d(t,\omega)\big) = \int_D E\left[\{X(t,\cdot)\}^2\right] m_L(dt)$$

$$= \int_D v(t,t)\, m_L(dt) < \infty$$

and also

$$\int_\Omega \left[\int_D \{Y(t,\omega)\}^2 m_L(dt)\right] P(d\omega) < \infty,$$

and hence

$$\int_D \{Y(t,\omega)\}^2 m_L(dt) < \infty \qquad \text{for a.e. } \omega \in \Omega.$$

This completes the proof of the lemma. □

Lemma 19.2 Let X be an extended real-valued measurable stochastic process on a probability space $(\Omega, \mathfrak{B}, P)$ and an interval $D = [a,b] \subset R^1$ with

$$\int_{D\times\Omega} \{X(t,\omega)\}^2 (m_L \times P)\big(d(t,\omega)\big) < \infty.$$

Then there exists a sequence of right-continuous step functions $\{\theta_n, n = 1,2,\cdots\}$ on D such that the sequence of stepwise, and hence measurable, stochastic processes $\{X_n, n = 1,2,\cdots\}$ defined by

$$X_n(t,\omega) = X\big(\theta_n(t), \omega\big) \qquad \text{for } t \in D \text{ and } \omega \in \Omega$$

satisfies the conditions that

$$X_n(t, \cdot) \in L_2(\Omega) \qquad \text{for } t \in D$$

and

$$\lim_{n\to\infty} \int_{D\times\Omega} \{X_n(t, \omega) - X(t, \omega)\}^2 \, (m_L \times P)\big(d(t, \omega)\big) = 0.$$

Proof This lemma is included in Lemma 24.9 which is to follow. □

Lemma 19.3 Let $D = [a, b] \subset R^1$ and $v(s, t)$ for $(s, t) \in D \times D$ be a real-valued continuous symmetric nonnegative definite function. Then the linear operator T defined on the real Hilbert space $L_2(D)$ by

$$(Tf)(t) = \int_D v(s, t) f(s) \, m_L(ds) \qquad \text{for } t \in D \text{ and } f \in L_2(D)$$

is a positive compact self-adjoint operator transforming $L_2(D)$ into $L_2(D)$.

Proof From the continuity of v on $D \times D$ it follows that Tf is a continuous function on D for $f \in L_2(D)$ so that $Tf \in L_2(D)$. The self-adjointness of T follows from the symmetry of v. The integrability of v^2 on $D \times D$ implies that T is a compact operator according to Theorem 18.2. It remains to show that the nonnegative definiteness of v, i.e.,

$$\sum_{j=1}^{n} \sum_{\ell=1}^{n} v(t_j, t_\ell) \, \xi_j \xi_\ell \geq 0 \qquad \text{whenever}$$

$$\{t_1, \cdots, t_n\} \subset D \text{ and } \{\xi_1, \cdots, \xi_n\} \subset R^1 \tag{1}$$

implies the positivity of T, i.e.,

$$(Tf, f) \geq 0 \qquad \text{for } f \in L_2(D). \tag{2}$$

Suppose $(Tf, f) < 0$ for some $f \in L_2(D)$. For $g \in L_2(D)$ we have

$$|(Tf, f) - (Tg, g| \le |(Tf, f) - (Tg, g)| \le |(Tf, f-g)|$$

$$\le \|T\| \; \|f\| \; \|f-g\| + \|T\| \; \|f-g\| \; \|g\|. \quad (3)$$

Since for every $\epsilon > 0$ there exists a continuous function g on D such that $\|f-g\| < \epsilon$ and since $\|g\| \le \|g-f\| + \|f\|$, the right side of (3) can be made as small as we wish. Thus in view of $(Tf, f) < 0$ there exists a continuous function g on D such that $(Tg, g) < 0$. Since both v and g are continuous, (Tg, g) can be given as a Riemann integral, i.e.,

$$(Tg, g) = \int_a^b \int_a^b v(s, t)\, g(s)\, g(t)\, ds\, dt$$

$$= \lim_{n\to\infty} \sum_{j=1}^{n} \sum_{\ell=1}^{n} v(t_j, t_\ell)\, g(t_j)\, g(t_\ell) \left(\frac{b-a}{n}\right)^2,$$

where $t_j = a + (j/n)(b-a)$ for $j = 1, 2, \cdots, n$, and similarly for t_ℓ. Since $(Tg, g) < 0$, the Riemann sum above is negative for sufficiently large n. This contradicts (1). Thus $(Tf, f) \ge 0$ for every $f \in L_2(D)$. □

Theorem 19.4 Let X be an extended real-valued measurable Gaussian process on a probability space $(\Omega, \mathfrak{A}, P)$ and an interval $D = [a, b] \subset R^1$ whose mean function $m(t) = E\left[X(t, \cdot)\right] = 0$ for $t \in D$ and covariance function $v(s, t) = E\left[X(s, \cdot)\, X(t, \cdot)\right]$, $(s, t) \in D \times D$, are continuous. Then

$$\int_{D\times\Omega} \left\{X(t, \omega)\right\}^2 (m_L \times P)\left(d(t, \omega)\right) < \infty, \quad (1)$$

and there exists $\Omega_0 \in \mathfrak{B}$ with $P(\Omega_0) = 1$ such that

$$X(\cdot, \omega) \in L_2(D) \qquad \text{for } \omega \in \Omega_0. \tag{2}$$

Let $\{e_k, k = 1, 2, \cdots\}$ be a full orthonormal system of eigenvectors corresponding to the nonzero eigenvalues $\{\lambda_k, k = 1, 2, \cdots\}$ of the positive compact self-adjoint operator T transforming the real Hilbert space $L_2(D)$ into $L_2(D)$ which is defined by

$$(Tf)(t) = \int_D v(s, t)\, f(s)\, m_L(ds) \quad \text{for } t \in D \text{ and } f \in L_2(D). \tag{3}$$

Let

$$Y_k(\omega) = \begin{cases} \left(X(\cdot, \omega), e_k\right) = \int_D X(t, \omega)\, e_k(t)\, m_L(dt) & \text{for } \omega \in \Omega_0 \\ 0 & \text{for } \omega \in \Omega_0^c \end{cases}. \tag{4}$$

Then $\{Y_k, k = 1, 2, \cdots\}$ is an independent Gaussian system of random variables on $(\Omega, \mathfrak{B}, P)$, and in fact Y_k is distributed normally with

$$E(Y_k) = 0 \quad \text{and} \quad V(Y_k) = \lambda_k \qquad \text{for } k = 1, 2, \cdots. \tag{5}$$

If T is strictly positive then writing $s - \Sigma$ to indicate strong convergence, i.e., convergence in the Hilbert norm of $L_2(D)$, we have

$$X(\cdot, \omega) = s - \sum_{k=1}^{\infty} Y_k(\omega)\, e_k(\cdot) \qquad \text{for } \omega \in \Omega_0. \tag{6}$$

Also

$$\sum_{k=1}^{\infty} \left\{Y_k(\omega)\right\}^2 = \|X(\cdot, \omega)\|^2 = \int_D \left\{X(t, \omega)\right\}^2 m_L(dt)$$

$$\text{for } \omega \in \Omega_0 \tag{7}$$

and

$$\sum_{k=1}^{\infty} \lambda_k = \int_D v(t, t)\, m_L(dt) < \infty. \tag{8}$$

Proof The measurability of X and the continuity of v imply (1) and (2), as we saw in Lemma 19.1. The continuity and the nonnegative definiteness of v imply that T is a positive compact self-adjoint operator transforming $L_2(D)$ into $L_2(D)$ by Lemma 19.3. Now according to Lemma 19.2, (1) implies the existence of a sequence of step functions $\{\theta_n, n = 1,2, \cdots\}$ on D such that the sequence of stepwise stochastic processes $\{X_n, n = 1,2, \cdots\}$ defined by

$$X_n(t, \omega) = X\big(\theta_n(t), \omega\big) \qquad \text{for } t \in D,\ \omega \in \Omega, \text{ and } n = 1,2, \cdots$$

satisfies

$$X_n(t, \cdot) \in L_2(\Omega) \qquad \text{for } t \in D \text{ and } n = 1,2, \cdots$$

and

$$\lim_{n\to\infty} \int_{D\times\Omega} \{X_n(t, \omega) - X(t, \omega)\}^2 (m_L \times P)\big(d(t, \omega)\big) = 0 .$$

By the Fubini theorem,

$$\lim_{n\to\infty} \int_\Omega \left[\int_D \{X_n(t, \omega) - X(t, \omega)\}^2 m_L(dt) \right] P(d\omega) = 0.$$

Since this is convergence of the sequence of random variables $\int_D \{X_n(t, \cdot) - X(t, \cdot)\}^2 m_L(dt)$, $n = 1,2, \cdots$, in the $L_1(\Omega)$ norm to 0 there exists a subsequence $\{X_{n_m}, m = 1,2, \cdots\}$ and $\Omega_1 \in \mathfrak{B}$ with $P(\Omega_1) = 1$ such that

$$\lim_{m\to\infty} \int_D \{X_{n_m}(t, \omega) - X(t, \omega)\}^2 m_L(dt) = 0 \qquad \text{for } \omega \in \Omega_1.$$

Then

$$\lim_{m\to\infty} \left(X_{n_m}(\cdot, \omega), e_k\right) = \left(X(\cdot, \omega), e_k\right)$$

$$\text{for } k = 1, 2, \cdots, \text{ when } \omega \in \Omega_1,$$

i.e.,

$$\lim_{m\to\infty} \int_D X_{n_m}(t, \omega)\, e_k(t)\, m_L(dt)$$

$$= \int_D X(t, \omega)\, e_k(t)\, m_L(dt) \quad \text{for } k = 1, 2, \cdots, \text{ when } \omega \in \Omega_1. \tag{9}$$

Now the sample functions of X_{n_m} are step functions and e_k is continuous on D since $Te_k = \lambda_k e_k$, i.e.,

$$e_k(t) = \frac{1}{\lambda_k} \int_D v(s, t)\, e_k(s)\, m_L(ds).$$

Thus the integral on the left side of (9) is equal to the Riemann integral for every $\omega \in \Omega$, i.e.,

$$\int_D X_{n_m}(t, \omega)\, e_k(t)\, m_L(dt)$$

$$= \int_a^b X_{n_m}(t, \omega)\, e_k(t)\, dt$$

$$= \lim_{\ell\to\infty} \sum_{q=1}^{\ell} X_{n_m}\left(a + \frac{q}{\ell}(b-a), \omega\right) e_k\left(a + \frac{q}{\ell}(b-a)\right) \frac{b-a}{\ell}. \tag{10}$$

From (10), (9), (4), Theorem 16.9, and Theorem 16.11, $\{Y_k, k = 1, 2, \cdots\}$ is a Gaussian system of random variables on $(\Omega, \mathfrak{B}, P)$. From the measurability of X we obtain, by applying the Fubini theorem,

$$E(Y_k) = E\left[\int_D X(t, \cdot)\, e_k(t)\, m_L(dt)\right]$$

$$= \int_D E\left[X(t,\cdot)\right] e_k(t)\, m_L(dt)$$

$$= \int_D m(t)\, e_k(t)\, m_L(dt) = 0. \tag{11}$$

Similarly

$$E(Y_j Y_\ell) = E\left[\left\{\int_D X(s,\cdot)\, e_j(s)\, m_L(ds)\right\}\left\{\int_D X(t,\cdot)\, e_\ell(t)\, m_L(dt)\right\}\right]$$

$$= \int_{D\times D} E\left[X(s,\cdot)\, X(t,\cdot)\right] e_j(s)\, e_\ell(t)\, m_L\big(d(s,t)\big)$$

$$= \int_{D\times D} v(s,t)\, e_j(s)\, e_\ell(t)\, m_L\big(d(s,t)\big)$$

$$= \int_D (Te_j)(t)\, e_\ell(t)\, m_L(dt)$$

$$= \lambda_j \int_D e_\ell(t)\, m_L(dt)$$

$$= \lambda_j\, \delta_{j\ell} \tag{12}$$

and, in particular,

$$V(Y_k) = \lambda_k. \tag{13}$$

Since $\{Y_k, k=1,2,\cdots\}$ is a Gaussian system, (12) implies that it is an independent system according to Theorem 16.13. Since $\{Y_k, k=1,2,\cdots\}$ is a Gaussian system, Y_k is normally distributed. Its mean and variance are given by (11) and (13), respectively.

When T is strictly positive then $\{e_k, k=1,2,\cdots\}$ is a complete orthonormal system in $L_2(D)$ so that (6) holds in view of the definition of Y_k by (4). The first equality in (7) is just the Parseval equality. Finally, by (5), the Monotone Convergence

Theorem, the Fubini theorem, and (7) we have

$$\sum_{k=1}^{\infty} \lambda_k = \sum_{k=1}^{\infty} E\left[Y_k^2\right] = E\left[\sum_{k=1}^{\infty} Y_k^2\right] = E\left[\int_D \{X(t,\cdot)\}^2 m_L(dt)\right]$$

$$= \int_D E\left[\{X(t,\cdot)\}^2\right] m_L(dt) = \int_D v(t,t)\, m_L(dt) < \infty,$$

which proves (8). This completes the proof of the theorem. □

The next theorem is a converse of Theorem 19.4. It asserts that from an arbitrary independent sequence of random variables $\{Z_n, n = 1, 2, \cdots\}$ on a probability space $(\Omega, \mathfrak{B}, P)$, each of which is distributed according to $N(0, 1)$, a Gaussian process on $(\Omega, \mathfrak{B}, P)$ and a finite interval D can be constructed as a series in $\{Z_n, n = 1, 2, \cdots\}$ to have an arbitrary real-valued continuous symmetric nonnegative definite function v on $D \times D$ as its covariance function. The proof is based in part on Mercer's theorem which we now state. A proof of this theorem can be found for instance in F. Smithies [1].

Mercer's theorem Let v be a not identically vanishing complex-valued continuous symmetric nonnegative function on $D \times D$ where D is a finite closed interval in R^1 and let $\{e_n, n = 1, 2, \cdots\}$ be a full orthonormal system of eigenvectors corresponding to the nonzero eigenvalues $\{\lambda_n, n = 1, 2, \cdots\}$ of the positive compact self-adjoint operator T transforming the complex Hilbert space $L_2(D)$ into $L_2(D)$ which is defined by

$$(Tf)(f) = \int_D v(s,t)\, f(s)\, m_L(ds) \qquad \text{for } t \in D \text{ and } f \in L_2(D).$$

Then

$$\sum_{n=1}^{\infty} \lambda_n < \infty$$

and

$$v(s,t) = \sum_{n=1}^{\infty} \lambda_n e_n(s) \overline{e_n(t)} \qquad \text{for } (s,t) \in D \times D,$$

the series being uniformly absolutely convergent on $D \times D$.

Theorem 19.5 (D. E. Varberg [1]). Let v be a real-valued continuous symmetric nonnegative function on $D \times D$ where $D = [a,b] \subset R^1$ and let $\{e_n, n = 1,2,\cdots\}$ be a full orthonormal system of eigenvectors corresponding to the nonnegative eigenvalues $\{\lambda_n, n = 1,2,\cdots\}$ of the positive compact self-adjoint operator T transforming the real Hilbert space $L_2(D)$ into $L_2(D)$ which is defined by

$$(Tf)(t) = \int_D v(s,t) f(s)\, m_L(ds) \qquad \text{for } t \in D \text{ and } f \in L_2(D).$$

Let $\{Z_n, n = 1,2,\cdots\}$ be a sequence of independent random variables on a probability space $(\Omega, \mathfrak{B}, P)$, each of which is distributed according to $N(0,1)$. Let A be the $\sigma(\mathfrak{M}_L \times \mathfrak{B})$-measurable subset of $D \times \Omega$ on which

$$G(t,\omega) = \sum_{n=1}^{\infty} \sqrt{\lambda_n}\, e_n(t) Z_n(\omega) \qquad \text{for } (t,\omega) \in D \times \Omega \tag{1}$$

converges. Then $(m_L \times P)(A^c) = 0$, and with the definition

$$G(t,\omega) = 0 \qquad \text{for } (t,\omega) \in A^c. \tag{2}$$

G is a measurable Gaussian process on $(\Omega, \mathfrak{B}, P)$ and D whose mean and covariance functions are given by

$$E\left[G(t,\cdot)\right] = 0 \qquad \text{for } t \in D \tag{3}$$

and

$$E\left[G(s,\cdot)\, G(t,\cdot)\right] = v(s,t) \qquad \text{for } (s,t) \in D \times D. \tag{4}$$

For every $t \in D$, the series in (1) converges for a.e. $\omega \in \Omega$ and for a.e. $\omega \in \Omega$ it converges both for a.e. $t \in D$ and in the Hilbert norm of $L_2(D)$.

Proof Let

$$G_n(t,\omega) = \sqrt{\lambda_n}\, e_n(t)\, Z_n(\omega) \quad \text{for } (t,\omega) \in D \times \Omega \text{ for } n = 1,2,\cdots. \tag{5}$$

Since G_n is $\sigma(\mathfrak{M}_D \times \mathfrak{B})$-measurable, $A \in \sigma(\mathfrak{M}_D \times \mathfrak{B})$. To show that $(m_L \times P)(A^c) = 0$ let us show first that for every $t \in D$, the series in (1) converges for a.e. $\omega \in \Omega$. Now from $E(Z_n) = 0$ and $V(Z_n) = 1$ we have

$$E\left[G_n(t,\cdot)\right] = 0 \text{ and } V\left[G_n(t,\cdot)\right] = \lambda_n\left\{e_n(t)\right\}^2 \quad \text{for } t \in D.$$

By Mercer's theorem,

$$\sum_{n=1}^{\infty} V\left[G_n(t,\cdot)\right] = \sum_{n=1}^{\infty} \lambda_n\left\{e_n(t)\right\}^2 = v(t,t) < \infty. \tag{6}$$

Thus for each $t \in D$, $\sum_{n=1}^{\infty} G_n(t,\cdot)$ converges for a.e. $\omega \in \Omega$ the exceptional subset of Ω depending on t (see Theorem B on p. 197 of Halmos [1]). Then $\chi_A(t,\omega) = 1$ for a.e. $\omega \in \Omega$ for each $t \in D$. By the Fubini theorem,

$$(m_L \times P)(A) = \int_D \left[\int_\Omega \chi_A(t,\omega)\, P(d\omega)\right] m_L(dt) = m_L(D).$$

Then since $(m_L \times P)(D \times \Omega) = m_L(D)$ we have $(m_L \times P)(A^c) = 0$.

Let us show that for a.e. $\omega \in \Omega$, the series in (1) converges for a.e. $\omega \in \Omega$. We have

$$b - a = (m_L \times P)(A) = \int_\Omega \left[\int_D \chi_A(t,\omega)\, m_L(dt)\right] P(d\omega).$$

For every $\omega \in \Omega$, the section of A at ω is Lebesgue measurable and $\int_D \chi_A(t,\omega)\, m_L(dt) \le b - a$. If $\int_D \chi_A(t,\omega)\, m_L(dt) < b - a$ for ω in a subset of Ω with a positive probability measure then

$$\int_\Omega \left[\int_D \chi_A(t,\omega)\, m_L(dt) \right] P(d\omega) < b - a,$$

contradicting $(m_L \times P)(A) = b - a$. Thus for a.e. $\omega \in \Omega$, we have $\int_D \chi_A(t,\omega)\, m_L(dt) = b - a$, i.e., for a.e. $\omega \in \Omega$ the series in (1) converges for a.e. $t \in D$.

Let us show next that for a.e. $\omega \in \Omega$, the series in (1) converges in the Hilbert norm of $L_2(D)$. According to Mercer's theorem, $\sum_{n=1}^{\infty} \lambda_n < \infty$. Thus there exists a positive interger N such that for $n \ge N$ we have $0 < \lambda_n < 1$ and hence $0 < \lambda_n^2 < \lambda_n < 1$. Then we have $\sum_{n=1}^{\infty} \lambda_n^2 < \infty$. Define a sequence of independent random variables $\{H_n, n = 1, 2, \cdots\}$ on $(\Omega, \mathfrak{B}, P)$ by

$$H_n(\omega) = \lambda_n \left[\{Z_n(\omega)\}^2 - 1 \right] \qquad \text{for } \omega \in \Omega. \tag{7}$$

Then from $E(Z_n^2) = V(Z_n) = 1$ we have $E(H_n) = 0$ and

$$\begin{aligned} V(H_n) &= E\left[\lambda_n^2 (Z_n^2 - 1)^2 \right] = \lambda_n^2\, E\left(Z_n^4 - 2Z_n^2 + 1 \right) \\ &= \lambda_n^2 (3 - 2 + 1) = 2\lambda_n^2, \end{aligned}$$

where we used (3) of Lemma 13.2 in obtaining

$$E\left(Z_n^4\right) = \sqrt{\frac{2^4}{\pi}}\; \Gamma\left(\tfrac{5}{2}\right) = 3.$$

Thus $\sum_{n=1}^{\infty} V(H_n) = 2\sum_{n=1}^{\infty} \lambda_n^2 < \infty$ and consequently $\sum_{n=1}^{\infty} H_n(\omega)$ converges for a.e. $\omega \in \Omega$. From this, (7), and $\sum_{n=1}^{\infty} \lambda_n < \infty$, we conclude that $\sum_{n=1}^{\infty} \lambda_n \{Z_n(\omega)\}^2$ converges for a.e. $\omega \in \Omega$. For each $\omega \in \Omega$ for which $\sum_{n=1}^{\infty} \lambda_n \{Z_n(\omega)\}^2$ converges, $\sum_{n=1}^{\infty} \sqrt{\lambda_n}\, Z_n(\omega)\, e_n(t)$, $t \in D$, converges in the Hilbert norm of $L_2(D)$ to some function $F(t, \omega)$, $t \in D$. Then there exists a subsequence $\{n_k, k = 1, 2, \cdots\}$ depending on ω such that $\sum_{n=1}^{\infty} \sqrt{\lambda_n}\, Z_n(\omega)\, e_n(t)$ converges to $F(t, \omega)$ for a.e. $t \in D$. On the other hand, as we have shown, for a.e. $\omega \in \Omega$, $\sum_{n=1}^{\infty} \sqrt{\lambda_n}\, Z_n(\omega)\, e_n(t)$ converges to $G(t, \omega)$ for a.e. $t \in D$. Thus for a.e. $\omega \in \Omega$, $F(\cdot, \omega)$ and $G(\cdot, \omega)$ are identical as elements of the Hilbert space $L_2(D)$, i.e., for a.e. $\omega \in \Omega$, $\sum_{n=1}^{\infty} \sqrt{\lambda_n}\, Z_n(\omega)\, e_n(t)$ converges to $G(t, \omega)$ in the Hilbert norm of $L_2(D)$.

To show that our stochastic process G is a Gaussian process whose mean and covariance functions are given by (3) and (4) we show that for $\{t_1, \cdots, t_k\} \subset D$ the characteristic function of the random vector $\left[G(t_1, \cdot), \cdots, G(t_k, \cdot)\right]$ is given by

$$E\left[\exp\left\{i \sum_{j=1}^{k} G(t_j, \cdot) y_j\right\}\right]$$

$$= \exp\left\{-\tfrac{1}{2} \sum_{j=1}^{k} \sum_{\ell=1}^{k} v(t_j, t_\ell) y_j y_\ell\right\} \qquad \text{for } (y_1, \cdots, y_k) \in R^k. \tag{8}$$

For simplicity let us write I for the left side of (8). Then by (1) and by the Bounded Convergence Theorem and finally by the independence of $\{Z_n, n = 1, 2, \cdots\}$,

$$I = E\left[\exp\left\{i \sum_{j=1}^{k} y_j \left[\sum_{n=1}^{\infty} \sqrt{\lambda_n}\, e_n(t_j)\, Z_n\right]\right\}\right]$$

$$= \lim_{N\to\infty} E\left[\exp\left\{i \sum_{n=1}^{N} Z_n\left[\sum_{j=1}^{k} y_j\sqrt{\lambda_n}\; e_n(t_j)\right]\right\}\right]$$

$$= \lim_{N\to\infty} \prod_{n=1}^{N} E\left[\exp\left\{i\, Z_n\left[\sum_{j=1}^{k} y_j\sqrt{\lambda_n}\; e_n(t_j)\right]\right\}\right].$$

Now since $Z_n \sum_{j=1}^{k} y_j\sqrt{\lambda_n}\; e_n(t_j)$ is distributed as $N\left(0, \left[\sum_{j=1}^{k} y_j\sqrt{\lambda_n}\; e_n(t_j)\right]^2\right)$ its characteristic function is given by

$$E\left[\exp\left\{i\, Z_n\left[\sum_{j=1}^{k} y_j\sqrt{\lambda_n}\; e_n(t_j)\right] y\right\}\right]$$

$$= \exp\left\{-\tfrac{1}{2}\left[\sum_{j=1}^{k} y_j\sqrt{\lambda_n}\; e_n(t_j)\right]^2 y^2\right\} \quad \text{for } y \in R^1.$$

Using this equality with $y = 1$ we have

$$I = \lim_{N\to\infty} \prod_{n=1}^{N} \exp\left\{-\tfrac{1}{2}\left[\sum_{j=1}^{k} y_j\sqrt{\lambda_n}\; e_n(t_j)\right]^2\right\}$$

$$= \lim_{N\to\infty} \prod_{n=1}^{N} \exp\left\{-\tfrac{1}{2} \sum_{j=1}^{k} \sum_{\ell=1}^{k} \lambda_n y_j y_\ell\; e_n(t_j)\; e_n(t_\ell)\right\}$$

$$= \lim_{N\to\infty} \exp\left\{-\tfrac{1}{2} \sum_{j=1}^{k} \sum_{\ell=1}^{k} y_j y_\ell\left[\sum_{n=1}^{N} \lambda_n e_n(t_j)\; e_n(t_\ell)\right]\right\}$$

$$= \exp\left\{-\tfrac{1}{2} \sum_{j=1}^{k} \sum_{\ell=1}^{k} y_j y_\ell\left[\sum_{n=1}^{\infty} \lambda_n e_n(t_j)\; e_n(t_\ell)\right]\right\},$$

which is equal to the right side of (8) by Mercer's theorem. This completes the proof of the theorem. □

§20. A STRONG LIMIT THEOREM FOR GAUSSIAN PROCESSES

For the standard Brownian motion process X (c.f. Theorem 17.1) on a probability space $(\Omega, \mathfrak{B}, P)$ and $D = [0,1] \subset R^1$, Lévy [1] and Cameron, and Martin [4] proved independently the following strong (i.e., almost everywhere) limit theorem:

$$P\left\{\omega \in \Omega ; \lim_{n\to\infty} \sum_{k=1}^{2^n} \left[X\left(\frac{k}{2^n}, \omega\right) - X\left(\frac{k-1}{2^n}, \omega\right)\right]^2 = 1\right\} = 1.$$

This result was extended by Baxter [1] to a large class of Gaussian processes whose covariance functions satisfy certain smoothness conditions. To prove Baxter's theorem, from which the above result of Lévy, Cameron, and Martin can be derived, we need the following lemmas.

<u>Lemma 20.1</u> Let f be a real-valued function which is defined and differentiable on (a, b) with $|f'(t)| \leq B$ for $t \in (a, b)$. Then $\lim_{t\downarrow a} f(t)$ and $\lim_{t\uparrow b} f(t)$ exist and satisfy

$$\left|\lim_{t\downarrow a} f(t) - f(c)\right| \leq B(c - a) \quad \text{and} \quad \left|\lim_{t\uparrow b} f(t) - f(c)\right| \leq B(b - c)$$

for $c \in (a, b)$.

<u>Proof</u> Let us prove the lemma for the endpoint a. Let $[a_0, c] \subset (a, b)$. Since f' is bounded on $[a_0, c]$, f is absolutely continuous there, and consequently

$$f(c) - f(a_0) = \int_{[a_0, c]} f'(t)\, m_L(dt).$$

Then $\lim_{a_0 \downarrow a} f(a_0)$ exists and satisfies

$$\left|f(c) - \lim_{a_0 \downarrow a} f(a_0)\right| \le \int_{(a,c]} |f'(t)|\, m_L(dt) \le B(c-a).$$

A similar proof can be given for the endpoint b. □

<u>Lemma 20.2</u> Let f be a real-valued function which is defined and differentiable on (a,b). If $\alpha = \lim_{t\downarrow a} f'(t)$ and $\beta = \lim_{t\uparrow b} f'(t)$ exist and are finite then the same holds for $\lim_{t\downarrow a} f(t)$ and $\lim_{t\uparrow b} f(t)$. If we define $f(a) = \lim_{t\downarrow a} f(t)$ and $f(b) = \lim_{t\uparrow b} f(t)$ then the right side derivative at a and the left side derivative at b exist for f and are equal to α and β, respectively.

<u>Proof</u> We prove the lemma for the endpoint a. Since α is finite f' is bounded on $(a, a+\delta)$ for some $\delta > 0$. By Lemma 20.1, $\lim_{t\downarrow a} f(t)$ exists and is finite. Let $f(a) = \lim_{t\downarrow a} f(t)$. Take $a_0 \in (a, a+\delta)$. From the boundedness of f' on $(a, a_0]$, f is absolutely continuous on $[a, a_0]$ and

$$f(a_0) - f(a) = \int_{[a,a_0]} f'(t)\, m_L(dt),$$

so that

$$\lim_{a_0\downarrow a} \left|\frac{f(a_0) - f(a)}{a_0 - a} - \alpha\right| \le \frac{1}{a_0 - a} \lim_{a_0 \downarrow a} \int_{[a,a_0]} |f'(t) - \alpha|\, m_L(dt) = 0.$$

This proves that the right side derivative of f at a is equal to α. A similar proof can be given for the endpoint b. □

<u>Lemma 20.3</u> Let $r(s,t)$ be a real-valued function

defined on the open triangle $\{(s,t) \in R^2;\ s \in (0,t)$ and $t \in (0,1)\}$. If $\partial^2 r/\partial s^2$ and $\partial^2 r/\partial t\,\partial s$ exist and satisfy $|\partial^2 r(s,t)/\partial s^2|$, $|\partial^2 r(s,t)/\partial t\,\partial s| \le B$ on the open triangle then, for every $t \in (0,1)$, the left side derivative

$$D^-(t) = \lim_{s\uparrow t} \frac{r(s,t) - r(t,t)}{s - t} \tag{1}$$

exists. Furthermore D^- is bounded and continuous on $(0,1)$ and satisfies

$$D^-(t) = \lim_{s\uparrow t} \frac{\partial r}{\partial s}(s,t), \tag{2}$$

$$\left| D^-(t) - \frac{\partial r}{\partial s}(s,t) \right| \le B(t-s), \tag{3}$$

$$|D^-(t') - D^-(t'')| \le 2B\,|t' - t''|. \tag{4}$$

Similar statements for

$$D^+(t) = \lim_{s\downarrow t} \frac{r(s,t) - r(t,t)}{s - t}$$

hold on the open triangle $\{(s,t) \in R^2;\ s \in (t,1),\ t \in (0,1)\}$.

<u>Proof</u> For a fixed $t \in (0,1)$ let $g(s) = r(s,t)$ for $s \in (0,t)$. From the boundedness of g'' on $(0,t)$ we have the existence and finiteness of $\lim_{s\downarrow 0} g'(s)$ and $\lim_{s\uparrow t} g'(s)$ according to Lemma 20.1. From the continuity of g' on $(0,t)$ implied by the existence of g'' there and from the existence of $\lim_{s\downarrow 0} g'(s)$ and $\lim_{s\uparrow t} g'(s)$ we have the boundedness of g' on $(0,t)$. From Lemma 20.1 we have

$$\left| \lim_{s\uparrow t} g'(s) - g'(s) \right| \le B(t-s). \tag{5}$$

By Lemma 20.2 the left side derivative $D^-(t)$ of g at t exists and is equal to $\lim_{s\uparrow t} g'(s)$. From the definition of g we have (2) and from (5) we have (3).

To prove (4) let $t', t'' \in (0,1)$ and consider the case $t'<t''$. Let $s \in (0,t')$. Then

$$
\begin{aligned}
|D^-(t') - D^-(t'')| &\le \left| D^-(t') - \frac{\partial r}{\partial s}(s,t') \right| + \left| \frac{\partial r}{\partial s}(s,t') - \frac{\partial r}{\partial s}(s,t'') \right| \\
&\quad + \left| \frac{\partial r}{\partial s}(s,t'') - D^-(t'') \right| \\
&\le B(t' - s) + \left| \frac{\partial^2 r}{\partial t\, \partial s}(s,t^*) \right| (t'' - t') + B(t'' - s) \\
&\le B(t' - s) + B(t'' - t') + B(t'' - s)
\end{aligned}
$$

with $t^* \in (t', t'')$. Since $s \in (0,t')$ is arbitrary, be letting $s \uparrow t'$ we have (4). □

<u>Theorem 20.4</u> (G. Baxter). Let X be a Gaussian process on a probability space $(\Omega, \mathfrak{B}, P)$ and $D = [0,1] \subset R^1$ whose mean function $m(t)$, $t \in D$, has a bounded first derivative on D and whose covariance function $r(s,t)$, $(s,t) \in D \times D$, is continuous on $D \times D$ and has bounded partial derivatives $\partial^2 r/\partial s^2$ and $\partial^2 r/\partial t\, \partial s$ on $D \times D$ except possibly on the diagonal $\{(s,t) \in D \times D ; s = t\}$. For $t \in (0,1)$ let

$$
\begin{aligned}
D^-(t) &= \lim_{s\uparrow t} \frac{r(s,t) - r(t,t)}{s - t}, \\
&\qquad\qquad\qquad\qquad\qquad\qquad\qquad\qquad (1) \\
D^+(t) &= \lim_{s\downarrow t} \frac{r(s,t) - r(t,t)}{s - t},
\end{aligned}
$$

and

$$f(t) = D^{-}(t) - D^{+}(t). \tag{2}$$

Then

$$P\left\{\omega \in \Omega ; \lim_{n\to\infty} \sum_{k=1}^{2^n} \left[X\left(\frac{k}{2^n}, \omega\right) - X\left(\frac{k-1}{2^n}, \omega\right)\right]^2 = \int_0^1 f(t)\, dt\right\} = 1. \tag{3}$$

<u>Proof</u> The covariance function r satisfies the conditions of Lemma 20.3. Let us first prove the theorem for the case where $m(t) = 0$ for $t \in D$. For each positive integer n let

$$Y_k^{(n)}(\omega) = X\left(\frac{k}{2^n}, \omega\right) - X\left(\frac{k-1}{2^n}, \omega\right)$$

and

$$Z_n(\omega) = \sum_{k=1}^{2^n} \left[Y_k^{(n)}(\omega)\right]^2 .$$

Since $\{Y_k^{(n)}, k = 1, 2, \cdots, 2^n\}$ is a collection of linear combinations of the Gaussian system of random variables $\{X(t, \cdot), t \in D\}$, it is a Gaussian system according to Theorem 16.9. Then $Y_n = \left(Y_1^{(n)}, \cdots, Y_{2^n}^{(n)}\right)$ is a random vector whose probability distribution is a 2^n-dimensional normal distribution with mean vector 0 and covariance matrix V_n given by

$$V_n = \left[v_{jk}^{(n)}, \ j, k = 1, 2, \cdots, 2^n\right], \quad \text{where } v_{jk}^{(n)} = E\left(Y_j^{(n)} Y_k^{(n)}\right).$$

Also Z_n is the inner product of the vector Y_n with itself, i.e.,

$$Z_n = (Y_n, Y_n).$$

Applying Theorem 16.16 with $C = I$, we have

$$E(Z_n) = E\left[(Y_n, Y_n)\right] = \mathrm{Tr}(V_n) = \sum_{k=1}^{2^n} v_{kk}^{(n)}, \tag{4}$$

$$E(Z_n^2) = E\left[(Y_n, Y_n)^2\right]$$

$$= 3\sum_{j=1}^{2^n}\left[v_{jj}^{(n)}\right]^2 + 2\sum_{j=1}^{2^n}\sum_{j<k}\left\{v_{jj}^{(n)} v_{kk}^{(n)} + 2\left[v_{jk}^{(n)}\right]^2\right\},$$

so that

$$V(Z_n) = E(Z_n^2) - \left[E(Z_n)\right]^2 = 2\sum_{j=1}^{2^n}\sum_{k=1}^{2^n}\left[v_{jk}^{(n)}\right]^2 \equiv v_n. \tag{5}$$

Now according to the Chebyshev inequality,

$$P\left\{\omega \in \Omega; |Z_n(\omega) - E(Z_n)| \geq \frac{n}{2^{n/2}}\right\} \leq \frac{2^n}{n^2} v_n .$$

Since $\lim_{n\to\infty} n/2^{n/2} = 0$ and $\sum_{n=1}^{\infty} 1/n^2 < \infty$, if we show that $2^n v_n$, $n = 1,2,\cdots$, are bounded, then by Theorem A5.1,

$$\lim_{n\to\infty}\left\{Z_n(\omega) - E(Z_n)\right\} = 0 \quad \text{for a.e. } \omega \in \Omega \tag{6}$$

We proceed to show that $2^n v_n$, $n = 1,2,\cdots$, are indeed bounded. Let $B \geq 0$ be a bound for $\partial^2 r/\partial s^2$ and $\partial^2 r/\partial t\,\partial s$ on $D \times D$ except possibly on the diagonal. For $j \neq k$ where $j, k = 1,2,\cdots,2^n$, we have

$$v_{jk}^{(n)} = E\left(Y_j^{(n)} Y_k^{(n)}\right)$$

$$= E\left[\left\{X\left(\frac{j}{2^n},\cdot\right) - X\left(\frac{j-1}{2^n},\cdot\right)\right\}\left\{X\left(\frac{k}{2^n},\cdot\right) - X\left(\frac{k-1}{2^n},\cdot\right)\right\}\right]$$

$$= r\left(\frac{j}{2^n},\frac{k}{2^n}\right) - r\left(\frac{j-1}{2^n},\frac{k}{2^n}\right) - r\left(\frac{j}{2^n},\frac{k-1}{2^n}\right) + r\left(\frac{j-1}{2^n},\frac{k-1}{2^n}\right).$$

$$= \left\{ \frac{\partial r}{\partial s}\left(\frac{j^*}{2^n}, \frac{k}{2^n}\right) - \frac{\partial r}{\partial s}\left(\frac{j^{**}}{2^n}, \frac{k-1}{2^n}\right) \right\} \frac{1}{2^n}$$

$$= \left\{ \frac{\partial r}{\partial s}\left(\frac{j^*}{2^n}, \frac{k}{2^n}\right) - \frac{\partial r}{\partial s}\left(\frac{j^{**}}{2^n}, \frac{k}{2^n}\right) + \frac{\partial r}{\partial s}\left(\frac{j^{**}}{2^n}, \frac{k}{2^n}\right) - \frac{\partial r}{\partial s}\left(\frac{j^{**}}{2^n}, \frac{k-1}{2^n}\right) \right\} \frac{1}{2^n}$$

$$= \left\{ \frac{\partial^2 r}{\partial s^2}\left(\frac{j^{***}}{2^n}, \frac{k}{2^n}\right) \frac{|j^* - j^{**}|}{2^n} + \frac{\partial^2 r}{\partial t\, \partial s}\left(\frac{j^{**}}{2^n}, \frac{k^*}{2^n}\right) \frac{1}{2^n} \right\} \frac{1}{2^n},$$

where $j^*, j^{**}, j^{***} \in (j-1, j)$ and $k^* \in (k-1, k)$. Thus

$$|v_{jk}^{(n)}| \le 2B\left(\frac{1}{2^n}\right)^2 \quad \text{and}$$

$$\left[v_{jk}^{(n)}\right]^2 \le 4B^2\left(\frac{1}{2^n}\right)^4 = O\left(\left(\frac{1}{2^n}\right)^4\right) \quad \text{for } j \ne k. \tag{7}$$

On the other hand, for $k = 1, 2, \cdots, 2^n$, we have

$$v_{kk}^{(n)} = E\left(\left[Y_k^{(n)}\right]^2\right) = E\left[\left\{X\left(\frac{k}{2^n}, \cdot\right) - X\left(\frac{k-1}{2^n}, \cdot\right)\right\}^2\right]$$

$$= r\left(\frac{k}{2^n}, \frac{k}{2^n}\right) - r\left(\frac{k-1}{2^n}, \frac{k}{2^n}\right) - r\left(\frac{k}{2^n}, \frac{k-1}{2^n}\right) + r\left(\frac{k-1}{2^n}, \frac{k-1}{2^n}\right)$$

$$= \left\{ \frac{\partial r}{\partial s}\left(\frac{k^*}{2^n}, \frac{k}{2^n}\right) - \frac{\partial r}{\partial s}\left(\frac{k^{**}}{2^n}, \frac{k-1}{2^n}\right) \right\} \frac{1}{2^n},$$

where $k^*, k^{**} \in (k-1, k)$. According to (2) and (3) of Lemma 20.3,

$$\lim_{s \uparrow k2^{-n}} \frac{\partial r}{\partial s}\left(s, \frac{k}{2^n}\right) = D^-\left(\frac{k}{2^n}\right) \quad \text{and}$$

$$\left| \frac{\partial r}{\partial s}\left(s, \frac{k}{2^n}\right) - D^-\left(\frac{k}{2^n}\right) \right| \le B\left(\frac{k}{2^n} - s\right),$$

so that

$$\frac{\partial r}{\partial s}\left(s, \frac{k}{2^n}\right) = D^-\left(\frac{k}{2^n}\right) + O\left(\frac{k}{2^n} - s\right).$$

Thus

$$\frac{\partial r}{\partial s}\left(\frac{k^*}{2^n}, \frac{k}{2^n}\right) = D^-\left(\frac{k}{2^n}\right) + O\left(\frac{1}{2^n}\right),$$

and similarly

$$\frac{\partial r}{\partial s}\left(\frac{k^{**}}{2^n}, \frac{k-1}{2^n}\right) = D^+\left(\frac{k-1}{2^n}\right) + O\left(\frac{1}{2^n}\right).$$

Then from the boundedness of $D^-(t)$ and $D^+(t)$ for $t \in (0, 1)$, according to Lemma 20.3,

$$v_{kk}^{(n)} = \left\{ D^-\left(\frac{k}{2^n}\right) - D^+\left(\frac{k-1}{2^n}\right)\right\}\frac{1}{2^n} + O\left(\left(\frac{1}{2^n}\right)^2\right) = O\left(\frac{1}{2^n}\right) \quad \text{and}$$

$$\left[v_{kk}^{(n)}\right]^2 = O\left(\left(\frac{1}{2^n}\right)^2\right). \tag{8}$$

Recalling the definition of v_n in (5) we have, by (7) and (8),

$$2^n v_n = 2^{n+1}\left\{2^n\, O\left(\left(\frac{1}{2^n}\right)^2\right) + 2^n(2^n - 1)\, O\left(\left(\frac{1}{2^n}\right)^4\right)\right\} = O(1).$$

This proves the boundedness of $2^n v_n$, $n = 1, 2, \cdots$, and hence (6). Now from (8) and from (4) of Lemma 20.3,

$$v_{kk}^{(n)} = \left\{D^-\left(\frac{k}{2^n}\right) - D^+\left(\frac{k}{2^n}\right) + O\left(\frac{1}{2^n}\right)\right\}\frac{1}{2^n} + O\left(\left(\frac{1}{2^n}\right)^2\right)$$

$$= f\left(\frac{k}{2^n}\right)\frac{1}{2^n} + O\left(\left(\frac{1}{2^n}\right)^2\right)$$

for $k = 1, 2, \cdots, 2^n - 1$. [Recall that $D^+(1)$ is not defined.] From this and (4) and also (8), for $k = 2^n$,

$$E(Z_n) = \sum_{k=1}^{2^n-1} \left\{ f\left(\frac{k}{2^n}\right)\frac{1}{2^n} + o\left(\left(\frac{1}{2^n}\right)^2\right) \right\} + o\left(\frac{1}{2^n}\right)$$

$$= \sum_{k=1}^{2^n-1} f\left(\frac{k}{2^n}\right)\frac{1}{2^n} + o\left(\frac{1}{2^n}\right),$$

so that

$$\lim_{n\to\infty} E(Z_n) = \int_0^1 f(t)\, dt, \tag{9}$$

where the last integral is an improper Riemann integral which exists since f is bounded and continuous on $(0, 1)$ according to Lemma 20.3. From (6) and (9) we have the theorem proved for the case where $m(t) = 0$ for $t \in D$.

Let us turn now to the case where the mean function m has a bounded first derivative on D, say $|m'(t)| \leq M$ for $t \in D$. The stochastic process $\widetilde{X}$ on $(\Omega, \mathfrak{B}, P)$ and D defined by

$$\widetilde{X}(t, \omega) = X(t, \omega) - m(t)$$

is a Gaussian process which has the same covariance function as X and an identically vanishing mean function. For simplicity let us write

$$\Delta_{n,k} X(\omega) = X\left(\frac{k}{2^n}, \omega\right) - X\left(\frac{k-1}{2^n}, \omega\right),$$

$$\Delta_{n,k} m = m\left(\frac{k}{2^n}\right) - m\left(\frac{k-1}{2^n}\right),$$

$$\Delta_{n,k} \widetilde{X}(\omega) = \widetilde{X}\left(\frac{k}{2^n}, \omega\right) - \widetilde{X}\left(\frac{k-1}{2^n}, \omega\right).$$

Since the theorem holds for $\widetilde{X}$ we have

$$\lim_{n\to\infty} \sum_{k=1}^{2^n} \left[\Delta_{n,k} \widetilde{X}(\omega)\right]^2 = \int_0^1 f(t)\, dt \quad \text{for a.e. } \omega \in \Omega. \tag{10}$$

Now

$$\sum_{k=1}^{2^n} (\Delta_{n,k} X)^2 = \sum_{k=1}^{2^n} (\Delta_{n,k} \widetilde{X} + \Delta_{n,k} m)^2$$

$$= \sum_{k=1}^{2^n} (\Delta_{n,k} \widetilde{X})^2 + 2 \sum_{k=1}^{2^n} (\Delta_{n,k} \widetilde{X})(\Delta_{n,k} m) + \sum_{k=1}^{2^n} (\Delta_{n,k} m)^2. \tag{11}$$

Here we have

$$\lim_{n\to\infty} \sum_{k=1}^{2^n} (\Delta_{n,k} m)^2 \le \lim_{n\to\infty} M^2 \sum_{k=1}^{2^n} \left(\frac{1}{2^n}\right)^2 = \lim_{n\to\infty} \frac{M^2}{2^n} = 0, \tag{12}$$

and, by means of the Schwarz inequality, (12) and (10),

$$\lim_{n\to\infty} \left\{ \sum_{k=1}^{2^n} \Delta_{n,k} \widetilde{X}(\omega) \cdot \Delta_{n,k} m \right\}^2$$
$$\le \lim_{n\to\infty} \left\{ \sum_{k=1}^{2^n} \left[\Delta_{n,k} \widetilde{X}(\omega)\right]^2 \cdot \sum_{k=1}^{2^n} [\Delta_{n,k} m]^2 \right\} = 0 \tag{13}$$

for a.e. $\omega \in \Omega$.

Using (12) and (13) in (11), we have

$$\lim_{n\to\infty} \sum_{k=1}^{2^n} \left[\Delta_{n,k} X(\omega)\right]^2 = \lim_{n\to\infty} \sum_{k=1}^{2^n} \left[\Delta_{n,k} \widetilde{X}(\omega)\right]^2 = \int_0^1 f(t)\, dt$$

for a.e. $\omega \in \Omega$,

proving the theorem for X. □

Corollary 20.5 Under the assumptions in Theorem 20.4, if in addition $\partial r(t, t)/\partial s$ exists for $t \in (0, 1)$ then

$$P\left\{\omega \in \Omega; \lim_{n\to\infty} \sum_{k=1}^{2^n} \left[X\left(\frac{k}{2^n}, \omega\right) - X\left(\frac{k-1}{2^n}, \omega\right)\right]^2 = 0\right\} = 1.$$

Proof If $\partial r(t, t)/\partial s$ exists for $t \in (0, 1)$, then

$$D^-(t) = D^+(t) = \frac{\partial r}{\partial s}(t, t) \qquad \text{and}$$

$$f(t) = D^-(t) - D^+(t) = 0 \qquad \text{for } t \in (0, 1),$$

so that $\int_0^1 f(t)\, dt = 0.$ □

Corollary 20.6 Let $a(t)$, $t \in D = [0, 1]$, be a real-valued function with a bounded first derivative on D, let $b(t)$, $t \in D$, be a monotone increasing function with a bounded second derivative on D and let c be a real number. For the generalized Brownian motion process X on a probability space $(\Omega, \mathfrak{B}, P)$ and D for which the probability distribution of $X(t'', \cdot) - X(t', \cdot)$, $t', t'' \in D$, $t' < t''$, is given by the normal distribution $N\left(a(t'') - a(t'), b(t'') - b(t')\right)$ and $X(0, \cdot) = c$ a.e. on Ω, we have

$$P\left\{\omega \in \Omega; \lim_{n\to\infty} \sum_{k=1}^{2^n} \left[X\left(\frac{k}{2^n}, \omega\right) - X\left(\frac{k-1}{2^n}, \omega\right)\right]^2 = \int_0^1 b'(t)\, dt\right\} = 1. \tag{1}$$

In particular for the standard Brownian motion process for which $a(t) = 0$ and $b(t) = t$ for $t \in D$ and $c = 0$ we have

$$P\left\{\omega \in \Omega; \lim_{n\to\infty} \sum_{k=1}^{2^n} \left[X\left(\frac{k}{2^n}, \omega\right) - X\left(\frac{k-1}{2^n}, \omega\right)\right]^2 = 1\right\} = 1. \tag{2}$$

Proof According to Theorem 17.1, the mean function m

and the covariance function r of our process X are given by

$$m(t) = E\left[X(t,\cdot)\right] = a(t) - a(0) + c \qquad \text{for } t \in D$$

$$\begin{aligned} r(s,t) &= C\left[X(s,\cdot), X(t,\cdot)\right] = b\left(\min\{s,t\}\right) - b(0) \\ &= \min\left\{b(s), b(t)\right\} - b(0) \\ &= \begin{cases} b(s) - b(0) & \text{for } s \le t,\ (s,t) \in D \times D \\ b(t) - b(0) & \text{for } s \ge t,\ (s,t) \in D \times D . \end{cases} \end{aligned}$$

Since $a'(t)$ and $b''(t)$ exist and are bounded on D , m and r satisfy the conditions in Theorem 20.4. Furthermore, for $t \in (0,1)$,

$$D^-(t) = \lim_{s \uparrow t} \frac{r(s,t) - r(t,t)}{s - t} = \lim_{s \uparrow t} \frac{b(s) - b(t)}{s - t} = b'(t) ,$$

$$D^+(t) = \lim_{s \downarrow t} \frac{r(s,t) - r(t,t)}{s - t} = \lim_{s \downarrow t} \frac{b(t) - b(t)}{s - t} = 0 ,$$

so that

$$f(t) = D^-(t) - D^+(t) = b'(t).$$

Using this in (3) of Theorem 20.4 we have our corollary. □

Corollary 20.7 Let X be a Gaussian process on a probability space $(\Omega, \mathfrak{B}, P)$ and $D = [0,1]$ whose mean function has a bounded first derivative on D and whose covariance function r is given by

$$r(s,t) = C\left[X(s,\cdot), X(t,\cdot)\right] = \begin{cases} u(s)\, v(t) & \text{for } s \le t,\ (s,t) \in D \times D \\ u(t)\, v(s) & \text{for } s \ge t,\ (s,t) \in D \times D , \end{cases}$$

where u and v are nonnegative functions on D satisfying

$$u(t'')\, v(t') - u(t')\, v(t'') \ge 0 \qquad \text{for } t', t'' \in D,\ t' < t'' .$$

If u and v have bounded second derivatives on D, then

$$P\left\{\omega \in \Omega ; \lim_{n\to\infty} \sum_{k=1}^{2^n} \left[X\left(\frac{k}{2^n}, \omega\right) - X\left(\frac{k-1}{2^n}, \omega\right)\right]^2 = \int_0^1 \left[u'(t)\, v(t) - u(t)\, v'(t)\right] dt \right\} = 1.$$

Proof For the existence of such a process see Theorem 17.5. Now since u'' and v'' exist and are bounded on D, r satisfies the conditions in Theorem 20.4. Also

$$D^-(t) = \lim_{s\uparrow t} \frac{r(s,t) - r(t,t)}{s - t} = \lim_{s\uparrow t} \frac{u(s)\,v(t) - u(t)\,v(t)}{s - t} = u'(t)v(t),$$

$$D^+(t) = \lim_{s\downarrow t} \frac{r(s,t) - r(t,t)}{s - t} = \lim_{s\downarrow t} \frac{u(t)\,v(s) - u(t)\,v(t)}{s - t} = u(t)v'(t),$$

and

$$f(t) = D^-(t) - D^+(t) = u'(t)\,v(t) - u(t)\,v'(t).$$

Then the corollary follows from (3) of Theorem 20.4. □

§21. CONTINUITY AND DIFFERENTIABILITY OF SAMPLE FUNCTIONS OF A GAUSSIAN PROCESS

Before we come to the discussion of the continuity of sample functions of Gaussian processes let us consider the stochastic continuity of a Gaussian process. As we saw in Theorem 5.2, the stochastic continuity of a process implies the existence of an extended real-valued equivalent process which is almost surely separable and measurable with respect to the completion of the product measure space of the probability measure and the Lebesgue measure on the domain of definition of the process. Our first theorem below asserts that the continuity of the mean function and the covariance function of a Gaussian process implies the stochastic continuity of the process.

Theorem 21.1 Let X be a Gaussian process on a probability space $(\Omega, \mathfrak{B}, P)$ and an interval $D \subset R^1$. If the mean function $m(t) = E[X(t, \cdot)]$, $t \in D$, is continuous at $t_0 \in D$ and the covariance function $v(s,t) = C[X(s, \cdot), X(t, \cdot)]$, $s, t \in D$, is continuous at $(t_0, t_0) \in D \times D$ then X is stochastically continuous at t_0.

Proof Let $t_0, t_1 \in D$. Since X is a Gaussian process, the probability distribution of the random vector $[X(t_0, \cdot), X(t_1, \cdot)]$ is a 2-dimensional normal distribution, and according to Theorem 16.3, the probability distribution of the random variable $X(t_1, \cdot) - X(t_0, \cdot)$ is the following normal distribution:

$$N\left(m(t_1) - m(t_0),\ v(t_1, t_1) - v(t_1, t_0) - v(t_0, t_1) + v(t_0, t_0)\right).$$

Now, for every $\epsilon > 0$,

$$\begin{aligned}
&P\{\omega \in \Omega;\ |X(t_1, \omega) - X(t_0, \omega)| \geq \epsilon\} \\
&\leq P\left\{\omega \in \Omega;\ \left|\{X(t_1, \omega) - X(t_0, \omega)\} - \{m(t_1) - m(t_0)\}\right| \geq \frac{\epsilon}{2}\right\} \\
&\quad + P\left\{\omega \in \Omega;\ |m(t_1) - m(t_0)| \geq \frac{\epsilon}{2}\right\} \\
&\leq \frac{4}{\epsilon^2} V[X(t_1, \cdot) - X(t_0, \cdot)] + P\left\{\omega \in \Omega;\ |m(t_1) - m(t_0)| \geq \frac{\epsilon}{2}\right\} \\
&= \frac{4}{\epsilon^2}\{v(t_1, t_1) - v(t_1, t_0) - v(t_0, t_1) + v(t_0, t_0)\} \\
&\quad + P\left\{\omega \in \Omega;\ |m(t_1) - m(t_0)| \geq \frac{\epsilon}{2}\right\},
\end{aligned}$$

where in obtaining the second inequality we applied the Chebyshev inequality. Since $v(s,t)$ is continuous at (t_0, t_0) and $m(t)$ is continuous at t_0, for every $\eta > 0$ there exists $\delta > 0$ such that

$$|v(s,t) - v(t_0,t_0)| < \eta \quad \text{and} \quad |m(t) - m(t_0)| < \eta$$

when $s, t \in (t_0 - \delta, t_0 - \delta)$.

Then for $t_1 \in (t_0 - \delta, t_0 + \delta)$ we have

$$|v(t_1,t_1) - v(t_1,t_0) - v(t_0,t_1) - v(t_0,t_0)|$$

$$\leq |v(t_1,t_1) - v(t_0,t_0)| + |v(t_0,t_0) - v(t_1,t_0)|$$

$$+ |v(t_0,t_1) - v(t_0,t_0)| < 3\eta,$$

so that with $\eta < \epsilon/2$ we have

$$P\left\{\omega \in \Omega ; |X(t_1,\omega) - X(t_0,\omega)| \geq \epsilon\right\} \leq \frac{12}{\epsilon^2}\eta + 0,$$

which proves the stochastic continuity of X at t_0. □

The following theorem asserts that, if the mean function is identically vanishing on the domain of definition D of a Gaussian process X and the variance $V\left[X(t',\cdot) - X(t'',\cdot)\right]$ satisfies a Lipschitz condition of order $\beta > 0$ for $t', t'' \in D$, then the process is stochastically continuous on D. This is a generalization of Theorem 13.7 for the Brownian motion process for which $V\left[X(t',\cdot) - X(t'',\cdot)\right] = c\,|t' - t''|$ for $t', t'' \in D$.

<u>Theorem 21.2</u> Let X be a Gaussian process on a probability space $(\Omega, \mathfrak{B}, P)$ and an interval $D \subset R^1$. If

$$E\left[X(t,\cdot)\right] = 0 \qquad \text{for } t \in D \tag{1}$$

$$V\left[X(t',\cdot) - X(t'',\cdot)\right] \leq B\,|t' - t''|^{\beta}$$

for $t', t'' \in D$ where $B, \beta > 0$ (2)

then X is stochastically continuous at every $t \in D$, and in fact, for every $\varepsilon > 0$ and $h \in R^1$,

$$P\left\{\omega \in \Omega ;\ |X(t+h,\omega) - X(t,\omega)| \geq \varepsilon\right\}$$

$$\leq \left\{\frac{2B|h|^\beta}{\pi}\right\}^{\frac{1}{2}} \frac{1}{\varepsilon} \exp\left\{-\frac{\varepsilon^2}{2B|h|^\beta}\right\} \tag{3}$$

holds.

Proof Since X is a Gaussian distribution, the probability distribution of the random vector $\left[X(t,\cdot),\ X(t+h,\cdot)\right]$, $t \in D$, $h \in R^1$, is a 2-dimensional normal distribution, and by Theorem 16.3 the random variable $X(t+h,\cdot) - X(t,\cdot)$ is normally distributed with mean m and variance v satisfying

$$m = E\left[X(t+h,\cdot) - X(t,\cdot)\right] = 0,$$

$$v = V\left[X(t+h,\cdot) - X(t,\cdot)\right] \leq B|h|^\beta$$

under the assumptions of (1) and (2). When $v = 0$ then (3) holds trivially, the left side of (3) being equal to 0, according to the Chebyshev inequality. On the other hand when $v > 0$ then we have, according to (2) of Lemma 13.5,

$$P\left\{\omega \in \Omega ;\ |X(t+h,\omega) - X(t,\omega)| \geq \varepsilon\right\}$$

$$= \frac{2}{(2\pi v)^{\frac{1}{2}}} \int_\varepsilon^\infty \exp\left\{-\frac{u^2}{2v}\right\} du$$

$$\leq \frac{2}{\sqrt{2\pi}} \exp\left\{-\frac{\varepsilon^2}{2v}\right\} \frac{v^{\frac{1}{2}}}{\varepsilon}$$

$$\leq \sqrt{\frac{2}{\pi}} \exp\left\{-\frac{\varepsilon^2}{2\beta|h|^\beta}\right\} \frac{\sqrt{B|h|^\beta}}{\varepsilon} ,$$

which is (3). □

The following theorem concerning the continuity of sample functions of a Gaussian process is due to A. N. Kolmogorov. Here we present a proof based on Theorem 6.2 by M. Loève. The proof resembles that of Theorem 13.8 for the Brownian motion process.

Theorem 21.3 A. N. Kolmogorov. If a Gaussian process X on a probability space $(\Omega, \mathfrak{B}, P)$ and an interval $D \subset R^1$ satisfies (1), (2) of Theorem 21.2 then it has an equivalent process which is almost surely continuous. If in addition, X is almost surely separable then X is itself almost surely continuous.

Proof Let $0 < a < \beta/2$. For the choice $\epsilon = |h|^a$ we have, according to (3) of Theorem 21.2,

$$P\{\omega \in \Omega ; |X(t+h, \omega) - X(t, \omega)| \geq |h|^a\}$$

$$\leq \sqrt{\frac{2B}{\pi}} \; |h|^{\frac{\beta}{2}-a} \exp\left\{-\frac{|h|^{2a-\beta}}{2B}\right\}.$$

Let

$$g(h) = |h|^a$$

and

$$q(h) = \sqrt{\frac{2B}{\pi}} \; |h|^{\frac{\beta}{2}-a} \exp\left\{-\frac{|h|^{2a-\beta}}{2B}\right\}.$$

Then

$$\sum_{n=1}^{\infty} g\left(\frac{1}{2^n}\right) = \sum_{n=1}^{\infty} \left(\frac{1}{2^a}\right)^n < \infty$$

and

$$\sum_{n=1}^{\infty} 2^n q\left(\frac{1}{2^n}\right) = \sqrt{\frac{2B}{\pi}} \sum_{n=1}^{\infty} 2^{n\left(1-\frac{\beta}{2}+a\right)} \exp\left\{-\frac{2^{n(\beta-2a)}}{2B}\right\} .$$

The convergence of this series can be verified by the logarithmic ratio test. In fact if we write u_n for the nth term of the series we have

$$\log \lim_{n\to\infty} \frac{u_{n+1}}{u_n}$$

$$= \left(1-\frac{\beta}{2}+a\right) \log 2 + \lim_{n\to\infty} \frac{1}{2B} 2^{n(\beta-2a)}\left(1-a^{\beta-2a}\right) = -\infty$$

since $\beta - 2a > 0$, $\lim_{n\to\infty} 2^{n(\beta-2a)} = \infty$, and $1 - 2^{\beta-2a} < 0$. Therefore by Theorem 6.2, X has an equivalent process which is almost surely continuous. If X is almost surely separable then by Theorem 6.5 it is itself almost surely continuous. □

Lemma 21.4 Let X be a Gaussian process on a probability space $(\Omega, \mathfrak{B}, P)$ and an interval $D \subset R^1$ which satisfies the conditions

$$E\left[X(t,\cdot)\right] = 0 \qquad \text{for } t \in D \tag{1}$$

$$V\left[X(t',\cdot) - X(t'',\cdot)\right] \geq A\,|t'-t''|^{\alpha} \qquad \text{for } t', t'' \in D$$

where $A, \alpha > 0$. (2)

Let $\lambda > \alpha/2$. Then for every $t \in D$ there exists $\Gamma_t \in \mathfrak{B}$ with $P(\Gamma_t) = 1$ such that, for every $\omega \in \Gamma_t$,

$$\limsup_{s\downarrow 0} \frac{|X(t+s,\omega) - X(t,\omega)|}{s^{\lambda}} = \infty , \tag{3}$$

$$\limsup_{s\downarrow 0} \frac{|X(t-s,\omega) - X(t,\omega)|}{s^{\lambda}} = \infty . \tag{4}$$

<u>Proof</u> For $t \in D$, $s > 0$, and positive integer k, let

$$\Gamma_{t,k,s} = \left\{\omega \in \Omega ;\ |X(t+s,\omega) - X(t,\omega)| < ms^{\lambda}\right\} \in \mathfrak{B} .$$

Since the random variable $X(t+s,\cdot) - X(t,\cdot)$ is normally distributed with mean m and variance v, where

$$m = E\left[X(t+s,\cdot) - X(t,\cdot)\right] = 0 ,$$

$$v = V\left[X(t+s,\cdot) - X(t,\cdot)\right] \geq As^{\alpha},$$

according to (1) and (2), we have

$$P(\Gamma_{t,k,s}) = \frac{1}{\sqrt{2\pi v}} \int_{|u| \leq ks^{\lambda}} \exp\left\{-\frac{u^2}{2v}\right\} du$$

$$\leq \frac{2}{\sqrt{2\pi A s^{\alpha}}}\, ks^{\lambda}$$

$$= \sqrt{\frac{2}{\pi A}}\, ks^{\lambda - \frac{\alpha}{2}} ,$$

from which follows that $\lim_{s\downarrow 0} P(\Gamma_{t,k,s}) = 0$ since $\lambda - \alpha/2 > 0$. Let $\{s_j, j = 1,2,\cdots\}$ be a sequence of positive numbers such that $s_j \downarrow 0$ and $\sum_{j=1}^{\infty} s_j^{\lambda-\alpha/2} < \infty$. Then $\sum_{j=1}^{\infty} P(\Gamma_{t,m,s_j}) < \infty$, so that, by the Borel-Cantelli theorem,

$$P(\Gamma_{t,k}) = 1, \qquad \text{where } \Gamma_{t,k} = \liminf_{j\to\infty} \Gamma_{t,k,s_j}^{c} .$$

Now for every $\omega \in \Gamma_{t,k}$ there exists a positive integer $J(\omega)$ such that

$$\frac{|X(t+s_j, \omega) - X(t, \omega)|}{s_j^{\lambda}} \geq k \qquad \text{for } j \geq J(\omega),$$

so that

$$\limsup_{s \downarrow 0} \frac{|X(t+s, \omega) - X(t, \omega)|}{s^{\lambda}}$$

$$= \lim_{\delta \downarrow 0} \sup_{0<s<\delta} \frac{|X(t+s, \omega) - X(t, \omega)|}{s^{\lambda}} \geq k.$$

Let $\Gamma_t^+ = \bigcap_{k=1}^{\infty} \Gamma_{t,k} \in \mathfrak{B}$. Then $P(\Gamma_t^+) = 1$ and, for $\omega \in \Gamma_t^+$, (3) holds.

Similarly there exists $\Gamma_t^- \in \mathfrak{B}$ with $P(\Gamma_t^-) = 1$ such that for $\omega \in \Gamma_t^-$ (4) holds. Let $\Gamma_t = \Gamma_t^+ \cap \Gamma_t^-$. Then $P(\Gamma_t) = 1$ and, for $\omega \in \Gamma_t$, (3) and (4) hold. □

Theorem 21.5 Let X be a Gaussian process on a probability space $(\Omega, \mathfrak{B}, P)$ and an interval $D \subset R^1$ which is almost surely continuous and satisfies the conditions (1) and (2) of Lemma 21.4. Let $\lambda > \alpha/2$. Then for a.e. $\omega \in \Omega$, (3) and (4) of Lemma 21.4 hold for a.e. $t \in D$, the exceptional subset of D with Lebesgue measure 0 depending on ω. In particular when $\alpha < 2$ so that λ can be chosen to be equal to 1, almost every sample function of X is almost everywhere nondifferentiable on D.

Proof We may assume without loss of generality that X is continuous. Consider first the case where D is a finite closed interval. Let

$$\Gamma = \{(t, \omega) \in D \times \Omega;\ (3) \text{ and } (4) \text{ of Lemma 21.4 hold}\}.$$

Consider the σ-field $\sigma(\mathfrak{B}_D \times \mathfrak{B})$ generated by $\mathfrak{B}_D \times \mathfrak{B}$ where $\mathfrak{B}_D$ is the σ-field of the Borel sets in R^1 that are contained in D. Let us show that $\Gamma \in \sigma(\mathfrak{B}_D \times \mathfrak{B})$ by showing that the left sides of (3) and (4) of Lemma 21.4 are $\sigma(\mathfrak{B}_D \times \mathfrak{B})$-measurable functions of (t, ω). To do this we extend $X(\cdot, \omega)$ beyond D so that $X(\cdot, \omega)$ is continuous on R^1 and is constant in each of the two disjoint intervals which constitute D^c. This is done for each $\omega \in \Omega$. Now for $(t, \omega) \in D \times \Omega$

$$\limsup_{s \downarrow 0} \frac{|X(t+s, \omega) - X(t, \omega)|}{s^\lambda} = \lim_{k\to\infty} \sup_{0<s<\frac{1}{k}} \frac{|X(t+s, \omega) - X(t, \omega)|}{s^\lambda}.$$

With fixed k, let $\{s_j, j = 1,2, \cdots\}$ be a countable dense subset of $(0, 1/k)$. From the continuity of $s^{-\lambda}|X(t+s, \omega) - X(t, \omega)|$ as a function of s on $(0, 1/k)$ for each $(t, \omega) \in D \times \Omega$,

$$\sup_{0<s<\frac{1}{k}} \frac{|X(t+s, \omega) - X(t, \omega)|}{s^\lambda} = \sup_j \frac{|X(t+s_j, \omega) - X(t, \omega)|}{s_j^\lambda}.$$

Since X is continuous, it is measurable with respect to $\sigma(\mathfrak{B}_D \times \mathfrak{B})$ according to Theorem 5.5. Thus the left side of (3) of Lemma 21.4 is $\sigma(\mathfrak{B}_D \times \mathfrak{B})$-measurable. So is the left side of (4) of Lemma 21.4. This proves that $\Gamma \in \sigma(\mathfrak{B}_D \times \mathfrak{B})$.

Let $\Gamma(t)$ be the section of Γ at $t \in D$, i.e.,

$$\Gamma(t) = \{\omega \in \Omega ; (t, \omega) \in \Gamma\} \in \mathfrak{B}.$$

Let Γ_t be the subset of Ω defined in Lemma 21.4. Then $\Gamma_t \subset \Gamma(t)$ for every $t \in D$. Since $P(\Gamma_t) = 1 = P(\Omega)$ we have

$$m_L(D) = (m_L \times P)(D \times \Omega) \geq (m_L \times P)(\Gamma)$$

$$= \int_D P\left(\Gamma(t)\right) m_L(dt) \geq \int_D P(\Gamma_t)\, m_L(dt)$$

$$= \int_D m_L(dt) = m_L(D),$$

so that

$$(m_L \times P)(\Gamma) = (m_L \times P)(D \times \Omega),$$

and hence

$$0 = (m_L \times P)(D \times \Omega - \Gamma) = \int_\Omega m_L\left\{t \in D;\, (t, \omega) \notin \Gamma\right\} P(d\omega).$$

Thus for a.e. $\omega \in \Omega$,

$$m_L\left\{t \in D;\, (t, \omega) \notin \Gamma\right\} = 0,$$

i.e., for a.e. $\omega \in \Omega$,

$$m_L\left\{t \in D;\, (t, \omega) \in \Gamma\right\} = m_L(D).$$

This proves the theorem for the case where D is a finite closed interval. For an arbitrary interval D, we express D as the union of countably many finite closed intervals and apply the above result. □

Chapter 5

STOCHASTIC INTEGRALS

§22. STOCHASTIC INTEGRAL OF A FUNCTION

Let X be a continuous stochastic process on a probability space $(\Omega, \mathfrak{B}, P)$ and an interval $D = [a, b]$. If f is a real-valued function of bounded variation, then the Riemann-Stieltjes integral $\int_a^b f(t)\, dX(t, \omega)$ exists as a real number for every $\omega \in \Omega$. The integral then is a real-valued function defined on Ω. Thus there arises question regarding its $\mathfrak{B}$-measurability and its distribution function in case it is $\mathfrak{B}$-measurable. We shall answer this question when X is a Brownian motion process. The stochastic integral of a function $f \in L_2[a, b]$ with respect to a Brownian motion process X on a probability space $(\Omega, \mathfrak{B}, P)$ and $D = [a, b]$ which we shall define is $\mathfrak{B}$-measurable and in fact normally distributed and, in particular, when X is continuous and f is of bounded variation then the stochastic integral is equal to the Riemann-Stieltjes integral $\int_a^b f(t)\, dX(t,\omega)$ for a. e. $\omega \in \Omega$.

Let $B = B(t, \omega)$, $(t,\omega) \in D \times \Omega$ be a Brownian motion process on a probability space $(\Omega, \mathfrak{B}, P)$ and an interval $D = [a, b]$ or $[a, b)$ where a is finite and b may be infinite. In addition let $B(a, .)$ be equal to a constant a. e. on Ω. Thus:

1° For $\{t_0, t_1, \cdots, t_n\} \subset D$, $t_0 < t_1 < \cdots < t_n$, the collection of random variables $\{B(t_j, \cdot) - B(t_{j-1}, \cdot), j = 1, 2, \cdots, n\}$ is an independent system.

2° For $t', t'' \in D$, $t' < t''$, the probability distribution of $B(t'', \cdot) - B(t', \cdot)$ is given by $N(0, t'' - t')$.

3° $B(a, \cdot) = c$ a.e. on Ω where $c \in R^1$.

As we saw in §17, a stochastic process satisfying the conditions 1°, 2°, 3° is a Gaussian process. Also from 1° and 2° follow

$$\{t_1, t_2, t_3, t_4\} \subset D, \quad t_1 < t_2 \leq t_3 < t_4$$

$$\Rightarrow E\left[\left\{B(t_2, \cdot) - B(t_1, \cdot)\right\}\left\{B(t_4, \cdot) - B(t_3, \cdot)\right\}\right] = 0,$$

$$t', t'' \in D, \quad t' < t'' \Rightarrow V\left[B(t'', \cdot) - B(t', \cdot)\right] = t'' - t'.$$

Consider the real Hilbert space $L_2(\Omega) = L_2(\Omega, \mathfrak{B}, P)$ where an element of $L_2(\Omega)$ is an equivalence class of random variables X on $(\Omega, \mathfrak{B}. P)$ with $E(X^2) < \infty$ relative to the equivalence relation of almost everywhere equality on Ω and where the inner product is defined by

$$(X, Y) = E(XY) \quad \text{for } X, Y \in L_2(\Omega).$$

In terms of this inner product and the associated Hilbert norm $\|\cdot\|$ we have

$$E(X^2) = (X, X) = \|X\|^2,$$

$$E(X) = (X, 1),$$

$$C(X, Y) = \big(X - E(X), \; Y - E(Y)\big),$$

$$V(X) = \|X - E(X)\|^2.$$

Consider also the real Hilbert space $L_2(D) = L_2(D, \mathfrak{M}_D, m_L)$

where $\mathfrak{M}_D$ is the σ-field of Lebesgue measurable sets in R^1 that are contained in D and m_L is the Lebesgue measure, an element of $L_2(D)$ is an equivalence class of almost everywhere equal functions f with $\int_D \{f(t)\}^2 m_L(dt) < \infty$ and the inner product is defined by

$$(f, g) = \int_D f(t)\, g(t)\, m_L(dt) \qquad \text{for } f, g \in L_2(D).$$

Let $S(D)$ be the collection of those elements of $L_2(D)$ which can be represented by step functions (with finitely many steps) of compact support on D. Here whether an individual interval appearing in the representation of a member of $S(D)$ as a step function is open, closed, or open at one end and closed at the other is immaterial. Clearly $S(D)$ is a dense linear subspace of $L_2(\Omega)$. We shall define our stochastic integral as an isometric linear transformation of $S(D)$ into $L_2(\Omega)$ first and then extend the domain of definition to $L_2(D)$.

<u>Definition 22.1</u> Let $f \in S(D)$ be represented as a step function as follows:

$$f = \sum_{k=1}^{n} c_k \chi_{J_k}, \tag{1}$$

where $\{c_k, k = 1, 2, \cdots, n\} \subset R^1$ and the interval J_k has t_k and t_{k+1} as its endpoints and $a \leq t_1 < t_2 < \cdots < t_{n+1} \leq b$. The stochastic integral $I(f)$ of f with respect to the Brownian motion process B is a random variable on $(\Omega, \mathfrak{B}, P)$ defined by

$$I(f)(\omega) = \sum_{k=1}^{n} c_k \left\{B(t_{k+1}, \omega) - B(t_k, \omega)\right\} \qquad \text{for } \omega \in \Omega. \tag{2}$$

Note that $I(f)(\omega)$ is defined for every $\omega \in \Omega$ and that $I(f)$ is determined by $f \in S(D)$ but is independent of the representation (1) of f as a step function.

Theorem 22.2 For $f, g \in S(D)$ and $\alpha, \beta \in R^1$ the following hold:

$$\left(I(f), 1\right) = E\left[I(f)\right] = 0, \tag{1}$$

$$\left(I(f), I(g)\right) = C\left(I(f), I(g)\right) = (f, g), \tag{2}$$

$$\| I(f)\|^2 = V\left[I(f)\right] = \|f\|^2, \tag{3}$$

$$I(f) \text{ is distributed according to } N\left(0, \|f\|^2\right), \tag{4}$$

$$I(\alpha f + \beta g)(\omega) = \alpha I(f)(\omega) + \beta I(g)(\omega) \quad \text{for every } \omega \in \Omega. \tag{5}$$

Proof To prove (1) note that if $f \in S(D)$ is represented as in (1) of Definition 22.1 then, by (2) of Definition 22.1,

$$E\left[I(f)\right] = \sum_{k=1}^{n} c_k E\left[B(t_{k+1}, \cdot) - B(t_k, \cdot)\right] = 0.$$

To prove (2) represent $f, g \in S(D)$ by step functions as

$$f = \sum_{k=1}^{n} c_k' \chi_{J_k} \quad \text{and} \quad g = \sum_{k=1}^{n} c_k'' \chi_{J_k},$$

$$\text{where } \{c_k', c_k'', k = 1, 2, \cdots, n\} \subset R^1. \tag{6}$$

Then

$$C\left(I(f), I(g)\right)$$

$$= E\left[\sum_{k=1}^{n} c_k'\left\{B(t_{k+1}, \cdot) - B(t_k, \cdot)\right\} \cdot \sum_{k=1}^{n} c_k''\left\{B(t_{k+1}, \cdot) - B(t_k, \cdot)\right\}\right]$$

$$= E\left[\sum_{k=1}^{n} c'_k c''_k \left\{B(t_{k+1}, \cdot) - B(t_k, \cdot)\right\}^2\right]$$

$$+ E\left[\sum_{j \neq k} c'_j c''_k \left\{B(t_{j+1}, \cdot) - B(t_j, \cdot)\right\}\left\{B(t_{k+1}, \cdot) - B(t_k, \cdot)\right\}\right]$$

$$= \sum_{k=1}^{n} c'_k c''_k (t_k - t_{k+1}) = \int_D f(t)\, g(t)\, m_L(dt) = (f, g),$$

which is (2). (3) is a particular case of (2).

Since $\{B(t, \cdot), t \in D\}$ is a Gaussian system of random variables the right-hand side of (2) in Definition 22.1 is normally distributed according to Theorem 16.4. This together with (1) and (3) proves (4).

To prove (5), use the representations (6) for $f, g \in S(D)$ and apply (2) of Definition 22.1. □

<u>Definition 22.3</u> Let $f \in L_2(D)$. From the denseness of $S(D)$ in $L_2(D)$ there exists a sequence $\{f_n, n = 1, 2, \cdots\} \subset S(D)$ satisfying $\lim_{n\to\infty} \|f_n - f\| = 0$. By (5) and (3) of Theorem 22.2,

$$\|I(f_m) - I(f_n)\| = \|f_m - f_n\|,$$

so that the fact that $\{f_n, n = 1, 2, \cdots\}$ is a Cauchy sequence in $L_2(D)$ implies that $\{I(f_n), n = 1, 2, \cdots\}$ is a Cauchy sequence in $L_2(\Omega)$. Thus there exists $X \in L_2(\Omega)$ such that

$$\lim_{n\to\infty} \|I(f_n) - X\| = 0.$$

We call X the stochastic integral of f with respect to the Brownian motion process B and write $I(f)$ for it. Thus

$$I(f) = s - \lim_{n\to\infty} I(f_n),$$

where we use $s - \lim_{n\to\infty}$ to indicate limit of strong convergence, i.e., convergence in the norm of $L_2(\Omega)$. Defined in this fashion, $I(f)$ is an element of the Hilbert space $L_2(\Omega)$ and is determined up to a set of probability measure 0. □

We remark that $I(f)$ as defined above is independent of the sequence $\{f_n, n=1,2,\cdots\}$. To show this, suppose $\{g_n, n=1,2,\cdots\}$ $\subset S(D)$ and $\lim_{n\to\infty} \|g_n - f\| = 0$ also. Then

$$\|I(g_n) - I(f_n)\| = \|g_n - f_n\| \le \|g_n - f\| + \|f_n - f\|,$$

so that $\lim_{n\to\infty} \|I(g_n) - I(f_n)\| = 0$, i.e., $s - \lim_{n\to\infty} I(g_n) =$ $s - \lim_{n\to\infty} I(f_n)$.

<u>Theorem 22.4</u> Let $f, g \in L_2(D)$ and $\alpha, \beta \in R^1$. Then (1), (2), (3), and (4) of Theorem 22.2 hold. Instead of (5) of Theorem 22.2 we have

$$I(\alpha f + \beta g)(\omega) = \alpha I(f)(\omega) + \beta I(g)(\omega) \quad \text{for a.e. } \omega \in \Omega. \tag{5}$$

The collection of random variables $\{I(f),\ f \in L_2(D)\}$ is a Gaussian system.

<u>Proof</u> (1), (2), (3) are immediate. Let us show (2) as an example. Thus let $\{f_n, n=1,2,\cdots\}$, $\{g_n, n=1,2,\cdots\} \subset S(D)$ and $f = s - \lim_{n\to\infty} f_n$, $g = s - \lim_{n\to\infty} g_n$. Then

$$\Big(I(f), I(g)\Big) = \left(s - \lim_{n\to\infty} I(f_n),\ s - \lim_{n\to\infty} I(g_n)\right) = \lim_{n\to\infty}\Big(I(f_n), I(g_n)\Big)$$

$$= \lim_{n\to\infty} (f_n, g_n) = \left(s - \lim_{n\to\infty} f_n,\ s - \lim_{n\to\infty}\right) = (f, g)$$

which proves (2).

Regarding (4), since $I(f) = s - \lim_{n\to\infty} I(f_n)$, the probability distribution of $I(f_n)$ converges to that of $I(f)$. But $I(f_n)$ is normally distributed. Thus by Lemma 16.10, $I(f)$ is normally distributed.

To prove (5) let f, g, f_n, g_n be as in the proof of (2). Then for $\alpha, \beta \in R^1$ we have $\alpha f_n + \beta g_n \in S(D)$ for $n = 1,2,\cdots$, and

$$\lim_{n\to\infty} \|(\alpha f_n + \beta g_n) - (\alpha f + \beta g)\| = 0.$$

so that

$$I(\alpha f + \beta g) = s - \lim_{n\to\infty} I(\alpha f_n + \beta g_n) = s - \lim_{n\to\infty} \alpha I(f_n) + s - \lim_{n\to\infty} \beta I(g_n)$$

$$= \alpha I(f) + \beta I(g).$$

Thus (5) holds.

Since $\{I(f),\ f \in S(D)\}$ is a collection of linear combinations of members of the Gaussian system $\{B(t, \cdot),\ t \in D\}$, it is a Gaussian system by an application of Theorem 16.9. Then since $\{I(f),\ f \in L_2(D)\}$ is a collection of strong limits of sequences of members of the Gaussian system $\{I(f), f \in S(D)\}$ it is a Gaussian system by Theorem 16.11. This completes the proof of the theorem. □

The following theorem relates our stochastic integral to the Riemann-Stieltjes integral.

Theorem 22.5 If the Brownian motion process B is continuous on $[a, b]$ and f is of bounded variation on $[a, b]$ then

$$I(f)(\omega) = \int_{\alpha}^{b} f(t)\, dB(t, \omega) \qquad \text{for a.e. } \omega \in \Omega.$$

Proof Consider first the case where f is real valued and monotone increasing on $[a, b]$. Let

$$M = f(b) - f(a)$$

and

$$D_{n,k} = \left\{ t \in [a, b]; f(a) + \frac{k}{n} M \leq f(t) < f(a) + \frac{k+1}{n} M \right\}$$

for $k = 0, 1, 2, \cdots, n-1$.

Since f is monotone, each $D_{n,k}$ is either an interval or a point or $\emptyset$. If $D_{n,k}$ is a point adjoin it to $D_{n,k-1}$ or $D_{n,k+1}$. In this way we have a decomposition of $[a, b]$ into finitely many intervals. If necessary, decompose these intervals further so that the lengths of the resulting intervals $J_{n,k}$, $k = 1, 2, \cdots, p(n)$, with end points $t_{n,k}$ and $t_{n,k+1}$ do not exceed $(b-a)/n$. Let

$$f_n = \sum_{k=1}^{p(n)} f(t_{n,k})\, \chi_{J_{n,k}} \qquad \text{for } n = 1, 2, \cdots.$$

Then $\{f_n, n = 1, 2, \cdots\} \subset S(D)$ and

$$|f_n(t) - f(t)| \leq 2\frac{M}{n} \qquad \text{for } t \in [a, b] \text{ and } n = 1, 2, \cdots,$$

so that

$$\lim_{n\to\infty} \|f_n - f\| = \lim_{n\to\infty} \int_{[a,b]} |f_n(t) - f(t)|^2\, m_L(dt) \leq \lim_{n\to\infty} \frac{4M^2}{n^2}(b-a) = 0.$$

Thus, according to Definition 22.3

$$I(f) = s - \lim_{n\to\infty} I(f_n),$$

and hence there exists a subsequence $\{f_{n_m}, m = 1, 2, \cdots\}$ such that

$$I(f)(\omega) = \lim_{m\to\infty} I(f_{n_m})(\omega) \quad \text{for a.e. } \omega \in \Omega.$$

Now, according to Definition 22.1

$$I(f_{n_m})(\omega) = \sum_{k=1}^{p(n)} f(t_{n_m,k}) \left\{B(t_{n_m,k+1}, \omega) - B(t_{n_m,k}, \omega)\right\},$$

which approximates the Riemann-Stieltjes integral $\int_a^b f(t)\, dB(t, \omega)$ which exists for every $\omega \in \Omega$. Thus

$$\lim_{m\to\infty} I(f_{n_m})(\omega) = \int_a^b f(t)\, dB(t, \omega) \quad \text{for every } \omega \in \Omega,$$

and hence

$$I(f)(\omega) = \int_a^b f(t)\, dB(t, \omega) \quad \text{for a.e. } \omega \in \Omega.$$

This proves the theorem for the case where f is monotone increasing. If f is of bounded variation we express it as the difference between two monotone increasing functions and apply the above result and (5) of Theorem 22.4. This completes the proof of the theorem. □

As we have seen in Theorem 22.4, for every $f \in L_2(D)$ the stochastic integral $I(f)$ is a random variable on $(\Omega, \mathfrak{B}, P)$ whose probability distribution is given by $N\left(0, \|f\|^2\right)$ and I is a linear transformation $L_2(D)$ into $L(\Omega)$. Let us turn to the study of $\{I(f), f \in L_2(D)\}$ as a linear subspace of $L_2(\Omega)$.

<u>Theorem 22.6</u> The stochastic integral I transforms $L_2(D)$ one-to-one into $L_2(\Omega)$. The image $\mathfrak{G}$ of $L_2(D)$ under the transformation I is a closed linear subspace of $L_2(\Omega)$ and I is an isomorphism between $L_2(D)$ and $\mathfrak{G}$ as Hilbert spaces.

Proof Since I transforms $f \in L_2(D)$ into a random variable whose probability distribution is given by $N\left(0, \|f\|^2\right)$, $0 \in L_2(D)$ is the only element of $L_2(D)$ that is transformed into $0 \in L_2(\Omega)$. This proves the one-to-one property of the transformation I.

From the linearity of I given by (5) of Theorem 22.4, $\mathfrak{G}$ is a linear subspace of $L_2(\Omega)$. To show that $\mathfrak{G}$ is closed we show that if $\{X_n, n = 1, 2, \cdots\} \subset \mathfrak{G}$, $X \in L_2(\Omega)$, and $X = s - \lim_{n \to \infty} X_n$ then $X \in \mathfrak{G}$. Now for $X_n \in \mathfrak{G}$ there exists $f_n \in L_2(D)$ such that $X_n = I(f_n)$. Since the transformation I preserves metric according to (3) of Theorem 22.4, so does the transformation I^{-1} of $\mathfrak{G}$ onto $L_2(D)$. Then the fact that $\{X_n, n = 1, 2, \cdots\}$ is a Cauchy sequence in $\mathfrak{G}$ implies that $\{f_n, n = 1, 2, \cdots\}$ is a Cauchy sequence in $L_2(D)$ and hence the existence of $f \in L_2(D)$ such that $\lim_{n \to \infty} \|f_n - f\| = 0$. Since the transformation I of $L_2(D)$ into $L_2(\Omega)$ preserves metric we have $\lim_{n \to \infty} \|I(f_n) - I(f)\| = 0$, i.e.,

$$X = s - \lim_{n \to \infty} X_n = s - \lim_{n \to \infty} I(f_n) = I(f) \in \mathfrak{G}.$$

This proves the closedness of $\mathfrak{G}$.

As a closed linear subspace of the Hilbert space $L_2(\Omega)$, $\mathfrak{G}$ is itself a Hilbert space. The fact that I is an isomorphism between $L_2(D)$ and $\mathfrak{G}$ as Hilbert spaces is from (2) and (5) of Theorem 22.4. □

Corollary 22.7 For $\{f_\alpha, \alpha \in A\} \subset L_2(D)$ the following hold.

(1) $\{f_\alpha, \alpha \in A\}$ is an orthonormal system in $L_2(D)$ if and only if $\{I(f_\alpha), \alpha \in A\}$ is an orthonormal system in $\mathfrak{G}$, and the former is complete if and only if the latter is.

(2) $\{f_\alpha, \alpha \in A\}$ is an orthonormal system in $L_2(D)$ if and only if $\{I(f_\alpha), \alpha \in A\}$ is an independent system of random variables.

Proof (1) is implied by the isomorphism of $L_2(D)$ and $\mathfrak{G}$ as Hilbert spaces. (2) is from the fact that $\{f_\alpha, \alpha \in A\}$ is an orthogonal system in $L_2(D)$ if and only if $\{I(f_\alpha), \alpha \in A\}$ is an orthogonal system in $L_2(\Omega)$ and the following corollary. □

Corollary 22.8 Let $\{X_\alpha, \alpha \in A\}$ be a Gaussian system of random variables on a probability space $(\Omega, \mathfrak{B}, P)$ with $E(X_\alpha) = 0$ for every $\alpha \in A$. Then $\{X_\alpha, \alpha \in A\}$ is an independent system of random variables if and only if it is an orthogonal system in the Hilbert space $L_2(\Omega)$.

Proof Since the independence of an infinite system of random variables is defined as the independence of every finite sybsystem, it is sufficient to prove the corollary for a finite Gaussian system $\{X_j, j = 1,2, \cdots, n\}$ with $E(X_j) = 0$ for $j = 1,2, \cdots, n$. Then since $(X_j, X_\ell) = C(X_j, X_\ell)$, the system is an independent system if and only if it is an orthogonal system according to Theorem 16.13. □

§23. ORTHOGONAL EXPANSIONS OF BROWNIAN MOTION PROCESSES

Let $B = B(t, \omega)$, $(t, \omega) \in \Omega$, be the Brownian motion process described in the second paragraph of §22, let $I(f)$, $f \in L_2(D)$, be the stochastic integral defined in Definition 22.3, and let $\mathfrak{G} = \{I(f), f \in L_2(D)\} \subset L_2(\Omega)$. To expand B in a series of orthogonal (in the Hilbert space $L_2(\Omega)$) random variables let us first summarize some pertinent results in §22 in the following theorem.

Theorem 23.1 The stochastic integral I defined on $L_2(D)$ is an isomorphism between $L_2(D)$ and $\mathfrak{G}$ as Hilbert spaces. If $\{\varphi_n, n = 0,1,2,\cdots\}$ is a complete orthonormal system in $L_2(D)$ then $\{X_n, n = 0,1,2,\cdots\}$, where $X_n = I(\varphi_n)$, is a complete orthonormal system in $L_2(\Omega)$. Each X_n is distributed according to $N(0,1)$ and $\{X_n, n = 0,1,2,\cdots\}$ is an independent system of random variables. For $f \in L_2(D)$, $f = s - \sum_{n=0}^{\infty}(f, \varphi_n)\varphi_n$ let $X = I(f)$. Then

$$X = s - \sum_{n=0}^{\infty} (X, X_n)X_n = s - \sum_{n=0}^{\infty} (f, \varphi_n)X_n \tag{1}$$

and

$$X(\omega) = \sum_{n=0}^{\infty} (X, X_n)\, X_n(\omega) = \sum_{n=0}^{\infty} (f, \varphi_n)\, X_n(\omega)$$

for a.e. $\omega \in \Omega$. (2)

Proof All the statements in this theorem except (2) have been proved in §22. The statement (2) follows from (1) since the strong convergence, i.e., convergence in the second moment, implies convergence in probability according to Theorem A5.4 and since convergence almost everywhere, convergence in probability, and convergence in distribution are all equivalent for a series of independent random variables according to Theorem A8.1. □

As a consequence of Theorem 23.1 we have the following orthogonal expansion of B.

Theorem 23.2 Let $\{\varphi_n, n = 0,1,2,\cdots\}$ be a complete orthonormal system in $L_2(D)$ and let $X_n = I(\varphi_n)$ for $n = 0,1,2,\cdots$.

Then for the Brownian motion process B we have for $t_0, t \in D$, $t_0 < t$,

$$B(t,\cdot) - B(t_0,\cdot) = s - \sum_{n=0}^{\infty} \left\{ \int_{[t_0,t]} \varphi_n(u)\, m_L(du) \right\} X_n \tag{1}$$

and also

$$B(t,\omega) - B(t_0,\omega) = \sum_{n=0}^{\infty} \left\{ \int_{[t_0,t]} \varphi_n(u)\, m_L(du) \right\} X_n(\omega)$$

for a.e. $\omega \in \Omega$. (2)

Proof For $t_0, t \in D$, $t_0 < t$, let $f(u) = \chi_{[t_0,t]}(u)$, $u \in D$. Then $f \in S(D)$ in the notation of §22 so that by Definition 22.1 we have, for $X = I(f)$,

$$X = I\left(\chi_{[t_0,t]}\right) = B(t,\cdot) - B(t_0,\cdot). \tag{3}$$

On the other hand, by (1) of Theorem 23.1,

$$X = s - \sum_{n=0}^{\infty} (f, \varphi_n)\, X_n = s - \sum_{n=0}^{\infty} \left\{ \int_{[t_0,t]} \varphi_n(u)\, m_L(du) \right\} X_n. \tag{4}$$

From (3) and (4) we have (1), from which follows (2) by Theorem A5.4 and Theorem A8.1. □

Theorem 23.3 Let $D = [0, \pi]$ and assume that the Brownian motion process B satisfies the condition that $B(0,\cdot) = 0$ a.e. on Ω. With the complete orthonormal system $\{\varphi_n, n = 0,1,2,\cdots\} \subset L_2(D)$ where

$$\varphi_0(t) = \frac{1}{\sqrt{\pi}} \quad \text{and} \quad \varphi_n(t) = \sqrt{\frac{2}{\pi}} \cos nt$$

for $n = 1,2,\cdots$, for $t \in D$, (1)

let

$$X_0 = I(\varphi_0) = \frac{1}{\sqrt{\pi}} B(\pi, \cdot) \text{ and } X_n = I(\varphi_n) \quad \text{for } n = 1,2,\cdots. \tag{2}$$

Then for every $t \in [0, \pi]$

$$B(t, \cdot) = \frac{t}{\sqrt{\pi}} X_0 + s - \sum_{n=1}^{\infty} \sqrt{\frac{2}{\pi}} \frac{\sin nt}{n} X_n \tag{3}$$

and

$$B(t, \omega) = \frac{t}{\sqrt{\pi}} X_0(\omega) + \sum_{n=1}^{\infty} \sqrt{\frac{2}{\pi}} \frac{\sin nt}{n} X_n(\omega)$$

for a.e. $\omega \in \Omega$. (4)

Proof This theorem is a particular case of Theorem 23.2. It suffices to note that with $t_0 = 0$ and with our $\{\varphi_n, n = 0,1,2,\cdots\}$,

$$\int_{[t_0,t]} \varphi_0(u)\, m_L(du) = \frac{t}{\sqrt{\pi}},$$

$$\int_{[t_0,t]} \varphi_n(u)\, m_L(du) = \int_0^t \sqrt{\frac{2}{\pi}} \cos nu\, du = \sqrt{\frac{2}{\pi}} \frac{\sin nt}{n}. \qquad \square$$

From an arbitrary independent system of random variables $\{X_n, n = 0,1,2,\cdots\}$ each of which is distributed according to $N(0,1)$ an almost surely continuous Brownian motion process can be constructed. This is done in the following theorem.

Theorem 23.4 Let $\{X_n, n = 0,1,2,\cdots\}$ be an arbitrary independent system of random variables on a probability space $(\Omega, \mathfrak{B}, P)$, each of which is distributed according to $N(0,1)$. Then there exists $\Omega_0 \in \mathfrak{B}$ with $P(\Omega_0) = 1$ such that, for every $\omega \in \Omega_0$,

$$W(t,\omega) = \frac{t}{\sqrt{\pi}} X_0(\omega) + \sum_{n=0}^{\infty} \left\{ \sum_{k=2^n+1}^{2^{n+1}} \sqrt{\frac{2}{\pi}} \frac{\sin kt}{k} X_k(\omega) \right\} \tag{1}$$

converges uniformly for t in $D = [0,\pi]$. For the real-valued function $W(t,\omega)$ defined by (1) for $(t,\omega) \in D \times \Omega_0$,

$$W(t,\cdot) = \frac{t}{\sqrt{\pi}} X_0 + s - \sum_{n=1}^{\infty} \sqrt{\frac{2}{\pi}} \frac{\sin nt}{n} X_n \tag{2}$$

holds for every $t \in D$. The function W is a Brownian motion process on $(\Omega, \mathfrak{B}, P)$ and D in which $W(0,\omega) = 0$ for $\omega \in \Omega_0$ and $W(t'',\cdot) - W(t',\cdot)$, $t', t'' \in D$, $t' < t''$, is distributed according to $N(0, t''-t')$. For every $\omega \in \Omega_0$, $W(\cdot,\omega)$ is continuous on D. Furthermore if we write $I_W(f)$, $f \in L_2(D)$, for the stochastic integral with respect to the Brownian motion process W then with the complete orthonormal system $\{\varphi_n, n = 0,1,2,\cdots\}$ in $L_2(D)$ where

$$\varphi_0(t) = \frac{1}{\sqrt{\pi}} \quad \text{and} \quad \varphi_n(t) = \sqrt{\frac{2}{\pi}} \cos nt$$

$$\text{for } n = 1,2,\cdots, \text{ for } t \in D \tag{3}$$

we have

$$I_W(\varphi_0)(\omega) = X_0(\omega) \quad \text{and} \quad I_W(\varphi_n)(\omega) = X_n(\omega)$$

$$\text{for } n = 1,2,\cdots, \text{ for a.e. } \omega \in \Omega. \tag{4}$$

<u>Proof</u> For positive integers m and ℓ where $m < \ell$ let

$$S_{m,\ell}(t,\omega) = \sum_{k=m+1}^{\ell} \frac{\sin kt}{k} X_k(\omega) \quad \text{for} \quad (t,\omega) \in D \times \Omega$$

and

$$T_{m,\ell}(\omega) = \sup_{t \in D} |S_{m,\ell}(t,\omega)| \quad \text{for } \omega \in \Omega .$$

To prove the first part of the theorem it suffices to show

$$\sum_{n=0}^{\infty} E\left(T_{2^n, 2^{n+1}}\right) < \infty, \tag{5}$$

for in view of $T_{2^n, 2^{n+1}}(\omega) \geq 0$ and the Monotone Convergence Theorem, (5) implies

$$E\left(\sum_{n=0}^{\infty} T_{2^n, 2^{n+1}}\right) < \infty,$$

and hence

$$\sum_{n=0}^{\infty} T_{2^n, 2^{n+1}}(\omega) < \infty \qquad \text{for a.e. } \omega \in \Omega,$$

which in turn implies that, for a.e. $\omega \in \Omega$, the series in (1) converges uniformly for t in D. To establish (5) let us observe that

$$S_{m,\ell}(t,\omega) = \sum_{k=m+1}^{\ell} \frac{\sin kt}{k} X_k(\omega) = \Im m \left\{ \sum_{k=m+1}^{\ell} \frac{e^{ikt}}{k} X_k(\omega) \right\},$$

so that

$$\begin{aligned}
|S_{m,\ell}(t,\omega)|^2 &\leq \left| \sum_{k=m+1}^{\ell} \frac{e^{ikt}}{k} X_k(\omega) \right|^2 \\
&= \left\{ \sum_{k=m+1}^{\ell} \frac{e^{ikt}}{k} X_k(\omega) \right\} \left\{ \sum_{k=m+1}^{\ell} \frac{e^{-ikt}}{k} X_k(\omega) \right\} \\
&= \sum_{k=m+1}^{\ell} \frac{\left[X_k(\omega)\right]^2}{k^2} + \sum_{\substack{h,k=m+1,\cdots,\ell \\ h \neq k}} \frac{X_h(\omega)}{h} \frac{X_k(\omega)}{k} e^{i(h-k)t}
\end{aligned}$$

$$= \sum_{k=m+1}^{\ell} \frac{\left[X_k(\omega)\right]^2}{k^2} + \sum_{p=1}^{\ell-m-1} \sum_{h=m+1}^{\ell-p} \frac{X_h(\omega)}{h} \frac{X_{h+p}(\omega)}{h+p} \cdot \left\{e^{-ipt} + e^{ipt}\right\}$$

and

$$\left\{T_{m,\ell}(\omega)\right\}^2 = \sup_{t \in D} |S_{m,\ell}(t, \omega)|^2$$

$$\leq \sum_{k=m+1}^{\ell} \frac{\left[X_k(\omega)\right]^2}{k^2} + 2 \sum_{p=1}^{\ell-m-1} \left| \sum_{h=m+1}^{\ell-p} \frac{X_h(\omega)\, X_{h+p}(\omega)}{h(h+p)} \right| .$$

By the Schwarz inequality,

$$\left\{E(T_{m,\ell})\right\}^2 \leq E(T_{m,\ell}^{\ 2})$$

$$\leq \sum_{k=m+1}^{\ell} \frac{1}{k^2} + 2 \sum_{p=1}^{\ell-m-1} E\left(\left| \sum_{h=m+1}^{\ell-p} \frac{X_h X_{h+p}}{h(h+p)} \right| \right), \tag{6}$$

and again by the Schwarz inequality,

$$\left\{E\left(\left|\sum_{h=m+1}^{\ell-p} \frac{X_h X_{h+p}}{h(h+p)}\right|\right)\right\}^2 \leq E\left(\left\{\sum_{n=m+1}^{\ell-p} \frac{X_h X_{h+p}}{h(h+p)}\right\}^2\right)$$

$$= \sum_{h=m+1}^{\ell-p} E\left(\frac{X_h^{\ 2} X_{h+p}^{\ 2}}{h^2 (h+p)^2}\right)$$

$$+ \ 2\sum_{m+1 \leq h < k \leq \ell - p} E\left(\frac{X_h X_{h+p} X_k X_{k+p}}{h(h+p)\ k(k+p)}\right). \tag{7}$$

From the independence of $\{X_h, X_{h+p}\}$ for $p \geq 1$, we have

$$E\left(X_h^{\ 2} X_{h+p}^{\ 2}\right) = E\left(X_h^{\ 2}\right) E\left(X_{h+p}^{\ 2}\right) = 1 . \tag{8}$$

For $h < k$ and $h+p \neq k$, $\{X_h, X_{h+p}, X_k, X_{k+p}\}$ is an independent system, while for $h < k$ and $h+p = k$, $\{X_h, X_{h+p}(=X_k), X_{k+p}\}$ is an independent system. In any case

$$E(X_h X_{h+p} X_k X_{k+p}) = E(X_h)\, E(X_{h+p} X_k X_{k+p}) = 0. \tag{9}$$

Using (7), (8), and (9) in (6) we have

$$\left\{E(T_{m,\ell})\right\}^2 \leq \sum_{k=m+1}^{\ell} \frac{1}{k^2} + 2\sum_{p=1}^{\ell-m-1} \left\{ \sum_{h=m+1}^{\ell-p} \frac{1}{h^2 (h+p)^2} \right\}^{\frac{1}{2}}$$

$$\leq \frac{\ell-m}{m^2} + 2(\ell-m) \left\{ (\ell-m \frac{1}{m^4} \right\}^{\frac{1}{2}} .$$

With the choice $\ell = 2m$,

$$\left\{E(T_{m,2m})\right\}^2 \leq \frac{1}{m} + 2m \frac{1}{m^{\frac{3}{2}}} = m^{-1} + 2m^{-\frac{1}{2}} \leq 3m^{-\frac{1}{2}},$$

and hence

$$E(T_{m,2m}) \leq \sqrt{3}\, m^{-\frac{1}{4}},$$

and consequently

$$\sum_{n=0}^{\infty} E\left(T_{2^n, 2^{n+1}}\right) \leq \sum_{n=0}^{\infty} \sqrt{3}\, 2^{-\frac{n}{4}} < \infty,$$

which proves (5).

We have just shown that there exists $\Omega_0 \in \mathfrak{B}$ with $P(\Omega_0) = 1$ such that for every $\omega \in \Omega_0$ the series in (1) converges uniformly for t in D. Let $W(t, \omega)$ be defined by (1) for $(t, \omega) \in D \times \Omega_0$. We may for instance define $W(t, \omega) = 0$ for $\omega \notin \Omega_0$. Then for every $t \in D$, $W(t, \cdot)$ is a random variable on $(\Omega, \mathfrak{B}, P)$ so that W is a stochastic process on $(\Omega, \mathfrak{B}, P)$ and D. Also $W(0, \cdot) = 0$ on

Ω and $W(\cdot, \omega)$ is continuous on D for $\omega \in \Omega_0$. Since $\{X_n, n = 0,1,2, \cdots\}$ is a Gaussian system of random variables according to Theorem 16.12, $W(t, \cdot)$, $t \in D$, is a Gaussian process by Theorem 16.11.

Let us turn now to the proof of (2). First of all for each $t \in D$ the strong sum on the right side of (2) exists in $L_2(\Omega)$ since $\{X_n, n = 0,1,2, \cdots\}$ is an orthonormal system in $L_2(\Omega)$ and the sum of the squares of the coefficients of the series is finite:

$$\frac{t^2}{\pi} + \sum_{n=1}^{\infty} \frac{2}{\pi} \frac{\sin^2 nt}{n^2} < \infty.$$

Let us call this strong sum $Y(t, \cdot)$ and show that it is equal to $W(t, \cdot)$ as an element of $L_2(\Omega)$. Now since the sequence of partial sums of the series in (1) is a subsequence of the sequence of partial sums of the series in (2) it too converges strongly to $Y(t, \cdot)$. Then there exists a subsequence of the sequence of partial sums of series in (1) which converges almost everywhere on Ω to $Y(t, \cdot)$. But this subsequence converges almost everywhere on Ω to $W(t, \cdot)$ also. Thus $Y(t, \omega) = W(t, \omega)$ for a.e. $\omega \in \Omega$ and (2) holds.

We use (2) to calculate the mean and the covariance functions of the Gaussian process W. By (2) and by the fact that $E(X_n) = 0$ for $n = 0,1,2, \cdots$, we have

$$E\left[W(t, \cdot)\right] = \left(W(t, \cdot), 1\right) = \frac{t}{\sqrt{\pi}} (X_0, 1) + \sum_{n=1}^{\infty} \sqrt{\frac{2}{\pi}} \frac{\sin nt}{n} (X_n, 1) = 0$$

for $t \in D$. (10)

To show

$$C\left[W(s, \cdot), W(t, \cdot)\right] = \min\{s, t\} \quad \text{for } s, t \in D \tag{11}$$

note that, by (10) and (2),

$$C\Big[W(s,\cdot),\ W(t,\cdot)\Big] = \Big(W(s,\cdot),\ W(t,\cdot)\Big)$$
$$= \frac{st}{\pi} + \sum_{n=1}^{\infty} \frac{2}{\pi} \frac{\sin ns}{n} \frac{\sin nt}{n}. \qquad (12)$$

We proceed to show that the right side of (12) is equal to $\min\{s,t\}$. For each fixed $s \in D$, let

$$f_s(t) = \min\{s,t\} - \frac{st}{\pi}. \qquad (13)$$

The problem then is translated to that of establishing

$$f_s(t) = \sum_{n=1}^{\infty} \sqrt{\frac{2}{\pi}} \frac{\sin ns}{n^2} \sqrt{\frac{2}{\pi}} \sin nt \quad \text{for } t \in D. \qquad (14)$$

With the complete orthonormal system $\{\psi_n, n = 1,2,\cdots\}$ in $L_2(D)$ where

$$\psi_n(t) = \sqrt{\frac{2}{\pi}} \sin nt \quad \text{for } t \in D \text{ and } n = 1,2,\cdots$$

we have, from (13),

$$(f_s, \psi_n) = \int_0^s \left(t - \frac{st}{\pi}\right)\sqrt{\frac{2}{\pi}} \sin nt\, dt$$
$$+ \int_s^{\pi} \left(s - \frac{st}{\pi}\right)\sqrt{\frac{2}{\pi}} \sin nt\, dt = \sqrt{\frac{2}{\pi}} \frac{\sin ns}{n^2}.$$

Thus the right side of (14) is the Fourier series of f_s corresponding to the complete orthonormal system $\{\psi_n, n = 1,2,\cdots\}$ and hence

$$f_s = s - \sum_{n=1}^{\infty} \sqrt{\frac{2}{\pi}} \frac{\sin ns}{n^2} \psi_n,$$

and consequently some subsequence of the sequence of partial sums of the series in (14) converges almost everywhere on D to f_s. On the other hand, since

$$\sum_{n=1}^{\infty} \left| \sqrt{\frac{2}{\pi}} \frac{\sin ns}{n^2} \sqrt{\frac{2}{\pi}} \sin nt \right| \leq \frac{2}{\pi} \sum_{n=1}^{\infty} \frac{1}{n^2} < \infty ,$$

the Weierstrass comparison test applies and the series in (14) converges uniformly on D to a continuous function on D. This continuous function is equal to f_s almost everywhere on D and then, from the continuity of f_s, actually everywhere on D. Therefore (14) holds. This proves (11).

The fact that W is a Gaussian process whose mean and covariance functions are given by (10) and (11) implies that W is an additive process. To show this let $t_0, t_1, \cdots, t_n \in D$, $0 \leq t_0 < t_1 < \cdots < t_n \leq \pi$ and for simplicity write W_k for $W(t_k, \cdot)$, $k = 0,1,2, \cdots, n$. Then for $j < k$, applying (10) and (11), we have

$$\begin{aligned} C(W_j - W_{j-1}, W_k - W_{k-1}) &= E\left[\{W_j - W_{j-1}\}\{W_k - W_{k-1}\}\right] \\ &= E(W_j W_k) - E(W_j W_{k-1}) \\ &\quad - E(W_{j-1} W_k) + E(W_{j-1} W_{k-1}) \\ &= t_j - t_j - t_{j-1} + t_{j-1} = 0. \end{aligned} \tag{15}$$

Since $\{W(t, \cdot), t \in D\}$ is a Gaussian process $\{W_k - W_{k-1}, k = 1,2,\cdots,n\}$ is a Gaussian system by Theorem 16.9. Then (15) implies that this system is an independent system by Theorem 16.13. Thus W is an additive process.

Next let us show that for $t', t'' \in D$, $t' < t''$, $W(t'', \cdot) - W(t', \cdot)$ is distributed according to $N(0, t'' - t')$. For brevity write W_1 and

W_2 for $W(t', \cdot)$ and $W(t'', \cdot)$, respectively. Now since $\{W(t, \cdot), t \in D\}$ is a Gaussian process, $W_2 - W_1$ is normally distributed. Its mean is equal to 0 by (10). For its variance we have, by (10) and (11),

$$V(W_2 - W_1) = E\left[W_2 - W_1)^2\right] = E(W_2{}^2) - 2E(W_1 W_2) + E(W_1{}^2)$$
$$= t'' - 2t' + t' = t'' - t'.$$

Thus $W(T'', \cdot) - W(t', \cdot)$ is distributed according to $N(0, t'' - t')$.

We have thus proved that W is a Brownian motion process on $(\Omega, \mathfrak{B}, P)$ and D for which $W(0, \omega) = 0$ for $\omega \in \Omega_0$; $W(t'', \cdot) - W(t', \cdot)$, where $t', t'' \in D$, $t' < t''$, is distributed according to $N(0, t'' - t')$ and $W(\cdot, \omega)$ is continuous on D for $\omega \in \Omega_0$. It remains to prove (4). For φ_0 we have, from Definition 22.1 and (1),

$$I_W(\varphi_0)(\omega) = \frac{1}{\sqrt{\pi}}\left\{W(\pi, \omega) - W(0, \omega)\right\}$$
$$= \frac{1}{\sqrt{\pi}} W(\pi, \omega) = X_0(\omega) \qquad \text{for } \omega \in \Omega.$$

For φ_n, $n \geq 1$, we use Theorem 22.5 to calculate $I_W(\varphi_0)(\omega)$ as a Riemann-Stieltjes integral for a.e. $\omega \in \Omega$. Thus for a.e. $\omega \in \Omega$,

$$I_W(\varphi_0)(\omega) = \int_0^{\pi} \sqrt{\frac{2}{\pi}} \cos nt \, dW(t, \omega)$$
$$= \sqrt{\frac{2}{\pi}} \cos n\pi \, W(\pi, \omega) + \sqrt{\frac{2}{\pi}} \int_0^{\pi} W(t, \omega) \, n \sin nt \, dt$$

by integration by parts and by the fact that $W(0, \omega) = 0$ for a.e. $\omega \in \Omega$. Substituting (1) for $W(t, \omega)$ in the last integral and interchanging integration and summation which is justified by the uniform convergence of the series in (1), we have, for a.e. $\omega \in \Omega$,

$$I_W(\varphi_0)(\omega) = \sqrt{\frac{2}{\pi}} \cos n\pi \, W(\pi, \omega) + \frac{\sqrt{2}}{\pi} X_0(\omega) \int_0^{\pi} tn \sin nt \, dt$$

$$+ \sum_{\ell=0}^{\infty} \sum_{k=2^{\ell}+1}^{2^{\ell+1}} \frac{2}{\pi} X_k(\omega) \int_0^{\pi} \frac{n \sin kt \sin nt}{k} dt$$

$$= \sqrt{\frac{2}{\pi}} \cos n\pi \, W(\pi, \omega) + \frac{\sqrt{2}}{\pi} \frac{1}{\sqrt{\pi}} W(\pi, \omega)(-\pi \cos n\pi)$$

$$+ \frac{2}{\pi} X_n(\omega) \int_0^{\pi} \sin^2 nt \, dt$$

$$= X_n(\omega).$$

This completes the proof of the theorem. □

Remark 23.5 If we use the collection of stochastic integrals $\{X_n, n = 0,1,2, \cdots\}$ given by (2) of Theorem 23.3 as the independent system of random variables each of which is distributed according to $N(0,1)$ in Theorem 23.4 and define W, then by (3) of Theorem 23.3 and (2) of Theorem 23.4 for each $t \in D$, $B(t, \cdot)$ and $W(t, \cdot)$ are equal as elements of $L_2(\Omega)$ so that $B(t,\omega) = W(t, \omega)$ for a.e. $\omega \in \Omega$. Thus B and W are equivalent processes. This gives yet another proof that the Brownian motion process B has an equivalent process in which almost every sample function is continuous.

§24. STOCHASTIC INTEGRALS

[1] Stochastic Integrals of Stochastic Processes

In §22 we considered stochastic integrals of function. We shall present now with some modification the theory of stochastic integrals of stochastic processes developed by K. Itô. Throughout this section we adopt the following notational conventions: B is the Brownian motion process on a probability space $(\Omega, \mathfrak{B}, P)$ and an interval $D = [a, b]$ as described in the second paragraph of §22 satisfying the additional conditions that $B(a, \cdot) = 0$ a.e. on Ω and that B is a continuous process on D, i.e., $B(\cdot, \omega)$ is continuous function on D for every $\omega \in \Omega$. We shall consider stochastic integral of a stochastic process $f(t, \omega)$, $(t, \omega) \in D \times \Omega$, with respect to the Brownian motion process B under the assumptions that f is a measurable process, $f(t, \cdot)$ is a Baire function of the Brownian motion process B up to and including the time point t for every $t \in D$ and that f satisfies certain integrability conditions. These conditions are discussed in the following.

To state the measurability condition which is to be imposed on the stochastic process f on $(\Omega, \mathfrak{B}, P)$ and $D = [a, b]$ let us agree on the following notations. For $t \in D$, let $\mathfrak{M}[a, t]$ be the σ-field of Lebesgue measurable subsets of $[a, t]$. As before we write $\mathfrak{M}_D$ for $\mathfrak{M}_{[a, b]}$. Let $\mathfrak{Z}_{[a, t]}$ be the smallest σ-field of subsets of Ω with respect to which all random variables $B(s, \cdot)$, $s \in [a, t]$, in our Brownian motion process B are measurable. We write $\mathfrak{Z}_D$ for $\mathfrak{Z}_{[a, b]}$. Thus

$$\mathfrak{Z}_{[a, t']} \subset \mathfrak{Z}_{[a, t'']} \subset \mathfrak{Z}_D \subset \mathfrak{B} \qquad \text{for } t', t'' \in D,\ t' < t''.$$

Let $\sigma\left(\mathfrak{M}_{[a, t]} \times \mathfrak{Z}_{[a, t]}\right)$ be the σ-field of subsets of $[a, t] \times \Omega$ generated by $\mathfrak{M}_{[a, t]} \times \mathfrak{Z}_{[a, t]}$. In terms of these notations the measurability condition on f is stated as follows:

((M)) For every $t \in D$, the restriction of f to $[a, t] \times \Omega$ is measurable with respect to $\left(\mathfrak{M}_{[a, t]} \times \mathfrak{Z}_{[a, t]}\right)$.

Under ((M)), the function f on $D \times \Omega$ is measurable with respect to $\sigma(\mathfrak{M}_D \times \mathfrak{Z}_D)$ and hence measurable with respect to $\sigma(\mathfrak{M}_D \times \mathfrak{B})$ and is thus a Lebesgue measurable process in the sense of Definition 5.1. The condition ((M)) also implies the following conditions:

((M_1)) For each $\omega \in \Omega$, $f(\cdot, \omega)$ is $\mathfrak{M}_D$-measurable on D

((M_2)) For each $t \in D$, $f(t, \cdot)$ is $\mathfrak{Z}_{[a,t]}$-measurable on Ω.

According to Theorem 7.17, the condition ((M_2)) is equivalent to the following condition:

((M_2')) For each $t \in D$, $f(t, \cdot)$ is a Baire function of the Brownian motion process B up to and including the time point t, i.e., $f(t, \cdot)$ is a Baire function of the random vector $\left(B(s, \cdot) - B(a, \cdot),\ s \in [a, t]\right)$, or in other words, there exists a $\mathfrak{B}^{[a,t]}$-measurable function $\varphi_{[a,t]}(x)$, $x \in R^{[a,t]}$, such that

$$f(t, \omega) = \varphi_{[a,t]}\left(B(\cdot, \omega) - B(a, \omega)\right) \quad \text{for every } \omega \in \Omega$$

where, as we defined in [I], §7, $R^{[a,t]}$ is the collection of all real-valued functions x on [a, t] and $\mathfrak{B}^{[a,t]}$ is the σ-field of Borel sets in $R^{[a,t]}$, i.e., $\mathfrak{B}^{[a,t]}$ is the σ-field of subsets of $R^{[a,t]}$ generated by the subsets of $R^{[a,t]}$ of the type

$$\left\{ x \in R^{[a,t]} ; \left[x(t_1), \cdots, x(t_n)\right] \in B \right\},$$

where $\{t_1, \cdots, t_n\} \subset [a, t]$, B is a member of the σ-field $\mathfrak{B}^n$ of Borel sets in R^n, and n is an arbitrary positive integer. As we saw in Lemma 7.5, $\mathfrak{B}^{[a, t]}$ is also the σ-field generated by the subsets of $R^{[a, t]}$ of the type

$$\left\{x \in R^{[a, t]}; x(t_j) \in J_j, \ j = 1, 2, \cdots, n\right\},$$

where J_j is an open interval in R^1 for $j = 1, 2, \cdots, n$.

Lemma 24.1 Let f be a stochastic process on $(\Omega, \mathfrak{M}, P)$ and D which satisfies the condition $((M_2'))$. For $t \in D$ let $\psi_{[u', u'']}(y)$, where $y \in R^{[u', u'']}$ and $a \leq t \leq u' < u'' \leq b$, be a real-valued $\mathfrak{B}^{[u', u'']}$-measurable function on $R^{[u', u'']}$. Then the two random variables $f(t, \cdot)$ and $\psi_{[u', u'']}\left(B(\cdot, \cdot) - B(u', \cdot)\right)$ are independent. In particular $f(t, \cdot)$ and $B(u'', \cdot) - B(u', \cdot)$ are independent, and consequently

$$E\left[f(t, \cdot)\left\{B(u'', \cdot) - B(u', \cdot)\right\}\right] = 0.$$

Proof We assert that the two random vectors

$$\left(B(s, \cdot) - B(a, \cdot), \ s \in [a, t]\right) \quad \text{and}$$
$$\left(B(v, \cdot) - B(u', \cdot), \ v \in [u', u'']\right) \tag{1}$$

are independent. To show this it suffices, according to Definition 7.11, to show that, for $a \leq s_1 < \cdots < s_m \leq t$ and $u' \leq v_1 < \cdots < v_n \leq u''$, the two random vectors

$$\left(B(s_j, \cdot) - B(a, \cdot), \ j = 1, 2, \cdots, m\right) \quad \text{and}$$
$$\left(B(v_k, \cdot) - B(u', \cdot), \ k = 1, 2, \cdots, n\right) \tag{2}$$

are independent. Now these last two random vectors are, respectively, Baire transformations of the two random vectors

$$\left(B(s_j, \cdot) - B(s_{j-1}, \cdot),\ j = 1, 2, \cdots, m\right) \quad \text{and}$$
$$\left(B(v_k, \cdot) - B(v_{k-1}, \cdot),\ k = 1, 2, \cdots, n\right) \tag{3}$$

with the understanding that $s_0 = a$ and $v_0 = u'$. Since B is an additive process, the two random vectors in (3) are independent by (1) of Theorem A6.5, and then the two random vectors in (2) are independent by Theorem A6.6. This proves the independence of the two random vectors in (1). Then since $f(t, \cdot)$ is a $\mathfrak{B}^{[a,t]}$-measurable function of the first random vector in (1), $f(t, \cdot)$ and $\psi_{[u', u'']}\left(B(\cdot, \cdot) - B(u', \cdot)\right)$ are independent by Theorem 7.12. □

The integrability conditions we shall impose on f are given in the following definition.

Definition 24.2 Let f be a stochastic process on $(\Omega, \mathfrak{B}, P)$ and D which satisfies the measurability condition ((M)). We say that $f \in S_0(D)$, $f \in S_1(D)$, or $f \in S_2(D)$ if it satisfies the integrability condition $((I_0))$, $((I_1))$, or $((I_2))$, respectively:

$((I_0))$ f is a stepwise stochastic process, i.e., there exists a partition of D by $a = a_1 < \cdots < a_{n+1} = b$ into subintervals $J_k = [a_k, a_{k+1})$, $k = 1, 2, \cdots, n-1$, and $J_n = [a_n, a_{n+1}]$ such that

$$f(t, \omega) = f(a_k, \omega) \quad \text{for } t \in J_k,\ k = 1, 2, \cdots, n \text{ and } \omega \in \Omega$$

and

$$f(a_k, \cdot) \in L_2(\Omega) \quad \text{for } k = 1, 2, \cdots, n.$$

$((I_1))$ $f \in L_2(D \times \Omega)$, i.e., $\int_{D\times\Omega} \{f(t,\omega)\}^2 (m_L \times P)\left(d(t, \omega)\right) < \infty$.

$((I_2))$ For a.e. $\omega \in \Omega$, $f(\cdot, \omega) \in L_2(D)$, i.e.,

$$\int_D \{f(t, \omega)\}^2 m_L(dt) < \infty .$$

Lemma 24.3 $S_0(D) \subset S_1(D) \subset S_2(D)$. Under pointwise addition and scalar multiplication on $D \times \Omega$, $S_i(D)$ is a linear subspace of $S_{i+1}(D)$ over the field of real numbers for $i = 0, 1$.

Proof It suffices to show that $((I_0))$ implies $((I_1))$ and that $((I_1))$ implies $((I_2))$. Now under $((I_0))$

$$\int_{D\times\Omega} \left[f(t, \omega)\right]^2 (m_L \times P)\left(d(t, \omega)\right)$$
$$= \sum_{k=1}^{n} \left\{\int \left[f(a_k, \omega)\right]^2 P(d\omega)\right\} (a_{k+1} - a_k) < \infty ,$$

so that $((I_1))$ holds. The implication of $((I_2))$ by $((I_1))$ is from the Fubini theorem. □

The stochastic integral $I(f)$ will be defined first for $f \in S_0(D)$ and then extended to $S_1(D)$ and $S_2(D)$. The following inequality which is an extension of the Kolmogorov inequality will be used in the consideration of $I(f)$ for $f \in S_0(D)$.

Lemma 24.4 Itô Inequality. Let $\{X_1, \cdots, X_n, Y_1, \cdots, Y_n\}$ be a collection of random variables on $(\Omega, \mathfrak{B}, P)$ which satisfy the following conditions:

1°. X_1 and Y_1 are independent and for $k = 2, 3, \cdots, n$, the random variable X_k and the random vector $(X_1, \cdots, X_{k-1}, Y_1, \cdots, Y_k)$ are independent.

2°. $E(X_k) = 0$ and $E(X_k^2) < \infty$ for $k = 1, 2, \cdots, n$.

3°. $E(Y_k^2) < \infty$ for $k = 1, 2, \cdots, n$.

Let $S_k = \sum_{i=1}^{k} X_i Y_i$. Then

$$E(S_k^2) = \sum_{i=1}^{k} E(X_i^2)\, E(Y_i^2) \qquad \text{for } k = 1, 2, \cdots, n, \tag{1}$$

and for every $c > 0$

$$P\left\{\omega \in \Omega ; \max\left\{|S_1(\omega)|, \cdots, |S_k(\omega)|\right\} \geq c\right\} \leq \frac{1}{c^2} E(S_k^2)$$

$$\text{for } k = 1, 2, \cdots, n. \tag{2}$$

<u>Proof</u> For $i < j$ we have, by 1° and the Schwarz inequality,

$$E\left(|X_i Y_i Y_j|\right) \leq \sqrt{E(X_i^2 Y_i^2)\, E(Y_j^2)}$$

$$= \sqrt{E(X_i^2)\, E(Y_i^2)\, E(Y_j^2)} < \infty, \tag{3}$$

and then by, 1° and 2°,

$$E(X_i Y_i X_j Y_j) = E(X_i Y_i Y_j)\, E(X_j) = 0. \tag{4}$$

By (4) and 1°,

$$E(S_k^2) = E\left[\left\{\sum_{i=1}^{k} X_i Y_i\right\}^2\right] = \sum_{i=1}^{k} E\left(X_i^2 Y_i^2\right) = \sum_{i=1}^{k} E(X_i^2)\, E(Y_i^2),$$

which is (1).

To prove (2), let

$$T_k(\omega) = \max\left\{|S_1(\omega)|, \cdots, |S_k(\omega)|\right\} \qquad \text{for } k = 1, 2, \cdots, n$$

and

$$T_0(\omega) = 0 \qquad \text{for } \omega \in \Omega.$$

Given $c > 0$ let $\varphi(x) = \chi_{[c,\infty)}(x)$, $x \in R^1$. Define a sequence of random variables Z_k, $k = 1, 2, \cdots, n$, on $(\Omega, \mathfrak{B}, P)$ by

$$Z_k(\omega) = \varphi\big(T_k(\omega)\big) - \varphi\big(T_{k-1}(\omega)\big) \qquad \text{for } k = 1, 2, \cdots, n.$$

Then

$$\varphi\big(T_k(\omega)\big) = \sum_{i=1}^{k} Z_i(\omega) \qquad \text{for } k = 1, 2, \cdots, n. \tag{5}$$

Since $T_k(\omega)$ is monotone increasing as k increases, $Z_k(\omega)$ assumes no values other than 0 and 1. Also

$$\{\omega \in \Omega ; Z_k(\omega) = 1\} = \{\omega \in \Omega ; \varphi\big(T_k(\omega)\big) = 1, \ \varphi\big(T_{k-1}(\omega)\big) = 0\}$$
$$= \{\omega \in \Omega ; T_k(\omega) \geq c, \ T_{k-1}(\omega) < c\}.$$

This implies in particular that

$$Z_k(\omega) = 1 \Rightarrow |S_k(\omega)| \geq c \qquad \text{for } k = 1, 2, \cdots, n. \tag{6}$$

From the fact that $Z_k(\omega)$, $k = 1, 2, \cdots, n$, can assume no values other than 0 and 1 and from the Schwarz inequality we have

$$E\big(|S_i Z_i Y_j|\big) \leq E\big(|S_i Y_j|\big) \leq \sqrt{E(S_i^2)\, E(Y_j^2)} < \infty. \tag{7}$$

For $i < j$, X_j and $S_i Z_i Y_j$ are independent according to 1°, so that, by 2° and (7),

$$E(S_i Z_i X_j Y_j) = E(X_j)\, E(S_i Z_i Y_j) = 0. \tag{8}$$

Then for $i < j < \ell$ we have, by (3),

$$E\big(|Z_i X_j Y_j Y_\ell|\big) \leq E\big(|X_j Y_j Y_\ell|\big) < \infty. \tag{9}$$

Further, by 1° X_ℓ and $Z_i X_j Y_j Y_\ell$ are independent so that, by

(9) and 2°,

$$E(Z_i X_j Y_j X_\ell Y_\ell) = E(Z_i X_j Y_j Y_\ell)\ E(X_\ell) = 0. \tag{10}$$

Using (8) and (10) and finally (6) we obtain

$$\begin{aligned} E(Z_i S_k^2) &= E\left[Z_i \{S_i + X_{i+1} Y_{i+1} + \cdots + X_k Y_k\}^2\right] \\ &= E(Z_i S_i^2) + E(Z_i X_{i+1}^2 Y_{i+1}^2) + \cdots + E(Z_i X_k^2 Y_k^2) \\ &\geq E(Z_i S_i^2) \geq c^2\ E(Z_i). \end{aligned} \tag{11}$$

Thus, by (5) and (11),

$$\begin{aligned} E(S_k^2) &\geq E\left[\varphi(T_k)\ S_k^2\right] = E\left[\left(\sum_{i=1}^{k} Z_i\right) S_k^2\right] = \sum_{i=1}^{k} E(Z_i S_k^2) \\ &\geq c^2 \sum_{i=1}^{k} E(Z_i) = c^2\ E\left(\sum_{i=1}^{k} Z_i\right) = c^2\ E\left[\varphi(T_k)\right] \\ &= c^2\ P\left\{\omega \in \Omega\,;\, \varphi\left(T_k(\omega)\right) = 1\right\} = c^2\ P\left\{\omega \in \Omega\,;\, T_k(\omega) \geq c\right\}, \end{aligned}$$

which proves (2). □

Corollary 24.5 Let $\{X_k, Y_k, k = 1, 2, \cdots\}$ be a collection of random variables on $(\Omega, \mathfrak{B}, P)$ such that, for each positive integer n, the collection $\{X_k, Y_k, k = 1, 2, \cdots, n\}$ satisfies the conditions 1°, 2°, 3° of Lemma 21.4. Let $S_k = \sum_{i=1}^{k} X_k Y_k$ for $k = 1, 2, \cdots$. Then for every $c > 0$

$$P\left\{\omega \in \Omega\,;\, \sup_n |S_n(\omega)| \geq c\right\} \leq \frac{1}{c^2} \sum_{i=1}^{\infty} E(X_i^2)\ E(Y_i^2).$$

Proof We have

$$\max_{k=1,\cdots,n} |S_k(\omega)| \uparrow \sup_n |S_n(\omega)| \quad \text{as } n \to \infty .$$

For $c > 0$ let $\delta > 0$ be so chosen that $c - \delta > 0$ and then let

$$A_n = \left\{ \omega \in \Omega ; \max_{k=1,\cdots,n} |S_k(\omega)| \geq c - \delta \right\} \quad \text{for } n = 1, 2, \cdots$$

and

$$A = \left\{ \omega \in \Omega ; \sup_n |S_n(\omega)| \geq c \right\} .$$

Then $\{A_n, n = 1, 2, \cdots\}$ is a monotone increasing sequence and $A \subset \bigcup_{n=1}^{\infty} A_n = \lim_{n\to\infty} A_n$ so that $P(A) \leq \lim_{n\to\infty} P(A_n)$. By Lemma 24.4,

$$P(A_n) \leq \frac{1}{(c-\delta)^2} \sum_{i=1}^{n} E(X_i^2)\, E(Y_i^2),$$

and hence

$$P(A) \leq \frac{1}{(c-\delta)^2} \sum_{i=1}^{\infty} E(X_i^2)\, E(Y_i^2).$$

Letting $\delta \downarrow 0$ we have a proof for the corollary. □

[II] Stochastic Integral for the Class $S_0(D)$

Definition 24.6 Let $f \in S_0(D)$ and let $a_1, \cdots, a_{n+1}$ be the partition points of D and $J_1, \cdots, J_n$ be the resulting subintervals of D as given in Definition 24.2. The stochastic integral $I(f)$ of f with respect to the Brownian motion process B is defined by

$$I(f)(t,\omega) = \sum_{i=1}^{k-1} f(a_i, \omega)\left\{B(a_{i+1}, \omega) - B(a_i, \omega)\right\} + f(a_k, \omega)\left\{B(t,\omega) - B(a_k, \omega)\right\}$$

for $t \in J_k$, $k = 1, 2, \cdots, n$, and $\omega \in \Omega$.

Thus defined, $I(f)(t, \cdot)$ is a random variable on $(\Omega, \mathfrak{B}, P)$ for each $t \in D$, so that $I(f)$ is a stochastic process on $(\Omega, \mathfrak{B}, P)$ and D. Also $I(f)(a, \omega) = 0$ for every $\omega \in \Omega$.

Theorem 24.7 For the stochastic integral $I(f)$, $f \in S_0(D)$, the following hold:

(1) If $f, g \in S_0(D)$ and $f(\cdot, \omega_0) = g(\cdot, \omega_0)$ on D for some $\omega_0 \in \Omega$ then

$$I(f)(\cdot, \omega_0) = I(g)(\cdot, \omega_0) \quad \text{on } D.$$

(2) If $f, g \in S_0(D)$ and $\alpha, \beta \in R^1$, then

$$I(\alpha f + \beta g)(t, \omega) = \alpha I(f)(t, \omega) + \beta I(g)(t, \omega) \quad \text{for } (t, \omega) \in D \times \Omega.$$

(3) For every $\omega \in \Omega$, $I(f)(\cdot, \omega)$ is a continuous function on D.

(4) For the mean of the random variable $I(f)(t, \cdot)$ we have

$$E\left[I(f)(t, \cdot)\right] = 0 \qquad \text{for } t \in D.$$

(5) For the variance of the random variable $I(f)(t, \cdot)$ we have

$$\|I(f)(t, \cdot)\| = \|f\|_{[a, t]} \qquad \text{for } t \in D,$$

where $\|I(f)(t, \cdot)\|$ is the Hilbert norm in $L_2(\Omega)$ and $\|f\|_{[a, t]}$ is the Hilbert norm in $L_2\big([a, t] \times \Omega\big)$.

(6) For every $c > 0$

$$c^2\, P\left\{\omega \in \Omega;\ \sup_{D} |I(f)(t, \omega)| > c\right\} \le \|f\|^2 ,$$

where $\|f\| = \|f\|_{[a,b]}$.

Proof The properties (1), (2), (3) are immediate from Definition 24.6. To prove (4) let $t \in D$, say $t \in J_k$. Then, by Lemma 24.1,

$$E\left[I(f)(t, \cdot)\right] = \sum_{i=1}^{k-1} E\left[f(a_i, \cdot)\left\{B(a_{i+1}, \cdot) - B(a_i, \cdot)\right\}\right]$$

$$+ E\left[f(a_k, \cdot)\left\{B(t, \cdot) - B(a_k, \cdot)\right\}\right] = 0.$$

To prove (5), again let $t \in J_k$. Then

$$\|I(f)(t, \cdot)\|^2 = E\left[\left\{I(f)(t, \cdot)\right\}^2\right]$$

$$= E\left(\left[\sum_{i=1}^{k-1} f(a_i, \cdot)\left\{B(a_{i+1}, \cdot) - B(a_i, \cdot)\right\}\right.\right.$$

$$\left.\left.+ f(a_k, \cdot)\left\{B(t, \cdot) - B(a_k, \cdot)\right\}\right]^2\right) .$$

From the independence of $f(a_i, \cdot)$ and $B(a_{i+1}, \cdot) - B(a_i, \cdot)$ according to Lemma 24.1 we have

$$E\left[\left\{f(a_i, \cdot)\right\}^2\left\{B(a_{i+1}, \cdot) - B(a_i, \cdot)\right\}^2\right] = E\left[\left\{f(a_i, \cdot)\right\}^2\right](a_{i+1} - a_i).$$

On the other hand for $i < j$ the two random variables $f(a_i, \cdot)\left\{B(a_{i+1}, \cdot) - B(a_i, \cdot)\right\}f(a_j, \cdot)$ and $B(a_{j+1}, \cdot) - B(a_j, \cdot)$ are independent by Lemma 24.1, so that

$$E\left[f(a_i, \cdot)\left\{B(a_{i+1}, \cdot) - B(a_i, \cdot)\right\} f(a_j, \cdot)\left\{B(a_{j+1}, \cdot) - B(a_j, \cdot)\right\}\right]$$

$$= E\left[f(a_i, \cdot)\left\{B(a_{i+1}, \cdot) - B(a_i, \cdot)\right\} f(a_j, \cdot)\right] E\left[B(a_{j+1}, \cdot) - B(a_j, \cdot)\right] = 0.$$

Thus

$$\|I(f)(t, \cdot)\|^2 = \sum_{i=1}^{k-1} E\left[\left\{f(a_i, \cdot)\right\}^2\right](a_{i+1} - a_i) + E\left[\left\{f(a_i, \cdot)\right\}^2\right](t - a_k)$$

$$= \int_{[a, t]\times\Omega} \left\{f(t, \omega)\right\}^2 (m_L \times P)\left(d(t, \omega)\right) = \|f\|^2_{[a, t]} .$$

This proves (5).

Let us now prove (6). From the denseness of $\{t_{\ell,k}, k = 0, 1, 2, \cdots, 2^\ell; \ell = 1, 2, \cdots\}$ in D where $t_{\ell,k} = a + k2^{-\ell}(b-a)$ and from the continuity of $I(f)(\cdot, \omega)$ on D for $\omega \in \Omega$ we have, for every $c > 0$,

$$\left\{\omega \in \Omega; \sup_D |I(f)(t, \omega)| > c\right\}$$

$$= \bigcup_{\ell=1}^{\infty} \left\{\omega \in \Omega; \max_{k=0, \cdots, 2^\ell} |I(f)(t_{\ell,k}, \omega)| > c\right\} . \tag{7}$$

The sequence of sets on the right side of (1) is monotone increasing as $\ell \to \infty$ so that the probability of the set on the left side is the limit as $\ell \to \infty$ of the probabilities of the sets on the right side. Thus we have

$$P\left\{\omega \in \Omega; \sup_D |I(f)(t, \omega)| > c\right\}$$

$$= \lim_{\ell\to\infty} P\left\{\omega \in \Omega; \max_{k=0, \cdots, 2^\ell} |I(f)(t_{\ell,k}, \omega)| > c\right\} . \tag{8}$$

In view of (8), to prove (6) it suffices to show that, for any partition of D, $a = s_1 < \cdots < s_m = b$, we have

$$c^2 P\left\{\omega \in \Omega;\ \max_{j=1,\cdots,m} |I(f)(s_j,\omega)| > c\right\} \le \|f\|^2. \tag{9}$$

Since an addition of more partition points of D increases the left side of (9) we do not lose generality in our proof by assuming that the partition points $\{a_1, \cdots, a_{n+1}\}$ of D in Definition 24.2 are included in the collection $\{s_1, \cdots, s_m\}$ already. Now

$$I(f)(s_j,\omega) = \sum_{i=1}^{j} f(s_i,\omega)\left\{B(s_{i+1},\omega) - B(s_i,\omega)\right\} \quad \text{for } j = 1,2,\cdots,m.$$

Let

$$X_i = B(s_{i+1},\cdot) - B(s_i,\cdot) \quad \text{and} \quad Y_i = f(s_i,\cdot) \quad \text{for } i = 1,2,\cdots,m.$$

Then by Lemma 24.1, X_1 and Y_1 are independent and for $j = 2,3,\cdots,m$, X_j and $(X_1,\cdots,X_{j-1},Y_1,\cdots,Y_j)$ are independent. Also

$$E(X_i) = 0,\ E(X_i^2) = s_{i+1} - s_i < \infty \quad \text{and} \quad E(Y_i^2) = E\left[\left\{f(s_i,\cdot)\right\}^2\right] < \infty$$

for $i = 1,2,\cdots,m$. Thus the conditions 1°, 2°, 3° of Lemma 24.4 are all satisfied, and consequently

$$\begin{aligned}
&c^2 P\left\{\omega \in \Omega;\ \max_{j=1,\cdots,m} |I(f)(s_j,\omega)| > c\right\} \\
&= c^2 P\left\{\omega \in \Omega;\ \max_{j=1,\cdots,m} \left|\sum_{i=1}^{j} X_i(\omega)\, Y_i(\omega)\right| > c\right\} \\
&\le \sum_{i=1}^{m} E(X_i^2)\, E(Y_i^2) = \sum_{i=1}^{m} E\left[\left\{f(s_i,\cdot)\right\}^2\right](s_{i+1} - s_i) \\
&= \int_{D\times\Omega} \left\{f(t,\omega)\right\}^2 (m_L \times P)\big(d(t,\omega)\big) = \|f\|^2.
\end{aligned}$$

This proves (9) and hence (6). □

[III] Stochastic Integral for the Class $S_1(D)$

In [II] we defined the stochastic integral $I(f)$ for $f \in S_0(D)$. To extend the definition to the class $S_1(D)$ we show that $S_0(D)$ is dense in $S_1(D)$ with respect to the Hilbert norm of $L_2(D \times \Omega)$ and then define $I(f)$ for $f \in S_1(D)$ by a limiting process. We need the following lemmas from real analysis for this purpose.

Lemma 24.8 Let $g \in L_2(R^1)$. If ψ is a real-valued function on R^1 and $\lim_{r \to r_0} \psi(r) = \psi(r_0)$ for some $r_0 \in R^1$ then

$$\lim_{r \to r_0} \int_{R^1} \left\{g\left(\psi(r)+s\right) - g\left(\psi(r_0)+s\right)\right\}^2 m_L(ds) = 0.$$

Proof The lemma follows from the fact that any $g \in L_2(R^1)$ can be approximated in the Hilbert norm by a continuous function with a compact support in R^1 and the fact that the latter function is uniformly continuous on R^1. Thus for $\varepsilon > 0$ let h be a continuous function with a compact support in R^1 which satisfies

$$\int_{R^1} \left\{g(s) - h(s)\right\}^2 m_L(ds) < \varepsilon . \tag{1}$$

Since for any real numbers a, b, and c, $(a+b)^2 \le 2(a^2+b^2)$ and then $\left\{a + (b+c)\right\}^2 \le 2a^2 + 4b^2 + 4c^2$ holds, we have

$$\int_{R^1} \left\{g\left(\psi(r)+s\right) - g\left(\psi(r_0)+s\right)\right\}^2 m_L(ds)$$

$$\le 2\int_{R^1} \left\{g\left(\psi(r)+s\right) - h\left(\psi(r)+s\right)\right\}^2 m_L(ds)$$

$$+ 4\int_{R^1} \{h(\psi(r)+s) - h(\psi(r_0)+s)\}^2 m_L(ds)$$

$$+ 4\int_{R^1} \{h(\psi(r_0)+s) - g(\psi(r_0)+s)\}^2 m_L(ds). \tag{2}$$

The first and the last integral on the right side of (2) are each less than ϵ by (1) for any $r \in R^1$ and the second integral can be made less than ϵ by choosing r sufficiently close to r_0 by virtue of the uniform continuity of h on R^1. This proves the lemma. □

Lemma 24.9 $S_0(D)$ is dense in $S_1(D)$ in the Hilbert norm of $L_2(D \times \Omega)$, i.e., for every $f \in S_1(D)$ there exists $\{f_n, n = 1,2,\cdots\} \subset S_1(D_0)$ such that $\lim_{n\to\infty} \|f_n - f\| = 0$.

Proof Let $f \in S_1(D)$. If $\theta_n(t)$, $t \in D$, is a step function and $f_n(t,\omega) = f(\theta_n(t),\omega)$ for $(t,\omega) \in D \times R$, then f_n is a stepwise stochastic process. Our problem then is to choose $\{\theta_n, n=1,2,\cdots\}$ so that the condition $\lim_{n\to\infty} \|f_n - f\| = 0$ as well as ((M)) and $((I_0))$ are satisfied by f_n.

For $f \in S_1(D)$, extend the domain of definition of the stochastic process f from $D = [a,b]$ to R^1 by setting

$$f(t,\omega) = 0 \quad \text{for} \quad t \in [a,b]^c \quad \text{and} \quad \omega \in \Omega.$$

Then

$$\int_{R^1\times\Omega} \{f(t,\omega)\}^2 (m_L \times P)(d(t,\omega)) = \int_{[a,b]\times\Omega} \{f(t,\omega)\}^2 (m_P \times P)(d(t,\omega)) < \infty,$$

and hence

$$\int_{R^1} \{f(t,\omega)\}^2 m_L(dt) < \infty \ \text{ i.e., } \ f(\cdot,\omega) \in L_2(R^1) \ \text{ for a.e. } \omega \in \Omega, \tag{1}$$

and similarly

$$\int_{\Omega} \{f(t,\omega)\}^2 P(d\omega) < \infty, \quad \text{i.e.} \quad f(t,\cdot) \in L_2(\Omega) \quad \text{for a.e.} \quad t \in R^1. \tag{2}$$

Let us define a sequence of functions $\{\varphi_\ell, \ell = 1,2,\cdots\}$ on R^1 by

$$\varphi_\ell(t) = \frac{k-1}{\ell} \quad \text{for} \quad t \in \left[\frac{k-1}{\ell}, \frac{k}{\ell}\right)$$

$$\text{for} \quad k = 0, \pm 1, \pm 2, \cdots, \quad \text{and} \quad \ell = 1,2,\cdots. \tag{3}$$

Then

$$\varphi_\ell(t) \le t \quad \text{for} \quad \ell = 1,2,\cdots \tag{4}$$

and

$$\lim_{\ell \to \infty} \varphi_\ell(t) = t \quad \text{for} \quad t \in R^1. \tag{5}$$

By (1), (5), and Lemma 24.8

$$\lim_{\ell \to \infty} \int_{R^1} \left\{f\left(\varphi_\ell(t) + s, \omega\right) - f(t+s,\omega)\right\}^2 m_L(ds) = 0$$

$$\text{for} \quad t \in R^1 \quad \text{for a.e.} \quad \omega \in \Omega. \tag{6}$$

The integral on the left side of (6) is a function of t and ω and is bounded as follows:

$$\int_{R^1} \left\{f\left(\varphi_\ell(t) + s, \omega\right) - f(t+s,\omega)\right\}^2 m_L(ds)$$

$$\le 2\int_{R^1} \left\{f\left(\varphi_\ell(t) + s, \omega\right)\right\}^2 m_L(ds) + 2\int_{R^1} \{f(t+s,\omega)\}^2 m_L(ds)$$

$$= 4\int_{R^1} \{f(s,\omega)\}^2 m_L(ds).$$

This bound, which is independent of ℓ, is integrable with respect to $m_L \times P$ on $[a-1,b] \times \Omega$:

$$\int_{[a-1,b]\times\Omega} \left[\int_{R^1} \{f(s,\omega)\}^2 m_L(ds)\right] (m_L \times P)\big(d(t,\omega)\big)$$

$$= \int_{[a-1,b]} \left[\int_{R^1 \times \Omega} \{f(s,\omega)\}^2 (m_L \times P)\big(d(s,\omega)\big)\right] m_L(dt) < \infty$$

since $f \in L_2(R^1 \times \Omega)$. Thus the Dominated Convergence Theorem may be applied to (6) and as the result we have

$$\lim_{\ell\to\infty} \int_{[a-1,b]\times\Omega} \left[\int_{R^1} \{f(\varphi_\ell(t)+s,\omega) - f(t+s,\omega)\}^2 m_L(ds)\right]$$
$$(m_L \times P)\big(d(t,\omega)\big) = 0. \tag{7}$$

Applying the Fubini theorem to the integral in (7) we obtain

$$\lim_{\ell\to\infty} \int_{R^1} \left[\int_{[a-1,b]\times\Omega} \{f(\varphi_\ell(t)+s,\omega) - f(t+s,\omega)\}^2\right.$$
$$\left.(m_L \times P)\big(d(t,\omega)\big)\right] m_L(ds) = 0. \tag{8}$$

According to the Riesz-Fischer theorem, convergence in the L_1 norm to 0 implies the existence of a subsequence which converges a.e. to 0. Thus there exists a subsequence $\{\ell_n, n = 1, 2, \cdots\}$ such that

$$\lim_{n\to\infty} \int_{[a-1,b]\times\Omega} \{f(\varphi_{\ell_n}(t)+s,\omega) - f(t+s,\omega)\}^2$$
$$(m_L \times P)\big(d(t,\omega)\big) = 0 \quad \text{for a.e. } s \in R^1.. \tag{9}$$

By (2), it is possible to choose $s_0 \in [0,1]$ so that not only (9) holds with $s = s_0$ but also

$$f\left(\frac{k}{\ell} + s_0, \cdot\right) \in L_2(\Omega) \quad \text{for } k = 0, \pm 1, \pm 2, \cdots, \text{ and } \ell = 1, 2, \cdots. \tag{10}$$

With such s_0 we have

$$\int_{[a,b]\times\Omega} \left\{f\left(\varphi_{\ell_n}(t - s_0) + s_0, \omega\right) - f(t, \omega)\right\}^2 (m_L \times P)\left(d(t, \omega)\right)$$

$$= \int_{[a-s_0, b-s_0]\times\Omega} \left\{f\left(\varphi_{\ell_n}(t) + s_0, \omega\right) - f(t + s_0, \omega)\right\}^2 (m_L \times P)\left(d(t, \omega)\right)$$

$$\leq \int_{[a-1, b]\times\Omega} \left\{f\left(\varphi_{\ell_n}(t) + s_0, \omega\right) - f(t + s_0, \omega)\right\}^2 (m_L \times P)\left(d(t, \omega)\right). \tag{11}$$

Let us define a sequence of stepwise stochastic processes $\{f_n, n = 1, 2, \cdots\}$ on $(\Omega, \mathfrak{B}, P)$ and D by

$$f_n(t, \omega) = f\left(\varphi_{\ell_n}(t - s_0) + s_0, \omega\right) \quad \text{for } t \in D \text{ and } \omega \in \Omega. \tag{12}$$

Thus the step function θ_n mentioned at the beginning of the proof takes the form $\theta_n(t) = \varphi_{\ell_n}(t - s_0) + s_0$ for $t \in D$. By (11) and (9),

$$\lim_{n\to\infty} \| f_n - f \| = 0 \tag{13}$$

holds. From (4),

$$\varphi_{\ell_n}(t - s_0) + s_0 \leq t - s_0 + s_0 = t.$$

This and (12) together with the fact that f satisfies ((M)) imply that f_n satisfies ((M)). Finally for $t \in R^1$, say $t \in \left[(k-1)/\ell + s_0, k/\ell + s_0\right)$ we have

$$t - s_0 \in \left[\frac{k-1}{\ell}, \frac{k}{\ell}\right), \quad \varphi_{\ell_n}(t - s_0) = \frac{k-1}{\ell}$$

by (3), and consequently, by (12) and (10),

$$f_n(t,\cdot) = f\left(\frac{k-1}{\ell} + s_0, \cdot\right) \in L_2(\Omega),$$

so that $((I_0))$ is satisfied. Thus $\{f_n, n = 1,2,\cdots\} \subset S_0(D)$, and this completes the proof. □

Lemma 24.10 Let $f \in S_1(D)$ and let $\{f_n, n = 1,2,\cdots\} \subset S_0(D)$ be such that $\lim_{n\to\infty} \|f_n - f\| = 0$. Then there exist a subsequence $\{f_{n_k}, k = 1,2,\cdots\}$, a set $\Omega_0 \in \mathfrak{B}$ with $P(\Omega_0) = 1$, and a real-valued function $X(t,\omega)$ on $D \times \Omega_0$ such that

$$\lim_{k\to\infty} I(f_{n_k})(t,\omega) = X(t,\omega) \quad \text{uniformly in } t \in D$$
$$\text{for each } \omega \in \Omega_0. \tag{1}$$

Let $X(t,\omega) = 0$ for $t \in D$ and $\omega \in \Omega_0^c$. Then $X(t,\cdot)$ is a random variable for each $t \in D$ and X is a continuous stochastic process on $(\Omega, \mathfrak{B}, P)$ and D. The sequence of random variables $\{I(f_n)(t,\cdot), n = 1,2,\cdots\}$ converges in probability to $X(t,\cdot)$ uniformly in $t \in D$, and in fact, for every $\epsilon > 0$,

$$P\left\{\omega \in \Omega ; \sup_D |I(f_n)(t,\omega) - X(t,\omega)| > \epsilon\right\} \le \frac{1}{\epsilon^2} \|f_n - f\|^2 \tag{2}$$

holds.

Proof Let $f \in S_1(D)$ and let $\{f_n, n = 1,2,\cdots\}$ be an arbitrary sequence from $S_0(D)$ with $\lim_{n\to\infty} \|f_n - f\| = 0$. Since $I(f_m)(\cdot,\omega) - I(f_n)(\cdot,\omega)$ is continuous on D for every $\omega \in \Omega$ according to (3) of Theorem 24.7,

$$\sup_D |I(f_m)(t,\omega) - I(f_n)(t,\omega)| = \sup_{D_0} |I(f_m)(t,\omega) - I(f_n)(t,\omega)|$$
$$\text{for each } \omega \in \Omega, \tag{3}$$

where D_0 is the countable collection of rational numbers in D. Thus this supremum over D is a $\mathfrak{B}$-measurable function on Ω. Then by (2) and (6) of Theorem 24.7, for every $\varepsilon > 0$,

$$\begin{aligned} &P\left\{\omega \in \Omega ; \sup_D |I(f_m)(t,\omega) - I(f_n)(t,\omega)| > \varepsilon\right\} \\ &= P\left\{\omega \in \Omega ; \sup_D |I(f_m - f_n)(t,\omega)| > \varepsilon\right\} \\ &\leq \frac{1}{\varepsilon^2} \|f_m - f_n\|^2, \end{aligned}$$

and hence

$$\lim_{m,n\to\infty} P\left\{\omega \in \Omega ; \sup_D |I(f_m)(t,\omega) - I(f_n)(t,\omega)| > \varepsilon\right\} = 0, \tag{4}$$

i.e., $\{I(f_n)(t,\cdot), n = 1,2,\cdots\}$ is a uniform (in $t \in D$) Cauchy sequence with respect to convergence in probability. By (4), for every positive integer k there exists a positive integer N(k) such that

$$P\left\{\omega \in \Omega ; \sup_D |I(f_{N(k)+q})(t,\omega) - I(f_{N(k)})(t,\omega)| > \frac{1}{2^k}\right\} \leq \frac{1}{2^k}$$

for $q = 1,2,\cdots$.

Choose $N(1) < N(2) < \cdots$. Then with $n_k = N(k)$, we have a subsequence $\{f_{n_k}, k = 1,2,\cdots\}$ for which

$$P\left\{\omega \in \Omega ; \sup_D |I(f_{n_{k+1}})(t,\omega) - I(f_{n_k})(t,\omega)| > \frac{1}{2^k}\right\} \leq \frac{1}{2^k}$$

for $k = 1,2,\cdots$.

Since $\sum_{k=1}^{\infty} 2^{-k} < \infty$, according to Theorem A5.2 there exists $\Omega_0 \in \mathfrak{B}$ with $P(\Omega_0) = 1$ such that

$$\sum_{k=1}^{\infty} \sup_{D} |I(f_{n_{k+1}})(t,\omega) - I(f_{n_k})(t,\omega)| < \infty \quad \text{for } \omega \in \Omega_0. \tag{5}$$

Let

$$Y(t,\omega) = \begin{cases} \sum_{k=1}^{\infty} \{I(f_{n_{k+1}})(t,\omega) - I(f_{n_k})(t,\omega)\} & \text{for } t \in D \text{ and } \omega \in \Omega_0 \\ 0 & \text{for } t \in D \text{ and } \omega \in \Omega_0^c, \end{cases}$$

where the series converges uniformly in $t \in D$ for each $\omega \in \Omega_0$ by (5). From this we have

$$Y(t,\omega) = \lim_{k\to\infty} I(f_{n_k})(t,\omega) - I(f_{n_1})(t,\omega) \qquad \text{for } t \in D \text{ and } \omega \in \Omega_0,$$

where the convergence is uniform in $t \in D$ for each $\omega \in \Omega_0$. Let

$$X(t,\omega) = \begin{cases} Y(t,\omega) + I(f_{n_1})(t,\omega) = \lim_{k\to\infty} I(f_{n_k})(t,\omega) & \text{for } t \in D \text{ and } \omega \in \Omega_0 \\ 0 & \text{for } t \in D \text{ and } \omega \in \Omega_0^c \end{cases} \tag{6}$$

where the convergence is uniform in $t \in D$ for each $\omega \in \Omega_0$. Thus defined $X(t, \cdot)$ is $\mathfrak{B}$-measurable for each $t \in D$ and consequently X is a stochastic process on $(\Omega, \mathfrak{B}, P)$ and D. It is a continuous process since for $\omega \in \Omega_0$, $X(\cdot, \omega)$ is continuous on D from the continuity of $I(f_{n_k})(\cdot, \omega)$ on D and the uniform convergence in (6) and since for $\omega \in \Omega_0^c$, $X(\cdot, \omega) = 0$ on D.

To prove (2) we shall prove first that with our subsequence $\{f_{n_k}, k = 1, 2, \cdots\}$, $\{I(f_{n_k})(t, \cdot), k = 1, 2, \cdots\}$ converges in probability to $X(t, \cdot)$ uniformly in $t \in D$, i.e., for every $\varepsilon > 0$,

$$\lim_{k\to\infty} P\left\{\omega \in \Omega ; \sup_{D} |I(f_{n_k})(t,\omega) - X(t,\omega)| > \varepsilon\right\} = 0. \tag{7}$$

Let Ω_1 be the subset of Ω consisting of all $\omega \in \Omega$ such that $\{I(f_{n_k})(\cdot, \omega), k = 1, 2, \cdots\}$ converges uniformly on D to $X(\cdot, \omega)$, i.e.,

$$\Omega_1 = \left\{ \omega \in \Omega ; \lim_{k\to\infty} \sup_D |I(f_{n_k})(t, \omega) - X(t, \omega)| = 0 \right\}. \tag{8}$$

Since $I(t_{n_k})$ and X are both continuous processes, the supremum over D in (8) is a $\mathfrak{B}$-measurable function for each k. Thus $\Omega_1 \in \mathfrak{B}$. Then since $\Omega_0 \subset \Omega_1$ we have $P(\Omega_1) = 1$. Now from (8) we have

$$\Omega_1 = \bigcap_{p=1}^{\infty} \bigcup_{\ell=1}^{\infty} \bigcap_{k\geq\ell} \left\{ \omega \in \Omega ; \sup_D |I(f_{n_k})(t, \omega) - X(t,\omega)| < \frac{1}{p} \right\},$$

and hence

$$0 = P\left(\Omega_1^c\right) = P\left(\bigcup_{p=1}^{\infty} \bigcap_{\ell=1}^{\infty} \bigcup_{k\geq\ell} A_{p,k} \right), \tag{9}$$

where

$$A_{p,k} = \left\{ \omega \in \Omega ; \sup_D |I(f_{n_k})(t, \omega) - X(t, \omega)| \geq \frac{1}{p} \right\}.$$

From (9) we have

$$P\left(\bigcap_{\ell=1}^{\infty} \bigcup_{k\geq\ell} A_{p,k} \right) = 0 \quad \text{for each } p. \tag{10}$$

Since $\{\bigcup_{k\geq\ell} A_{p,k}, \ell = 1, 2, \cdots\}$ is a monotone decreasing sequence we have, from (10),

$$\lim_{\ell\to\infty} P\left(\bigcup_{k\geq\ell} A_{p,k} \right) = 0 \quad \text{for each } p.$$

Thus for each p there exists a positive integer $L(p)$ such that

$$P\left(\bigcup_{k\geq\ell} A_{p,k} \right) < \frac{1}{p} \quad \text{for } \ell \geq L(p),$$

and hence for each p

$$P\left\{\omega \in \Omega ; \sup_D |I(f_{n_k})(t,\omega) - X(t,\omega)| \geq \frac{1}{p}\right\} < \frac{1}{p} \quad \text{for } k \geq L(p).$$

This proves (7).

We turn now to the proof of (2). According to (7), for arbitrary ϵ, δ, $\eta > 0$ there exists a positive integer M such that

$$P\left\{\omega \in \Omega ; \sup_D |I(f_{n_k})(t,\omega) - X(t,\omega)| > \frac{\eta}{1+\eta}\,\epsilon\right\} < \delta$$

$$\text{for } k \geq M. \tag{11}$$

Now

$$\left\{\omega \in \Omega ; \sup_D |I(f_n)(t,\omega) - X(t,\omega)| > \epsilon\right\}$$

$$\subset \left\{\omega \in \Omega ; \sup_D |I(f_n)(t,\omega) - I(f_{n_k})(t,\omega)| > \frac{1}{1+\eta}\,\epsilon\right\}$$

$$\cup \left\{\omega \in \Omega ; \sup_D |I(f_{n_k})(t,\omega) - X(t,\omega)| > \frac{\eta}{1+\eta}\,\epsilon\right\}. \tag{12}$$

This follows from the fact that any $\omega \in \Omega$ which is in none of the two sets on the right side cannot be in the set on the left side. For $k \geq M$ applying (6) of Theorem 24.7 and (11) to (12) we have

$$P\left\{\omega \in \Omega ; \sup_D |I(f_n)(t,\omega) - X(t,\omega)| > \epsilon\right\} \leq \frac{(1+\eta)^2}{\epsilon^2}\, \| f_n - f_{n_k} \|^2 + \delta .$$

Letting $k \to \infty$ we have $\lim_{k\to\infty} \|f_n - f_{n_k}\| = \|f_n - f\|$. Then from the arbitrariness of η and δ we have (2). This completes the proof. □

<u>Remark 24.11</u> For $f \in S_1(D)$ the stochastic process X in Lemma 24.10 is determined uniquely by f up to almost sure equality. It is, up to almost sure equality, independent of the approximating sequence $\{f_n, n = 1, 2, \cdots\} \subset S_0(D)$ and the

subsequence $\{f_{n_k}, k=1,2,\cdots\}$ used in constructing it.

Proof For $f \in S_1(D)$ let $\{f_n, n=1,2,\cdots\}$ and $\{g_n, n=1,2,\cdots\}$ be two sequences from $S_0(D)$ satisfying the conditions $\lim_{n\to\infty} \|f_n - f\| = 0$ and $\lim_{n\to\infty} \|g_n - f\| = 0$. Let X_1 and X_2 be, respectively, the stochastic processes X in Lemma 24.10 corresponding to $\{f_n, n=1,2,\cdots\}$ and corresponding to $\{g_n, n=1,2,\cdots\}$. From (2) of Lemma 24.10,

$$X_1(t,\cdot) = P - \lim_{n\to\infty} I(f_n)(t,\cdot) \quad \text{and}$$

$$X_2(t,\cdot) = P - \lim_{n\to\infty} I(g_n)(t,\cdot) \quad \text{for } t \in D.$$

Let $\{h_n, n=1,2,\cdots\}$ be the sequence from $S_0(D)$ obtained by setting

$$h_1 = f_1, \quad h_2 = g_1, \quad h_3 = f_2, \quad h_4 = g_2, \quad \cdots.$$

Then $\lim_{n\to\infty} \|h_n - f\| = 0$. Let X_3 be the stochastic process X in Lemma 24.10 corresponding to the sequence $\{h_n, n=1,2,\cdots\}$. Again by (2) of Lemma 24.10

$$X_3(t,\cdot) = P - \lim_{n\to\infty} I(h_n)(t,\cdot) \quad \text{for } t \in D.$$

Since $\{f_n, n=1,2,\cdots\}$ and $\{g_n, n=1,2,\cdots\}$ are subsequences of $\{h_n, n=1,2,\cdots\}$, we have

$$P - \lim_{n\to\infty} I(f_n)(t,\cdot) = X_3(t,\cdot) \quad \text{and}$$

$$P - \lim_{n\to\infty} I(g_n)(t,\cdot) = X_3(t,\cdot) \quad \text{for } t \in D.$$

Since the limit of convergence in probability of a sequence of random variables is unique up to a set of probability measure 0 we have $X_1(t,\cdot) = X_3(t,\cdot) = X_2(t,\cdot)$ almost everywhere for each $t \in D$. Thus X_1 and X_2 are equivalent processes. Since X_1 and X_2 are both continuous processes, this implies that they are almost surely equal processes by Remark 1.3. □

Definition 24.12 For $f \in S_1(D)$, the stochastic integral $I(f)$ of f with respect to the Brownian motion process B is defined to be the stochastic process X of Lemma 24.10. According to Remark 24.11, $I(f)$ is determined up to almost sure equality.

Theorem 24.13 For the stochastic integral $I(f)$, $f \in S_1(D)$, the following hold:

(1) If $f, g \in S_1(D)$ and $f(\cdot,\omega) = g(\cdot,\omega)$ on D for $\omega \in A$ where $A \in \mathfrak{B}$ then

$$I(f)(\cdot,\omega) = I(g)(\cdot,\omega) \quad \text{on } D \text{ for } \omega \in A_0$$

where A_0 is a $\mathfrak{B}$-measurable subset of A with $P(A_0) = P(A)$.

(2) If $f, g \in S_1(D)$ and $\alpha, \beta \in R^1$, then

$$I(\alpha f + \beta g)(\cdot,\omega) = \alpha I(f)(\cdot,\omega) + \beta I(g)(\cdot,\omega) \quad \text{on } D$$

for a.e. $\omega \in \Omega$.

(3) For every $\omega \in \Omega$, $I(f)(\cdot,\omega)$ is a continuous function on D.

(4) For the mean of the random variable $I(f)(t,\cdot)$ we have

$$E\left[I(f)(t,\cdot)\right] = 0 \quad \text{for } t \in D.$$

(5) For the variance of the random variable $I(f)(t,\cdot)$ we have

$$\|I(f)(t,\cdot)\| \le \|f\|_{[a,t]} \quad \text{for } t \in D.$$

(6) For every $c > 0$

$$c^2 P\left\{\omega \in \Omega;\ \sup_D |I(f)(t,\omega)| > c\right\} \le \|f\|^2.$$

Proof To prove (1) let $f, g \in S_1(D)$. Choose the subsequence $\{\varphi_{\ell_n}, n = 1,2,\cdots\}$ of the sequence $\{\varphi_\ell, \ell = 1,2,\cdots\}$ given by (3) in the proof of Lemma 24.9 in such a way that (9) in that proof holds for both f and g. Similarly choose s_0 so that (10) in the same proof holds for both f and g. Then let

$$f_n(t,\omega) = f\left(\varphi_{\ell_n}(t - s_0) + s_0, \omega\right) \quad \text{for } (t,\omega) \in D \times \Omega, \tag{7}$$

$$g_n(t,\omega) = g\left(\varphi_{\ell_n}(t - s_0) + s_0, \omega\right) \quad \text{for } (t,\omega) \in D \times \Omega. \tag{8}$$

By (13) of the same proof, we have $\lim_{n\to\infty} \|f_n - f\| = 0$ and $\lim_{n\to\infty} \|g_n - g\| = 0$. Thus we may use these two sequences to define $I(f)$ and $I(g)$, respectively, as in Lemma 24.10 and Definition 24.12. By Lemma 24.10 we can select a subsequence $\{n_k, k = 1,2,\cdots\}$ such that

$$\lim_{k\to\infty} I(f_{n_k})(t,\omega) = I(f)(t,\omega), \tag{9}$$

$$\lim_{k\to\infty} I(g_{n_k})(t,\omega) = I(g)(t,\omega) \tag{10}$$

uniformly in $t \in D$ for $\omega \in \Omega_0$ where $\Omega_0 \in \mathfrak{B}$ and $P(\Omega_0) = 1$. Now suppose $f(\cdot,\omega) = g(\cdot,\omega)$ on D for $\omega \in A$ where $A \in \mathfrak{B}$. Then, from (7) and (8),

$$f_{n_k}(\cdot, \omega) = g_{n_k}(\cdot, \omega) \qquad \text{on } D \text{ for } \omega \in A.$$

Since f_{n_k}, $g_{n_k} \in S_0(D)$, we have, by (1) of Theorem 24.7,

$$I(f_{n_k})(\cdot, \omega) = I(g_{n_k})(\cdot, \omega) \qquad \text{on } D \text{ for } \omega \in A.$$

Then by (9) and (10)

$$I(f)(\cdot, \omega) = I(g)(\cdot, \omega) \qquad \text{for } \omega \in A \cap \Omega_0.$$

Let $A_0 = A \cap \Omega_0$ and we have a proof of part (1).

To prove part (2) let $f, g \in S_1(D)$ and $\alpha, \beta \in R^1$. Let $\{f_n, n = 1,2, \cdots\}$ and $\{g_n, n = 1,2, \cdots\}$ be sequences from $S_0(D)$ such that $\lim_{n\to\infty} \| f_n - f \| = 0$ and $\lim_{n\to\infty} \| g_n - g \| = 0$. Then $\{\alpha f_n + \beta g_n, n = 1,2, \cdots\}$ is a sequence from $S_0(D)$ and

$$\lim_{n\to\infty} \|(\alpha f_n + \beta g_n) - (\alpha f + \beta g)\| = 0.$$

By (2) of Theorem 24.7

$$I(\alpha f_n + \beta g_n)(t,\omega) = \alpha I(f_n)(t,\omega) + \beta I(g_n)(t,\omega) \qquad \text{for } (t,\omega) \in D \times \Omega. \tag{11}$$

By Lemma 24.10 and Definition 24.12 we can select a subsequence $\{n_k, k = 1,2, \cdots\}$ and $\Omega_0 \in \mathfrak{B}$ with $P(\Omega_0) = 1$ in such a way that $I(f_{n_k})(t, \omega)$, $I(g_{n_k})(t, \omega)$, and $I(\alpha f_{n_k} + \beta g_{n_k})(t, \omega)$ converge, respectively, to $I(f)(t, \omega)$, $I(g)(t, \omega)$, and $I(\alpha f + \beta g)(t, \omega)$ for $t \in D$ when $\omega \in \Omega_0$ as $k \to \infty$. On the other hand, from (2) of Theorem 24.7,

$$I(\alpha f_n + \beta g_n)(t, \omega) = \alpha I(f_n)(t, \omega) + \beta I(g_n)(t, \omega) \qquad \text{for } (t, \omega) \in D \times \Omega.$$

Thus we have (2).

(3) is contained in Lemma 24.10 already.

We shall prove (6) next and then (5) and finally (4). For every $c > 0$, $\left\{\omega \in \Omega ; \sup_D |I(f)(t, \omega)| > c\right\} \in \mathfrak{B}$ since $I(f)(\cdot, \omega)$ is continuous on D for every $\omega \in \Omega$. Let $\{f_n, n = 1, 2, \cdots\}$ be a sequence from $S_0(D)$ such that $\lim_{n\to\infty} \|f_n - f\| = 0$. Then for $\eta > 0$ we have

$$\begin{aligned}
&P\left\{\omega \in \Omega ; \sup_D |I(f)(t,\omega)| > c\right\} \\
&\le P\left\{\omega \in \Omega ; \sup_D |I(f)(t, \omega) - I(f_n)(t, \omega)| > \frac{\eta}{1+\eta} c\right\} \\
&\quad + P\left\{\omega \in \Omega ; \sup_D |I(f)(t, \omega)| > \frac{1}{1+\eta} c\right\} \\
&\le \left(\frac{1+\eta}{c\eta}\right)^2 \|f_n - f\|^2 + \left(\frac{1+\eta}{c}\right)^2 \|f_n\|^2
\end{aligned}$$

by (2) of Lemma 24.10 and (6) of Theorem 24.7. Letting $n \to \infty$ and taking into account the arbitrariness of η we have (6).

To prove (5) we use the fact that, according to Lemma 24.10 and Definition 24.12, there exists a subsequence $\{f_{n_k}, k = 1, 2, \cdots\}$ such that $\lim_{k\to\infty} I(f_{n_k})(t, \omega)$ for $t \in D$ for a.e. $\omega \in \Omega$. Then, at each $t \in D$, by Fatou's lemma and (5) of Theorem 24.7,

$$\|I(f)(t, \cdot)\|^2 \le \liminf_{k\to\infty} \|I(f_{n_k})(t, \cdot)\|^2 = \liminf_{k\to\infty} \|f_{n_k}\|_{[a, t]}^2 .$$

Now $\lim_{n\to\infty} \|f_n - f\| = 0$ implies $\lim_{n\to\infty} \|f_n - f\|_{[a, t]} = 0$ which in turn implies $\lim_{n\to\infty} \|f_n\|_{[a, t]} = \|f\|_{[a, t]}$. Thus we have (5).

To prove (4) observe that, by (4) of Theorem 24.7 the Schwarz inequality, and (5),

$$\left\{E\left[I(f)(t,\cdot)\right]\right\}^2 = \left\{E\left[I(f)(t,\cdot)\right] - E\left[I(f_n)(t,\cdot)\right]\right\}^2$$

$$= \left\{E\left[I(f-f_n)(t,\cdot)\right]\right\}^2$$

$$\le E\left[\left\{I(f-f_n)(t,\cdot)\right\}^2\right] \le \|f-f_n\|^2_{[a,t]} .$$

Since $\lim_{n\to\infty} \|f-f_n\|^2_{[a,t]} = 0$ we have (4). This completes the proof of the theorem. □

[IV] Stochastic Integral for the Class $S_2(D)$

We shall show that by trancating the sample functions of $f \in S_2(D)$ appropriately we can obtain a stochastic process belonging in the class $S_1(D)$ for which the stochastic integral was defined in [III]. We then define the stochastic integral of f as the limit of the stochastic integrals of the truncated processes.

Lemma 24.14 Let $f \in S_2(D)$. For each positive integer n define

$$f_n(t,\omega) = \chi_{[0,n]}\left(\int_{[a,t]} \{f(u,\omega)\}^2 m_L(du)\right) f(t,\omega) \quad \text{for } (t,\omega) \in D \times \Omega .$$

Then $f_n \in S_1(D)$.

Proof To show that $f_n \in S_1(D)$ we show that it satisfies the measurability condition ((M)) and the integrability condition ((I_1)). Consider ((M)) first. Thus we are to show that for each $t \in D$, $f_n(s,\omega)$, $(s,\omega) \in [a,t] \times \Omega$, is measurable with respect to $\sigma\left(\mathfrak{M}_{[a,t]} \times \mathfrak{F}_{[a,t]}\right)$. For simplicity let us write

$$h(s,\omega) = \int_{[a,s]} \{f(u,\omega)\}^2 \, m_L(du)$$

$$= \int_{[a,t]} \chi_{[a,s]}(u) \{f(u,\omega)\}^2 \, m_L(du) \quad \text{for} \quad (s,\omega) \in [a,t] \times \Omega.$$

Now $\chi_{[a,s]}(u)$, $(u,s) \in [a,t] \times [a,t]$, is measurable with respect to $\sigma\left(\mathfrak{M}_{[a,t]} \times \mathfrak{M}_{[a,t]}\right)$. As a function of $(u,\omega) \in [a,t] \times \Omega$, $f(u,\omega)$ is measurable with respect to $\sigma\left(\mathfrak{M}_{[a,t]} \times \mathfrak{F}_{[a,t]}\right)$ since f satisfies the condition ((M)) on $D \times \Omega$. Thus the integrand in the last integral, as a function of $(u,s,\omega) \in [a,t] \times [a,t] \times \Omega$, is measurable with respect to $\sigma\left(\mathfrak{M}_{[a,t]} \times \mathfrak{M}_{[a,t]} \times \mathfrak{F}_{[a,t]}\right)$, and consequently the integral, namely $h(s,\omega)$ as a function of $(s,\omega) \in [a,t] \times \Omega$, is measurable with respect to $\sigma\left(\mathfrak{M}_{[a,t]} \times \mathfrak{F}_{[a,t]}\right)$. Then

$$f_n(s,\omega) = \chi_{[0,n]}\left(h(s,\omega)\right) f(s,\omega) \quad \text{for} \quad (s,\omega) \in [a,t] \times \Omega$$

is measurable with respect to $\sigma\left(\mathfrak{M}_{[a,t]} \times \mathfrak{F}_{[a,t]}\right)$. Thus f_n satisfies the condition ((M)) on $D \times \Omega$.

To show that f_n satisfies the condition $((I_1))$ let us note that

$$\int_{D \times \Omega} \{f_n(t,\omega)\}^2 \, (m_L \times P)\left(d(t,\omega)\right)$$

$$= \int_\Omega \left[\int_D \{f_n(t,\omega)\}^2 \, m_L(dt)\right] P(d\omega) \le \int_\Omega nP(d\omega) = n < \infty.$$

This completes the proof of the lemma. □

<u>Lemma 24.15</u>. For $f \in S_2(D)$ let f_n be the truncated process defined in Lemma 24.14 for $n = 1, 2, \cdots$. Let

$$F_n = \left\{ \omega \in \Omega ;\ \int_D \{f(t,\omega)\}^2 m_L(dt) \le n \right\}. \tag{1}$$

Then $\{F_n, n = 1,2,\cdots\}$ is a monotone increasing sequence of sets from $\mathfrak{B}$ with $P\left(\bigcup_{n=1}^{\infty} F_n\right) = 1$ and

$$F_n \subset \{\omega \in \Omega ; f(\cdot,\omega) = f_{n+m}(\cdot,\omega) \text{ on } D \text{ for } m = 0,1,2,\cdots\}. \tag{2}$$

Also there exists $G_n \subset F_n$ such that $G_n \in \mathfrak{B}$, $P(G_n) = P(F_n)$, $\{G_n, n = 1,2,\cdots\}$ is a monotone increasing sequence, $P\left(\bigcup_{n=1}^{\infty} G_n\right) = 1$, and

$$I(f_n)(\cdot,\omega) = I(f_{n+m})(\cdot,\omega) \text{ on } D \text{ for } m = 1,2,\cdots, \text{ when } \omega \in G_n. \tag{3}$$

Proof From the fact that f is a $\sigma(\mathfrak{M}_D \times \mathfrak{B})$-measurable function of $(t,\omega) \in D \times \Omega$ follows that $\int_D \{f(t,\omega)\}^2 m_L(dt)$ is a $\mathfrak{B}$-measurable function of $\omega \in \Omega$, and hence $F_n \in \mathfrak{B}$. The fact that $\{F_n, n = 1,2,\cdots\}$ is a monotone increasing sequence is obvious. Since f satisfies the integrability condition $((I_2))$, almost every $\omega \in \Omega$ belongs to F_n for some n depending on ω. Thus $P\left(\bigcup_{n=1}^{\infty} F_n\right) = 1$.

For a fixed $\omega \in \Omega$,

$$\int_D \{f(t,\omega)\}^2 m_L(dt) \le n \Rightarrow \int_{[a,t]} \{f(u,\omega)\}^2 m_L(du) \le n \text{ for all } t \in D$$

$$\Rightarrow f(\cdot,\omega) = f_{n+m}(\cdot,\omega) \quad \text{on } D \text{ for } m = 0,1,2,\cdots.$$

Thus (2) holds.

From (2),

$$f_n(\cdot,\omega) = f_{n+m}(\cdot,\omega) \quad \text{on } D \quad \text{for } m = 0,1,2,\cdots \quad \text{when } \omega \in F_n,$$

so that by (1) of Theorem 24.13 there exists $H_n \subset F_n$ such that $H_n \in \mathfrak{B}$, $P(H_n) = P(F_n)$, and

$$I(f_n)(\cdot,\omega) = I(f_{n+m})(\cdot,\omega) \quad \text{on } D \quad \text{for } m = 1,2,\cdots$$

when $\omega \in H_n$. □

<u>Definition 24.16</u> For $f \in S_2(D)$, the stochastic integral $I(f)$ with respect to the Brownian motion process B is defined by

$$I(f)(t,\omega) = \begin{cases} I(f_n)(t,\omega) & \text{for } t \in D \text{ and } \omega \in G_n \\ 0 & \text{for } t \in D \text{ and } \omega \in \left(\bigcup_{n=1}^{\infty} G_n\right)^c, \end{cases}$$

where $\{f_n, n = 1,2,\cdots\}$ and $\{G_n, n = 1,2,\cdots\}$ are as in Lemma 24.15.

<u>Remark 24.17</u> For each $t \in D$, since $I(f_n)(t,\cdot)$ is a random variable and since $G_n \in \mathfrak{B}$, $I(f)(t,\cdot)$ as defined above is a random variable and $I(f)$ is a stochastic process on $(\Omega, \mathfrak{B}, P)$ and D. It is a stochastic process which is determined up to almost sure equality since $I(f_n)$ has this property. Also it is a continuous process since $I(f_n)$ is. Finally in view of (3) of Lemma 24.15 we may write

$$I(f)(t,\omega) = \lim_{n\to\infty} I(f_n)(t,\omega) \quad \text{for } t \in D \text{ and } \omega \in \bigcup_{n=1}^{\infty} G_n. \tag{1}$$

<u>Theorem 24.18</u> For the stochastic integral $I(f)$, $f \in S_2(D)$, the following hold:

(1) If $f, g \in S_2(D)$ and $f(\cdot, \omega) = g(\cdot, \omega)$ on D for $\omega \in A$ where $A \in \mathfrak{B}$, then

$$I(f)(\cdot, \omega) = I(g)(\cdot, \omega) \quad \text{on } D \text{ for } \omega \in A_0$$

where A_0 is a $\mathfrak{B}$-measurable subset of A with $P(A_0) = P(A)$.

(2) If $f, g \in S_2(D)$ and $\alpha, \beta \in R^1$, then

$$I(\alpha f + \beta g)(\cdot, \omega) = \alpha I(f)(\cdot, \omega) + \beta I(g)(\cdot, \omega) \quad \text{on } D$$

for a.e. $\omega \in \Omega$.

(3) For every $\omega \in \Omega$, $I(f)(\cdot, \omega)$ is a continuous function on D.

(4) If $f \in S_2(D)$ and $\{f_n, n = 1, 2, \cdots\} \subset S_2(D)$ also, then the condition

1° $\int_D \{f_n(t, \cdot) - f(t, \cdot)\}^2 m_L(dt)$ converges to 0 in probability as $n \to \infty$, i.e., for every $\varepsilon > 0$,

$$\lim_{n\to\infty} P\{\omega \in \Omega ; \| f_n(\cdot, \omega) - f(\cdot, \omega)\| > \varepsilon\} = 0$$

implies the condition

2° $\sup_D |I(f_n)(t, \cdot) - I(f)(t, \cdot)|$ converges to 0 in probability as $n \to \infty$.

Proof To prove (1) let $f(\cdot, \omega) = g(\cdot, \omega)$ on D for $\omega \in A$ where $A \in \mathfrak{B}$. Then for the truncated processes f_n and g_n of f and g, respectively, as defined in Lemma 24.14, we have $f_n(\cdot, \omega) = g_n(\cdot, \omega)$ on D for $\omega \in A$. By (1) of Theorem 24.13, there exists a $\mathfrak{B}$-measurable subset A_1 of A with $P(A_1) = P(A)$ such that

$$I(f_n)(\cdot, \omega) = I(g_n)(\cdot, \omega) \quad \text{on } D \quad \text{for } n = 1, 2, \cdots \text{ when } \omega \in A_1.$$

On the other hand by (1) of Remark 24.17 there exists a $\mathfrak{B}$-measurable subset A_2 of Ω with $P(A_2) = 1$ such that

$$I(f)(\cdot, \omega) = \lim_{n\to\infty} I(f_n)(\cdot, \omega) \quad \text{on } D \text{ for } \omega \in A_2,$$

$$I(g)(\cdot, \omega) = \lim_{n\to\infty} I(g_n)(\cdot, \omega) \quad \text{on } D \text{ for } \omega \in A_2.$$

With $A_0 = A_1 \cap A_2$ we have (1).

Similarly (2) follows from (2) of Theorem 24.13 and (1) of Remark 24.17.

As we pointed out in Remark 24.17, $I(f)(\cdot, \omega)$ is continuous on D for each $\omega \in \Omega$.

Regarding (4), since $f_n - f \in S_2(D)$, it suffices to show that the condition

$$P\text{-}\lim_{n\to\infty} \int_D \left\{f_n(t, \cdot)\right\}^2 m_L(dt) = 0 \tag{5}$$

implies

$$P\text{-}\lim_{n\to\infty} \sup_D \left| I(f_n)(t, \cdot) \right| = 0. \tag{6}$$

Let

$$h_n(t,\omega) = \chi_{[0,1]}\left[\int_{[a,t]} \left\{f_n(t,\omega)\right\}^2 m_L(du) \right] f_n(t,\omega) \quad \text{for } (t,\omega) \in D \times \Omega.$$

By the same argument as the one used in the proof of Lemma 24.14, h_n satisfies the measurability condition ((M)) on $D \times \Omega$. Also

$$\int_D \left\{h_n(t, \omega)\right\}^2 m_L(dt) \le 1 \quad \text{for a.e. } \omega \in \Omega, \tag{7}$$

so that h_n satisfies the integrability condition $((I_1))$. Thus $h_n \in S_1(D)$. Now (5) and the fact that

$$\int_D \{h_n(t,\omega)\}^2 m_L(dt) \leq \int_D \{f_n(t,\omega)\}^2 m_L(dt) \quad \text{for a.e. } \omega \in \Omega$$

imply

$$P\text{-}\lim_{n\to\infty} \int_D \{h_n(t,\cdot)\}^2 m_L(dt) = 0. \tag{8}$$

With (7) and (8) we can apply the Dominated Convergence Theorem under convergence in probability to obtain

$$\lim_{n\to\infty} \int_\Omega \left\{ \int_D \{h_n(t,\omega)\}^2 m_L(dt) \right\} P(d\omega) = 0,$$

i.e.,

$$\lim_{n\to\infty} \| h_n \| = 0. \tag{9}$$

Since $h_n \in S_1(D)$ we have by (6) of Theorem 24.13 that, for every $c > 0$,

$$P\left\{\omega \in \Omega ; \sup_D |I(h_n)(t,\omega)| > c\right\} \leq \frac{1}{c^2} \| h_n \|^2, \tag{10}$$

which, in view of (9), implies

$$P\text{-}\lim_{n\to\infty} \sup_D |I(h_n)(t,\cdot)| = 0,$$

i.e., for every $\varepsilon, \eta > 0$ there exists N_1 such that

$$P\left\{\omega \in \Omega ; \sup_D |I(h_n)(t,\omega)| > \varepsilon\right\} < \eta \quad \text{for } n \geq N_1. \tag{11}$$

On the other hand, by (5), there exists N_2 such that

$$P\left\{\omega \in \Omega ; \int_D \{f_n(t,\omega)\}^2 m_L(dt) > 1\right\} < \eta \quad \text{for } n \geq N_2,$$

i.e.,

$$P(A_n) \geq 1 - \eta \quad \text{for } n \geq N_2 \tag{12}$$

where

$$A_n = \left\{ \omega \in \Omega ; \int_D \{f_n(t, \omega)\}^2 m_L(dt) \leq 1 \right\} .$$

Now $f_n(\cdot, \omega) = h_n(\cdot, \omega)$ on D for $\omega \in A_n$. Thus by (1) there exists a $\mathfrak{B}$-measurable subset B_n of A_n with $P(B_n) = P(A_n)$ such that

$$I(h_n)(\cdot, \omega) = I(f_n)(\cdot, \omega) \quad \text{on } D \text{ for } \omega \in B_n .$$

Then

$$\left\{ \omega \in \Omega ; \sup_D |I(f_n)(t, \omega)| > \epsilon \right\}$$

$$= \left\{ \omega \in \Omega ; \sup_D |I(f_n)(t, \omega)| > \epsilon \right\} \cap (B_n \cup B_n^c)$$

$$\subset \left\{ \omega \in \Omega ; \sup_D |I(h_n)(t, \omega)| > \epsilon \right\} \cup B_n^c . \tag{13}$$

Let $N = \max\{N_1, N_2\}$. Then for $n \geq N$ we have, by (13), (11), and $P(B_n) = P(A_n) \geq 1 - \eta$,

$$P\left\{ \omega \in \Omega ; \sup_D I(f_n)(t, \omega) | > \epsilon \right\} < \eta + \eta = 2\eta ,$$

which proves (2). This completes the proof of the theorem. □

<u>Remark 24.19</u> For $f \in S_2(D)$ let f_n be the truncated process defined in Lemma 24.14. Then for the sequence $\{f_n, n = 1, 2, \cdots\}$ we have

$$\lim_{n \to \infty} \int_D \{f_n(t, \cdot) - f(t, \cdot)\}^2 m_L(dt) = 0 \quad \text{a.e. on } \Omega ,$$

so that in particular it satisfies the condition 1° of Theorem 24.18.

Proof For each $\omega \in \Omega$ for which $\int_D \{f(t,\omega)\}^2 m_L(dt) < \infty$ we have

$$\int_D \{f_n(t,\omega) - f(t,\omega)\}^2 m_L(dt) = \int_D \{f(t,\omega)\}^2 \theta_n(t,\omega)\, m_L(dt)$$

where

$$\theta_n(t,\omega) = \left\{\chi_{[0,n]}\left(\int_{[a,t]} \{f(u,\omega)\}^2 m_L(du)\right) - 1\right\}^2 \quad \text{for } t \in D.$$

Now $\lim_{n\to\infty} \theta_n(t,\omega) = 0$ for $t \in D$, so that by the Dominated Convergence Theorem

$$\lim_{n\to\infty} \int_D \{f_n(t,\omega) - f(t,\omega)\}^2 m_L(dt) = 0.$$

This proves the Remark. □

Remark 24.20 An implication of 2° of Theorem 24.18 is that, for every positive integer k, there exists a positive integer n_k such that

$$P\left\{\omega \in \Omega ; \sup_D |I(f_{n_k})(t,\omega) - I(f)(t,\omega)| > \frac{1}{2^k}\right\} \le \frac{1}{2^k}.$$

We may choose n_k so that $n_1 < n_2 < n_3 < \cdots$. Now since $\sum_{k=1}^\infty 1/2^k < \infty$ and

$$\sum_{k=1}^\infty P\left\{\omega \in \Omega ; \sup_D |I(f_{n_k})(t,\omega) - I(f)(t,\omega)| > \frac{1}{2^k}\right\} < \infty,$$

we have, according to Theorem A5.2,

$$\sum_{k=1}^\infty \sup_D |I(f_{n_k})(t,\omega) - I(f)(t,\omega)| < \infty \quad \text{for a.e. } \omega \in \Omega,$$

and hence

$$\lim_{k\to\infty} \sup_{D} \left| I(f_{n_k})(t,\omega) - I(f)(t,\omega) \right| = 0 \qquad \text{for a.e. } \omega \in \Omega,$$

i.e., for a.e. $\omega \in \Omega$,

$$\lim_{k\to\infty} I(f_{n_k})(t,\omega) = I(f)(t,\omega) \qquad \text{uniformly for } t \in D.$$

Thus the stochastic process $I(f)$ which is unique up to almost sure equality can be realized as $\lim_{k\to\infty} I(f_{n_k})(t,\omega)$.

Chapter 6

GAUSSIAN MEASURES IN FUNCTION SPACES

As we saw in [III] of §2, an arbitrary stochastic process X on a probability space $(\Omega, \mathfrak{B}, P)$ and an interval $D \subset R^1$ induces a probability measure μ on the space R^D of all real-valued functions on D. We call the measure μ a Gaussian measure when X is a Gaussian process. Feldman [1] and Hájek [2] showed independently that if X_1 and X_2 are two Gaussian processes then the Gaussian measures μ_1 and μ_2 induced on R^D by X_1 and X_2, respectively, are either equivalent or singular. In this chapter we present a proof of the Feldman-Hájek dichotomy following the approach of Hájek.

§25. THE J-DIVERGENCE BETWEEN TWO PROBABILITY MEASURES

Let μ_1, μ_2, and μ_0 be measures on a measurable space $(X, \mathfrak{F})$. We say that μ_1 is absolutely continuous with respect to μ_2 and write $\mu_1 << \mu_2$ if $\mu_1(E) = 0$ for every $E \in \mathfrak{F}$ with $\mu_2(E) = 0$. Clearly $\mu_1 << \mu_0$ and $\mu_0 << \mu_2$ imply $\mu_1 << \mu_2$. We say that μ_1 and μ_2 are equivalent and write $\mu_1 \sim \mu_2$ if $\mu_1 << \mu_2$ and $\mu_2 << \mu_1$. If $\mu_1 \sim \mu_0$ and $\mu_0 \sim \mu_2$ then $\mu_1 \sim \mu_2$. The two measures μ_1 and μ_2 are said to be singular and written $\mu_1 \perp \mu_2$ if there exist $E_1, E_2 \in \mathfrak{F}$ such that $E_1 \cap E_2 = \emptyset$, $E_1 \cup E_2 = X$, $\mu_1(E_2) = 0$, and

$\mu_2(E_1) = 0$. When μ_1 and μ_2 are finite measures, the conditions $\mu_1(E_2) = 0$ and $\mu_2(E_1) = 0$ are equivalent to the conditions $\mu_1(E_1) = \mu_1(X)$ and $\mu_2(E_2) = \mu_2(X)$.

Let μ_1 and μ_2 be probability measures on a measurable space $(X, \mathfrak{Z})$ and let $\mu_1 \sim \mu_2$. Let μ_0 be an arbitrary probability measure on $(X, \mathfrak{Z})$ such that $\mu_0 \sim \mu_1$ as well as $\mu_0 \sim \mu_2$. (We may for instance take $\mu_0 = \lambda_1\mu_1 + \lambda_2\mu_2$ where $\lambda_1, \lambda_2 \geqq 0$ and $\lambda_1 + \lambda_2 = 1$.) Since $\mu_1 \sim \mu_0 \sim \mu_2$, if $\mu_i(E) = 0$ for $E \in \mathfrak{Z}$ for one of $i = 0, 1, 2$, then $\mu_i(E) = 0$ for all of $i = 0, 1, 2$ so that in saying "almost everywhere on X" we need not specify with respect to which of the three probability measures. Note also that if $\mu_i(E) > 0$ for one of $i = 0, 1, 2$, then $\mu_i(E) > 0$ for all of $i = 0, 1, 2$. Let $f_i = d\mu_i/d\mu_0$ for $i = 1, 2$, i.e., the Radon-Nikodym derivative of μ_i with respect to μ_0 for $i = 1, 2$ which is a nonnegative valued $\mathfrak{Z}$-measurable function on X, determined up to a set of measure 0 and satisfies $\mu_i(E) = \int_E f_i(x)\,\mu_0(dx)$ for every $E \in \mathfrak{Z}$. From the finiteness of $\mu_i(X)$, f_i is finite a.e. on X and from the finiteness of $d\mu_0/d\mu_i = \left[d\mu_i/d\mu_0\right]^{-1} = [f_i]^{-1}$, $f_i > 0$ a.e. on X also.

<u>Definition 25.1</u> Let μ_1 and μ_2 be two equivalent probability measures on a measurable space $(X, \mathfrak{Z})$. Let μ_0 be a probability measure on $(X, \mathfrak{Z})$ such that $\mu_0 \sim \mu_1$ and $\mu_0 \sim \mu_2$ and let $f_i = d\mu_i/d\mu_0$ for $i = 1, 2$. We define $I(\mu_1;\mu_2)(E)$ for $E \in \mathfrak{Z}$ by

$$I(\mu_1:\mu_2)(E) = \begin{cases} \dfrac{1}{\mu_1(E)} \displaystyle\int_E \log \frac{d\mu_1}{d\mu_2}(x)\, \mu_1(dx) \\ = \dfrac{1}{\mu_1(E)} \displaystyle\int_E f_1(x) \log \frac{f_1(x)}{f_2(x)}\, \mu_0(dx) & \text{when } \mu_1(E) > 0 \\ 0 & \text{when } \mu_1(E) = 0. \end{cases}$$

Lemma 25.2 Let $I(\mu_1;\mu_2)$ be as in Definition 25.1. If $E \in \mathfrak{F}$ and $\mu_1(E) > 0$ then

$$I(\mu_1:\mu_2)(E) \geq \log \frac{\mu_1(E)}{\mu_2(E)} > -\infty, \tag{1}$$

where the equality holds if and only if

$$\frac{f_1(x)}{f_2(x)} = \frac{\mu_1(E)}{\mu_2(E)} \quad \text{for a. e.} \quad x \in E, \tag{2}$$

i. e., when restricted to E, the two measures μ_1 and μ_2 satisfy $\mu_1 = c\mu_2$ where $c = \mu_1(E)/\mu_2(E)$. In particular

$$I(\mu_1:\mu_2)(X) \geq 0, \tag{3}$$

where the equality holds if and only if $\mu_1 = \mu_2$.

Proof For $E \in \mathfrak{F}$ with $\mu_1(E) > 0$ we have, from Definition 25.1,

$$I(\mu_1:\mu_2)(E) - \log \frac{\mu_1(E)}{\mu_2(E)}$$

$$= \frac{1}{\mu_1(E)} \int_E \log \frac{f_1(x)}{f_2(x)}\, \mu_1(dx) - \log \frac{\mu_1(E)}{\mu_2(E)} \frac{1}{\mu_1(E)} \int_E \mu_1(dx)$$

$$= \frac{1}{\mu_1(E)} \int_E \log \frac{f_1(x)\mu_2(E)}{f_2(x)\mu_1(E)}\, \mu_1(dx) .$$

Let

$$g(x) = \frac{f_1(x)\,\mu_2(E)}{f_2(x)\,\mu_1(E)}$$

so that $0 < g(x) < \infty$ for a.e. $x \in X$ and

$$\mu_1(dx) = f_1(x)\,\mu_0(dx) = \frac{\mu_1(E)}{\mu_2(E)}\; g(x)\,\mu_2(dx)$$

In terms of g we have

$$I(\mu_1 : \mu_2)(E) - \log \frac{\mu_1(E)}{\mu_2(E)} = \frac{1}{\mu_2(E)} \int_E g(x) \log g(x)\,\mu_2(dx). \quad (4)$$

To estimate the last integral consider the function

$$\varphi(t) = t \log t \quad \text{for} \quad t > 0.$$

According to Taylor's theorem,

$$\varphi(t) = \varphi(1) + \varphi'(1)(t-1) + \tfrac{1}{2}\varphi''(\tau)(t-1)^2 = (t-1) + \frac{1}{2\tau}(t-1)^2$$

for $t > 0$ with τ between 1 and t. Applying this to $g(x)$ which satisfies $0 < g(x) < \infty$ for a.e. $x \in X$ we have

$$g(x) \log g(x) = \varphi\left[g(x)\right] = \left\{g(x) - 1\right\} + \tfrac{1}{2}\frac{1}{h(x)}\left\{g(x) - 1\right\}^2 \quad (5)$$

for a.e. $x \in X$ with $h(x)$ between 1 and $g(x)$. Now

$$\begin{aligned}\int_E g(x)\,\mu_2(dx) &= \int_E \frac{f_1(x)\mu_2(E)}{f_2(x)\mu_1(E)}\, f_2(x)\mu_0(dx) \\ &= \frac{\mu_2(E)}{\mu_1(E)} \int_E \mu_1(dx) = \mu_2(E). \quad (6)\end{aligned}$$

Using (5) and (6) in (4) we obtain

$$I(\mu_1:\mu_2)(E) - \log \frac{\mu_1(E)}{\mu_2(E)}$$

$$= \frac{1}{\mu_2(E)} \int_E \frac{1}{2h(x)} \{g(x)-1\}^2 \mu_2(dx) \geq 0,$$

where the equality holds if and only if $g(x) = 1$ for a.e. $x \in E$, i.e., (2) holds. (3) is immediate from (1). □

Remarks 25.3 The value ∞ may be actually assumed by $I(\mu_1:\mu_2)(E)$. To show this by an example let μ_1 be the Lebesgue measure m_L on $[0, 1] \subset R^1$. Let μ_2 be the probability measure on $[0, 1]$ which is absolutely continuous with respect to μ_1 and is defined by the Radon-Nikodym derivative

$$\frac{d\mu_2}{d\mu_1}(x) = ke^{-1/x} \quad \text{for} \quad x \in (0, 1]$$

where $k = \left[\int_{[0,1]} e^{-1/x} m_L(dx) \right]^{-1}$

Then μ_1 is absolutely continuous with respect to μ_2 with

$$\frac{d\mu_1}{d\mu_2}(x) = \frac{1}{k} e^{1/x} \quad \text{for} \quad x \in (0, 1]$$

so that $\mu_1 \sim \mu_2$ and

$$I(\mu_1:\mu_2)\big([0,1]\big) = \int_{[0,1]} \log \frac{d\mu_1}{d\mu_2}(x)\, \mu_1(dx)$$

$$= \int_{[0,1]} \left\{-\log k + \frac{1}{x}\right\} m_L(dx) = \infty. \qquad \square$$

Lemma 25.4 Let $(X, \mathfrak{X})$, $\mu_1, \mu_2, \mu_0, f_1,$ and f_2 be as in Definition 25.1. Let $(Y, \mathfrak{G})$ be a measurable space and T be a measurable transformation of X into Y. Define probability measures ν_i, $i = 0, 1, 2,$ on $(Y, \mathfrak{G})$ by

$$\nu_i(G) = \mu_i\left[T^{-1}(G)\right] \quad \text{for every } G \in \mathfrak{G}. \tag{1}$$

Then $\nu_1 \sim \nu_2 \sim \nu_0$ and

$$I(\mu_1 : \mu_2)\left[T^{-1}(G)\right] \geq I(\nu_1 : \nu_2)(G) \quad \text{for every } G \in \mathfrak{G}. \tag{2}$$

When $I(\nu_1 : \nu_2)(G) = \infty$, the equality in (2) holds trivially. When $I(\nu_1 : \nu_2)(G) < \infty$, the equality in (2) holds if and only if

$$\frac{f_1(x)}{f_2(x)} = \frac{(g_1 T)(x)}{(g_2 T)(x)} \quad \text{for a. e. } x \in T^{-1}(G) \tag{3}$$

where $g_1 = d\nu_1/d\nu_0$ and $g_2 = d\nu_2/d\nu_0$.

Proof From (1) and $\mu_1 \sim \mu_2 \sim \mu_0$ follows $\nu_1 \sim \nu_2 \sim \nu_0$. Let us prove (2) and (3). First of all if $G \in \mathfrak{G}$ and $\nu_1(G) = 0$ then $\mu_1\left[T^{-1}(G)\right] = 0$ and, by Definition 25.1,

$$I(\mu_1 : \mu_2)\left[T^{-1}(G)\right] = 0 = I(\nu_1 : \nu_2)(G),$$

so that in this case the equality in (2) holds. Note also that in this case since we have $\mu_1\left[T^{-1}(G)\right] = 0$, (3) holds trivially. Let us then consider the case when $G \in \mathfrak{G}$ and $\nu_1(G) > 0$. Assume further that $I(\nu_1 : \nu_2)(G)$ is finite and it is possible to subtract this quantity. Then, by Definition 25.1,

$$I(\mu_1:\mu_2)\left[T^{-1}(G)\right] - I(\nu_1:\nu_2)(G)$$

$$= \frac{1}{\mu_1\left[T^{-1}(G)\right]} \int_{T^{-1}(G)} \log \frac{f_1(x)}{f_2(x)} \mu_1(dx)$$

$$- \frac{1}{\nu_1(G)} \int_G \log \frac{g_1(y)}{g_2(y)} \nu_1(dy)$$

$$= \frac{1}{\mu_1\left[T^{-1}(G)\right]} \int_{T^{-1}(G)} \log \frac{f_1(x)}{f_2(x)} \mu_1(dx)$$

$$- \frac{1}{\mu_1\left[T^{-1}(G)\right]} \int_{T^{-1}(G)} \log \frac{(g_1T)(x)}{(g_2T)(x)} \mu_1(dx)$$

$$= \frac{1}{\mu_1\left[T^{-1}(G)\right]} \int_{T^{-1}(G)} \log \frac{f_1(x)(g_2T)(x)}{f_2(x)(g_1T)(x)} \mu_1(dx).$$

Let

$$g(x) = \frac{f_1(x)(g_2T)(x)}{f_2(x)(g_1T)(x)}$$

so that $0 < g(x) < \infty$ for a.e. $x \in X$ since $0 < f_i(x) < \infty$ for a.e. $x \in X$ and $0 < g_i(y) < \infty$ for a.e. $y \in Y$. Also

$$\mu_1(dx) = f_1(x)\,\mu_0(dx) = \frac{(g_1T)(x)}{(g_2T)(x)} g(x)\, f_2(x)\, \mu_0(dx)$$

$$= \frac{(g_1T)(x)}{(g_2T)(x)} g(x)\, \mu_2(dx).$$

Then

$$I(\mu_1:\mu_2)\left[T^{-1}(G)\right] - I(\nu_1:\nu_2)(G)$$

$$= \frac{1}{\mu_1\left[T^{-1}(G)\right]} \int_{T^{-1}(G)} \frac{(g_1 T)(x)}{(g_2 T)(x)}\, g(x) \log g(x)\, \mu_2(dx). \tag{4}$$

Now

$$\int_{T^{-1}(G)} \frac{(g_1 T)(x)}{(g_2 T)(x)}\, g(x)\, \mu_2(dx)$$

$$= \int_{T^{-1}(G)} \frac{f_1(x)}{f_2(x)}\, \mu_2(dx) = \int_{T^{-1}(G)} \mu_1(dx) = \mu_1\left[T^{-1}(G)\right] \tag{5}$$

and

$$\int_{T^{-1}(G)} \frac{(g_1 T)(x)}{(g_2 T)(x)}\, \mu_2(dx)$$

$$= \int_G \frac{g_1(y)}{g_2(y)}\, \nu_2(dy) = \int_G \nu_1(dy) = \nu_1(G) = \mu_1\left[T^{-1}(G)\right]. \tag{6}$$

Applying (5) of Lemma 25. 2 and the above (5) and (6) to (4) we obtain

$$I(\mu_1:\mu_2)\left[T^{-1}(G)\right] - I(\nu_1:\nu_2)(G)$$

$$= \frac{1}{\mu_1\left[T^{-1}(G)\right]} \int_{T^{-1}(G)} \frac{(g_1 T)(x)}{(g_2 T)(x)}\, \frac{1}{2h(x)} \left\{g(x) - 1\right\}^2 \mu_2(dx) \geq 0,$$

where the equality holds if and only if $g(x) = 1$ for a. e. $x \in T^{-1}(G)$, i. e., (3) holds. This proves (2) and (3) under the assumption that $I(\nu_1:\nu_2)(G)$ is finite. Let us remove this assumption. Since $I(\nu_1:\nu_2)(G) > -\infty$ according to Lemma 25. 2 we need to consider the case $I(\nu_1:\nu_2)(G) = \infty$ only. Since the integrand of

$$I(\nu_1:\nu_2)(G) = \frac{1}{\nu_1(G)} \int_G \log \frac{g_1(y)}{g_2(y)} \nu_1(dy)$$

is finite a.e. on G, G can be decomposed into countably many disjoint members $\{G_n, n = 1, 2, \cdots\} \subset \mathfrak{G}$ such that the integrand is bounded and the integral is finite on G_n for each n. Then by the above result we have

$$I(\mu_1:\mu_2)\left[T^{-1}(G_n)\right] \geq I(\nu_1:\nu_2)(G_n) \quad \text{for } n = 1, 2, \cdots .$$

Multiplying both sides by $\mu_1\left[T^{-1}(G_n)\right] = \nu_1(G_n)$ and the summing over n we obtain (2). This completes the proof. □

Definition 25.5 The J-divergence between two probability measures μ_1 and μ_2 on a measurable space $(X, \mathfrak{B})$ is defined by

$$J(\mu_1, \mu_2) = \begin{cases} I(\mu_1:\mu_2)(X) + I(\mu_2:\mu_1)(X) & \text{when } \mu_1 \sim \mu_2 \\ \infty & \text{otherwise.} \end{cases}$$

Remark 25.6 For the J-divergence $J(\mu_1, \mu_2)$ just defined the following hold:

(1) When $\mu_1 \sim \mu_2$, we have from Definition 25.1

$$J(\mu_1, \mu_2) = \int_X \log \frac{d\mu_1}{d\mu_2}(x)\, \mu_1(dx) + \int_X \log \frac{d\mu_2}{d\mu_1}(x)\, \mu_2(dx)$$

$$= \int_X \log \frac{d\mu_1}{d\mu_2}(x) \frac{d\mu_1}{d\mu_2}(x)\, \mu_2(dx)$$

$$- \int_X \log \frac{d\mu_1}{d\mu_2}(x)\, \mu_2(dx)$$

$$= \int_X \left\{ \frac{d\mu_1}{d\mu_2}(x) - 1 \right\} \log \frac{d\mu_1}{d\mu_2}(x)\, \mu_2(dx). \quad (1)$$

A similar expression holds in which the roles of μ_1 and μ_2 are interchanged.

(2) $J(\mu_1, \mu_2) \geq 0$ where the equality holds if and only if $\mu_1 = \mu_2$. This follows from (3) of Lemma 25.2 It can also be derived from (1) above as follows. For $0 < t < \infty$ we have $(t - 1) \log t \geq 0$ since $t - 1$ and $\log t$ have the same sign. Also $(t - 1) \log t = 0$ if and only if $t = 1$. Then since $0 < d\mu_1(x)/d\mu_2 < \infty$ for a.e. $x \in X$, the integrand in (1) is nonnegative for a.e. $x \in X$ so that $J(\mu_1, \mu_2) \geq 0$. Also $J(\mu_1, \mu_2) = 0$ if and only if the integrand is equal to 0 for a.e. $x \in X$, i.e., $d\mu_1(x)/d\mu_2 = 1$ for a.e. $x \in X$, in other words $\mu_1 = \mu_2$.

(3) Even when $\mu_1 \sim \mu_2$, $J(\mu_1, \mu_2) = \infty$ can occur. The example in Remark 25.3 is such a case.

Lemma 25.7 Let P and Q be probability measures on a measurable space $(\Omega, \mathfrak{B})$. For σ-fields $\mathfrak{Z}_\alpha$ and $\mathfrak{Z}_\beta$ of subsets of Ω contained in $\mathfrak{B}$ let

$$P_\alpha = P \mid \mathfrak{Z}_\alpha, \quad Q_\alpha = Q \mid \mathfrak{Z}_\alpha, \quad P_\beta = P \mid \mathfrak{Z}_\beta \text{ and } Q_\beta = Q \mid \mathfrak{Z}_\beta,$$

i.e., the restrictions of P and Q to $\mathfrak{Z}_\alpha$ and $\mathfrak{Z}_\beta$, and consider the probability spaces $(\Omega, \mathfrak{Z}_\alpha, P_\alpha)$, etc. Then under the assumption that $\mathfrak{F}_\beta \subset \mathfrak{F}_\alpha$ we have

$$P_\alpha << Q_\alpha \Rightarrow P_\beta << Q_\beta,\ P_\alpha \sim Q_\alpha \Rightarrow P_\beta \sim Q_\beta \text{ and } P_\beta \perp Q_\beta \Rightarrow P_\alpha \perp Q_\alpha . \quad (1)$$

Also writing $J_\alpha = J(P_\alpha, Q_\alpha)$ and $J_\beta = J(P_\beta, Q_\beta)$ we have

$$\mathfrak{F}_\beta \subset \mathfrak{F}_\alpha \Rightarrow J_\beta \leq J_\alpha \quad (2)$$

When $J_\beta = \infty$, the equality in (2) holds trivially. When $J_\beta < \infty$ the equality in (2) holds if and only if

$$\frac{dP_\alpha}{dQ_\alpha}(\omega) = \frac{dP_\beta}{dQ_\beta}(\omega) \qquad \text{for } \omega \in \Lambda, \quad (3)$$

where $\Lambda \in \mathfrak{F}_\beta$ and $P_\beta(\Lambda) = Q_\beta(\Lambda) = 0$. (Note that, when $J_\beta < \infty$ we have $P_\beta \sim Q_\beta$).

<u>Proof</u> The implications in (1) are obvious. In proving (2) and (3) we apply Lemma 25.4 by identifying $(X, \mathfrak{F})$, μ_1, μ_2 and $(Y, \mathfrak{G})$ with $(\Omega, \mathfrak{F}_\alpha)$, P_α, Q_α and $(\Omega, \mathfrak{F}_\beta)$ and T with the identity mapping of Ω onto Ω. Then from (1) of Lemma 25.4

$$\nu_1(G) = \mu_1\left[T^{-1}(G)\right] = P_\beta(G) \quad \text{and}$$

$$\nu_2(G) = \mu_2\left[T^{-1}(G)\right] = Q_\beta(G) \quad \text{for} \quad G \in \mathfrak{F}_\beta .$$

From (2) of Lemma 25.4,

$$I(P_\alpha : Q_\alpha)(\Omega) \geq I(P_\beta : Q_\beta)(\Omega) \quad (1)$$

and

$$I(Q_\alpha : P_\alpha)(\Omega) \geq I(Q_\beta : P_\beta)(\Omega) , \quad (2)$$

so that $J_\alpha \geq J_\beta$. When $J_\beta < \infty$ the right side of (1) and that of (2) are both finite and $J_\alpha = J_\beta$ if and only if the equality holds in both (1) and (2) or equivalently (3) holds in view of (3) of Lemma 25.4. □

Theorem 25.8 Given two probability measures P and Q on a measurable space $(\Omega, \mathfrak{B})$. For a monotone increasing sequence of sub-σ-fields of $\mathfrak{B}$ $\{\mathfrak{F}_n, n=1,2,\cdots\}$ let

$$P_n = P|\mathfrak{F}_n, \quad Q_n = Q|\mathfrak{F}_n \quad \text{and}$$

$$J_n = J(P_n, Q_n) \quad \text{for } n = 1, 2, \cdots$$

and

$$P_\infty = P|\mathfrak{F}_\infty, \quad Q_\infty = Q|\mathfrak{F}_\infty \quad \text{and} \quad J_\infty = J(P_\infty, Q_\infty) \quad \text{where}$$

$\mathfrak{F}_\infty = \sigma\left(\bigcup_{n=1}^{\infty} \mathfrak{F}_n\right)$ so that $J_n \uparrow$, $J_n \leq J_\infty$ and $\lim_{n\to\infty} J_n \leq J_\infty$. Then

$$J_\infty = \lim_{n\to\infty} J_n \tag{1}$$

and

$$\lim_{n\to\infty} J_n < \infty \Rightarrow P_\infty \sim Q_\infty . \tag{2}$$

Proof (1) Let us prove (2) first. When we assume $\lim_{n\to\infty} J_n < \infty$ we are also assuming that $J_n < \infty$ and, in view of Definition 25.5, $P_n \sim Q_n$ for $n=1,2,\cdots$. To prove $P_\infty \sim Q_\infty$ let us assume the contrary, i.e., at least one of $P_\infty \ll Q_\infty$ and $Q_\infty \ll P_\infty$ does not hold. Suppose that the former does not hold. Then there exists some $E \in \mathfrak{F}_\infty$ such that $Q(E) = 0$ while

$P(E) = \varepsilon > 0$. We proceed to show that for $k = 2, 3, \cdots$, there exists $E_k \in \mathfrak{F}_{n_k}$ such that

$$P(E_k) > \frac{3}{4}\varepsilon \quad \text{and} \quad Q(E_k) < \frac{\varepsilon}{4(k-1)} . \tag{3}$$

According to Lemma 9.12, if μ is a finite measure on a measurable space $(X, \mathfrak{F})$ and if $\mathfrak{A}$ is a field of subsets of X such that $\sigma(\mathfrak{A}) = \mathfrak{F}$ then for every $E \in \mathfrak{F}$ and $\varepsilon > 0$ there exists $A \in \mathfrak{A}$ such that $\mu(E \Delta A) < \varepsilon$. Thus for our $E \in \mathfrak{F}_\infty = \sigma\left(\bigcup_{n=1}^\infty \mathfrak{F}_n\right)$ and $\varepsilon > 0$ there exists some $E_k \in \mathfrak{F}_{n_k}$ such that

$$\left\{P + (k-1)Q\right\}(E \Delta E_k) < \frac{\varepsilon}{4} \quad \text{for } k = 2, 3, \cdots,$$

so that from the nonnegativity of P and $(k-1)Q$,

$$P(E \Delta E_k) < \frac{\varepsilon}{4} \quad \text{and} \quad Q(E \Delta E_k) < \frac{\varepsilon}{4(k-1)} \quad \text{for } k = 2, 3, \cdots, \tag{4}$$

Then from (4) and $P(E) = \varepsilon$ we have

$$P(E - E_k) < \frac{\varepsilon}{4}, \quad P(E \cap E_k) > \frac{3}{4}\varepsilon \quad \text{and} \quad P(E_k) > \frac{3}{4}\varepsilon$$

and similarly from (4) and $Q(E) = 0$ we have

$$Q(E_k - E) < \frac{\varepsilon}{4(k-1)} \quad \text{and} \quad Q(E_k) < \frac{\varepsilon}{4(k-1)} .$$

Thus our E_k satisfies (3).

Let

$$F_k = \left\{ \omega \in E_k ; \frac{dP_{n_k}}{dQ_{n_k}}(\omega) \geq k \right\} \in \mathfrak{F}_{n_k} \quad \text{for } k = 2, 3, \cdots .$$

Then, from (3),

$$\frac{\varepsilon}{2} < P(E_k) - Q(E_2) \le P(E_k) - Q(E_k)$$

$$= \int_{E_k} \left\{ \frac{dP_{n_k}}{dQ_{n_k}}(\omega) - 1 \right\} Q_{n_k}(d\omega)$$

$$\le \int_{F_k} \left\{ \frac{dP_{n_k}}{dQ_{n_k}}(\omega) - 1 \right\} Q_{n_k}(d\omega) + (k-1)Q_{n_k}(E-F_k) \qquad \text{for } k = 2, 3, \cdots$$

where the last term is less than $\varepsilon/4$ according to (3). Thus

$$\int_{F_k} \left\{ \frac{dP_{n_k}}{dQ_{n_k}}(\omega) - 1 \right\} Q_{n_k}(d\omega) > \frac{\varepsilon}{4} \qquad \text{for } k = 2, 3, \cdots . \tag{5}$$

Now from the nonnegativity of the integrand in (1) of Remark 25.6 as we pointed out in part (2) of the same, we have

$$J_{n_k} \ge \int_{F_k} \left\{ \frac{dP_{n_k}}{dQ_{n_k}}(\omega) - 1 \right\} \log \frac{dP_{n_k}}{dQ_{n_k}}(\omega)\, Q_{n_k}(d\omega)$$

$$\text{for } k = 2, 3, \cdots .$$

Noting that, on F_k, we have $dP_{n_k}/dQ_{n_k} \ge k$ so that both of the two factors in the last integrand are nonnegative for $k = 2, 3, \cdots$, we have, using (5),

$$J_{n_k} \geq \log k \int_{F_k} \left\{ \frac{dP_{n_k}}{dQ_{n_k}}(\omega) - 1 \right\} Q_{n_k}(d\omega) > \frac{\varepsilon}{4} \log k \quad \text{for } k = 2, 3, \cdots$$

so that $\lim_{k\to\infty} J_{n_K} = \infty$, a contradiction to the assumption that $\lim_{n\to\infty} J_n < \infty$. Therefore $P_\infty \sim Q_\infty$.

(2) Let us prove (1) now. Since $J_n \leq J_\infty$ for all n, (1) holds trivially when $\lim_{n\to\infty} J_n = \infty$. Thus let us consider the case where $\lim_{n\to\infty} J_n < \infty$. Here $P_\infty \sim Q_\infty$ by (2) so that, by (1) of Remark 25.6

$$J_\infty = \int_\Omega \left\{ \frac{dP_\infty}{dQ_\infty}(\omega) - 1 \right\} \log \frac{dP_\infty}{dQ_\infty}(\omega)\, Q_\infty(d\omega). \tag{6}$$

A similar expression holds for J_n since $P_n \sim Q_n$. Let us show then that $\lim_{n\to\infty} dP_n(\omega)/dQ_n = dP_\infty(\omega)/dQ_\infty$ for a.e. $\omega \in \Omega$. To do this, identify $(\Omega, \mathfrak{B}, P)$, X, and $\{\mathfrak{F}_n, n = 1, 2, \cdots\}$, of Theorem 11.2 with our $(\Omega, \mathfrak{F}_\infty, Q_\infty)$, dP_∞/dQ_∞, and $\{\mathfrak{F}_n, n = 1, 2, \cdots\}$ respectively, so that $X_n = E(X|\mathfrak{F}_n)$ and $X_\infty = E(X|\mathfrak{F}_\infty)$ there are identified with our dP_n/dQ_n and dP_∞/dQ_∞, respectively. Then by the conclusion of Theorem 11.2 that $\lim_{n\to\infty} X_n(\omega) = X_\infty(\omega)$ for a.e. $\omega \in \Omega$ we have $\lim_{n\to\infty} dP_n(\omega)/dQ_n = dP_\infty(\omega)/dQ_\infty$ for a.e. $\omega \in \Omega$. Using this together with Fatou's lemma in (6) we obtain

$$J_\infty \leq \liminf_{n\to\infty} \int_\Omega \left\{ \frac{dP_n}{dQ_n}(\omega) - 1 \right\} \log \frac{dP_n}{dQ_n}(\omega)\, Q_n(d\omega) = \liminf_{n\to\infty} J_n = \lim_{n\to\infty} J_n.$$

But $J_n \leq J_\infty$ for all n. Thus $\lim_{n\to\infty} J_n = J_\infty$. □

§26. EQUIVALENCE AND SINGULARITY OF GAUSSIAN MEASURES ON A FUNCTION SPACE

[I] Gaussian Measures in a Function Space

Let R^D be the collection of all real-valued functions x defined on an interval $D \subset R^1$. Let $\mathfrak{T}$ be the collection of all strictly increasing finite sequences $T = \{t_1, \cdots, t_n\}$ of elements of D. For each $T = \{t_1, \cdots, t_n\} \in \mathfrak{T}$ let p_T be the projection of R^D onto R^n defined by

$$p_T(x) = \left[x(t_1), \cdots, x(t_n)\right] \in R^n \qquad \text{for } x \in D. \tag{1}$$

Then for the σ-field $\mathfrak{B}^n$ of Borel sets in R^n,

$$\mathfrak{Z}_T = p_T^{-1}(\mathfrak{B}^n) \tag{2}$$

is a σ-field of subsets of R^D. With the σ-field $\sigma(\mathfrak{Z})$ of subsets of R^D generated by the field $\mathfrak{Z} = \bigcup_{T \in \mathfrak{T}} \mathfrak{Z}_T$, we have a measurable space $\left(R^D, \sigma(\mathfrak{Z})\right)$.

Let us define a real-valued function X on $D \times R^D$ by

$$X(t, x) = x(t) \qquad \text{for } (t, x) \in D \times R^D. \tag{3}$$

Let $T = \{t_1, \cdots, t_n\} \in \mathfrak{T}$. For the σ-field of subsets of R^D generated by $X(t_1, \cdot), \cdots, X(t_n, \cdot)$, namely, the smallest σ-field of subsets of R^D with respect to which each of the transformations $X(t_1, \cdot), \cdots, X(t_n, \cdot)$ of R^D into $(R^1, \mathfrak{B}^1)$ is measurable, we have

$$\sigma\left\{X(t_1,\cdot)^{-1}(\mathfrak{B}^1),\cdots,X(t_n,\cdot)^{\ 1}(\mathfrak{B}^1)\right\}$$

$$= \left[X(t_1,\cdot)\cdots,X(t_n,\cdot)\right]^{-1}(\mathfrak{B}^n) - p_T^{-1}(\mathfrak{B}^n) = \mathfrak{Z}_T \tag{4}$$

where the first equality is from Lemma 7.15. Similarly for an arbitrary subset D_0 of D, if we let

$$p_{D_0}(x) = \left[x(t), t\in D_0\right] \in R^{D_0}, \tag{5}$$

then, for the σ-field of Borel sets $\mathfrak{B}^{D_0}$ in R^{D_0},

$$\mathfrak{Z}_{D_0} = p_{D_0}^{-1}(\mathfrak{B}^{D_0}) \tag{6}$$

is a σ-field of subsets of R^D. Again by Lemma 7.15, for the σ-field of subsets of R^D generated by all $X(t,\cdot)$, $t\in D_0$, we have

$$\sigma\left\{X(t,\cdot)^{-1}(\mathfrak{B}^1),\ t\in D_0\right\}$$

$$=\left[X(t,\cdot).\,t\in D_0\right]^{-1}(\mathfrak{B}^{D_0}) = p_{D_0}^{-1}(\mathfrak{B}^{D_0}) = \mathfrak{Z}_{D_0}. \tag{7}$$

In this connection note also that

$$\mathfrak{Z}_D = \sigma\left(\bigcup_{T\in\mathfrak{T}}\mathfrak{Z}_T\right) = \sigma(\mathfrak{Z}) \tag{8}$$

from the fact that the two σ-fields (3) and (5) in Lemma 7.15 are identical.

Now let μ be a probability measure defined on the measurable space $\left(R^D, \sigma(\mathfrak{Z})\right)$. Then for each $t\in D$, $X(t,\cdot)$ is $\mathfrak{Z}_{\{t\}}$-measurable according to (4) so that it is certainly

$\sigma(\mathfrak{Z})$-measurable and is hence a random variable on the probaba-bility space $\left(R^D, \sigma(\mathfrak{Z}), \mu\right)$. Thus X is a stochastic process on $\left(R^D, \sigma(\mathfrak{Z}), \mu\right)$ and D. If μ is the probability measure induced on $\left(R^D, \sigma(\mathfrak{Z})\right)$ by a stochastic process Y on some probability space $(\Omega, \mathfrak{B}, P)$ and D then our X is a representation of Y on R^D as we saw in [II] of §2.

Definition 26.1 A probability measure μ on the measurable space $\left(R^D, \sigma(\mathfrak{Z})\right)$ is called a Gaussian measure if it is induced by a Gaussian process on some probability space $(\Omega, \mathfrak{B}, P)$ and D, or equivalently, if the stochastic process $X(t, x) = x(t)$ for $(t, x) \in D \times R^D$ is a Gaussian process on the probability space $\left(R^D, \sigma(\mathfrak{Z}), \mu\right)$ and D.

The fact that the first formulation in Defintion 26.1 implies the second is from the consideration in the preceding paragraph. The converse is from the fact that the measure induced on $\left(R^D, \sigma(\mathfrak{Z})\right)$ by the Gaussian process X on $\left(R^D, \sigma(\mathfrak{Z}), \mu\right)$ and D is μ itself.

[II] The J-Divergence of Two Probability Measures on a Function Space

Throughout the rest of §26, $R^D, T, \mathfrak{T}, \mathfrak{Z}_T, \mathfrak{Z}, \sigma(\mathfrak{Z})$, and $\mathfrak{Z}_{D_0}$ will be as defined in [I].

Theorem 26.2 Let μ and ν be two probability measures on the measurable space $\left(R^D, \sigma(\mathfrak{Z})\right)$ and let

$$\mu_T = \mu|\mathfrak{Z}_T, \quad \nu_T = \nu|\mathfrak{Z}_T \quad \text{and} \quad J_T = J(\mu_T, \nu_T) \quad \text{for } T \in \mathfrak{T}$$

and

$$J = J(\mu, \nu)$$

so that $J_T \leq J$ for every $T \in \mathfrak{T}$ and $\sup_{T\in\mathfrak{T}} J_T \leq J$. Then

$$J = \sup_{T\in\mathfrak{T}} J_T \tag{1}$$

and

$$\sup_{T\in\mathfrak{T}} J_T < \infty \Rightarrow \mu \sim \nu . \tag{2}$$

Proof (1) Let us prove (2) first. Assume $\sup_{T\in\mathfrak{T}} J_T < \infty$. If μ and ν are not equivalent then at least one of the two is not absolutely continuous with respect to the other, say, μ is not absolutely continuous with respect to ν. Then there exists $E \in \sigma(\mathfrak{Z})$ such that $\nu(E) = 0$ while $\mu(E) = \varepsilon > 0$. Since E is $\sigma(\mathfrak{Z})$-measurable and since $\sigma(\mathfrak{Z})$ is the σ-field generated by the transformations $\{X(t,\cdot), t \in D\}$ as we saw in (8) and (7) of [I], there exists a countable subset $D_0 \subset D$ such that E is $\mathfrak{Z}_{D_0}$-measurable where $\mathfrak{Z}_{D_0}$ is the σ-field generated by the transformation $\{X(t,\cdot), t \in D_0\}$ according to Theorem 7.19. With $\mu_{D_0} = \mu|\mathfrak{Z}_{D_0}$ and $\nu_{D_0} = \nu|\mathfrak{Z}_{D_0}$ we have $\nu_{D_0}(E) = 0$ while $\mu_{D_0}(E) = \varepsilon$ so that μ_{D_0} and ν_{D_0} are not equivalent and $J_{D_0} = J(\mu_{D_0}, \nu_{D_0}) = \infty$ by Definition 25.5. Let $D_0 = \{s_n, n = 1, 2, \cdots\}$ be an arbitrary enumeration of the elements of D_0. For each n, let $T_n \in \mathfrak{T}$ be the finite sequence obtained by arranging $s_1, \dots, s_n$ in the increasing order and let $J_{T_n} = J(\mu_{T_n}, \nu_{T_n})$. Since $\mathfrak{Z}_{D_0} = \sigma\left(\bigcup_{n=1}^{\infty} \mathfrak{Z}_{T_n}\right)$ by Lemma 7.15 we have $\lim_{n\to\infty} J_{T_n} = J_{D_0} = \infty$ from (1) of Theorem 25.8. On the other hand since $T_n \in \mathfrak{T}$ and $\sup_{T\in\mathfrak{T}} J_T < \infty$ we have $\lim_{n\to\infty} J_{T_n} < \infty$, a contradiction. Therefore μ and ν must be equivalent. This proves (2).

(2) Now let us prove (1). If μ and ν are not equivalent then as we saw in (1) there exists a countable subset $D_0 \subset D$ such that $J_{D_0} = \infty$. Since $J_{D_0} \le J$, (1) holds trivially in this case.

When $\mu \sim \nu$ then $d\mu/d\nu$ exists and is $\sigma(\mathfrak{Z})$-measurable. Now according to Theorem 7.19 there exists a countable subset $D_0 \subset D$ such that the random variable $d\mu/d\nu$ is measurable with respect to the σ-field $\mathfrak{Z}_{D_0}$ generated by the transformations $\{X(t,\cdot),\ t \in D_0\}$. Thus

$$\frac{d\mu}{d\nu}(x) = \frac{d\mu_{D_0}}{d\nu_{D_0}}(x) \quad \text{for a.e. } x \in R^D \text{ with respect to } \nu_{D_0}.$$

Then

$$J = J_{D_0} = \lim_{n\to\infty} J_{T_n} \le \sup_{T\in\mathfrak{T}} J_T$$

with $T_n \in \mathfrak{T}$ as defined in part (1). On the other hand $J \ge J_T$ for every $T \in \mathfrak{T}$ so that $J \ge \sup_{T\in\mathfrak{T}} J_T$. Thus (1) holds. □

[III] The J-Divergence of Two Gaussian Measures

In [II] we showed that if the J-divergence between two probability measures on $\left(R^D, \sigma(\mathfrak{J})\right)$ is finite then the two measures are equivalent. We will show next that if the two measures are Gaussian and their J-divergence is infinite then they are singular. Let us start by discussing the equivalence and singularity of two n-dimensional normal distributions.

An n-dimensional normal distribution $\Phi = N(m, V)$ is a probability measure on $(R^n, \mathfrak{B}^n)$ whose characteristic function φ is given by

$$\varphi(y) = \int_{R^n} e^{i(x,y)} \Phi(dx) = \exp\left\{i(m,y) - \tfrac{1}{2}(Vy, y)\right\} \quad \text{for } y \in R^n$$

where $m \in R^n$ and V is a positive (but not necessarily strictly positive) symmetric linear operator on R^n into R^n. When V is strictly positive [i.e., $(Vy, y) = 0$ if and only if $y = 0$] then Φ is absolutely continuous with respect to the Lebesgue measure m_L on $(R^n, \mathfrak{B}^n)$, and the density function Φ' is given by

$$\Phi'(x) = \frac{d\Phi}{dm_L}(x) = \frac{1}{\{2\pi \det V\}^{\frac{1}{2}}} \exp\left\{-\tfrac{1}{2}(V^{-1}x, x)\right\} \quad \text{for } x \in R^n$$

where $\det V$ is the determinant of the matrix of V with respect to an orthonormal basis of R^n. Since Φ' is positive on R^n, m_L is absolutely continuous with respect to Φ so that $\Phi \sim m_L$ when V is strictly positive. Let us call an n-dimensional normal distribution $\Phi = N(m, V)$ with strictly positive V a regular, or nondegenerate, n-dimensional normal distribution. When V is not strictly positive Φ will be called a degenerate normal distribution. Thus Φ is regular if and only if rank $(V) = n$ or equivalently if and only if all the n nonnegative eigenvalues of V are in fact positive. It will follow from

Lemma 26.3 that a degenerate n-dimensional normal distribution is not absolutely continuous with respect to m_L on $(R^n, \mathfrak{B}^n)$ and has no density function.

Lemma 26.3 Given an n-dimensional normal distribution $\Phi = N(0, V)$, let $k = \text{rank}(V)$. When $k = 0$, Φ is a unit distribution at $0 \in R^n$. When $k \geq 1$, there exist a k-dimensional linear subspaces S_1 and an $n - k$ dimensional linear subspace S_2 of R^n such that

1° $R^n = S_1 \oplus S_2$

2° $\Phi(S_1) = \Phi(R^n) = 1$ and $\Phi(E) = 0$ for $E \in \mathfrak{B}^n$ such that $E \cap S_1 = \emptyset$.

3° Φ is absolutely continuous with respect to m_L when restricted to S_1 and in fact it is a regular k-dimensional normal distribution when restricted to S_1.

A decomposition of R^n satisfying 1°, 2°, 3° is unique.

Proof For $\Phi = N(0, V)$, the characteristic function φ is given by

$$\varphi(y) = \exp\left\{ -\tfrac{1}{2}(Vy, y) \right\} \qquad \text{for } y \in R^n .$$

Since $\text{rank}(V) = k$, exactly k of the n eigenvalues of V, say $\lambda_1, \cdots, \lambda_k$, are positive and the remaining $n - k$ are zero. Let $\{e_1, \cdots, e_k\}$ be an orthonormal system of eigenvectors corresponding to $\{\lambda_1, \cdots, \lambda_k\}$ and extend this system to be an orthonormal basis $\{e_1, \cdots, e_n\}$ of R^n. Let $\{v_{j,\ell}, j, \ell = 1, 2, \cdots, n\}$ be the matrix of V with respect to this basis. Then

$$\varphi(y) = \exp\left\{-\frac{1}{2}\sum_{j=1}^{k} \lambda_j y_j^2\right\} \qquad \text{for } y = (y_1, \cdots, y_n) \in R^n .$$

Let us define a probability measure Ψ on $(R^n, \mathfrak{B}^n)$ as follows: on the k-dimensional linear subspace S_1 of R^n spanned by $\{e_1, \cdots, e_k\}$ let Ψ_1 be a regular k-dimensional normal distribution with the density function

$$\psi_1(y_1, \cdots, y_k) = \exp\left\{-\frac{1}{2}\sum_{j=1}^{k} \lambda_j y_j^2\right\} \quad \text{for } (y_1, \cdots, y_k) \in S_1 ,$$

and on the $n - k$ dimensional linear subspace S_2 of R^n spanned $\{e_{k+1}, \cdots, e_n\}$ let Ψ_2 be the unit distribution at $0 \in S_2$ with the characteristic function

$$\psi_2(y_{k+1}, \cdots, y_n) = 1 \qquad \text{for } (y_{k+1}, \cdots, y_n) \in S_2$$

and finally let Ψ be the product measure of Ψ_1 and Ψ_2 on R^n. [Note that $\sigma(\mathfrak{B}^k \times \mathfrak{B}^{n-k}) = \mathfrak{B}^n$.] Since $\Psi = \Psi_1 \times \Psi_2$, the characteristic function of Ψ is the product of ψ_1 and ψ_2 which is precisely φ. From the one-to-one correspondence between probability measures and characteristic functions we have $\Phi = \Psi = \Psi_1 \times \Psi_2$. Thus our S_1 and S_2 satisfy 1°, 2°, and 3°. It is easy to verify that a decomposition of R^n satisfying 1°, 2°, and 3° is unique. □

Definition 26.4 Given an n-dimensional normal distribution $\Phi = N(m, V)$. Let $k = \text{rank}(V)$. When $k \geq 1$ let

$R^n = S_1 \oplus S_2$ be the decomposition in Lemma 26.3 corresponding to the n-dimensional normal distribution $\Phi_0 = N(0, V)$ so that $\Phi(S_1 + m) = \Phi(R^n) = 1$, $\Phi(E) = 0$ for $E \in \mathfrak{B}^n$ such that $E \cap (S_1 + m) = \phi$ and when restricted to $S_1 + m$, Φ is a regular k-dimensional normal distribution. $S_1 + m$ is called the carrier or the support of Φ and will be denoted by car. Φ. Thus

$$\text{car.}\,\Phi = S_1 + m.$$

When $k = 0$, we define

$$\text{car.}\,\Phi = \{m\}.$$

Lemma 26.5 Let Φ_1 and Φ_2 be two n-dimensional normal distributions on $(R^n, \mathfrak{B}^n)$. Then

$$\text{car.}\,\Phi_1 = \text{car.}\,\Phi_2 \Leftrightarrow \Phi_1 \sim \Phi_2$$

and

$$\text{car.}\,\Phi_1 \neq \text{car.}\,\Phi_2 \Leftrightarrow \Phi_1 \perp \Phi_2 .$$

Proof Let $M_1 =$ car. Φ_2 and $M_2 =$ car. Φ_2. If we show that $M_1 = M_2$ implies $\Phi_1 \sim \Phi_2$ and that $M_1 \neq M_2$ implies $\Phi_1 \perp \Phi_2$ then we have shown that any two n-dimensional normal distributions are either equivalent or singular and also that the converses of the above implications hold.

Suppose $M_1 = M_2 = M$. Let $E \in \mathfrak{B}^n$ and $\Phi_2(E) = 0$. Then $\Phi_2(E \cap M) = 0$. Since $\Phi_1 \sim m_L$ and $m_L \sim \Phi_2$ when restricted to M, $\Phi_1(E \cap M) = 0$. On the other hand since $\Phi_1(M^c) = 0$,

$\Phi_1(E \cap M^c) = 0$. Thus $\Phi_1(E) = 0$ and $\Phi_1 << \Phi_2$. Similarly $\Phi_2 << \Phi_1$ and consequently $\Phi_1 \sim \Phi_2$.

Suppose $M_1 \neq M_2$. If $M_1 \cap M_2 = \phi$ then from the definition of the carrier, $\Phi_1 \perp \Phi_2$. It remains to consider the case where $M_1 \neq M_2$ and $M_1 \cap M_2 \neq \phi$. This is divided into two subcases: $M_1 \subset M_2$ (or $M_2 \subset M_1$) and $M_1 \not\subset M_2$ (or $M_2 \not\subset M_1$). If $M_1 \subset M_2$ then from $M_1 \neq M_2$ we have $\dim M_1 < \dim M_2$. Now $\Phi_1(M_1) = \Phi_1(R^n) = 1$ and $\Phi_1(M_1^c) = 0$. On the other hand since $\Phi_2 << m_L$ on M_2 and $\dim M_1 < \dim M_2$ we have $\Phi_2(M_1) = 0$. Thus $\Phi_1 \perp \Phi_2$. If $M_1 \not\subset M_2$ then $\dim M_1 \cap M_2 < \dim M_1$, $\dim M_2$. From the fact that $\Phi_1 << m_L$ on M_1 and $\Phi_2 << m_L$ on M_2, we have

$$\Phi_1(M_1 \cap M_2) = \Phi_2(M_1 \cap M_2) = 0$$

and consequently

$$\Phi_1\left[M_1 - (M_1 \cap M_2)\right] = \Phi_2\left[M_2 - (M_1 \cap M_2)\right] = 1,$$

i.e., $\Phi_1 \perp \Phi_2$. □

<u>Lemma 26.6</u> Let P and Q be two regular n-dimensional normal distributions on $(R^n, \mathfrak{B}^n)$ with density functions

$$p(x) = \frac{dP}{dm_L}(x) = \frac{1}{(2\pi)^{\frac{n}{2}}} \exp\left\{-\tfrac{1}{2}\sum_{j=1}^{n} x_i^2\right\} \qquad (1)$$

$$q(x) = \frac{dQ}{dm_L}(x) = \frac{1}{(2\pi)^{\frac{n}{2}} \prod_{i=1}^{n} \sigma_i} \exp\left\{ -\frac{1}{2} \sum_{i=1}^{n} \left(\frac{x_i - \mu_i}{\sigma_i} \right)^2 \right\}$$

$$= \frac{1}{(2\pi)^{\frac{n}{2}}} \exp\left\{ -\frac{1}{2} \sum_{i=1}^{n} \left[\left(\frac{x_i - \mu_i}{\sigma_i} \right)^2 + \log \sigma_i^2 \right] \right\} \quad (2)$$

with $\mu_i \in R^1$ and $\sigma_i > 0$ for $i = 1, 2, \cdots, n$, for $x = (x_1, \cdots, x_n) \in R^n$ with respect to an orthonormal basis of R^n. From $P \sim m_L$ and $Q \sim m_L$ we have $P \sim Q$ and

$$\frac{dP}{dQ}(x) = \frac{p(x)}{q(x)} \quad .$$

Let M_P and D_P be the mean and variance with respect to the probability space $(R^n, \mathfrak{B}^n, P)$ and M_Q and D_Q be those with respect to the probability space $(R^n, \mathfrak{B}^n, Q)$ of the random variable.

$$\log \frac{dP}{dQ}(x) = \log \frac{p(x)}{q(x)} = \frac{1}{2} \sum_{i=1}^{n} \left[\left(\frac{x_i - \mu_i}{\sigma_i} \right)^2 - x_i^2 + \log \sigma_i^2 \right] \quad (3)$$

Then

$$M_P = \frac{1}{2} \sum_{i=1}^{n} \left[\frac{1 + \mu_i^2}{\sigma_i^2} - 1 + \log \sigma_i^2 \right] \quad (4)$$

$$D_P = \frac{1}{2} \sum_{i=1}^{n} \left[\left(\frac{1}{\sigma_i^2} - 1 \right)^2 + 2 \frac{\mu_i^2}{\sigma_i^4} \right] \quad (5)$$

$$M_Q = \frac{1}{2}\sum_{i=1}^{n}\left[1 - \mu_i^2 - \sigma_i^2 + \log \sigma_i^2\right] \tag{6}$$

$$D_Q = \frac{1}{2}\sum_{i=1}^{n}\left[\left(\sigma_i^2 - 1\right)^2 + 2\mu_i^2\sigma_i^2\right] \tag{7}$$

and for the J-divergence J between P and Q, namely,

$$J = \int_{R^n} \log \frac{dP}{dQ}(x)\, P(dx) + \int_{R^n} \log \frac{dQ}{dP}(x)\, Q(dx) = M_P - M_Q, \tag{8}$$

in view of $\log\,[dQ(x)/dP] = -\log\,[dP(x)/dQ]$, we have

$$J = \frac{1}{2}\sum_{i=1}^{n}\left[\frac{\left(\sigma_i^2 - 1\right)^2}{\sigma_i^2} + \mu_i^2\left(1 + \frac{1}{\sigma_i^2}\right)\right]. \tag{9}$$

Proof Let us evaluate M_P and D_P first. From the defintion of M_P we have

$$M_P = \int_{R^n} \log \frac{p(x)}{q(x)}\, p(x)\, m_L(dx)\,.$$

Since $p(x)$ is given by (1) and $\log\,[p(x)/q(x)]$ is given by (3), M_P can be interpreted as the expectation of

$$\frac{1}{2}\sum_{i=1}^{n}\left[\left(\frac{X_i(\omega) - \mu_i}{\sigma_i}\right)^2 - \left(X_i(\omega)\right)^2 + \log \sigma_i^2\right] \tag{10}$$

where $\{X_i, i = 1, 2, \cdots, n\}$ is an independent system of random variables on some probability space $(\Omega, \mathfrak{B}, P)$ and each X_i is distributed according to $N(0, 1)$. Then since the expectation of a sum is the sum of the expectations we have

$$M_P = \tfrac{1}{2}\sum_{i=1}^{n}\int_{R^1}\left[\left(\frac{x_i-\mu_i}{\sigma_i}\right)^2 - x_i^2 + \log \sigma_i^2\right]\frac{1}{\sqrt{2\pi}}\exp\left\{-\tfrac{1}{2}x_i^2\right\} m_L(dx_i). \tag{11}$$

Using

$$\int_{R^1} x^k \frac{1}{\sqrt{2\pi}}\exp\{-\tfrac{1}{2}x^2\}\,dx = 1,0,1,0,3 \quad \text{respectively for} \quad k = 0,1,2,3,4 \tag{12}$$

in (11) we obtain (4). As for D_P, since $\{X_i, i = 1,2,\cdots,n\}$ is an independent system, so is

$$\left\{\left(\frac{X_i-\mu_i}{\sigma_i}\right)^2 - X_i + \log \sigma_i^2,\ i = 1,2,\cdots,n\right\}.$$

Now since the variance of the sum of n independent random variables is the sum of the variances of the random variables, and since $V(X) = E(X^2) - [E(X)]^2$, we have

$$D_P = \tfrac{1}{4}\sum_{i=1}^{n}\int_{R^1}\left[\left(\frac{x_i-\mu_i}{\sigma_i}\right)^2 - x_i^2 + \log \sigma_i^2\right]^2\frac{1}{\sqrt{2\pi}}\exp\left\{-\tfrac{1}{2}x_i^2\right\} m_L(dx_i)$$
$$- \tfrac{1}{4}\sum_{i=1}^{n}\left[\frac{1+\mu_i^2}{\sigma_i^2} - 1 + \log \sigma_i^2\right]^2 \tag{13}$$

Using (12) in (13) we obtain (5) after some simplification.

In calculating M_Q and D_Q, since $q(x)$ is given by (2) we may interpret M_Q and D_Q as the expectation and the mean of the sum (10) where now $\{X_i, i = 1,2,\cdots,n\}$ is an independent system of random variables and each X_i is distributed accordingly to $N(\mu_i, \sigma_i^2)$. Then

$$M_Q = \tfrac{1}{2}\sum_{i=1}^{n}\int_{R^1}\left[\left(\frac{x_i-\mu_i}{\sigma_i}\right)^2 - x_i^2 + \log \sigma_i^2\right]$$

$$\frac{1}{\sqrt{2\pi}\,\sigma_i} \exp\left\{-\tfrac{1}{2}\left(\frac{x_i-\mu_i}{\sigma_i}\right)^2\right\} m_L(dx_i). \tag{14}$$

Using

$$\int_{R^1} \left(\frac{x-\mu}{\sigma}\right)^k \frac{1}{\sqrt{2\pi}\,\sigma} \exp\left\{-\tfrac{1}{2}\left(\frac{x-\mu}{\sigma}\right)^2\right\} dx = 1,0,1,0,3$$

respectively for $k = 0, 1, 2, 3, 4,$ (15)

$$x^2 = \left[\left(\frac{x-\mu}{\sigma}\right)^2 + \frac{2\mu}{\sigma}\left(\frac{x-\mu}{\sigma}\right) + \frac{\mu^2}{\sigma^2}\right]\sigma^2 \tag{16}$$

in (14) we obtain (6). Similarly using (15) and (16) in

$$D_Q = \tfrac{1}{4}\sum_{i=1}^{n}\left[\int_{R^1}\left[\left(\frac{x_i-\mu_i}{\sigma_i}\right)^2 - x_i^2 + \log \sigma_i^2\right]^2 \frac{1}{\sqrt{2\pi}\,\sigma_i}\exp\left\{-\tfrac{1}{2}\left(\frac{x_i-\mu_i}{\sigma_i}\right)^2\right\} m_L(dx_i)\right]$$
$$- \tfrac{1}{4}\sum_{i=1}^{n}\left[1 - \mu_i^2 - \sigma_i^2 + \log \sigma_i^2\right]^2 \tag{17}$$

we obtain (7). Finally (9) is from (8) and (4) and (6). □

Lemma 26.7 Let P, Q, M_P, D_P, M_Q, D_Q and J be as in Lemma 26.6. Then for the subsets of R^n defined by

$$A = \left\{x \in R^n;\ \log\frac{p(x)}{q(x)} < M_P - \tfrac{1}{2}J\right\}$$
$$= \left\{x \in R^n;\ \log\frac{p(x)}{q(x)} < M_Q + \tfrac{1}{2}J\right\} \tag{1}$$

$$B_i = \left\{x \in R^n;\ x_i^2 > \sigma_i\right\} \quad \text{for } i = 1, 2, \cdots, n \tag{2}$$

$$C_i = \left\{ x \in R^n ;\ (x_i - \mu_i)^2 < \sigma_i \right\} \qquad \text{for } i = 1, 2, \cdots, n, \tag{3}$$

we have

$$P(A) \le \frac{D_P}{(\frac{1}{2}J)^2} \qquad Q(A) \ge 1 - \frac{D_Q}{(\frac{1}{2}J)^2} \tag{4}$$

$$P(B_i) = 2\left[1 - \Phi(\sqrt{\sigma_i})\right] \qquad Q(B_i) \ge 2\left[1 - \Phi\left(\frac{1}{\sqrt{\sigma_i}}\right)\right] \tag{5}$$

$$P(C_i) \le 1 - 2\left[1 - \Phi(\sqrt{\sigma_i})\right] \qquad Q(C_i) = 1 - 2\left[1 - \Phi\left(\frac{1}{\sqrt{\sigma_i}}\right)\right], \tag{6}$$

where

$$\Phi(\lambda) = \frac{1}{\sqrt{2\pi}} \int_{-\infty}^{\lambda} e^{-x^2/2}\, dx$$

$$= \frac{1}{\sqrt{2\pi}\,\sigma} \int_{-\infty}^{\sigma\lambda} e^{-x^2/2\sigma^2}\, dx \qquad \text{for } \lambda \in R^1 \text{ and } \sigma > 0. \tag{7}$$

<u>Proof</u> With regard to (1) note that

$$M_P - \tfrac{1}{2}J = M_P - \tfrac{1}{2}(M_P - M_Q) = M_Q + \tfrac{1}{2}J.$$

To prove (4) note that since $J \ge 0$ we have

$$A \subset \left\{ x \in R^n ;\ \left| \log \frac{p(x)}{q(x)} - M_P \right| > \tfrac{1}{2}J \right\},$$

so that, by the Chebyshev inequality, the estimate of $P(A)$ in (4) holds. On the other hand from the second expression of A in (1) we have

$$A^c = \left\{ x \in R^n ;\ \log \frac{p(x)}{q(x)} - M_Q \ge \tfrac{1}{2}J \right\}$$

$$\subset \left\{ x \in R^n ;\ \left| \log \frac{p(x)}{q(x)} - M_Q \right| \ge \tfrac{1}{2}J \right\},$$

so that by the Chebyshev inequality we have

$$Q(A^c) \le \frac{D_Q}{(\frac{1}{2}J)^2} ,$$

which implies the estimate of $Q(A)$ in (4).

The equality in (5) for $P(B_i)$ is immediate from (2) and (7). On the other hand from

$$\int_{x^2>a} \exp\left\{-\frac{(x-\mu)^2}{2\sigma^2}\right\} dx \ge \int_{x^2>a} \exp\left\{-\frac{x^2}{2\sigma^2}\right\} dx ,$$

which is immediately clear if we simply consider the areas under the two curves, we have

$$\begin{aligned} Q(B_i) &= \frac{1}{\sqrt{2\pi}\,\sigma_i} \int_{x_i^2>\sigma_i} \exp\left\{-\frac{(x_i-\mu_i)^2}{2\sigma_i^2}\right\} dx_i \\ &\ge \frac{1}{\sqrt{2\pi}\,\sigma_i} \int_{x_i^2>\sigma_i} \exp\left\{-\frac{x_i^2}{2\sigma_i^2}\right\} dx_i \\ &= \frac{2}{\sqrt{2\pi}\,\sigma_i} \int_{x_i>\sqrt{\sigma_i}} \exp\left\{-\frac{x_i^2}{2\sigma_i^2}\right\} dx_i = 2\left[1-\Phi\left(\frac{1}{\sqrt{\sigma_i}}\right)\right], \end{aligned}$$

which is the estimate of $Q(B_i)$ in (5). The estimate of $P(C_i)$ and the equality for $Q(C_i)$ in (6) follow likewise. □

<u>Lemma 26.8</u> For every $\varepsilon > 0$ there exists $K_\varepsilon \ge 0$ such that for any positive integer n and any pair of regular n-dimensional normal distributions P and Q on $(R^n, \mathfrak{B}^n)$ with the J-divergence $J = J(P, Q) > K_\varepsilon$ there exists $\Lambda \in \mathfrak{B}^n$ such that

$$P(\Lambda) < \varepsilon \qquad \text{and} \qquad Q(\Lambda) > 1 - \varepsilon .$$

Proof (1) Consider first the case where the density functions of P and Q are given by (1) and (2) of Lemma 26.6. Let $\lambda_\epsilon > 0$ be so large that, for the function Φ given by (7) of Lemma 26.7,

$$2\left[1 - \Phi(\lambda_\epsilon)\right] < \epsilon \quad \text{and} \quad 2\left[1 - \Phi\left(1 - \Phi\left(\frac{1}{\lambda_\epsilon}\right)\right]\right] > 1 - \epsilon \tag{1}$$

hold. Now if at least one of σ_i, $i = 1, 2, \cdots, n$, say σ_{i_0}, satisfies $\sqrt{\sigma_{i_0}} > \lambda_\epsilon$, then, by (5) of Lemma 26.7 and (1),

$$P(B_{i_0}) = 2\left[1 - \Phi\left(\sqrt{\sigma_{i_0}}\right)\right] \le 2\left[1 - \Phi(\lambda_\epsilon)\right] < \epsilon,$$

$$Q(B_{i_0}) \ge 2\left[1 - \Phi\left(\frac{1}{\sqrt{\sigma_{i_0}}}\right)\right] \ge 2\left[1 - \Phi\left(\frac{1}{\sqrt{\lambda_\epsilon}}\right)\right] > 1 - \epsilon,$$

and $\Lambda = B_{i_0}$ will do. Similarly if $\sqrt{\sigma_{i_0}} < 1/\lambda_\epsilon$ for some i_0 then, by (6) of Lemma 26.7 and (1),

$$P(C_{i_0}) \le 1 - 2\left[1 - \Phi\left(\sqrt{\sigma_{i_0}}\right)\right] \le 1 - 2\left[1 - \Phi\left(\frac{1}{\lambda_\epsilon}\right)\right] < \epsilon,$$

$$Q(C_{i_0}) = 1 - 2\left[1 - \Phi\left(\frac{1}{\sqrt{\sigma_{i_0}}}\right)\right] \ge 1 - 2\left[1 - \Phi(\lambda_\epsilon)\right] > 1 - \epsilon,$$

and $\Lambda = C_{i_0}$ will do.

Consider the case where neither $\sqrt{\sigma_i} > \lambda_\epsilon$ nor $\sqrt{\sigma_i} < 1/\lambda_\epsilon$ is satisfied for any i, i.e., $1/\lambda_\epsilon \le \lambda_\epsilon$ for $i = 1, 2, \cdots, n$, or equivalently

$$\frac{1}{\lambda_\epsilon^4} \le \sigma_i^2 \le \lambda_\epsilon^4 \qquad \text{for } i = 1, 2, \cdots, n. \tag{2}$$

By (5) and (7) of Lemma 26.6,

$$\frac{1}{4\lambda_\epsilon^4}\left\{D_P + D_Q\right\} = \frac{1}{8\lambda_\epsilon^4}\sum_{i=1}^{n}\left[\left(\sigma_i^2 - 1\right)^2\left(1 + \frac{1}{\sigma_i^4}\right) + 2\mu_i^2\left(\sigma_i^2 + \frac{1}{\sigma_i^4}\right)\right]. \tag{3}$$

For J given by (9) of Lemma 26.6 we have, from (3) and (2)

$$J \geq \frac{1}{4\lambda_\epsilon^4}\{D_P + D_Q\}. \tag{4}$$

From (4) of Lemma 26.7 and (4),

$$P(A) \leq \frac{D_P}{(\frac{1}{2}J)^2} \leq D_P\left\{\frac{1}{4}J \frac{1}{4\lambda_\epsilon^4} D_P\right\}^{-1} = \frac{16\lambda_\epsilon^4}{J},$$

$$Q(A) \geq \frac{D_Q}{(\frac{1}{2}J)^2} \geq 1 - D_Q\left\{\frac{1}{4}J \frac{1}{4\lambda_\epsilon^4} D_Q\right\}^{-1} = 1 - \frac{16\lambda_\epsilon^4}{J}.$$

Thus if we take $K_\epsilon = 16\lambda_\epsilon^4 \epsilon^{-1}$ then, for $J > K_\epsilon$, $\Lambda = A$ will do.

(2) Let us turn now to the general case where the density functions of P and Q are given, respectively, by

$$p(x) = \frac{1}{\{(2\pi)^n \det W\}^{\frac{1}{2}}} \exp\left\{-\frac{1}{2}\left(V^{-1}[x-a], x-a\right)\right\} \quad \text{for } x \in R^n,$$

$$q(x) = \frac{1}{\{(2\pi)^n \det W\}^{\frac{1}{2}}} \exp\left\{-\frac{1}{2}\left(W^{-1}[x-b], x-b\right)\right\} \quad \text{for } x \in R^n,$$

where $a, b \in R^n$ andd V and W are $n \times n$ positive definite symmetric matrices of real numbers. Now since V and W^{-1} are positive definite symmetric matrices there exist $n \times n$ positive definite symmetric matrices of real numbers M and N such that

$$MM' = M^2 = V \qquad \text{and} \qquad NN' = N^2 = W^{-1}.$$

Then $MW^{-1}M$ is a positive definite symmetric matrix so that there exists an orthogonal matrix O such that $O'MW^{-1}MO$ is a diagonal matrix with positive diagonal entries which we call σ_i^{-2} with $\sigma_i > 0$ for $i = 1, 2, \cdots, n$. Let $y, \mu \in R^n$ be defined by

$$y = (MO)^{-1}[x-a] \qquad \text{and} \qquad \mu = (MO)^{-1}[b-a],$$

i.e.,

$$x-a = MOy \qquad \text{and} \qquad b-a = MO\mu.$$

Then

$$\left(V^{-1}[x-a], x-a\right) = (M^{-2}MOy, MOy) = (O'MM^{-2}MOy, y) = (y, y) = \sum_{i=1}^{n} y_i^2$$

and from

$$x-b = [x-a] - [b-a] = MO[y-\mu]$$

we have

$$\left(W^{-1}[x-b], x-b\right) = \left(W^{-1}MO[y-\mu], MO[y-\mu]\right)$$

$$= \left(O'MW^{-1}MO[y-\mu], y-\mu\right)$$

$$= \sum_{i=1}^{n} \left(\frac{y_i-\mu_i}{\sigma_i}\right)^2 .$$

Since

$$\sqrt{\det V} = \det M \qquad \text{and} \qquad \sqrt{\det W} = \prod_{i=1}^{n} \sigma_i \det M,$$

we have under the transformation $x = MOy-a$, with the Jacobian $\det M$,

$$p(x)m_L(dx) = \frac{1}{(2\pi)^{n/2}\det M} \exp\left\{-\tfrac{1}{2}\sum_{i=1}^{n} y_i^2\right\} \det M\, m_L(dy)$$

and

$$q(x)\, m_L(dx)$$

$$= \frac{1}{(2\pi)^{n/2} \prod_{i=1}^{n} \sigma_i \det M} \exp\left\{-\tfrac{1}{2}\sum_{i=1}^{n}\left(\frac{y_i-\mu_i}{\sigma_i}\right)^2\right\} \det M\, m_L(dy),$$

which are the types of density functions considered in part (1). It remains to show that the J-divergence remains invariant under the transformation. But this invariance follows from Lemma 25.4 since after all our transformation is a one-to-one transformation of R^n onto R^n, and the inequality (2) in Lemma 25.4 can be applied to both the transformation and its inverse. □

Theorem 26.9 Let μ and ν be two Gaussian measures on the measurable space $(R^D, \sigma(\mathfrak{Z}))$. If $J(\mu, \nu) = \infty$ then $\mu \perp \nu$.

Proof Recall that $\mathfrak{Z} = \bigcup_{T \in \mathfrak{T}} \mathfrak{Z}_T$ and $\mathfrak{Z}_T = p_T^{-1}(\mathfrak{B}^n)$ for $T = \{t_1, \cdots, t_n\} \in \mathfrak{T}$. Let μ_T and ν_T be the restriction of μ and ν to $\mathfrak{Z}_T$ and $J_T = J(\mu_T, \nu_T)$. For $J = J(\mu, \nu)$, we have $J = \sup_{T \in \mathfrak{T}} J_T$ according to Theorem 26.2. Since μ and ν are Gaussian measures on $(R^D, \sigma(\mathfrak{Z}))$, i.e., probability measures induced by two Gaussian processes, there exist n-dimensional normal distributions P_T and Q_T on $(R^n, \mathfrak{B}^n)$ such that for every member E of $\mathfrak{Z}_T$, say $E = p_T^{-1}(B)$ where $B \in \mathfrak{B}^n$ we have

$$\mu_T(E) = P_T(B) \quad \text{and} \quad \nu_T(E) = Q_T(B).$$

If $\text{car.}\, P_T \neq \text{car.}\, Q_T$ for some $T \in \mathfrak{Z}$, then $P_T \perp Q_T$ by Lemma 26.5 and consequently $\mu_T \perp \nu_T$ and $\mu \perp \nu$.

Assume now that $\text{car.}\, P_T = \text{car.}\, Q_T$ for every $T \in \mathfrak{T}$. If the common carrier consists of a single point (i.e., P_T and Q_T are unit distributions at the same point) then both dP_T/dQ_T and dQ_T/dP_T are equal to 1 on R^n so that, by Definition 25.5 and Definition 25.1, $J_T = J(P_T, Q_T) = 0$. On the other hand if the common carrier is not a single point then P_T and Q_T are regular k-dimensional normal distributions when restricted to the common carrier with the same $k = 1, 2, \cdots,$ or n. According to Lemma 26.8 for every $\epsilon > 0$ there exists $K_\epsilon \geq 0$ such that for any $T \in \mathfrak{T}$ with $J_T = J(P_T, Q_T) > K_\epsilon$ there exists $B \in \mathfrak{B}^n$ such that $P_T(\Lambda) < \epsilon$ and $Q_T(\Lambda) > 1 - \epsilon$ and consequently for $\Lambda = p_T^{-1}(B) \in \mathfrak{Z}_T$ we have $\mu_T(\Lambda) < \epsilon$ and $\nu_T(\Lambda) > 1 - \epsilon$. In the last two inequalities the subscripts T can be dropped since μ_T and ν_T are after all restrictions of μ and ν to $\mathfrak{Z}_T$. Now let $\epsilon = 1/2^m$ for $m = 1,2,\cdots,$ Since $J = \infty$, there exists $T_m \in \mathfrak{T}$ such that $J_{T_m} = J\left(P_{T_m}, Q_{T_m}\right) > K_{2^{-m}}$. Then there exists $\Lambda_m \in \mathfrak{Z}_{T_m}$ such that

$$\mu(\Lambda_m) \leq \frac{1}{2^m} \qquad \text{and} \qquad \nu(\Lambda_m) > 1 - \frac{1}{2^m}.$$

Since $\sum_{m=1}^{\infty} \mu(\Lambda_m) < \infty$, by the Borel-Cantelli theorem we have $\mu(\lim_{m\to\infty} \sup \Lambda_m) = 0$. Similarly from $\nu(\Lambda_m^c) < 1/2^m$ and $\sum_{m=1}^{\infty} \nu(\Lambda_m^c) < \infty$ we have $\nu(\lim_{m\to\infty} \sup \Lambda_m^c) = 0$, or equivalently $\nu(\lim_{m\to\infty} \inf \Lambda_m) = 1$ and a fortiori $\nu(\lim_{m\to\infty} \sup \Lambda_m) = 1$. Let $\Lambda = \lim_{m\to\infty} \sup \Lambda_m \in \sigma(\mathfrak{Z})$. Then $\mu(\Lambda) = 0$ and $\nu(\Lambda) = 1$ so that $\mu \perp \nu$. □

Combining Theorem 26.2 and Theorem 26.9 we have

Theorem 26.10 Let μ and ν be two Gaussian measures on the measurable space $\left(R^D, \sigma(\mathfrak{Z})\right)$. Then either $J(\mu, \nu) < \infty$ and $\mu \sim \nu$ or $J(\mu, \nu) = \infty$ and $\mu \perp \nu$.

[IV] An Example

Theorem 26.11 Let Y_1 and Y_2 be two Gaussian processes on a probability space $(\Omega, \mathfrak{B}, P)$ and $D = [0,1] \subset R^1$ whose mean and covariance functions satisfy the conditions in Theorem 20.4. Let f_1 and f_2 be as defined in (2) of Theorem 20.4 for Y_1 and Y_2, respectively. Let μ_1 and μ_2 be the Gaussian measures on the measurable space $\left(R^D, \sigma(\mathfrak{Z})\right)$ induced by Y_1 and Y_2, respectively. If

$$\int_0^1 f_1(t)\, dt \neq \int_0^1 f_2(t)\, dt \tag{1}$$

then $\mu_1 \perp \mu_2$, and in fact with the subsets of R^D defined by

$$E_i = \left\{ x \in R^D ; \lim_{n\to\infty} \sum_{k=1}^{2^n} \left[x\left(\frac{k}{2^n}\right) - x\left(\frac{k-1}{2^n}\right) \right]^2 = \int_0^1 f_i(t)dt \right\} \quad \text{for } i = 1,2, \tag{2}$$

we have

$$\mu_i(E_j) = \delta_{ij} . \tag{3}$$

Proof If we let

$$X_i(t,x) = x(t) \quad \text{for} \quad (t,x) \in D \times R^D \quad \text{and } i = 1, 2, \tag{4}$$

then X_i is a Gaussian process on the probability space $\left(R^D, \sigma(\mathfrak{Z}), \mu_i\right)$ and D which has the same mean and covariance functions as Y_i for $i = 1, 2$. Thus Theorem 20.4 is applicable to X_i for $i = 1, 2,$. In view of (4), the conclusion (3) of Theorem 20.4 becomes

$$\mu_i(E_i) = 1 \quad \text{for} \quad i = 1, 2, \tag{5}$$

where E_i, $i = 1, 2$, are defined by (2). If (1) holds then $E_1 \cap E_2 = \emptyset$ so that from (5) we have (3) and hence $\mu_1 \perp \mu_2$. □

Chapter 7

WIENER MEASURE AND WIENER INTEGRAL

§27. WIENER MEASURE

The Wiener space C_w is the collection of all real-valued continuous functions x on $[0,1]$ with $x(0) = 0$. The Wiener measure m_w is a probability measure defined on a σ-field of subsets of C_w which includes sets of the type

$$J = \left\{x \in C_w;\ \alpha_i < x(t_i) \leq \beta_i,\quad i = 1, 2, \cdots, n\right\} \tag{1}$$

where $0 = t_0 < t_1 < \cdots < t_n \leq 1$, $-\infty \leq \alpha_i < \beta_i \leq \infty$ for $i = 1, 2, \cdots, n$, for which m_w assumes the value

$$m_w(J) = \left\{(2\pi)^n \prod_{i=1}^{n} (t_i - t_{i-1})\right\}^{-\frac{1}{2}} \int_{\alpha_1}^{\beta_1} (n) \int_{\alpha_n}^{\beta_n} \exp\left\{-\frac{1}{2}\sum_{i=1}^{n} \frac{(\xi_i - \xi_{i-1})^2}{t_i - t_{i-1}}\right\} d\xi_1 \cdots d\xi_n \tag{2}$$

where $\xi_0 \equiv 0$. This measure is related to the probability measure induced on the space of all real-valued functions on $(0,1]$ by a standard Brownian motion process whose domain of definition is $[0,1]$. To show this let Z be a standard Brownian motion process on a probability space $(\Omega, \mathfrak{B}, P)$ and $D = [0,1]$, i.e., Z is an additive process in which $Z(t'', \cdot) - Z(t, \cdot)$ is distributed according to $N(0, t'' - t')$ for $t', t'' \in D, t' < t''$, and $Z(0, \cdot) = 0$ a.e. on Ω. According to Theorem 17.3 [with $a(t) = 0$, $b(t) = t$ for $t \in D$ and $c = 0$], the probability distribution of the n-dimensional random vector $\left[Z(t_1, \cdot), \cdots, Z(t_n, \cdot)\right]$, where

$0 = t_0 < t_1 < \cdots < t_n \le 1$, is an n-dimensional normal distribution whose density function is given by

$$\left\{(2\pi)^n \prod_{i=1}^{n} (t_i - t_{i-1})\right\}^{-\frac{1}{2}} \exp\left\{-\frac{1}{2}\sum_{i=1}^{n} \frac{\left(\xi_i - \xi_{i-1}\right)^2}{t_i - t_{i-1}}\right\} \tag{3}$$

Let $R^{(0,1]}$ be the collection of all real-valued functions on $(0,1]$ and let $X = \{0\} \times R^{(0,1]}$. There exist the obvious one-to-one correspondences between the elements of X and those of $R^{(0,1]}$ and between the subsets of X and those of $R^{(0,1]}$. The Borel cylinders in $R^{(0,1]}$ are defined as in §2. Thus for $\{t_1, \cdots, t_n\} \subset (0,1]$ where $0 < t_1 < \cdots < t_n \le 1$, the projection $p_{t_1 \cdots t_n}$ of $R^{(0,1]}$ onto R^n is defined by

$$p_{t_1 \cdots t_n}(x) = \left[x(t_1), \cdots, x(t_n)\right] \in R^n \quad \text{for } x \in R^{(0,1]}. \tag{4}$$

The Borel cylinder in $R^{(0,1]}$ with base $B \in \mathfrak{B}^n$ is defined by

$$p_{t_1 \cdots t_n}^{-1}(B) = \left\{x \in R^{(0,1]}; \left[x(t_1), \cdots, x(t_n)\right] \in B\right\}. \tag{5}$$

Let

$$\mathfrak{Z}_{t_1 \cdots t_n} = p_{t_1 \cdots t_n}^{-1}(\mathfrak{B}^n) \quad \text{and} \quad \mathfrak{Z} = \bigcup \mathfrak{Z}_{t_1 \cdots t_n}. \tag{6}$$

Let μ_Z be the probability measure induced on the measurable space $\left(R^{(0,1]}, \sigma(\mathfrak{Z})\right)$ by Z. Consider the subset of $R^{(0,1]}$

$$I = \left\{x \in R^{(0,1]}; \alpha_i < x(t_i) \le \beta_i,\ i = 1, 2, \cdots, n\right\} \in \mathfrak{Z}_{t_1 \cdots t_n}. \tag{7}$$

According to (2) and (3) in [III] of §2,

$$\mu_Z(I) = P\left\{\omega \in \Omega; \alpha_i < Z(t_i, \omega) \le \beta_i,\ i = 1, 2, \cdots, n\right\}. \tag{8}$$

Thus, by (3) and (2),

$$\mu_Z(I) = m_w(J). \tag{9}$$

Note that $J = I \cap C_w$ from (7) and (1). [Strictly speaking, $J = \left(\{0\} \times I\right) \cap C_w$, but we do not distinguish between corresponding subsets of $R^{(0,1]}$ and $X = \{0\} \times R^{(0,1]}$.] The equality (9) is the relationship between the Wiener measure m_w and the probability measure μ_Z induced on $\left(R^{(0,1]}, \sigma(\mathfrak{Z})\right)$ by the standard Brownian motion process Z which we mentioned before. Although we will not prove it here it is known (see for instance Kac [1], p. 162) that $C_w \notin \sigma(\mathfrak{Z})$ and $I \cap C_w \notin \sigma(\mathfrak{Z})$ and consequently $\mu_Z(C_w)$ and $\mu_Z(J)$ are not defined. (This situation is not improved even when we assume that Z is a continuous process, i.e., every sample function of Z is continuous, since $\sigma(\mathfrak{Z})$ is a σ-field of subsets of $R^{(0,1]}$ which is defined independently of the process Z.) To define the Wiener measure m_w we show that the Carathéodory outer measure of C_w derived from the probability measure μ_Z on $\left(R^{(0,1]}, \sigma(\mathfrak{Z})\right)$ is equal to one and then we show that this fact implies that m_w defined by (9) to be equal to $\mu_Z(I)$ for the subsets J of C_w of the type (1) can be extended to be a probability measure on a σ-field of subsets of C_w. This program is carried out in the rest of §27 and in §28.

<u>Definition 27.1</u> Let $R^{(0,1]}$ be the collection of all real-valued functions x on $(0,1]$ and let $\mathfrak{Z}$ be the field of Borel cylinders in $R^{(0,1]}$ as defined by (6) above. For $I \in \mathfrak{Z}$, say $I \in \mathfrak{Z}_{t_1 \cdots t_n}$, $I = p_{t_1 \cdots t_n}^{-1}(B)$ where $B \in \mathfrak{B}^n$, let

$$m(I) = \left\{(2\pi)^n \prod_{i=1}^{n} (t_i - t_{i-1})\right\}^{-\frac{1}{2}} \int_B \exp\left\{-\frac{1}{2}\sum_{i=1}^{n} \frac{(\xi_i - \xi_{i-1})^2}{t_i - t_{i-1}}\right\} m_L(d\xi) \tag{1}$$

where $t_0 = 0$, $\xi_0 \equiv 0$ and $\xi = (\xi_1, \cdots, \xi_n) \in R^n$.

Lemma 27.2 The set function m on the field $\mathfrak{J}$ of subsets of $R^{(0,1]}$ in Definition 27.1 is well defined and it is a probability measure on the σ-field $\mathfrak{J}_{t_1 \cdots t_n}$ for each $\{t_1, \cdots, t_n\}$. Thus, according to the Kolmogorov extension theorem, it can be extended uniquely to be a probability measure on $\sigma(\mathfrak{J})$.

Proof The lemma follows from the fact that our m is in fact the probability measure μ_Z induced by a standard Brownian motion process Z on a probability space $(\Omega, \mathfrak{B}, P)$ and $[0,1]$ on $R^{(0,1]}$. □

Definition 27.3 Let Y be an arbitrary subset of $X = \{0\} \times R^{(0,1]}$. For $\{t_1, \cdots, t_n\} \subset (0,1]$ where $0 < t_1 < \cdots < t_n \leq 1$, let

$$q_{t_1 \cdots t_n}(x) = \left[x(t_1), \cdots, x(t_n)\right] \in R^n \quad \text{for } x \in Y \tag{1}$$

$$q_{t_1 \cdots t_n}^{-1}(B) = \left\{x \in Y; \left[x(t_1), \cdots, x(t_n)\right] \in B\right\}$$

$$= p_{t_1 \cdots t_n}^{-1}(B) \cap Y \quad \text{for } B \in \mathfrak{B}^n \tag{2}$$

$$\mathfrak{G}_{t_1 \cdots t_n} = q_{t_1 \cdots t_n}^{-1}(\mathfrak{B}^n) \quad \text{and } \mathfrak{G} = \bigcup \mathfrak{G}_{t_1 \cdots t_n}. \tag{3}$$

For $J \in \mathfrak{G}$, say $J \in \mathfrak{G}_{t_1 \cdots t_n}$, $J = q_{t_1 \cdots t_n}^{-1}(B) = I \cap Y$ where $I = p_{t_1 \cdots t_n}^{-1}(B)$ where $p_{t_1 \cdots t_n}$ is a projection defined on X and $B \in \mathfrak{B}^n$, define

$$m_Y(J) = m(I). \tag{4}$$

Without additional conditions on Y, there is no one-to-one correspondence between the members of $\mathfrak{B}^n$ and those of $\mathfrak{F}_{t_1 \cdots t_n}$ and m_Y as given above is not well defined on $\mathfrak{F}_{t_1 \cdots t_n}$, let alone $\mathfrak{F}$. To show this by an example consider the case where Y consists of just one element of X, say the identically vanishing function on $[0, 1]$. Let $t_1 \in (0, 1)$ be fixed and let $B_1 = (0, \infty)$, $B_2 = R^1 - \{0\}$, $B_3 = [0, \infty)$, and $B_4 = R^1$, all members of $\mathfrak{B}^1$. Writing $\varphi(\xi_1) = (2\pi t_1)^{-\frac{1}{2}} \exp\left\{-\frac{1}{2}\xi_1^2/t_1\right\}$ for $\xi_1 \in R^1$ we have

$$m_Y(\emptyset) = \int_{B_1} \varphi(\xi_1)d\xi_1 = \tfrac{1}{2} \qquad \text{since } \emptyset = q_{t_1}^{-1}(B_1)$$

as well as

$$m_Y(\emptyset) = \int_{B_2} \varphi(\xi_1)d\xi_1 = 1 \qquad \text{since } \emptyset = q_{t_1}^{-1}(B_2).$$

Similarly we have

$$m_Y(Y) = \int_{B_3} \varphi(\xi_1)d\xi_1 = \tfrac{1}{2} \qquad \text{since } Y = q_{t_1}^{1}(B_3)$$

as well as

$$m_Y(Y) = \int_{B_4} \varphi(\xi_1)d\xi_1 = 1 \qquad \text{since } Y = q_{t_1}^{-1}(B_4).$$

Thus m_Y is not well defined on $\mathfrak{F}_{t_1}$.

<u>Lemma 27.4</u> Let $Y \subset X$ be such that for some $\{t_1, \cdots, t_n\} \subset (0, 1]$ where $0 < t_1 < \cdots < t_n \le 1$ and every $\{\gamma_1, \cdots, \gamma_n\} \subset R^n$ there exists $x \in Y$ such that $[x(t_1), \cdots, x(t_n)]$

$= [\gamma_1, \cdots, \gamma_n]$. Then there is a one-to-one correspondence between the members of $\mathfrak{B}^n$ and those of $\mathfrak{G}_{t_1 \cdots t_n}$, and consequently m_Y is well defined on $\mathfrak{G}_{t_1 \cdots t_n}$ and is a probability measure there.

<u>Proof</u> Under the above additional condition on Y, $q_{t_1 \cdots t_n}$ maps Y onto R^n so that for every $B \in \mathfrak{B}^n$ we have $q_{t_1 \cdots t_n}\left[q_{t_1 \cdots t_n}^{-1}(B)\right] = B$. Thus if $B_1, B_2 \in \mathfrak{B}^n$ and $B_1 \neq B_2$ then $q_{t_1 \cdots t_n}^{-1}(B_1) \neq q_{t_1 \cdots t_n}^{-1}(B_2)$. This establishes a one-to-one correspondence between the members of $\mathfrak{B}^n$ and those of $\mathfrak{G}_{t_1 \cdots t_n}$. Then m_Y is well defined on $\mathfrak{G}_{t_1 \cdots t_n}$ and is a probability measure there. □

Under the assumption of the condition in Lemma 27.4 for every $\{t_1, \cdots, t_n\} \subset (0, 1]$, m_Y is well defined on $\mathfrak{G}_{t_1 \cdots t_n}$ and is a probability measure there. However m_Y is not well defined on $\mathfrak{G}$ yet. Let $\{J_k, k = 1, 2, \cdots\} \subset \mathfrak{G}$ be a disjoint collection and assume that $J_\infty \equiv \bigcup_{k=1}^\infty J_k \in \mathfrak{G}$ also. Then $J_k = I_k \cap Y$ for some $I_k \in \mathfrak{J}$ for $k = 1, 2, \cdots, \infty$ and

$$I_\infty \cap Y = J_\infty = \left\{\bigcup_{k=1}^\infty I_k\right\} \cap Y.$$

This does not imply $I_\infty = \bigcup_{k=1}^\infty I_k$, nor does it imply $\bigcup_{k=1}^\infty I_k \in \mathfrak{J}$. We only have $\bigcup_{k=1}^\infty I_k \in \sigma(\mathfrak{J})$. If we assume further that $\bigcup_{k=1}^\infty I_k \in \mathfrak{J}$ then we have, from the above two expressions of J_∞,

$$m_Y(J_\infty) = m(I_\infty) \quad \text{as well as} \quad m_Y(J_\infty) = m\left(\bigcup_{k=1}^{\infty} I_k\right).$$

But these two values for $m_Y(J_\infty)$ may not agree since $I_\infty = \bigcup_{k=1}^{\infty} I_k$ does not hold in general. We shall show below that if the Carathéodory outer measure of Y derived from the probability measure m on the field $\mathfrak{F}$ is equal to 1 then m_Y is well defined on $\mathfrak{G}$. To fix terminology let us recall the following. Given $(S, \mathfrak{A}, \mu)$ where μ is a measure on a field $\mathfrak{A}$ of subsets of S. Let O be a countable union of members of $\mathfrak{A}$. Then $O \in \sigma(\mathfrak{A})$ and $\mu(O)$ is uniquely determined. The Carathéodory outer measure μ^* of an arbitrary set $E \subset S$ derived from μ is defined by

$$\mu^*(E) = \inf_{E \subset O} \mu(O).$$

The collection $\mathfrak{A}^*$ of all Carathéodory measurable sets, $E \subset S$, i.e., those sets E which satisfy

$$\mu^*(A) = \mu^*(E \cap A) + \mu^*(E^c \cap A) \qquad \text{for every } A \subset S$$

is a σ-field which contains $\mathfrak{A}$, $\mu^* = \mu$ on $\mathfrak{A}$, and $(S, \mathfrak{A}^*, \mu^*)$ is a complete measure space.

Lemma 27.5 (J. L. Doob) Given $(S, \mathfrak{A}, \mu)$ where μ is a finite measure on a field $\mathfrak{A}$ of subsets of S. Let $T \subset S$. Then in order that

$$E_1, E_2 \in \mathfrak{A}^*, \qquad E_1 \cap T = E_2 \cap T \Rightarrow \mu^*(E_1) = \mu^*(E_2) \tag{1}$$

it is necessary and sufficient that

$$\mu^*(T) = \mu(S) . \tag{2}$$

Proof Suppose (1) holds. To prove (2) let O be a countable union of members of $\mathfrak{A}$ which contains T. With

$E_1 = O$ and $E_2 = S$ in (1) we have $E_1 \cap T = E_2 \cap T$ so that $\mu^*(E_1) = \mu^*(E_2)$, i.e., $\mu(O) = \mu(S)$. Then $\mu^*(T) = \inf_{T \subset O} \mu(O) = \mu(S)$.

Conversely assume (2). To prove (1) we note that if we let $E = E_1 - (E_1 \cap E_2)$ then $E \in \mathfrak{A}^*$ and also $E \cap T = \phi$. From $E \in \mathfrak{A}^*$ we have

$$\mu^*(S) \geq \mu^*(E \cup T) = \mu^*\Big((E \cup T) \cap E\Big) + \mu^*\Big((E \cup T) \cap E^c\Big) = \mu^*(E) + \mu^*(T).$$

Thus by (2), $\mu^*(E) = 0$ so that

$$0 = \mu^*\Big(E_1 - (E_1 \cap E_2)\Big) = \mu^*(E_1) - \mu^*(E_1 \cap E_2),$$

and hence

$$\mu^*(E_1) = \mu^*(E_1 \cap E_2).$$

Interchanging the roles of E_1 and E_2 we have $\mu^*(E_2) = \mu^*(E_1 \cap E_2)$ and consequently $\mu^*(E_1) = \mu^*(E_2)$. □

<u>Theorem 27.6</u> Let $Y \subset X = \{0\} \times R^{(0,1]}$ be such that for every $\{t_1, \cdots, t_n\} \subset (0,1]$ where $0 < t_1 < \cdots < t_n \leq 1$ and every $\{\gamma_1, \cdots, \gamma_n\} \subset R^1$ there exists $x \in Y$ such that $\left[x(t_1), \cdots, x(t_n)\right] = [\gamma_1, \cdots, \gamma_n]$ so that m_Y is well defined and is a probability measure on the σ-field $\mathfrak{F}_{t_1 \cdots t_n}$ for each $\{t_1, \cdots, t_n\}$. If $m^*(Y) = 1$ then m_Y is well defined on the field $\mathfrak{F}$ and is a probability measure there and consequently can be extended to be a probability measure on $\sigma(\mathfrak{F})$.

<u>Proof</u> Assume $m^*(Y) = 1$. To show that m_Y is well

defined on $\mathfrak{G}$ let $J \in \mathfrak{G}$ be given as $J = I_1 \cap Y$ as well as $J = I_2 \cap Y$ with $I_1, I_2 \in \mathfrak{J}$. Then by Definition 27.3 we have $m_Y(J) = m(I_1)$ as well as $m_Y(J) = m(I_2)$. But $m^*(Y) = 1$ implies, according to Lemma 27.5, that $m(I_1) = m(I_2)$. Thus m_Y is well defined on $\mathfrak{G}$. To show that m_Y is a probability measure on $\mathfrak{G}$, it suffices to show that m_Y is countably additive on $\mathfrak{G}$. Thus let $\{J_k, k = 1, 2, \cdots\} \subset \mathfrak{G}$ be a disjoint collection with $J_\infty \equiv \bigcup_{k=1}^{\infty} J_k \in \mathfrak{G}$. Then $J_k = I_k \cap Y$ with $I_k \in \mathfrak{J}$ for $k = 1, 2, \cdots$, and $k = \infty$ also. Now

$$I_\infty \cap Y = J_\infty = \left\{ \bigcup_{k=1}^{\infty} I_k \right\} \cap Y,$$

and, from Lemma 27.5,

$$m_Y(J_\infty) = m(I_\infty) = m\left(\bigcup_{k=1}^{\infty} I_k \right).$$

The disjointness of the collection $\{J_k, k = 1, 2, \cdots\}$ implies the disjointness of the collection $\{I_k, k = 1, 2, \cdots\}$. To show this take two distinct suffixes i and j. Then $J_i = I_i \cap Y$ and $J_j = I_j \cap Y$ and, with an appropriately chosen $\{t_1, \cdots, t_n\}$, $I_i = p_{t_1 \cdots t_n}^{-1}(B')$ and $I_j = p_{t_1 \cdots t_n}^{-1}(B'')$. Thus $J_i \cap J_j = \phi$ implies $B' \cap B'' = \phi$ which in turn implies $I_i \cap I_j = \phi$. With the disjointness of the collection $\{I_k, k = 1, 2, \cdots\}$ we have

$$m_Y(J_\infty) = \sum_{k=1}^{\infty} m(I_k) = \sum_{k=1}^{\infty} m_Y(J_k).$$

This proves the countable additivity of m_Y on $\mathfrak{G}$. □

§28. WIENER MEASURE ON THE SPACE OF CONTINUOUS FUNCTIONS

In Theorem 27.6 we showed that if a subset Y of $X = \{0\} \times R^{(0,1]}$ has the property that for every $\{t_1, \cdots, t_n\} \subset (0,1]$ where $0 < t_1 < \cdots < t_n \le 1$ and every $\{\gamma_1, \cdots, \gamma_n\} \subset R^1$ there exists $x \in Y$ with $\left[x(t_1), \cdots, x(t_n)\right] = [\gamma_1, \cdots, \gamma_n]$ and if $m^*(Y) = 1$ where m^* is the Carathéodory outer measure defined from the measure m on the field $\mathfrak{F}$ of subsets of X in Definition 27.1 then the set function m_Y on the field $\mathfrak{G}$ of subsets of Y in Definition 27.3 is well defined and is a probability measure on $\mathfrak{G}$ and consequently can be extended to be a probability measure on $\sigma(\mathfrak{G})$.

The Wiener space C_w consisting of all continuous functions x on $[0,1]$ with $x(0) = 0$ satisfies the first condition on Y above. Thus if we show that $m^*(C_w) = 1$ then m_{C_w}, which we shall abbreviate as m_w, is well defined on $\mathfrak{G}$ and can be extended to be a probability measure on $\sigma(\mathfrak{G})$. This measure m_w is the Wiener measure on C_w. In what follows we show that $m^*(C_w) = 1$.

<u>Definition 28.1</u> For $\alpha > 0$, let C_α be the collection of those members of C_w which are Hölder α-continuous functions on $[0,1]$, i.e.,

$$C_\alpha = \left\{ x \in C_w ;\ \exists h = h(x) \text{ such that } |x(t') - x(t'')| \le h\,|t' - t''|^\alpha \right.$$
$$\left. \text{for } t', t'' \in [0,1] \right\}.$$

Let S be the collection of binary rationals in $[0,1]$. Let B_w

be the collection of those members x of X whose restrictions to S are uniformly continuous on S, i.e., for every $\varepsilon > 0$ there exists $\delta > 0$ such that $|x(s')-x(s'')| < \varepsilon$ whenever $s', s'' \in S$, $|s'-s''| < \delta$. (A member x of B_w need not be continuous on $[0,1]$. Note that $C_w \subset B_w$ since continuity on $[0,1]$ implies uniform continuity on $[0,1]$ and hence on S also. On the other hand for every $x \in B_w$ there exists uniquely $\tilde{x} \in C_w$ such that $x(s) = \tilde{x}(s)$ for $s \in S$. In fact from the uniform continuity of x on S, x can be extended uniquely to be a continuous function on $[0,1]$. The converse does not hold, i.e., given $x \in C_w$ there exist $x_1, x_2 \in B_w$, $x_1 \neq x_2$, such that $x_1(s) = x_2(s) = x(s)$ for $s \in S$. This is so since the members of B need not be continuous on $[0,1]$). For $\alpha > 0$, let

$$B_\alpha = \Big\{x \in B_w; \exists h = h(x) \text{ such that } |x(s')-x(s'')| \leq h|s'-s''|^\alpha$$
$$\text{for } s', s'' \in S\Big\}.$$

For $\alpha > 0$ and $h > 0$ let

$$H_\alpha[h] = \Big\{x \in X; \exists s', s'' \in S \text{ such that } |x(s')-x(s'')| > h|s'-s''|^\alpha\Big\}$$

and for $\alpha > 0$ let

$$H_\alpha = \Big\{x \in X; \forall h > 0, \exists s' s'' \in S \text{ such that } |x(s')-x(s'')| > h|s'-s''|^\alpha\Big\}.$$

As immediate consequences of the above definitions we have

Lemma 28.2

$$0 < \alpha < \beta \Rightarrow \begin{array}{ccccccc} C_\beta & \subset & C_\alpha & \subset & C_w & & \\ \cap & & \cap & & \cap & & \\ B_\beta & \subset & B_\alpha & \subset & B_w & \subset & X, \end{array} \tag{1}$$

$$h' < h'' \Rightarrow H_\alpha[h''] \subset H_\alpha[h'], \tag{2}$$

$$H_\alpha = \bigcap_{h>0} H_\alpha[h] = \bigcap_{i=1}^{\infty} H_\alpha[h_i] \text{ for } h_i > 0,\ i = 1, 2, \cdots, \text{ and } h_i \uparrow \infty, \tag{3}$$

$$H_\alpha = X - B_\alpha . \tag{4}$$

Lemma 28.3 Let $\alpha > 0$ and $h > 0$. If $x \in X$ satisfies

$$\left| x\left(\frac{\ell}{2^k}\right) - x\left(\frac{\ell+1}{2^k}\right) \right| \le h\left(\frac{1}{2^k}\right)^\alpha \tag{1}$$

for all natural numbers k and ℓ where $0 \le \ell \le 2^k - 1$ and $k = 0, 1, 2, \cdots,$ then

$$x \notin H_\alpha\left[2h\left\{1 - \left(\frac{1}{2}\right)^\alpha\right\}^{-1}\right], \tag{2}$$

so that $x \notin H_\alpha$ and $x \in B_\alpha$.

Proof Let us show that if $x \in X$ satisfies (1), then it satisfies (2), i.e., for every $s_1, s_2 \in S$, $s_1 < s_2$, we have

$$|x(s_1) - x(s_2)| \le 2h\left\{1 - \left(\frac{1}{2}\right)^\alpha\right\}^{-1} (s_2 - s_1)^\alpha. \tag{3}$$

Note that when $[s_1, s_2] = [0, 1]$, then from (1) with $k = 0$ and $\ell = 0$ we have (3). Thus we need only to consider $[s_1, s_2] \neq [0, 1]$.

Each $s \in S$ being a binary rational in $[0, 1]$ can be expressed as $s = q2^{-p}$ where p and q are natural numbers and p is chosen to be the smallest possible for the given s. Thus for $s = 0$ we have $p = 0$ and $q = 0$ and for $s = 1$ we have $p = 0$ and $q = 1$. These are the only two cases in which

$p = 0$. Note also that for $s \neq 0$, q is always odd.

Take $[s_1, s_2] \neq [0,1]$. Let s_0 be the one with the smallest p among all the binary rationals in $[s_1, s_2]$. There is certainly at least one such s_0 since p is bounded below by 0. Now if one of s_1 and s_2 is 0 or 1 then s_0 is 0 or 1 with $p = 0$ and s_0 is the only one with $p = 0$. If none of s_1 and s_2 is 0 or 1 and there are two binary rationals in $[s_1, s_2]$ with the smallest p, say $q_1 2^{-p}$ and $q_2 2^{-p}$, $q_1 < q_2$, then since q_1 and q_2 are both odd there exists a positive integer r such that $q_1 < 2r < q_2$. Then we have $2r2^{-p} = r2^{-(p-1)} \in [s_1, s_2]$ contradicting the fact that p is the smallest.

Now if $s_0 \neq s_1$ then $s_0 - s_1 = \sum_{i=1}^{m} 2^{-k_i}$ and if $s_0 \neq s_2$ then $s_2 - s_0 = \sum_{j=1}^{n} 2^{-\ell_j}$ where $\{k_i, i = 1,2,\cdots,m\}$ and $\{\ell_j, j = 1,2,\cdots,n\}$ are strictly increasing finite sequences of natural numbers. Consider the two sequences of intervals

$$\left[s_0 - \frac{1}{2^{k_1}}, s_0\right], \left[s_0 - \frac{1}{2^{k_1}} - \frac{1}{2^{k_2}}, s_0 - \frac{1}{2^{k_1}}\right], \cdots, \left[s_1, s_0 - \frac{1}{2^{k_1}} - \cdots - \frac{1}{2^{k_{m-1}}}\right]$$

and

$$\left[s_0, s_0 + \frac{1}{2^{\ell_1}}\right], \left[s_0 + \frac{1}{2^{\ell_1}}, s_0 + \frac{1}{2^{\ell_1}} + \frac{1}{2^{\ell_2}}\right], \cdots, \left[s_0 + \frac{1}{2^{\ell_1}} + \cdots + \frac{1}{2^{\ell_{n-1}}}, s_2\right].$$

If $s_0 = s_1$ or $s_0 = s_2$ then we have to deal with only one of the two sequences of intervals. If however $s_1 < s_0 < s_2$ then $[s_1, s_2]$ is decomposed into the above two sequences of intervals. Let $p = \min\{k_1, \ell_1\}$ and $q = \max\{k_m, \ell_n\}$. By (1)

$$|x(s_1)-x(s_2)| \le 2h \sum_{k=p}^{q} \left(\frac{1}{2^k}\right)^{\alpha} = 2h\left(\frac{1}{2^p}\right)^{\alpha} \sum_{k=0}^{q-p} \left(\frac{1}{2^k}\right)^{\alpha}$$

$$\le 2h\left(\frac{1}{2^p}\right)^{\alpha} \frac{1}{1-\left(\frac{1}{2}\right)^{\alpha}} \le \frac{2h}{1-\left(\frac{1}{2}\right)^{\alpha}} (s_2 - s_1)^{\alpha} ,$$

which proves (4). □

<u>Lemma 28.4</u> For $\alpha > 0$ and $h > 0$

$$m^*\left(H_\alpha\left[2h\left\{1-\left(\frac{1}{2}\right)^{\alpha}\right\}^{-1}\right]\right) \le \sqrt{\frac{2}{\pi}}\, \frac{1}{h} \sum_{k=0}^{\infty} 2^{k(\frac{1}{2}+\alpha)} \exp\left\{-\frac{h^2}{2} 2^{k(1-2\alpha)}\right\}. \quad (1)$$

The series in (1) [not including the factor $\sqrt{2/\pi}(1/h)$] diverges for $\alpha \ge \frac{1}{2}$ and converges for $0 < \alpha < \frac{1}{2}$ to a sum which decreases monotonically with increasing h. For $0 < \alpha < \frac{1}{2}$,

$$\lim_{h\to\infty} m^*\left(H_\alpha\left[2h\left\{1-\left(\frac{1}{2}\right)^{\alpha}\right\}^{-1}\right]\right) = 0 \quad (2)$$

and

$$\lim_{h\to\infty} m^*\left(H_\alpha[h]\right) = 0 , \quad (3)$$

and H_α is Carathéodory measurable with respect to m^* with $m^*(H_\alpha) = 0$. The set B_α which is Carathéodory measurable with respect to m^* for $\alpha > 0$ has $m^*(B_\alpha) = 1$ for $0 < \alpha < \frac{1}{2}$.

<u>Proof</u> Let $\alpha > 0$ and $h > 0$ and $x \in H_\alpha\left[2h\left\{1-\left(\frac{1}{2}\right)^{\alpha}\right\}^{-1}\right]$. According to Lemma 28.3 there exist a natural number k and a positive integer n with $1 \le n \le 2^k$ such that

$x \in I_{\alpha, h, k, n}$ where $I_{\alpha, h, k, n} = \left\{ x \in X; \left| x\left(\frac{n}{2^k}\right) - x\left(\frac{n-1}{2^k}\right) \right| > h2^{-k\alpha} \right\}.$

Then

$$H_\alpha\left[2h\left\{1 - \left(\frac{1}{2}\right)^\alpha\right\}^{-1}\right] \subset \bigcup_{k=0}^{\infty} \bigcup_{n=1}^{2^k} I_{\alpha, h, k, n},$$

so that

$$m^*\left(H_\alpha\left[2h\left\{1 - \left(\frac{1}{2}\right)^\alpha\right\}^{-1}\right]\right) \leq \sum_{k=0}^{\infty} \sum_{n=1}^{2^k} m(I_{\alpha, h, k, n}). \tag{4}$$

Now

$$I_{\alpha, h, k, n} \in \mathfrak{J}_{t_1 t_2} \quad \text{and} \quad I_{\alpha, h, k, n} = p_{t_1 t_2}^{-1}(B)$$

where $t_1 = (n-1)2^{-k}$, $t_2 = n2^{-k}$, and

$$B = \left\{ [\xi_1, \xi_2] \in R^2; \ |\xi_2 - \xi_1| > h2^{-k\alpha} \right\} \in \mathfrak{B}^2,$$

so that by Definition 27.1

$$m(I_{\alpha, h, k, n}) = \left\{ (2\pi)^2 \frac{n-1}{2^k} \right\}^{-\frac{1}{2}} \times$$

$$\iint_{|\xi_2 - \xi_1| > h2^{-k\alpha}} \exp\left\{ -\tfrac{1}{2}\left[\frac{\xi_1^2}{(n-1)2^{-k}} - \frac{(\xi_2 - \xi_1)^2}{2^{-k}} \right] \right\} d\xi_1 d\xi_2 .$$

Letting $\xi = \left\{ 2(n-1)2^{-k} \right\}^{-\frac{1}{2}} \xi_1$ and $\eta = \{2 \cdot 2^{-k}\}^{-\frac{1}{2}}(\xi_2 - \xi_1)$ we obtain

$$m(I_{\alpha, h, k, n}) = \frac{1}{\pi}\left\{ \int_{-\infty}^{\infty} e^{-\xi^2} d\xi \right\} \left\{ 2 \int_{h2^{-\frac{1}{2}} 2^{k(\frac{1}{2} - \alpha)}}^{\infty} e^{-\eta^2} d\eta \right\} .$$

From the well-known inequality

$$\int_{\lambda}^{\infty} e^{-\xi^2} d\xi \le \frac{1}{2\lambda} e^{-\lambda^2} \quad \text{for} \quad \lambda > 0$$

we have

$$m(I_{\alpha, h, k, n}) \le \sqrt{\frac{2}{\pi}} \frac{1}{h} 2^{k(\alpha - \frac{1}{2})} \exp\left\{-\frac{h^2}{2} 2^{k(1-2\alpha)}\right\}. \tag{5}$$

Using (5) in (4) we obtain (1).

Consider the series in (1) excluding the factor $\sqrt{2/\pi}(1/h)$. For $\alpha = \frac{1}{2}$, the series reduces to $\sum_{k=0}^{\infty} 2^k = \infty$. For $\alpha > \frac{1}{2}$, say $\alpha = \frac{1}{2} + \delta$ where $\delta > 0$, the series becomes

$$\sum_{k=0}^{\infty} 2^{k(1+\delta)} \exp\left\{-\frac{h^2}{2} 2^{-2\delta k}\right\}$$

which is divergent since $2^{k(1+\delta)} \uparrow \infty$ while $2^{-2\delta k} \downarrow 0$, $-\frac{1}{2}h^2 2^{-2\delta k} \uparrow 0$ and $\exp\left\{-\frac{1}{2}h^2 2^{-2\delta k}\right\} \uparrow 1$ as $k \to \infty$. When $0 < \alpha < \frac{1}{2}$, say $\alpha = \frac{1}{2} - \delta$ where $0 < \delta < \frac{1}{2}$, the series becomes

$$\sum_{k=0}^{\infty} 2^{k(1-\delta)} \exp\left\{-\frac{h^2}{2} 2^{2\delta k}\right\}.$$

Observe that we can choose $B > 0$ such that

$$\log B + \frac{h^2}{2} 2^{2\delta k} - k \log 4 \ge 0.$$

With such B we have

$$-\frac{h^2}{2} 2^{2\delta k} \le \log B + \log 4^{-k} = \log\left\{B4^{-k}\right\},$$

$$\exp\left\{-\frac{h^2}{2} 2^{2\delta k}\right\} \le B4^{-k},$$

and

$$2^{k(1-\delta)} \exp\left\{-\frac{h^2}{2} 2^{2\delta k}\right\} \le 2^k B 4^{-k} = B \frac{1}{2^k}.$$

Thus by a comparison test with $\sum_{k=0}^{\infty} 1/2^k < \infty$, our series converges. It is obvious that the sum is monotone decreasing as h increases. Now with the factor $\sqrt{2/\pi}(1/h)$, the right side of (1) converges to 0 as $h \to \infty$ when $0<\alpha<\frac{1}{2}$ and this proves (2). Note that (3) is equivalent to (2). From (3) of Lemma 28.2, the monotonicity of m^*, and (3), we have $m^*(H_\alpha) = 0$ for $0 < \alpha < \frac{1}{2}$. This implies also that H_α is Carathéodory measurable with respect to m^* for $0 < \alpha \frac{1}{2}$.

For $\alpha > 0$,

$$B_\alpha = \{x \in X; \exists h = h(x) \text{ such that } |x(s') - x(s'')| \le h|s' - s''|^\alpha, s', s'' \in S\} = \bigcup_{\ell=1}^{\infty} B_\alpha^{(\ell)},$$

where

$$B_\alpha^{(\ell)} = \{x \in X; |x(s') - x(s'')| \le \ell |s' - s''|^\alpha, s', s'' \in S\}$$

for $\ell = 1, 2, \cdots$.

Enumerate the elements of S arbitrarily. Thus $S = \{s_i, i = 1, 2, \cdots\}$. Then

$$B_\alpha^{(\ell)} = \bigcap_{n=1}^{\infty} B_\alpha^{(\ell, n)}$$

where

$$B_\alpha^{(\ell, n)} = \bigcap_{i, j=1, 2, \cdots, n} \{x \in X; |x(s_i) - x(s_j)| \le \ell |s_i - s_j|^\alpha\}.$$

Thus $B_\alpha^{(\ell,n)} \in \mathfrak{J}$, $B_\alpha^{(\ell)} \in \sigma(\mathfrak{J})$, and $B_\alpha \in \sigma(\mathfrak{J})$ and B_α is certainly Carathéodory measurable with respect to m^*. From this and from (4) of Lemma 28.2 we have

$$1 = m(X) = m^*(X \cap B_\alpha) + m^*(X \cap H_\alpha) = m^*(B_\alpha) + m^*(H_\alpha) = m^*(B_\alpha)$$

since $m^*(H_\alpha) = 0$. □

Theorem 28.5 For $0 < \alpha < \frac{1}{2}$, $m^*(C_\alpha) = 1$ holds and consequently $m^*(C_w) = 1$.

Proof Suppose $m^*(C_\alpha) = 1 - \varepsilon$ for some $\alpha \in (0, \frac{1}{2})$ and $\varepsilon > 0$. Let us show that this implies $m^*\left(X - H_\alpha[h]\right) < 1 - \varepsilon/4$ for every $h > 0$. Now if $m^*(C_\alpha) = 1 - \varepsilon$ then there exists a collection $\{I_n, n = 1, 2, \cdots\} \subset \mathfrak{J}$ such that

$$C_\alpha \subset \bigcup_{n=1}^{\infty} I_n \quad \text{and} \quad \sum_{n=1}^{\infty} m(I_n) < 1 - \frac{\varepsilon}{2}. \tag{1}$$

Let $I_n \in \mathfrak{J}$ be a member of $\mathfrak{J}_{t_{n,1} \cdots t_{n,p_n}}$ where $0 < t_{n,1} < \cdots < t_{n,p_n} \le 1$, say

$$I_n = P^{-1}_{t_{n,1} \cdots t_{n,p_n}}(B_n) \qquad \text{where } B_n \in \mathfrak{B}^{p_n}, \tag{2}$$

so that, by Definition 27.1,

$$m(I_n) = \left\{ (2\pi)^{p_n} \prod_{i=1}^{p_n} (t_{n,i} - t_{n,i-1}) \right\}^{-\frac{1}{2}} \int_{B_n} \exp\left\{ -\frac{1}{2} \sum_{i=1}^{p_n} \frac{\left(\xi_i - \xi_{i-1}\right)^2}{t_{n,i} - t_{n,i-1}} \right\} m_L(d\xi). \tag{3}$$

Let us call a subset of R^n of the type $(a_1, b_1] \times \cdots \times (a_n, b_n]$ an interval in R^n. Then for $B_n \in \mathfrak{B}^{p_n}$ and an arbitrary $\eta > 0$ there exists a countable disjoint collection of intervals $\{A_{n,j}, j = 1, 2, \cdots\}$ in R^{p_n} such that

$$B_n \subset A_n = \bigcup_{j=1}^{n} A_{n,j} \quad \text{and} \quad m_L(A_n - B_n) < \eta .$$

Let

$$K_n = p_{t_{n,1} \cdots t_{n,p_n}}^{-1}(A_n) .$$

From $B_n \subset A_n$ we have $I_n \subset K_n$. By choosing $\eta > 0$ sufficiently small we have

$$m(K_n - I_n) < \frac{\varepsilon}{4} \frac{1}{2^n} \quad \text{and hence} \quad m(K_n) < m(I_n) + \frac{\varepsilon}{4} \frac{1}{2^n} .$$

This is possible since $m(K_n - I_n)$ is given by replacing the domain of integration B_n on the right side of (3) by $A_n - B_n$ and since $m_L(A_n - B_n) < \eta$. Since this is true of each n we have

$$C_\alpha \subset \bigcup_{n=1}^{\infty} K_n \quad \text{and} \quad \sum_{n=1}^{\infty} m(K_n) < 1 - \frac{\varepsilon}{2} + \sum_{n=1}^{\infty} \frac{\varepsilon}{4} \frac{1}{2^n} = 1 - \frac{\varepsilon}{4} . \tag{4}$$

From $A_n = \bigcup_{j=1}^{n} A_{n,j}$ and from the fact that this is a disjoint union we have

$$K_n = \bigcup_{j=1}^{n} p_{t_{n,1} \cdots t_{n,p_n}}^{-1}(A_{n,j}) \quad \text{and}$$

$$m(K_n) = \sum_{j=1}^{\infty} m\left(p_{t_{n,1} \cdots t_{n,p_n}}^{-1}(A_{n,j})\right) . \tag{5}$$

Using (5) in (4) we obtain

$$C_\alpha \subset \bigcup_{n=1}^{\infty} \bigcup_{j=1}^{n} p_{t_{n,1} \cdots t_{n,p_n}}^{-1}(A_{n,j}) \quad \text{and}$$

$$\sum_{n=1}^{\infty} \sum_{j=1}^{n} m\left(p_{t_{n,1} \cdots t_{n,p_n}}^{-1}(A_{n,j})\right) < 1 - \frac{\varepsilon}{4} .$$

Thus, rather than covering C_α by countably many Borel cylinders in X with Borel sets in Euclidean spaces as bases as in (1) and (2) we can cover C_α by countably many Borel cylinders in X whose bases are intervals in Euclidean spaces. Therefore under the assumption that $m^*(C_\alpha) = 1 - \varepsilon$ for some $\alpha \in (0, \frac{1}{2})$ and $\varepsilon > 0$ we have (1) where instead of (2) we have now

$$I_n = p_{t_{n,1} \cdots t_{n,p_n}}^{-1}(B_n) = \left\{ x \in X;\ \alpha_{n,i} < x(t_{n,i}) \le \beta_{n,i},\ i = 1,2,\cdots,p_n \right\} \quad (6)$$

and

$$B_n = \left\{ [\xi_1, \cdots, \xi_{p_n}] \in R^{p_n};\ \alpha_{n,i} < \xi_i \le \beta_{n,i},\ i = 1,2,\cdots,p_n \right\}. \quad (7)$$

With I_n given by (6) and (7) we have

$$m(I_n) = \left\{ (2\pi)^{p_n} \prod_{i=1}^{p_n} (t_{n,i} - t_{n,i-1}) \right\}^{-\frac{1}{2}} \times$$
$$\int_{\alpha_{n,1}}^{\beta_n} \cdots \int_{\alpha_{n,p_n}}^{\beta_{n,p_n}} \exp\left\{ -\frac{1}{2} \sum_{i=1}^{p_n} \frac{(\xi_1 - \xi_{i-1})^2}{t_{n,i} - t_{n,i-1}} \right\} d\xi \cdots d\xi_{p_n}. \quad (8)$$

Now, for each $h > 0$ let

$$I_{h,n} = \left\{ x \in X;\ \alpha_{n,i} - h\,|t_{n,i} - s_{n,i}|^\alpha < x(s_{n,i}) \right.$$
$$\left. \le \beta_{n,i} + h\,|t_{n,i} - s_{n,i}|^\alpha,\ i = 1,2,\cdots,p_n \right\} \quad (9)$$

where $s_{n,i} \in S$ are chosen so close to $t_{n,i}$ that

$$m(I_{h,n}) < m(I_n) + \frac{\varepsilon}{4} \frac{1}{2^n}. \quad (10)$$

This is possible since $m(I_{h,n})$ is given by replacing $t_{n,i}$, $\alpha_{n,i}$

and $\beta_{n,i}$ on the right side of (8) by $s_{n,i}$, $\alpha_{n,i} - h|t_{n,i} - s_{n,i}|^{\alpha}$ and $\beta_{n,i} + h|t_{n,i} - s_{n,i}|^{\alpha}$, respectively.

We proceed to show that $X - H_{\alpha}[h] \subset \bigcup_{n=1}^{\infty} I_{h,n}$. (Compare this with $C_{\alpha} \subset \bigcup_{n=1}^{\infty} I_n$). Let $x \in X - H_{\alpha}[h] \subset X - H_{\alpha} = B_{\alpha}$. Then there exists a unique $\tilde{x} \in C_{\alpha}$ such that $\tilde{x}(s) = x(s)$ for $s \in S$. Since $C_{\alpha} \subset \bigcup_{n=1}^{\infty} I_n$ we have $\tilde{x} \in I_n$ for some n. With such n we have

$$\alpha_{n,i} < \tilde{x}(t_{n,i}) \leq \beta_{n,i} \qquad \text{for } i = 1, 2, \cdots, p_n . \tag{11}$$

On the other hand since $x \notin H_{\alpha}[h]$ we have

$$|x(s') - x(s'')| \leq h|s' - s''|^{\alpha} \qquad \text{for all } s', s'' \in S,$$

and consequently

$$|\tilde{x}(s') - \tilde{x}(s'')| \leq h|s' - s''|^{\alpha} \qquad \text{for all } s', s'' \in S,$$

and finally, from the fact that S is dense in $[0,1]$ and $\tilde{x}$ is continuous on $[0,1]$,

$$|\tilde{x}(t') - \tilde{x}(t'')| \leq h|t' - t''|^{\alpha} \qquad \text{for all } t', t'' \in [0.1].$$

With the choice $t' = t_{n,i}$ and $t'' = s_{n,i}$ for $i = 1, 2, \cdots, p_n$, the last inequality gives

$$\tilde{x}(t_{n,i}) - h|t_{n,i} - s_{n,i}|^{\alpha} \leq \tilde{x}(s_{n,i}) \leq \tilde{x}(t_{n,i}) + h|t_{n,i} - s_{n,i}|^{\alpha}$$

for $i = 1, 2, \cdots, p_n$.

By (11) and the fact that $\tilde{x}(s_{n,i}) = x(s_{n,i})$, we have then

$$\alpha_{n,i} - h|t_{n,i} - s_{n,i}|^{\alpha} < x(s_{n,i}) \leq \beta_{n,i} + h|t_{n,i} - s_{n,i}|^{\alpha}$$

for $i = 1, 2, \cdots, p_n$,

i.e., $x \in I_{h,n}$. This proves $X - H_\alpha[h] \subset \bigcup_{n=1}^{\infty} I_{h,n}$ for each $h > 0$.

Now we have for each $h > 0$, by (10) and (1),

$$m^*\left(X - H_\alpha[h]\right) \leq \sum_{n=1}^{\infty} m(I_{h,n}) < 1 - \frac{\varepsilon}{2} + \sum_{n=1}^{\infty} \frac{\varepsilon}{4} \frac{1}{2^n} = 1 - \frac{\varepsilon}{4}, \tag{12}$$

which is what we set out to prove. To complete the proof of the theorem recall that according to (3) of Lemma 28.4

$$m^*\left(H_\alpha[h]\right) < \frac{\varepsilon}{8} \qquad \text{for sufficiently large } h.$$

For such h we have by

$$1 = m^*(X) \leq m^*\left(H_\alpha[h]\right) + m^*\left(X - H_\alpha[h]\right) < \frac{\varepsilon}{8} + 1 - \frac{\varepsilon}{4} = 1 - \frac{\varepsilon}{8} < 1,$$

a contradiction. Thus for $0 < \alpha < \frac{1}{2}$, $m^*(C_\alpha) = 1$. Then from (1) of Lemma 28.2, $m^*(C_w) = 1$. □

To show that $m^*(C_\alpha) = 0$ for $\alpha > \frac{1}{2}$ let us recall that according to the definitions of B_α and B_w in Definition 28.1, for $\alpha > 0$,

$$B_\alpha = \Big\{ x \in X; \exists h = h(x) \text{ such that}$$

$$|x(s') - x(s'')| \leq h|s' - s''|^\alpha \text{ for } s', s'' \in S \Big\}.$$

For $\alpha > 0$ and $h < 0$ let

$$B_\alpha[h] = \left\{ x \in X; \ |x(s') - x(s'')| \leq h\,|s' - s''|^\alpha \text{ for } s', s'' \in S \right\}.$$

Then

$$h' < h'' \Rightarrow B_\alpha[h'] \subset B_\alpha[h''],$$

$$C_\alpha \subset B_\alpha = \bigcup_{h>0} B_\alpha[h] = \bigcup_{i=1}^{\infty} B_\alpha[h_i]$$

for $h_i > 0$, $i = 1, 2, \cdots$, and $h_i \uparrow \infty$.

Theorem 28.6 For $\alpha > \frac{1}{2}$ and $h > 0$, $m^*\left(B_\alpha[h]\right) = 0$ holds and consequently $m^*(B_\alpha) = 0$ and $m^*(C_\alpha) = 0$.

Proof For $\alpha > 0$, $h > 0$, and $k = 1, 2, \cdots$, let

$$I_{\alpha,h,k} = \left\{x \in X;\ \left| x\left(\frac{i}{2^k}\right) - x\left(\frac{i-1}{2^k}\right)\right| \le h\left(\frac{1}{2^k}\right)^\alpha,\ i = 1, 2, \cdots, 2^k\right\}.$$

Then

$$B_\alpha[h] \subset I_{\alpha,h,k} \quad \text{and} \quad m^*\left(B_\alpha[h]\right) \le m(I_{\alpha,h,k}) \quad \text{for } k = 1, 2, \cdots.$$

Now

$$m(I_{\alpha,h,k}) = \left\{(2\pi)^{2^k}\left(\frac{1}{2^k}\right)^{2^k}\right\}^{-\frac{1}{2}} \times$$

$$\int^{(2^k)}_B \int \exp\left\{-\frac{1}{2}\sum_{i=1}^{2^k} \frac{\left(\xi_i - \xi_{i-1}\right)^2}{2^{-k}}\right\} d\xi_1 \cdots d\xi_{2^k}$$

where

$$B = \left\{\left[\xi_1, \cdots, \xi_{2^k}\right] \in R^{2^k};\ |\xi_i - \xi_{i-1}| \le h\left(\frac{1}{2^k}\right)^\alpha,\ i = 1, 2, \cdots, 2^k\right\} \in \mathfrak{B}^{2^k}.$$

By the transformation $\eta_i = \left[2\cdot(1/2^k)\right]^{-\frac{1}{2}}(\xi_i - \xi_{i-1})$,

$$m(I_{\alpha,h,k}) = \left\{\pi^{2^k}\right\}^{-\frac{1}{2}} \prod_{i=1}^{2}\left\{\int_{|\eta_i| \le 2^{-\frac{1}{2}} h (2^{-k})^{\alpha - \frac{1}{2}}} e^{-\eta_i^2}\, d\eta_i\right\}$$

$$\le \left\{\sqrt{\frac{2}{\pi}}\ h\left(\frac{1}{2^k}\right)^{\alpha - \frac{1}{2}}\right\}^{2^k}.$$

For $\alpha > \frac{1}{2}$, let $\delta = \alpha - \frac{1}{2} > 0$. Then

$$\lim_{k\to\infty} \log\left\{\sqrt{\frac{2}{\pi}}\, h\left(\frac{1}{2^k}\right)^{\alpha-\frac{1}{2}}\right\}^{2^k} = \lim_{k\to\infty} 2^k\left\{\log\sqrt{\frac{2}{\pi}}\, h - k\delta \log 2\right\} = -\infty,$$

so that

$$\lim_{k\to\infty}\left\{\sqrt{\frac{2}{\pi}}\, h\left(\frac{1}{2^k}\right)^{\alpha-\frac{1}{2}}\right\}^{2^k} = 0.$$

Thus

$$\lim_{k\to\infty} m(I_{\alpha,h,k}) = 0, \quad m^*\left(B_\alpha[h]\right) = 0, \quad m^*(B_\alpha) = 0, \quad m^*(C_\alpha) = 0. \ \square$$

§29. WIENER INTEGRAL

[I] Wiener Measure Space, Wiener Integral, and Wiener Process

As a summary of §27 and §28 and in order to fix notations we state the following:

Theorem 29.1 Let C_w be the Wiener space, i.e., the collection of real-valued continuous functions x on $[0,1]$ with $x(0) = 0$. For $\{t_1, \cdots, t_n\} \subset (0,1]$ where $0 = t_0 < t_1 < \cdots < t_n \le 1$ let

$$q_{t_1 \cdots t_n}(x) = \left[x(t_1), \cdots, x(t_n)\right] \in R^n \quad \text{for } x \in C_w,$$

$$\mathfrak{W}_{t_1 \cdots t_n} = q_{t_1 \cdots t_n}^{-1}(\mathfrak{B}^n) \quad \text{and} \quad \mathfrak{W} = \bigcup \mathfrak{W}_{t_1 \cdots t_n}.$$

For $J \in \mathfrak{W}$, say $J \in \mathfrak{W}_{t_1 \cdots t_n}$ and $J = q_{t_1 \cdots t_n}^{-1}(B)$ where $B \in \mathfrak{B}^n$, let

$$m_w(J) = \left\{(2\pi)^n \prod_{i=1}^{n} (t_i - t_{i-1})\right\}^{-\frac{1}{2}} \int_B \exp\left\{-\frac{1}{2}\sum_{i=1}^{n} \frac{\left(\xi_i - \xi_{i-1}\right)^2}{t_i - t_{i-1}}\right\} m_L(d\xi),$$

where $\xi_0 \equiv 0$ and $\xi = (\xi_1, \cdots, \xi_n) \in R^n$. Then m_w is well defined on the field $\mathfrak{W}$ of subsets of C_w and is a probability measure there so that it can be extended uniquely to be a probability measure on the σ-field $\sigma(\mathfrak{W})$.

Definition 29.2 Let $\mathfrak{W}^*$ be the σ-field of Carathéodory measurable subsets of C_w with respect to the outer measure derived from the probability measure m_w on the field $\mathfrak{W}$. (Thus, in particular, $\sigma(\mathfrak{W}) \subset \mathfrak{W}^*$). The Carathéodory extension of m_w to $\mathfrak{W}^*$, which we again denote by m_w, is called the Wiener measure. The probability space $(C_w, \mathfrak{W}^*, m_w)$, which is a complete measure space, is called the Wiener measure space. An extended real-valued function F on C_w is said to be Wiener measurable if it is measurable with respect to $\mathfrak{W}^*$. Its integral with respect to m_w, if it exists, is called its Wiener integral. The notation $E^w[F]$ is also used for this integral. Thus

$$E^w[F] = \int_{C_w} F[x]\, m_w(dx).$$

Definition 29.3 The Wiener process W is the stochastic process on the probability space $(C_w, \mathfrak{W}^*, m_w)$ and $[0,1]$ defined by

$$W(t,x) = x(t) \qquad \text{for} \quad (t,x) \in [0,1] \times C_w.$$

Theorem 29.4 The Wiener process W as defined in Definition 29.3 is a stochastic process in which the sample space coincides with the space of sample functions. Thus it is a continuous process and as such it is a separable and measurable process. It is also a standard Brownian motion process.

Proof The fact that the real-valued function W on $[0,1] \times C_w$ is a stochastic process on $(C_w, \mathfrak{B}^*, m_w)$ and $[0,1]$, i.e., the fact that $W(t,\cdot)$ is $\mathfrak{B}^*$-measurable for each $t \in [0,1]$, follows from the fact that for $t \in (0,1]$

$$\{x \in C_w; x(t) \in B\} = q_t^{-1}(B) \in \mathfrak{B}_t \subset \mathfrak{B}^* \qquad \text{for every } B \in \mathfrak{B}^1$$

and the fact that, for $t = 0$,

$$\{x \in C_w; x(0) \in B\} = C_w \text{ or } \emptyset$$

for every $B \in \mathfrak{B}^1$ depending on whether $0 \in B$ or $0 \notin B$. In this connection note also that, for $t \in (0,1]$,

$$m_w\{x \in C_w; x(t) \in B\} = m_w\left(q_t^{-1}(B)\right) = \frac{1}{\sqrt{2\pi t}} \int_B \exp\left\{-\frac{\xi^2}{2t}\right\} m_L(d\xi)$$

according to Theorem 29.1, so that $W(t,\cdot)$ is distributed according to $N(0,t)$ and that for $t = 0$ the probability distribution of $W(0,\cdot)$ is the unit distribution with the unit mass at $0 \in R^1$.

Since C_w is both the sample space and the space of sample functions, our process W is a continuous process and is thus separable and measurable according to Theorem 5.5.

Let us show that W is a standard Brownian motion process. As we have pointed out already, the probability distribution of $W(0,\cdot)$ is the unit distribution with the unit mass at $0 \in R^1$. For $0 < t_1 < t_2 \leq 1$, and $B \in \mathfrak{B}^1$ we have, by Theorem 29.1,

$$m_w\{x \in C_w; x(t_2) - x(t_1) \in B\}$$

$$= \left\{(2\pi)^2 t_1(t_2 - t_1)\right\}^{-\frac{1}{2}} \int_{\xi_2 - \xi_1 \in B} \exp\left\{-\frac{1}{2}\frac{\xi_1^2}{t_1} - \frac{1}{2}\frac{(\xi_2 - \xi_1)^2}{t_2 - t_1}\right\} m_L(d\xi) \qquad (1)$$

where $\xi = (\xi_1, \xi_2) \in R^2$. With the transformation $\eta_1 = \xi_1, \eta_2 = \xi_2 - \xi_1$, the above integral becomes

$$\left\{(2\pi)^2 t_1(t_2-t_1)\right\}^{-\frac{1}{2}} \left\{\int_{R^1} \exp\left\{-\frac{1}{2}\frac{\eta_1^2}{t_1}\right\} m_L(d\eta_1)\right\} \times$$

$$\left\{\int_B \exp\left\{-\frac{1}{2}\frac{\eta_2^2}{t_2-t_1}\right\} m_L(d\eta_2)\right\} = \left\{2\pi(t_2-t_1)\right\}^{-\frac{1}{2}} \int_B \exp\left\{-\frac{1}{2}\frac{\eta_2^2}{t_2-t_1}\right\} m_L(d\eta_2). \tag{2}$$

Thus $x(t_2)-x(t_1)$, i.e., $W(t_2,\cdot) - W(t_1,\cdot)$ is distributed according to $N(0, t_2 - t_1)$. To prove that W is an additive process, i.e., a process with independent increments, let $0 = t_0 < t_1 < \cdots < t_n \le 1$ and $B_1, \cdots, B_n \in \mathfrak{B}^1$. Then, according to Theorem 29.1,

$$m_W\left\{x \in C_W; x(t_i) - x(t_{i-1}) \in B_i,\ i=1,2,\cdots,n\right\}$$

$$= \left\{(2\pi)^n \prod_{i=1}^n (t_i - t_{i-1})\right\}^{-\frac{1}{2}} \int_B \exp\left\{-\frac{1}{2}\sum_{i=1}^n \frac{(\xi_i - \xi_{i-1})^2}{t_i - t_{i-1}}\right\} m_L(d\xi) \tag{3}$$

where $\xi_0 \equiv 0$ and

$$B = \left\{\xi = [\xi_i, \cdots, \xi_n] \in R^n; \xi_i - \xi_{i-1} \in B_i,\ i = 1, 2, \cdots, n\right\} \in \mathfrak{B}^n.$$

With the transformation $\eta_i = \xi_i - \xi_{i-1}$, $i = 1, 2, \cdots, n$, the above integral becomes

$$\left\{(2\pi)^n \prod_{i=1}^n (t_i - t_{i-1})\right\}^{-\frac{1}{2}} \prod_{i=1}^n \left\{\int_{B_i} \exp\left\{-\frac{1}{2}\frac{\eta_i^2}{t_i - t_{i-1}}\right\} m_L(d\eta_i)\right\}$$

$$= \prod_{i=1}^n m_W\left\{x \in C_W; x(t_i) - x(t_{i-1}) \in B_i\right\} \tag{4}$$

from (1) and (2). From (3) and (4) we have the independence of the system of random variables $\{x(t_i) - x(t_{i-1}),\ i = 1, 2, \cdots, n\}$, i.e., $\{W(t_i,\cdot) - W(t_{i-1},\cdot),\ i=1,2,\cdots,n\}$. Thus W is an additive process. This completes the proof that W is a standard Brownian motion process. □

Corollary 29.5 For $0 = t_0 < t_1 < \cdots < t_n \le 1$, the probability distribution of the n-dimensional random vector $[x(t_1),\cdots,x(t_n)] = [W(t_1,\cdot),\cdots,W(t_n,\cdot)]$ is an n-dimensional distribution Φ whose density function Φ' is given by

$$\Phi'(\xi) = \left\{(2\pi)^n \prod_{i=1}^{n}(t_i - t_{i-1})\right\}^{-\frac{1}{2}} \exp\left\{-\frac{1}{2}\sum_{i=1}^{n}\frac{(\xi_i - \xi_{i-1})^2}{t_i - t_{i-1}}\right\}$$

for $\xi = (\xi_1,\cdots,\xi_n) \in R^n$ with $\xi_0 \equiv 0$.

Proof The Corollary follows from (2) of Theorem 17.3.

[II] Examples of Wiener Integrals

Let us show first some examples of Wiener integrals of Wiener measurable functionals $F[x]$, $x \in C_w$, which depend on the values of x at finitely many fixed values of t in $[0,1]$.

Example 1 For $t', t'' \in [0,1]$, $t' < t''$,

$$\int_{C_w} \{x(t'') - x(t')\}^p \, m_w(dx) = 0 \tag{1}$$

when p is an odd natural number and

$$\int_{C_w} |x(t'') - x(t')|^p \, m_w(dx) = \left\{\frac{2^p}{\pi}(t''-t')^p\right\}^{\frac{1}{2}} \Gamma\left(\frac{p}{2}+\frac{1}{2}\right) \tag{2}$$

when p is a natural number and where Γ is the gamma function, i.e., $\Gamma(q) = \int_0^\infty \zeta^{q-1} e^{-\zeta} d\zeta$.

Proof (1) and (2) follow from the fact that $x(t'') - s(t')$ is a Wiener measurable functional on C_w whose probability distribution is given by $N(0, t''-t')$ and from the fact that the pth moment and the pth absolute moment of a random variable which is distributed according to $N(0, v)$ are given, respectively, by

$$\frac{1}{\sqrt{2\pi v}} \int_{-\infty}^{\infty} \xi^p e^{-\frac{\xi^2}{2v}} d\xi = 0$$

when p is an odd natural number and

$$\frac{1}{\sqrt{2\pi v}} \int_{-\infty}^{\infty} |\xi|^p e^{-\frac{\xi^2}{2v}} d\xi = \sqrt{\frac{2}{\pi v}} \int_0^\infty \xi^p e^{-\frac{\xi^2}{2v}} d\xi$$

$$= \sqrt{\frac{2}{\pi}}\, v^{\frac{p}{2}} \int_0^\infty \eta^p e^{-\frac{\eta^2}{2}} d\eta = \sqrt{\frac{2^p v^p}{\pi}}\, \Gamma\left(\frac{p+1}{2}\right)$$

when p is a natural number. □

Example 2 For $t', t'' \in [0,1]$, $t' < t''$.

$$\int_{C_w} x(t')\, x(t'')\, m_w(dx) = t'.$$

Proof From the fact that $W(t, x) = x(t)$ for $(t, x) \in [0,1] \times C_w$ is a standard Brownian motion process on the probability space $(C_w, \mathfrak{B}^*, m_w)$ and the interval $[0,1]$,

$$\int_{C_w} x(t')x(t'')\, m_w(dx) = E^w\left[x(t')x(t'')\right]$$

$$= E^w\left[x(t')\left\{x(t'')-x(t')+x(t')\right\}\right]$$

$$= E^w\left[x(t')\right] E^w\left[x(t'')-x(t')\right] + E^w\left[\left\{x(t')\right\}^2\right]$$

$$= 0\cdot 0 + t'. \qquad \square$$

The foregoing examples are particular cases of the following theorem:

<u>Theorem 29.6</u> Let $F[x]$, $x \in C_w$, be given by

$$F[x] = f\left[x(t_1), \cdots, x(t_n)\right]$$

where $0 < t_1 < \cdots < t_n \le 1$ and $f(\xi_1, \cdots, \xi_n)$ is an extended real-valued Baire (i.e., $\mathfrak{B}^n$-measurable) function on R^n. Then F is Wiener measurable and

$$\int_{C_w} F[x]\, m_w(dx) = \left\{(2\pi)^n \prod_{i=1}^{n} (t_i - t_{i-1})\right\}^{-\frac{1}{2}} \times$$

$$\int_{R^n} f(\xi_1, \cdots, \xi_n) \exp\left\{-\frac{1}{2}\sum_{i=1}^{n} \frac{\left(\xi_i - \xi_{i-1}\right)^2}{t_i - t_{i-1}}\right\} m_L(d\xi)$$

in the sense that the existence of one side implies that of the other and the equality.

<u>Proof</u> Since $x(t_1), \cdots, x(t_n)$ are random variables on the probability space $(C_w, \mathfrak{M}^*, m_L)$ and $f(\xi_1, \cdots, \xi_n)$ is a Baire function on R^n, $f\left[x(t_1), \cdots, x(t_n)\right]$ is a random variable on

$(C_w, \mathfrak{W}^*, m_L)$, i.e., it is Wiener measurable. Since the probability distribution of the random vector $[x(t_1), \cdots, x(t_n)]$ is an n-dimensional normal distribution Φ whose density function Φ' is as given in Corollary 29.5, we have

$$\int_{C_w} f[x(t_1), \cdots, x(t_n)]\, m_w(dx)$$

$$= E^w\left[f[x(t_1), \cdots, x(t_n)]\right] = \int_{R^n} f(\xi_1, \cdots, \xi_n)\, \Phi'(\xi)\, m_L(d\xi)$$

in the sense that if one of the Wiener integral and the Lebesgue integral above exists then so does the other and the two are equal according to Theorem A1.6. □

As an example of the Wiener integral of a Wiener measurable functional $F[x]$, $x \in C_w$, which depends on the values $x(t)$ for all $t \in [0,1]$, we have the following:

Example 3

$$\int_{C_w} \left\{ \int_0^1 \{x(t)\}^p\, dt \right\} m_w(dx) = 0 \tag{1}$$

for an odd natural number p and

$$\int_{C_w} \left\{ \int_0^1 |x(t)|^p dt \right\} m_w(dx) = \left\{ \frac{2}{\pi} \right\}^{\frac{1}{2}} \frac{2^{\frac{p+2}{2}}\, \Gamma\left(\frac{p}{2}+\frac{1}{2}\right)}{p+2} \tag{2}$$

for a natural number p.

Proof Since the Wiener process $W(t,x) = x(t)$ for $(t,x) \in [0,1] \times C_w$ is a measurable process, we have, by the Fubini theorem and Example 1,

$$\int_{C_w}\left\{\int_0^1 \{x(t)\}^p\, dt\right\} m_w(dx)$$

$$= \int_{[0,1]}\left\{\int_{C_w} \{x(t)\}^p\, m_w(dx)\right\} m_L(dt) = \int_{[0,1]} 0\, m_L(dt) = 0$$

when p is an odd natural number and

$$\int_{C_w}\left\{\int_0^1 |x(t)|^p\, dt\right\} m_w(dx) = \int_{[0,1]}\left\{\int_{C_w} |x(t)|^p\, m_w(dx)\right\} m_L(dt)$$

$$= \left(\frac{2^p}{\pi}\right)^{\frac{1}{2}} \Gamma\left(\frac{p}{2}+\frac{1}{2}\right) \int_{[0,1]} t^{p/2}\, m_L(dt) = \left(\frac{2^p}{\pi}\right)^{\frac{1}{2}} \Gamma\left(\frac{p}{2}+\frac{1}{2}\right) \frac{1}{\frac{p}{2}+1}$$

when p is a natural number. □

As an example of approximation of a Wiener integral by Lebesgue integrals on Euclidean spaces we have the following:

Example 4 Let f and g be real-valued functions on R^1 satisfying

$$|f(\xi)| \le M \qquad \text{for } \xi \in R^1 \text{ where } M \ge 0, \tag{1}$$

$$|f(\xi') - f(\xi'')| \le A|\xi' - \xi''| \text{ for } \xi', \xi'' \in R^1 \text{ where } A \ge 0, \tag{2}$$

$$|g(\eta') - g(\eta'')| \le B|\eta' - \eta''|$$

$$\text{for } \eta', \eta'' \in R^1 \text{ and } |\eta'|, |\eta''| \le M \text{ where } B \ge 0. \tag{3}$$

Then the functionals F and F_n, $n = 1, 2, \cdots$, defined on C_w by

$$F[x] = g\left(\int_0^1 f\left[x(t)\right] dt\right) \quad \text{and} \quad F_n[x] = g\left(\frac{1}{n}\sum_{i=1}^{n} f\left[x\left(\frac{i}{n}\right)\right]\right) \tag{4}$$

are Wiener measurable and bounded on C_w and hence Wiener

integrable, and their Wiener integrals satisfy

$$\left| \int_{C_w} F[x]\, m_w(dx) - \int_{C_w} F_n[x]\, m_w(dx) \right| \le \frac{2}{3}\sqrt{\frac{2}{\pi}}\, AB \frac{1}{\sqrt{n}} \tag{5}$$

for $n = 1, 2, \cdots$, where the Wiener integral of F_n can be evaluated as a Lebesgue integral on R^n, i.e.,

$$\int_{C_w} F_n[x]\, m_w(dx)$$
$$= \left(\frac{n}{2\pi}\right)^{n/2} \int_{R^n} g\left(\frac{1}{n}\sum_{i=1}^{n} f(\xi_i)\right) \exp\left\{-\frac{1}{2}\sum_{i=1}^{n} \frac{(\xi_i - \xi_{i-1})^2}{t_i - t_{i-1}}\right\} m_L(d\xi). \tag{6}$$

Proof From the continuity of f and g on R^1 implied by (2) and (3), the function $g\left[(1/n)\sum_{i=1}^{n} f(\xi_i)\right]$ of $(\xi_1, \cdots; \xi_n) \in R^n$ is continuous on R^n. Thus the continuous function $F_n[x]$ of the random vector $\left[x(t_1), \cdots, x(t_n)\right]$ on the probability space $(C_w, \mathfrak{B}^*, m_w)$ given by (5) is a random variable on $(C_w, \mathfrak{B}^*, m_w)$, i.e., it is Wiener measurable. From the continuity of $x(t), t \in [0, 1]$, and the continuity of $f(\xi), \xi \in R^1$,

$$\lim_{n\to\infty} \frac{1}{n}\sum_{i=1}^{n} f\left[x\left(\frac{i}{n}\right)\right] = \int_0^1 f\left[x(t)\right] dt,$$

so that from the continuity of $g(\eta)$, $\eta \in R^1$, we have

$$\lim_{n\to\infty} g\left(\frac{1}{n}\sum_{i=1}^{n} f\left[x\left(\frac{i}{n}\right)\right]\right) = g\left(\int_0^1 f\left[x(t)\right] dt\right) \quad \text{for } x \in C_w,$$

i.e., $\lim_{n\to\infty} F_n[x] = F[x]$ for $x \in C_w$. This establishes the Wiener measurability of F. The boundedness of F and F_n on C_w follows from (1) and (4).

Now

$$D = \left| \int_{C_w} \{F[x] - F_n[x]\} m_w(dx) \right|$$

$$= \left| E^w \left\{ g\left(\int_0^1 f[x(t)]\,dt\right) - g\left(\frac{1}{n}\sum_{i=1}^n f\left[x\left(\frac{i}{n}\right)\right]\right)\right\}\right|$$

$$\leq BE^w \left\{ \left| \int_0^1 f[x(t)]\,dt - \frac{1}{n}\sum_{i=1}^n f\left[x\left(\frac{i}{n}\right)\right] \right| \right\}$$

$$\leq BE^w \left\{ \sum_{i=1}^n \int_{\frac{i-1}{n}}^{\frac{i}{n}} \left| f[x(t)] - f\left[x\left(\frac{i}{n}\right)\right] \right| dt \right\}$$

$$\leq AB \sum_{i=1}^n E^w \left\{ \int_{\left[\frac{i-1}{n}, \frac{i}{n}\right]} \left| x(t) - x\left(\frac{i}{n}\right) \right| m_L(dt) \right\}$$

$$= AB \sum_{i=1}^n \int_{\left[\frac{i-1}{n}, \frac{i}{n}\right]} E^w\left[\left| x(t) - x\left(\frac{i}{n}\right) \right| \right] m_L(dt)$$

$$= AB \sum_{i=1}^n \int_{\left[\frac{i-1}{n}, \frac{i}{n}\right]} \sqrt{\frac{2}{\pi}} \left(\frac{i}{n} - t\right)^{\frac{1}{2}} m_L(dt)$$

by Example 1 with $p = 1$ and $\Gamma(1) = 1$. Thus

$$D \leq \sqrt{\frac{2}{\pi}}\, AB \sum_{i=1}^n \frac{2}{3}\left(\frac{i}{n} - t\right)^{\frac{3}{2}} \Bigg|_{i/n}^{(i-1)/n}$$

$$= \sqrt{\frac{2}{\pi}}\, \frac{2}{3} AB \sum_{i=1}^n \left(\frac{1}{n}\right)^{\frac{3}{2}} = \sqrt{\frac{2}{\pi}}\, \frac{2}{3} AB \frac{1}{\sqrt{n}}$$

This proves (5). Finally (6) is from Theorem 29.6. □

Theorem 29.7 (R. E. A. C. Paley and N. Wiener)
Let $\{\varphi_i, i = 1,2,\cdots,n\}$ be an orthornormal system in the real

Hilbert space $L_2[0,1]$ and assume that each φ_i has a representative which is a function of bounded variation on $[0,1]$. Then the n Riemann-Stieltjes integrals $\int_0^1 \varphi_i(t)\,dx(t)$, $i = 1, 2, \cdots, n$, which exist for every $x \in C_w$, constitute an independent system of random variables on the probability space $(C_w, \mathfrak{W}^*, m_w)$, each of which is distributed according to $N(0,1)$. If $f(\xi_1, \cdots, \xi_n)$ is an extended real-valued Baire function on R^n then the functional F on C_w defined by

$$F[x] = f\left[\int_0^1 \varphi_1(t)\,dx(t), \cdots, \int_0^1 \varphi_n(t)\,dx(t)\right] \quad \text{for } x \in C_w \qquad (1)$$

is Wiener measurable and

$$\int_{C_w} F[x]\, m_w(dx) = (2\pi)^{-n/2} \int_{R^n} f(\xi_1, \cdots, \xi_n) \exp\left\{-\sum_{i=1}^{n} \frac{\xi_i^2}{2}\right\} m_L(d\xi) \qquad (2)$$

in the sense that the existence of one side implies that of the other and the equality of the two.

<u>Proof</u> As we pointed out in Theorem 29.4, $W(t,x) = x(t)$ for $(t,x) \in [0,1] \times C_w$ is a continuous standard Brownian motion process on $(C_w, \mathfrak{W}^*, m_w)$ and $[0,1]$. For our φ_i, consider the stochastic integral $I(\varphi_i)$ with respect to W as defined in Definition 22.3. Then since $\|\varphi_i\| = 1$, the random variable $I(\varphi_i)$ on $(C_w, \mathfrak{W}^*, m_w)$ is distributed according to $N(0,1)$ by Theorem 22.4. Furthermore since $\{\varphi_i, i = 1, 2, \cdots, n\}$ is an orthogonal system in $L_2[0,1]$, the system of random variables $\{I(\varphi_i), i = 1, 2, \cdots, n\}$ is independent system according to Corollary 22.7.

Now since φ_i is of bounded variation on $[0,1]$ and every $x \in C_w$ is continuous on $[0,1]$, the Riemann-Stieltjes integral $\int_0^1 \varphi_i(t)\,dx(t)$ exists for every $x \in C_w$. But according to Theorem

22.5

$$I(\varphi_i)(x) = \int_0^1 \varphi_i(t)\, dW(t,x) = \int_0^1 \varphi_i(t)\, dx(t) \quad \text{for a.e.} \quad x \in C_w.$$

Thus from the completeness of the measure space $(C_w, \mathfrak{W}^*, m_w)$, $\int_0^1 \varphi_i(t)\, dx(t)$ as a function of $x \in C_w$ is $\mathfrak{W}^*$-measurable. Therefore $\left\{\int_0^1 \varphi_i(t)\, dx(t),\ i = 1, 2, \cdots, n\right\}$ is an independent system of random variables on $(C_w, \mathfrak{W}^*, m_w)$, each of which is distributed according to $N(0,1)$. This implies that the probability distribution of the random vector $\left[\int_0^1 \varphi_1(t)\, dx(t), \cdots, \int_0^1 \varphi_n(t)\, dx(t)\right]$ is an n-dimensional normal distribution Φ whose density function Φ' is given by

$$\Phi'(\xi) = \prod_{i=1}^{n} (2\pi)^{-\frac{1}{2}} \exp\left\{-\frac{\xi_i^2}{2}\right\} \quad \text{for} \quad \xi = (\xi_1, \cdots, \xi_n) \in R^n. \quad (3)$$

If $f(\xi_1, \cdots, \xi_n)$ is an extended real-valued Baire function on R^n then F as defined by (1) is an extended real valued random variable on $(C_w, \mathfrak{W}^*, m_w)$ and (2) holds by Theorem A1.6 and (3). □

§30. UNIFORM TOPOLOGY AND WIENER MEASURABILITY

Let $|||\cdot|||$ be the uniform norm in C_w, i.e., $|||x||| = \max_{[0,1]} |x(t)|$ for $x \in C_w$. We refer to the metric topology of C_w determined by the uniform norm as the uniform topology in C_w. A subset $K(x_0, \varepsilon)$ of C_w defined by

$$K(x_0, \varepsilon) = \{x \in C_w ; |||x - x_0||| < \varepsilon\} \quad \text{where} \quad x_0 \in C_w \quad \text{and} \quad \varepsilon > 0$$

will be called an open sphere in C_w with center x_0 and radius ε. The open spheres in C_w constitute a base for the uniform topology in C_w. Note also that C_w is complete with respect to the uniform norm and is therefore a real Banach space.

Lemma 30.1 In its uniform topology, C_w is separable. In fact if $Q^{(n)}$ is the collection of polygonal functions on $[0,1]$ whose steps are the subintervals $[t_{i-1}, t_i]$ of $[0,1]$ where $t_i = i/n$ for $i = 1, 2, \cdots, n$, and which vanish at $t = 0$ and assume rational values at t_i, $i = 1, 2, \cdots, n$, then the countable collection $Q = \bigcup_{n=1}^{\infty} Q^{(n)}$ is dense in C_w in the uniform topology. Every open set in C_w is a union of countably many open spheres with centers in Q and rational radii.

Proof To show that Q is dense in C_w in the uniform topology we show that an arbitrary open sphere in C_w, $K(x_0, \varepsilon)$, contains a member of Q. From the uniform continuity of x_0 on $[0,1]$ there exists a positive integer n such that $|x_0(t') - x_0(t'')| < \varepsilon/5$ for $t', t'' \in [t_{i-1}, t_i]$ where $t_i = i/n$ for $i = 1, 2, \cdots, n$. Let η_i be a rational number satisfying $|\eta_i - x_0(t_i)| < \varepsilon/5$ for $i = 1, 2, \cdots, n$, and let y be the member of $Q^{(n)}$ with $y(t_i) = \eta_i$ for $i = 1, 2, \cdots, n$. Then for $t \in [t_{i-1}, t_i]$, we have

$$|y(t) - x_0(t)| \le |y(t) - y(t_{i-1})| + |y(t_{i-1}) - x_0(t_{i-1})| + |x_0(t_{i-1}) - x_0(t)|$$

$$< |y(t) - y(t_{i-1})| + \frac{2}{5}\varepsilon ,$$

and from the linearity of y on $[t_{i-1}, t_i]$

$$|y(t) - y(t_{i-1})| \le |y(t_i) - y(t_{i-1})|$$

$$\le |y(t_i) - x_0(t_i)| + |x_0(t_i) - x_0(t_{i-1})|$$

$$+ |x_0(t_{i-1}) - y(t_{i-1})| < \frac{3}{5}\varepsilon .$$

Thus

$$|y(t) - x_0(t)| < \varepsilon,$$

i.e., $y \in K(x_0, \varepsilon)$. This proves the denseness of Q in C_w.

Let G be an arbitrary open set in C_w in the uniform topology. For $x_0 \in G$, let $\varepsilon > 0$ be such that $K(x_0, \varepsilon) \subset G$. Let $y \in Q$ and $y \in K(x_0, \varepsilon/3)$ and let η be a rational number in $(\varepsilon/3, \varepsilon/2)$. Then $x_0 \in K(y, \eta) \subset K(x_0, \varepsilon) \subset G$. Therefore G is a union of countably many open spheres with centers in Q and rational radii. □

<u>Lemma 30.2</u> An open set in the uniform topology of C_w is $\sigma(\mathfrak{W})$-measurable and hence Wiener measurable.

<u>Proof</u> According to Lemma 30.1, every open set in the uniform topology of C_w is a countable union of open spheres. Thus, to prove our lemma it suffices to show that an arbitrary open sphere $K(x_0, \varepsilon)$ is $\sigma(\mathfrak{W})$-measurable. Now

$$K(x_0, \varepsilon) = \left\{x \in C_w; |||x - x_0||| < \varepsilon\right\} = \bigcup_{n=1}^{\infty} \left\{x \in C_w; |||x - x_0||| \le \varepsilon - \frac{1}{n}\right\}$$

and, with the rational numbers $\{s_i, i = 1, 2, \cdots,\}$ in $[0, 1]$,

$$\left\{x \in C_w; |||x - x_0||| \le \varepsilon - \frac{1}{n}\right\} = \left\{x \in C_w; \sup_i |x(s_i) - x_0(s_i)| \le \varepsilon - \frac{1}{n}\right\}$$

$$= \bigcap_{i=1}^{\infty} \left\{x \in C_w; |x(s_i) - x_0(s_i)| \le \varepsilon - \frac{1}{n}\right\}.$$

Since

$$\left\{x \in C_w; |x(s_i) - x_0(s_i)| \le \varepsilon - \frac{1}{n}\right\} \in \mathfrak{W}_{s_i}$$

we have $K(x_0, \varepsilon) \in \sigma(\mathfrak{W})$. □

<u>Theorem 30.3</u> A real-valued function $F[x]$, $x \in C_w$, which is continuous with respect to the uniform topology of

C_w is $\sigma(\mathfrak{W})$-measurable and hence Wiener measurable. In particular, if $G(\xi)$, $\xi \in R^1$, is a continuous real-valued function, then $G\left(|||x|||\right)$, $x \in C_w$, is $\sigma(\mathfrak{W})$-measurable.

<u>Proof</u> Let us show that if $F[x]$, $x \in C_w$, is continuous then it is a measurable transformation of $\left(C_w, \sigma(\mathfrak{W})\right)$ into $(R^1, \mathfrak{B}^1)$, i.e.,

$$F^{-1}(B) \in \sigma(\mathfrak{W}) \qquad \text{for every} \quad B \in \mathfrak{B}^1. \tag{1}$$

From the continuity of F, for every open set $O \subset R^1$, $F^{-1}(O)$ is open and hence $F^{-1}(O) \in \sigma(\mathfrak{W})$ by Lemma 30.2. Let

$$\mathfrak{A} = \left\{A \subset R^1;\ F^{-1}(A) \in \sigma(\mathfrak{W})\right\}.$$

Since $\sigma(\mathfrak{W})$ is a σ-field, so is $\mathfrak{A}$. But $\mathfrak{A}$ includes all the open sets in R^1 as we have already seen. Thus $\mathfrak{B}^1 \subset \mathfrak{A}$ and (1) holds.

Since $|||x|||$, $x \in C_w$, is a continuous function on C_w with respect to the uniform topology, $G\left(|||x|||\right)$, $x \in C_w$, is continuous and hence $\sigma(\mathfrak{W})$-measurable. □

Chapter 8

TRANSFORMATIONS OF WIENER INTEGRALS

§31. PROBABILITY MEASURE INDUCED IN THE WIENER SPACE BY A TRANSFORMATION OF THE WIENER PROCESS

Let the families of subsets of the Wiener space $C_w, \mathfrak{W}_{t_1 \cdots t_n}, \mathfrak{W}, \sigma(\mathfrak{W})$, and $\mathfrak{W}^*$ be as given in Theorem 29.1 and consider the Wiener measure space $(C_w, \mathfrak{W}^*, m_w)$. Let X (instead of W as in Definition 29.3) be the Wiener process, i.e., the stochastic process on $(C_w, \mathfrak{W}^*, m_w)$ and $[0,1]$ defined by

$$X(t, x) = x(t) \qquad \text{for } (t, x) \in [0,1] \times C_w. \tag{1}$$

As we saw in Theorem 29.4, X is then a standard Brownian motion process in which C_w is both the sample space and the space of sample functions.

Let T be a transformation of C_w satisfying the following conditions:

1° T maps C_w one-to-one onto C_w.

2° For any $\{t_1, \cdots, t_n\} \in [0,1]$ where $0 < t_1 < \cdots < t_n \leq 1$, and $B \in \mathfrak{B}^n$,

$$\left\{x \in C_w ; \left[(Tx)(t_1), \cdots, (Tx)(t_n)\right] \in B\right\} \in \mathfrak{W}^*.$$

Define a real-valued function Y on $[0,1] \times C_w$ by

$$Y(t, s) = (Tx)(t) \qquad \text{for } (t, x) \in [0,1] \times C_w. \tag{2}$$

On account of 2°, Y is a stochastic process on the probability space $(C_w, \mathfrak{W}^*, m_w)$ and $[0,1]$. As a result of 1°, the space of sample functions $Y(\cdot, x) = Tx$, $x \in C_w$, coincides with the sample space C_w.

To define the probability measures induced by the two processes X and Y on the field $\mathfrak{W}$ of subsets of C_w, let $F \in \mathfrak{W}$, say $F \in \mathfrak{W}_{t_1 \cdots t_n}$, where $0 < t_1 < \cdots < t_n \leq 1$ and in fact

$$F = \left\{x \in C_w ; \left[x(t_1), \cdots, x(t_n)\right] \in B\right\} \quad \text{where } B \in \mathfrak{B}^n. \tag{3}$$

With the same B as in (3), let

$$E = \left\{x \in C_w ; \left[(Tx)(t_1), \cdots, (Tx)(t_n)\right] \in B\right\}. \tag{4}$$

Note that, by 2°, $E \in \mathfrak{W}^*$. Now if $x \in E$ then $\left[(Tx)(t_1), \cdots, (Tx)(t_n)\right] \in B$ so that $Tx \in F$ and hence $TE \subset F$. Conversely if $x \in F$ then $\left[x(t_1), \cdots, x(t_n)\right] \in B$ and $\left[(TT^{-1}x)(t_1), \cdots, (TT^{-1}x)(t_n)\right] \in B$ so that $T^{-1}x \in E$ and hence $T^{-1}F \subset E$, i.e., $F \subset TE$. Therefore

$$F = TE \quad \text{and} \quad E = T^{-1}F. \tag{5}$$

We define two set functions μ_X and μ_Y on the field $\mathfrak{W}$ by

$$\mu_X(F) = m_w(F) \quad \text{for } F \in \mathfrak{W}, \tag{6}$$

$$\mu_Y(F) = m_w(E) \quad \text{for } F \in \mathfrak{W} \text{ and } E = T^{-1}F. \tag{7}$$

As defined by (6), μ_X is nothing but the restriction of m_w to $\mathfrak{W}$. Thus we may extend μ_X to $\mathfrak{W}^*$ merely by setting $\mu_X = m_w$ on $\mathfrak{W}^*$. With this extension, we have, from (7) and the fact that $E \in \mathfrak{W}^*$,

$$\mu_Y(F) = \mu_X(E) \quad \text{for } F \in \mathfrak{W} \text{ and } E = T^{-1}F. \tag{8}$$

Consider the set function μ_Y on $\mathfrak{W}$ defined by (7). Since $T^{-1}F$ is uniquely determined by F and $T^{-1}F \in \mathfrak{W}^*$, μ_Y is well defined on $\mathfrak{W}$. It is easy to see that μ_Y is actually a probability measure on the field $\mathfrak{W}$. To verify for instance its countable additivity on $\mathfrak{W}$ let $\{F_n, n = 1, 2, \cdots\} \subset \mathfrak{W}$ be a disjoint collection and assume that $\bigcup_{n=1}^{\infty} F_n \in \mathfrak{W}$. Then $\{T^{-1}F_n, n = 1, 2, \cdots\} \subset \mathfrak{W}^*$ is a disjoint collection, and hence by the countable additivity of m_w on $\mathfrak{W}^*$

$$\mu_Y\left(\bigcup_{n=1}^{\infty} F_n\right) = m_w\left(T^{-1}\left(\bigcup_{n=1}^{\infty} F_n\right)\right) = m_w\left(\bigcup_{n=1}^{\infty} T^{-1} F_n\right)$$

$$= \sum_{n=1}^{\infty} m_w\left(T^{-1} F_n\right) = \sum_{n=1}^{\infty} \mu_Y(F_n),$$

which proves the countable additivity of μ_Y on $\mathfrak{W}$. Now that μ_Y is a probability measure on the field $\mathfrak{W}$ it can be extended uniquely to be a probability measure on $\sigma(\mathfrak{W})$. Summarizing the above discussion we have:

Theorem 31.1 Let X be the Wiener process and let Y be a stochastic process on the probability space $(C_w, \mathfrak{W}^*, m_w)$ and $[0,1]$ defined by (2) where T is a transformation of C_w satisfying the conditions $1°$ and $2°$. The set functions μ_X and μ_Y on the field $\mathfrak{W}$ defined by (6) and (7) determine two probability measures on $\sigma(\mathfrak{W})$. In fact μ_X is just the restriction of m_w to $\sigma(\mathfrak{W})$.

In §§ 32-34 we investigate the relationship between $\mu_X = m_w$ and μ_Y under transformations T satisfying the conditions $1°$ and $2°$.

§32. LINEAR TRANSFORMATIONS OF THE WIENER SPACE

Let T be a linear transformation of the Wiener space C_w defined by

$$Tx = \lambda x \quad \text{for} \quad x \in C_w \quad \text{where} \quad \lambda \in R^1 \quad \text{and} \quad \lambda \neq 0.$$

This transformation obviously satisfies the condition 1° of §31. Let $0 < t_1 < \cdots < t_n \leq 1$ and $B \in \mathfrak{B}^n$. Writing $cB = \{c\xi ; \xi \in B\} \in \mathfrak{B}^n$ for $c \in R^1$ we have

$$\left\{x \in C_w ; \left[(Tx)(t_1), \cdots, (Tx)(t_n)\right] \in B\right\}$$

$$= \left\{x \in C_w ; \left[x(t_1), \cdots, x(t_n)\right] \in \frac{1}{\lambda} B\right\} \in \mathfrak{W}_{t_1 \cdots t_n} .$$

Thus T satisfies 2° of §31.

Consider the stochastic process Y on the probability space $(C_w, \mathfrak{W}^*, m_w)$ and $[0,1]$ defined by

$$Y(t,x) = (Tx)(t) \qquad \text{for} \quad (t,x) \in [0,1] \times C_w .$$

To show that Y is a Brownian motion process let us show that it is a process with independent increments. Thus let $0 = t_0 < t_1 < \cdots < t_n \leq 1$ and $B_1, \cdots, B_n \in \mathfrak{B}^1$. Then

$$m_w\left\{x \in C_w ; (Tx)(t_i) - (Tx)(t_{i-1}) \in B_i, \ i = 1,2, \cdots, n\right\}$$

$$= m_w\left\{x \in C_w ; x(t_i) - x(t_{i-1}) \in \frac{1}{\lambda} B_i , \ i = 1,2, \cdots, n\right\}$$

$$= \prod_{i=1}^{n} m_w\left\{x \in C_w ; x(t_i) - x(t_{i-1}) \in \frac{1}{\lambda} B_i\right\}$$

$$= \prod_{i=1}^{n} m_w\left\{x \in C_w ; (Tx)(t_i) - (Tx)(t_{i-1}) \in B_i\right\} .$$

This proves the independence of increments of Y. For $t', t'' \in [0,1]$, $t' < t''$, $x(t'') - x(t')$ is distributed according to $N(0, t'' - t')$, so that $(Tx)(t'') - (Tx)(t') = \lambda\{x(t'') - x(t')\}$ is distributed according to $N\left(0, \lambda^2(t'' - t')\right)$. Note also that $Y(0,x) = 0$ for every $x \in C_w$. This completes the proof that Y is a Brownian motion process.

Theorem 32.1 Let X be the Wiener process, i.e., $X(t,x) = x(t)$ for $(t,x) \in [0,1] \times C_w$, and let Y be a Brownian motion process on $(C_w, \mathfrak{W}^*, m_w)$ and $[0,1]$ defined $Y(t,x) = (Tx)(t)$ for $(t,x) \in [0,1] \times C_w$ where T is a linear transformation of C_w defined by $Tx = \lambda x$ with $\lambda \in R^1$, $\lambda \neq 0$. Let $\mu_X = m_w$ and μ_Y be the probability measures on $\sigma(\mathfrak{W})$ induced by X and Y, respectively. If $\lambda = 1$ or -1, then $\mu_X = \mu_Y$ on $\sigma(\mathfrak{W})$. If $\lambda \neq 1$ or -1 then $\mu_X \perp \mu_Y$ on $\sigma(\mathfrak{W})$ and in fact for the two disjoint subsets Γ_1 and Γ_2 of C_w defined by

$$\Gamma_1 = \left\{x \in C_w ; \lim_{n\to\infty} \sum_{k=1}^{2^n} \left[x\left(\frac{k}{2^n}\right) - x\left(\frac{k-1}{2^n}\right)\right]^2 = 1\right\} \tag{1}$$

and

$$\Gamma_2 = \left\{x \in C_w ; \lim_{n\to\infty} \sum_{k=1}^{2^n} \left[x\left(\frac{k}{2^n}\right) - x\left(\frac{k-1}{2^n}\right)\right]^2 = \lambda^2\right\} \tag{2}$$

we have $\mu_X(\Gamma_1) = 1$ and $\mu_Y(\Gamma_2) = 1$. However the restrictions of μ_X and μ_Y on $\mathfrak{W}_{t_1 \cdots t_n}$ are equivalent and

$$\frac{d\left(\mu_Y|\mathfrak{W}_{t_1\cdots t_n}\right)}{d\left(\mu_X|\mathfrak{W}_{t_1\cdots t_n}\right)}(\xi) = \frac{1}{\lambda^n} \exp\left\{-\frac{1}{2}\left(\frac{1}{\lambda^2} - 1\right)\sum_{i=1}^{n} \frac{\left(\xi_i - \xi_{i-1}\right)^2}{t_i - t_{i-1}}\right\}, \tag{3}$$

where $\xi_0 \equiv 0$ and $\xi = (\xi_1, \cdots, \xi_n) \in R^n$.

Proof When $\lambda = 1$, $X = Y$ and hence $\mu_X = \mu_Y$ on $\sigma(\mathfrak{W})$.

When $\lambda = -1$, to show that $\mu_X = \mu_Y$ on $\sigma(\mathfrak{W})$ let us show first that the equality holds on $\mathfrak{W}$. Thus let $F \in \mathfrak{W}$, say $F \in \mathfrak{W}_{t_1 \cdots t_n}$ where $0 < t_1 < \cdots < t_n \le 1$, and

$$F = \left\{x \in C_w ; \left[x(t_1), \cdots, x(t_n)\right] \in B\right\} \quad \text{with } B \in \mathfrak{B}^n. \tag{4}$$

With the same B as in (4) let

$$E = \left\{x \in C_w ; \left[x(t_1), \cdots, x(t_n)\right] \in -B\right\}. \tag{5}$$

Then $F = TE$ and $E = T^{-1}F$. By (6) and (8) of §31

$$\mu_X(F) = m_w(F) \quad \text{while} \quad \mu_Y(F) = \mu_X(E) = m_w(E). \tag{6}$$

For simplicity, let

$$N = \left\{(2\pi)^n \prod_{i=1}^{n} (t_i - t_{i-1})\right\}^{-\frac{1}{2}}. \tag{7}$$

Then

$$m_w(E) = N \int_{-B} \exp\left\{-\frac{1}{2} \sum_{i=1}^{n} \frac{(\xi_i - \xi_{i-1})^2}{t_i - t_{i-1}}\right\} m_L(d\xi) \tag{8}$$

$$= N \int_{B} \exp\left\{-\frac{1}{2} \sum_{i=1}^{n} \frac{(\eta_i - \eta_{i-1})^2}{t_i - t_{i-1}}\right\} m_L(d\eta) = m_w(F)$$

by the transformation $\xi = -\eta$ whose Jacobian is equal to 1. From (6) and (8) we have $\mu_X(F) = \mu_Y(F)$. Thus $\mu_X = \mu_Y$ on $\mathfrak{W}$. Since a probability measure on $\sigma(\mathfrak{W})$ is uniquely determined by its values on $\mathfrak{W}$, this implies that $\mu_X = \mu_Y$ on $\sigma(\mathfrak{W})$.

Let us turn now to the case where $\lambda \neq 1$ or -1. The set

Γ_1 defined by (1) is a member of $\sigma(\mathfrak{W})$. For our transformation T it is obvious that $T\mathfrak{W}_{t_1 \cdots t_n} = \mathfrak{W}_{t_1 \cdots t_n}$ and $T\mathfrak{W} = \mathfrak{W}$. From this follows that $T\left[\sigma(\mathfrak{W})\right] \subset \sigma(\mathfrak{W})$. The same holds for T^{-1} and consequently $T\left[\sigma(\mathfrak{W})\right] = \sigma(\mathfrak{W})$. Thus for the set Γ_2 defined by (2) we have $\Gamma_2 = T\Gamma_1 \in \sigma(\mathfrak{W})$. Since μ_X is the restriction of m_w to $\sigma(\mathfrak{W})$ we have

$$\mu_X(\Gamma_1) = m_w(\Gamma_1). \tag{9}$$

Consider μ_Y on $\sigma(\mathfrak{W})$. The set function $m_w T^{-1}$ defined by

$$(m_w T^{-1})(\Gamma) = m_w\left(T^{-1}\Gamma\right) \qquad \text{for } \Gamma \in \sigma(\mathfrak{W})$$

is a probability measure on $\sigma(\mathfrak{W})$. According to (8) of §31

$$\mu_Y(F) = \mu_X(T^{-1}F) = m_w(T^{-1}F) \qquad \text{for } F \in \mathfrak{W}.$$

Thus the two probability measures $m_w T^{-1}$ and μ_Y on $\sigma(\mathfrak{W})$ are equal on $\mathfrak{W}$ and hence must be equal on $\sigma(\mathfrak{W})$ as well. Therefore

$$\mu_Y(\Gamma_2) = (m_w T^{-1})(\Gamma_2) = m_w\left(T^{-1}\Gamma_2\right) = m_w(\Gamma_1). \tag{10}$$

From (9) and (10) we have

$$\mu_X(\Gamma_1) = \mu_Y(\Gamma_2) = m_w(\Gamma_1). \tag{11}$$

Applying (2) of Corollary 20.6 to the Wiener process X which is a standard Brownian motion process and to the set Γ_1 defined by (1) we have

$$m_w(\Gamma_1) = 1. \tag{12}$$

From (11) and (12) we have $\mu_X(\Gamma) = \mu_Y(\Gamma_2) = 1$. But $\Gamma_1 \cap \Gamma_2 = \phi$.

Thus $\mu_X \perp \mu_Y$ on $\sigma(\mathfrak{B})$.

To show that when $\lambda \neq 1$ or -1, the restrictions of μ_X and μ_Y to $\mathfrak{B}_{t_1 \cdots t_n}$ for an arbitrary $\{t_1, \cdots, t_n\} \subset [0,1]$ with $0 = t_0 < t_1 < \cdots < t_n \leq 1$ are equivalent, take an arbitrary member F of $\mathfrak{B}_{t_1 \cdots t_n}$ given by (4). Let $E = T^{-1}F$, i.e.,

$$E = \left\{x \in C_w ; \left[x(t_1), \cdots, x(t_n)\right] \in \lambda^{-1}B\right\}.$$

Then with N as given by (7), we have

$$\mu_X(F) = m_w(F) = \int_B N \exp\left\{-\frac{1}{2}\sum_{i=1}^{n} \frac{(\xi_i - \xi_{i-1})^2}{t_i - t_{i-1}}\right\} m_L(d\xi) \tag{13}$$

and

$$\mu_Y(F) = \mu_X(E) = m_w(E) = \int_{\lambda^{-1}B} N \exp\left\{-\frac{1}{2}\sum_{i=1}^{n} \frac{(\eta_i - \eta_{i-1})^2}{t_i - t_{i-1}}\right\} m_L(d\eta)$$

$$= \int_B \frac{N}{\lambda^n} \exp\left\{-\frac{1}{2\lambda^2}\sum_{i=1}^{n} \frac{(\xi_i - \xi_{i-1})^2}{t_i - t_{i-1}}\right\} m_L(d\xi) \tag{14}$$

with the transformation $\eta = \lambda^{-1}\xi$ whose Jacobian is equal to λ^{-n}. When $\mu_X(F) = 0$ then from the positivity of the integrand in (13) we have $m_L(B) = 0$ and hence $\mu_Y(F) = 0$ from (14). Thus $\mu_Y \ll \mu_X$ on $\mathfrak{B}_{t_1 \cdots t_n}$. Similarly $\mu_X \ll \mu_Y$ and hence μ_X and μ_Y are equivalent on $\mathfrak{B}_{t_1 \cdots t_n}$. The Radon Nikodym derivative (3) is obtained by dividing the density function of μ_Y by that of μ_X, i.e., by dividing the integrand in (14) by that in (13). □

§33. TRANSFORMATION OF THE WIENER MEASURE AND WIENER INTEGRALS BY A TRANSLATION

[I] Introduction

Let T be a translation of the Wiener space C_w defined by

$$Tx = x + x_0 \quad \text{for } x \in C_w$$

where x_0 is a fixed element of C_w. Clearly T is a one-to-one transformation of C_w onto C_w. Also for $0 < t_1 < \cdots < t_n \le 1$ and $B \in \mathfrak{B}^n$

$$\left\{x \in C_w ; \left[(Tx)(t_1), \cdots, (Tx)(t_n)\right] \in B\right\}$$

$$= \left\{x \in C_w ; \left[x(t_1), \cdots, x(t_n)\right] \in B - \left[x_0(t_1), \cdots, x_0(t_n)\right]\right\} \in \mathfrak{W}_{t_1 \cdots t_n}$$

where by $B - \left[x_0(t_1), \cdots, x_0(t_n)\right]$ we mean $\left\{\xi \in R^n ; \xi + \left[x_0(t_1), \cdots, x_0(t_n)\right] \in B\right\}$. Thus T satisfies the conditions 1° and 2° of §31, and consequently the real-valued function $Y(t,x) = (Tx)(t)$ for $(t,x) \in [0,1] \times C_w$ is a stochastic process on $(C_w, \mathfrak{W}^*, m_w)$ and $[0,1]$ whose sample space and sample functions are both C_w. Proceeding as in §32, we can show that $Y(0,x) = 0$ for every $x \in C_w$, Y is an additive process, and for $t', t'' \in [0,1]$, $t' < t''$, $Y(t'', \cdot) - Y(t', \cdot)$ is distributed according to $N\left(x_0(t'') - x_0(t'), t''-t'\right)$. Thus Y is a generalized Brownian motion which we considered in §17.

Let μ_X and μ_Y be the probability measures induced on $\sigma(\mathfrak{W})$ by the Wiener process $X(t,x) = x(t)$ for $(t,x) \in [0,1] \times C_w$ and our process Y. We shall show that if x_0 is such that x_0' exists and is of bounded variation on $[0,1]$, then $\mu_X (= m_w)$ and

μ_Y are equivalent on $\sigma(\mathfrak{W})$ with the Radon-Nikodym derivative given by

$$\frac{d\mu_Y}{d\mu_X}(x) = \exp\left\{-\tfrac{1}{2}\int_0^1 \left[x_0'(t)\right]^2 dt + \int_0^1 x_0'(t)\, dx(t)\right\} \quad \text{for } x \in C_w.$$

In this connection let us remark that since $x_0' \in$ B.V. $[0,1]$ the Riemann-Stieltjes integral $\int_0^1 x_0'(t)\, dx(t)$ exists for every $x \in C_w$. We remark also that since x_0' exists on $[0,1]$ and $x_0' \in$ B.V.$[0,1]$, the Riemann integral $\int_0^t x_0'(s)\, ds$ exists for $t \in [0,1]$, and according to the Fundamental Theorem of Integral Calculus, $x_0(t) = \int_0^t x_0'(s)\, ds$ for $t \in [0,1]$, so that x_0 is absolutely continuous on $[0,1]$.

[II] Translation Theorem for Wiener Integrable Functionals Which Are Continuous and Bounded on Bounded Sets

Definition 33.1 Let $P^{(n)}$ be the collection of polygonal functions on $[0,1]$ with n equal steps $[t_{i-1}, t_i]$ where $t_i = i/n$ for $i = 1, 2, \cdots, n$, and vanishing at $t = 0$. Let $L^{(n)}$ be the transformation of C_w onto $P^{(n)}$ defined by assigning to each member of C_w the corresponding polygonal function in $P^{(n)}$, i.e.,

$$\left(L^{(n)}y\right)(t) = y(t_{i-1}) + \frac{y(t_i) - y(t_{i-1})}{t_i - t_{i-1}}(t - t_{i-1})$$

for $t \in [t_{i-1}, t_i]$, $i = 1, 2, \cdots, n$, and $y \in C_w$.

It is obvious that $\lim_{n\to\infty} \left\| L^{(n)}y - y \right\| = 0$ for every $y \in C_w$, i.e., $\lim_{n\to\infty}\left(L^{(n)}y\right)(t) = y(t)$ uniformly in $t \in [0,1]$ for every

$y \in C_w$. Note also that for $y \in P^{(n)}$, $y \sim [y(1/n), \cdots, y(n/n)]$ establishes a one-to-one correspondence between $P^{(n)}$ and R^n, so that the transformation $L^{(n)}$ of C_w onto R^n can be represented by the transformation $q_{t_1 \cdots t_n}$ of C_w onto R^n where

$$q_{t_1 \cdots t_n}(y) = [y(t_1), \cdots, y(t_n)] \quad \text{for } y \in C_w$$

with $t_i = i/n$, $i = 1, 2, \cdots, n$.

Lemma 33.2 Let F be a real-valued functional on C_w. Then for the function $(FL^{(n)})[y] = F[L^{(n)}[y]]$, $y \in C_w$, there exists a real-valued function $H[\eta_1, \cdots, \eta_n]$ on R^n such that

$$(FL^{(n)})[y] = H\left[y\left(\frac{1}{n}\right), \cdots, y\left(\frac{n}{n}\right)\right] \quad \text{for } y \in C_w. \tag{1}$$

If F is continuous with respect to the uniform topology of C_w then H is continuous with respect to the uniform topology of R^n.

Proof Since the transformation $L^{(n)}$ of C_w covers $P^{(n)}$ and since there is a one-to-one correspondence between $P^{(n)}$ and R^n there exists a real-valued function H on R^n which satisfies the condition (1).

Let F be continuous with respect to the uniform topology of C_w. To show the continuity of H at an arbitrary $[\zeta_1, \cdots, \zeta_n] \in R^n$ in the uniform topology of R^n, let $\varepsilon > 0$ be given. Let $z \in P^{(n)}$ be such that $[z(1/n), \cdots, z(n/n)] = [\zeta_1, \cdots, \zeta_n]$. From the continuity of F on C_w and in particular at z, there exists $\delta > 0$ such that $|F[y] - F[z]| < \varepsilon$ whenever $y \in C_w$ and $|||y - z||| < \delta$. Consider $[\eta_1, \cdots, \eta_n] \in R^n$ with $|\eta_i - \zeta_i| < \delta$ for

$i = 1,2,\cdots,n$. Let $y \in P^{(n)}$ be such that $y(i/n) = \eta_i$ for $i = 1,2,\cdots,n$. Then $|y(i/n) - z(i/n)| = |\eta_i - \zeta_i| < \delta$ for $i = 1,2,\cdots,n$, and hence $|||y - z||| < \delta$ since $y, z \in P^{(n)}$. Then

$$|H[\eta_1,\cdots,\eta_n] - H[\zeta_1,\cdots,\zeta_n]|$$

$$= \left|H\left[y\left(\tfrac{1}{n}\right),\cdots,y\left(\tfrac{n}{n}\right)\right] - H\left[z\left(\tfrac{1}{n}\right),\cdots,z\left(\tfrac{n}{n}\right)\right]\right|$$

$$= |F[y] - F[z]| < \varepsilon,$$

so that H is continuous at $[\zeta_1,\cdots,\zeta_n]$. □

Definition 33.3 For $M > 0$ and $n = 1,2,\cdots$, let

$$C_M = \{y \in C_w ;\ |||y||| \le M\} \quad \text{and} \quad C_M^{(n)} = \{y \in C_w ;\ |||L^{(n)}y||| \le M\}.$$

In connection with C_M and $C_M^{(n)}$, note that $C_M^{(2n)} \subset C_M^{(n)}$, so that $C_M^{(2^k)} \downarrow$ as $k \to \infty$ and $\lim_{k\to\infty} C_M^{(2^k)} = C_M$. For $M' < M''$ we have $C_{M'} \subset C_{M''}$ and $\lim_{M\to\infty} C_M = C_w$. For $M' < M''$ we have $C_{M'} \subset C_{M''}$ and $\lim_{M\to\infty} C_M = C_w$. Note also that $C_M^{(n)}, C_M \in \sigma(\mathfrak{T})$.

Lemma 33.4 Let F be a real-valued function on C_w which is continuous with respect to the uniform topology of C_w. With the transformation $y = Tx$ where $Tx = x + x_0$ with a fixed $x_0 \in C_w$ we have

$$\int_{C_M^{(n)}} F\left[L^{(n)}y\right] m_w(dy)$$

$$= \int_{T^{-1}C_M^{(n)}} F\left[L^{(n)}[x+x_0]\right] \exp\left\{-\frac{1}{2}\sum_{i=1}^{n} \frac{\left[x_0(t_i) - x_0(t_{i-1})\right]^2}{t_i - t_{i-1}}\right\}$$

$$\times \exp\left\{-\sum_{i=1}^{n} \frac{\left[x_0(t_i) - x_0(t_{i-1})\right]\left[x(t_i) - x(t_{i-1})\right]}{t_i - t_{i-1}}\right\} m_w(dx) , \quad (1)$$

where $L^{(n)}$ is as defined in Definition 33.1 and $t_i = i/n$ for $i = 1,2,\cdots,n$. □

Proof According to Lemma 33.2 there exists a real-valued continuous function $H[\eta_1,\cdots,\eta_n]$ on R^n such that

$$F\left[L^{(n)}y\right] = H\left[y\left(\frac{1}{n}\right),\cdots,y\left(\frac{n}{n}\right)\right] \quad \text{for } y \in C_w .$$

Then

$$\chi_{C_M^{(n)}}[y]\, F\left[L^{(n)}y\right]$$

$$= \chi_{[-M,M]\times\cdots\times[-M,M]}\left[y\left(\frac{1}{n}\right),\cdots,y\left(\frac{n}{n}\right)\right] H\left[y\left(\frac{1}{n}\right),\cdots,y\left(\frac{n}{n}\right)\right],$$

so that, by Theorem 29.6,

$$\int_{C_M^{(n)}} F\left[L^{(n)}y\right] m_w(dy)$$

$$= \int_{C_w} \chi_{C_M^{(n)}}[y]\, F\left[L^{(n)}y\right] m_w(dy)$$

$$= \left\{(2\pi)^n \prod_{i=1}^{n} (t_i - t_{i-1})\right\}^{-\frac{1}{2}} \int_{-M}^{M}{}^{(n)} \int_{-M}^{M} H[\eta_1,\cdots,\eta_n]$$

$$\times \exp\left\{-\frac{1}{2} \sum_{i=1} \frac{(\eta_i - \eta_{i-1})^2}{t_i - t_{i-1}}\right\} d\eta_1\cdots d\eta_n. \quad (2)$$

With the translation

$$\eta_i = \xi_i + a_i \quad \text{where } a_i = x_0(t_i) \text{ for } i = 1,2,\cdots,n$$

in the integral on the right side of (2), we obtain

$$\int_{C_M^{(n)}} F\left[L^{(n)}y\right] m_w(dy)$$

$$= \left\{(2\pi)^n \prod_{i=1}^{n}(t_i - t_{i-1})\right\}^{-\frac{1}{2}} \int_{-M-a_1}^{M-a_1} (n) \int_{-M-a_n}^{M-a_n} H[\xi_1 + a_1, \cdots, \xi_n + a_n]$$

$$\times \exp\left\{-\frac{1}{2}\sum_{i=1}^{n}\frac{(\xi_i - \xi_{i-1})^2}{t_i - t_{i-1}}\right\} \exp\left\{-\frac{1}{2}\sum_{i=1}^{n}\frac{(a_i - a_{i-1})^2}{t_i - t_{i-1}}\right\}$$

$$\times \exp\left\{-\sum_{i=1}^{n}\frac{(a_i - a_{i-1})(\xi_i - \xi_{i-1})}{t_i - t_{i-1}}\right\} d\xi_1 \cdots d\xi_n . \tag{3}$$

On the other hand since $L^{(n)}[x+x_0] = L^{(n)}x + L^{(n)}x_0$ we have

$$F\left[L^{(n)}[x+x_0]\right] = H\left[x\left(\frac{1}{n}\right) + x_0\left(\frac{1}{n}\right), \cdots, x\left(\frac{n}{n}\right) + x_0\left(\frac{n}{n}\right)\right].$$

Also $x \in T^{-1}C_M^{(n)}$ if and only if $-M-a_i \le x(i/n) \le M - a_i$ for $i = 1, 2, \cdots, n$. If we use these facts in the right side of (1) and apply Theorem 29.6, then we see that the right side of (1) is equal to the right side of (3). This proves (1). □

<u>Theorem 33.5</u> (R. H. Cameron and W. T. Martin [1]) Let F be a real-valued functional on C_w which is continuous on C_w and bounded on every bounded subset of C_w in the uniform topology of C_w and is furthermore Wiener integrable on C_w. Let $x_0 \in C_w$ be such that x_0' exists and $x_0' \in B.V.[0,1]$. Then with the change of variable of integration $y = x + x_0$ we have

$$\int_{C_w} F[y]\, m_w(dy) = \int_{C_w} F[x+x_0]\, J(x_0, x)\, m_w(dx), \tag{1}$$

where "Jacobian" $J(x_0, \cdot)$ is given by

$$J(x_0, x) = \exp\left\{-\tfrac{1}{2}\int_0^1 \left[x_0'(t)\right]^2 dt\right\} \exp\left\{-\int_0^1 x_0'(t)\, dx(t)\right\}. \tag{2}$$

Proof With $n = 2^k$ in (1) of Lemma 33.4 we have

$$\int_{C_M^{(2^k)}} F\left[L^{(2^k)} y\right] m_w(dy)$$

$$= \int_{T^{-1} C_M^{(2^k)}} F\left[L^{(2^k)}[x + x_0]\right] \exp\left\{-\tfrac{1}{2} \sum_{i=1}^{2^k} \frac{\left[x_0(t_i) - x_0(t_{i-1})\right]^2}{t_i - t_{i-1}}\right\}$$

$$\times \exp\left\{-\sum_{i=1}^{2^k} \frac{\left[x_0(t_i) - x_0(t_{i-1})\right]\left[x(t_i) - x(t_{i-1})\right]}{t_i - t_{i-1}}\right\} m_w(dx). \tag{3}$$

We shall prove (1) be letting $k \to \infty$ and then $M \to \infty$ in (3).

Consider the left side of (1). Since $\lim_{k\to\infty} \left\| L^{(2^k)} y - y \right\| = 0$ and F is continuous with respect to the uniform topology of C_w, we have

$$\lim_{k\to\infty} F\left[L^{(2^k)} y\right] = F[y] \qquad \text{for } y \in C_w.$$

Let us write the left side of (1) as

$$\int_{C_M^{(2^k)}} F\left[L^{(2^k)} y\right] m_w(dy)$$

$$= \int_{C_M^{(2^k)} - C_M} F\left[L^{(2^k)} y\right] m_w(dy) + \int_{C_M} F\left[L^{(2^k)} y\right] m_w(dy). \tag{4}$$

Let B_M be a bound of F on C_M. For $y \in C_M^{(2^k)}$ we have

$L^{(2^k)}y \in C_M$ so that $\left|F\left[L^{(2^k)}y\right]\right| \le B_M$ for $y \in C_M^{(2^k)}$. Then since $C_M^{(2^k)} \downarrow C_M$ as $k \to \infty$ we have

$$\lim_{k\to\infty} \left| \int_{C_M^{(2^k)} - C_M} F\left[L^{(2^k)}y\right] m_w(dy) \right|$$

$$\le \lim_{k\to\infty} B_M\, m_w\left(C_M^{(2^k)} - C_M\right) = 0. \tag{5}$$

Also by the Bounded Convergence Theorem we have

$$\lim_{k\to\infty} \int_{C_M} F\left[L^{(2^k)}y\right] m_w(dy) = \int_{C_M} F[y]\, m_w(dy). \tag{6}$$

Using (5) and (6) in (4) we have

$$\lim_{k\to\infty} \int_{C_M^{(2^k)}} F\left[L^{(2^k)}y\right] m_w(dy) = \int_{C_M} F[y]\, m_w(dy). \tag{7}$$

Regarding the right side of (2), let

$$s_k[x] = \frac{1}{2}\sum_{i=1}^{2^k} \frac{\left[x_0(t_i)-x_0(t_{i-1})\right]^2}{t_i - t_{i-1}} + \sum_{i=1}^{2^k} \frac{\left[x_0(t_i) - x_0(t_{i-1})\right]\left[x(t_i) - x(t_{i-1})\right]}{t_i - t_{i-1}}.$$

We claim that

$$\lim_{k\to\infty} s_k[x] = \frac{1}{2}\int_0^1 \left[x_0'(t)\right]^2 dt + \int_0^1 x_0'(t)\, dx(t) \tag{8}$$

and that for every $M \ge 0$ there exists $b_M \ge 0$ such that

$$|s_k[x]| \le b_M \quad \text{for } k = 1, 2, \cdots \text{ and } x \in C_M. \tag{9}$$

To show (8) and (9) let

$$z(t) = \tfrac{1}{2}x_0(t) + x(t).$$

Then by the Mean Value Theorem

$$s_k[x] = \sum_{i=1}^{2^k} \frac{x_0(t_i) - x_0(t_{i-1})}{t_i - t_{i-1}} \left[z(t_i) - z(t_{i-1})\right]$$

$$= \sum_{i=1}^{2^k} x_0'(t_i^*)\left[z(t_i) - z(t_{i-1})\right] \tag{10}$$

for some $t_i^* \in (t_{i-1}, t_i)$ for $i = 1, 2, \cdots, 2^k$. Since $x_0' \in$ B.V. $[0,1]$ and $z \in C_w$ we have $\lim_{k\to\infty} s_k[x] = \int_0^1 x_0'(t)\, dz(t)$. The last Riemann-Stieltjes integral is equal to the right side of (8). Thus (8) holds. To prove (9) let us note that by Abel's transformation applied to the right side of (10) we have

$$s_k[x] = x_0'\left(t^*_{2^k}\right) z(1) - \sum_{i=1}^{2^k} \left[x_0'(t^*_{i+1}) - x_0'(t_i^*)\right] z(t_i). \tag{11}$$

Let

$$A = \max\left\{ |||x_0|||,\ \text{Var}\ x_0',\ |||x_0'||| \right\},$$

where Var x_0' is the variation of x_0' on $[0,1]$ and $|||x_0'||| = \sup_{[0,1]} |x_0'(t)| < \infty$. Then, from (11),

$$|s_k[x]| \le 2A(\tfrac{1}{2}A + M) = A^2 + 2AM \qquad \text{for } x \in C_M.$$

If we let $b_M = A^2 + 2AM$, then (9) holds. With s_k, the right side of (3) can be written as

$$\int_{T^{-1}C_M^{(2^k)}} F\left[L^{(2^k)}[x+x_0]\right] \exp\left\{-s_k[x]\right\} m_w(dx)$$

$$= \int_{T^{-1}\left(C_M^{(2^k)}-C_M\right)} \cdots\, m_w(dx) + \int_{T^{-1}C_M} \cdots\, m_w(dx). \tag{12}$$

For $x \in T^{-1}C_M^{(2^k)}$ we have $x+x_0 \in C_M^{(2^k)}$ and $L^{(2^k)}[x+x_0] \in C_M$, so that by the definition of B_M and by (9)

$$\left| F\left[L^{(2^k)}[x+x_0] \exp\left\{-s_k[x]\right\}\right| \le B_M e^{b_M}.$$

Since $C_M^{(2^k)} \downarrow C_M$ and $T^{-1}C_M^{(2^k)} \downarrow T^{-1}C_M$ as $k \to \infty$ the first term on the right side of (12) converges to 0 as $k \to \infty$. Applying the Bounded Convergence Theorem to the second term on the right side of (12) and using (8) we have

$$\lim_{k\to\infty} \int_{T^{-1}C_M^{(2^k)}} F\left[L^{(2^k)}[x+x_0]\right] \exp\left\{-s_k[x]\right\} m_w(dx)$$

$$= \int_{T^{-1}C_M} F[x+x_0]\, J(x_0, x)\, m_w(dx). \tag{13}$$

From (7), (13), and (3) we have

$$\int_{C_M} F[y]\, m_w(dy) = \int_{T^{-1}C_M} F[x+x_0]\, J(x_0, x)\, m_w(dx). \tag{14}$$

Finally, since $C_M \uparrow C_w$ and $T^{-1}C_M \uparrow C_w$ as $M \to \infty$ and since F is integrable on C_w, we obtain (1) by letting $M \to \infty$ in (14). □

[III] The Translation Theorem

As a preparation for the translation theorem for an arbitrary Wiener measurable functional we introduce, in addition to $\mathfrak{W}_{t_1 \cdots t_n}$, $\mathfrak{W}$, $\sigma(\mathfrak{W})$, and $\mathfrak{W}^*$ which were defined in Theorem 29.1 and Definition 29.2, the following families of subsets of C_w:

Definition 33.6 Let $\mathfrak{I}$ be the subcollection of the field $\mathfrak{W}$ of subsets of C_w consisting of Borel cylinders whose bases are semiopen semiclosed intervals in Euclidean spaces, i.e., $\mathfrak{I}$ consists of subsets of C_w of the type

$$\left\{x \in C_w ; \alpha_i < x(t_i) \le \beta_i,\ i = 1, 2, \cdots, n\right\}$$

where $0 < t_1 < \cdots < t_n \le 1$ and $-\infty \le \alpha_i < \beta_i \le \infty$ for $i = 1, 2, \cdots, n$. Let $\mathfrak{I}^\sigma$ be the collection of countable unions of members of $\mathfrak{I}$ and let $\mathfrak{I}^{\sigma\downarrow}$ be the collection of limits of monotone decreasing sequences of members of $\mathfrak{I}^\sigma$.

It is obvious that $\mathfrak{I} \subset \mathfrak{I}^\sigma \subset \mathfrak{I}^{\sigma\downarrow}$ and $\mathfrak{I}^\sigma, \mathfrak{I}^{\sigma\downarrow} \in \sigma(\mathfrak{W})$. Also $\mathfrak{I}$ and $\mathfrak{I}^\sigma$ are closed under intersection. We proceed to show that if $\Gamma \in \mathfrak{W}^*$ then $\Gamma = G - N$ where $G \in \mathfrak{I}^{\sigma\downarrow}$ and $N \subset G$, $N \in \mathfrak{W}^*$, with $m_w(N) = 0$.

Lemma 33.7 Let $E \in \mathfrak{W}$, say $E \in \mathfrak{W}_{t_1 \cdots t_n}$, $0 < t_1 < \cdots < t_n \le 1$, and

$$E = \left\{x \in C_w ; \left[x(t_1), \cdots, x(t_n)\right] \in B\right\} \quad \text{with } B \in \mathfrak{B}^n. \tag{1}$$

For every $\epsilon > 0$ there exist a compact set B' and an open set B'' in R^n such that $B' \subset B \subset B''$ and $m_w(E - E') < \epsilon$ and $m_w(E'' - E) < \epsilon$ where E' and E'' are members of $\mathfrak{W}_{t_1 \cdots t_n}$

obtained by replacing B in (1) by B' and B'', respectively.

<u>Proof</u> For $B \in \mathfrak{B}^n$ (and in fact for any Lebesgue measurable set in R^n), given $\eta > 0$ there exists an open set B'' in R^n such that $B \subset B''$ and $m_L(B'' - B) < \eta$. (This is obvious from the definition of the outer measure when B is bounded. When B is not bounded, we can reduce the case to the bounded case by the σ-finiteness of m_L.) For brevity let

$$N = \left\{(2\pi)^n \prod_{i=1}^{n} (t_i - t_{i-1})\right\}^{-\frac{1}{2}} \quad \text{and} \quad W(\xi) = \exp\left\{-\tfrac{1}{2}\sum_{i=n}^{n} \frac{(\xi_i - \xi_{i-1})^2}{t_i - t_{i-1}}\right\}.$$

Then with $\eta > 0$ so chosen that $\eta < \epsilon N^{-1}$ we have

$$m_L(E'' - E) = N\int_{B''-B} W(\xi)\, m_L(d\xi) \leq N m_L(B'' - B) < \epsilon.$$

To find the desired compact set B' let $M \geq 0$ be so large that

$$N \int_{B_M^c} W(\xi)\, m_L(d\xi) < \frac{\epsilon}{2} \qquad \text{where } B_M = \left\{\xi \in R^n ; \sqrt{\sum_{i=1}^{n} \xi_i^2} \leq M\right\}.$$

Let $*$ denote complementation in the subspace B_M of R^n which has a finite measure. From the foregoing result, for an arbitrary $\eta > 0$ there exists an open set B'' in B_M such that $(B \cap B_M)^* \subset B''$ and $m_L\left(B'' - (B \cap B_M)^*\right) < \eta$. Let $B' = (B'')^*$. Then B' is a closed set in B_M, $B' \subset B \cap B_M$, and $m_L\left((B \cap B_M) - B'\right) < \eta$. Now B' which is closed in B_M is also closed in R^n so that it is a compact set. With $\eta = \frac{1}{2}\epsilon N^{-1}$ we have

$$m_w(E - E') = N \int_{B-B'} W(\xi)\, m_L(d\xi).$$

From $B - B' \subset B_M^c \cup \{(B \cap B_M) - B'\}$ we obtain $m_w(E - E') < \varepsilon$. □

Lemma 33.8 Let $\Gamma \in \mathfrak{W}^*$. Then for every $\varepsilon > 0$ there exists $G \in \mathfrak{J}^\sigma$ such that $\Gamma \subset G$ and $m_w(G - \Gamma) < \varepsilon$.

Proof Since $\Gamma \in \mathfrak{W}^*$, there exists a subset O of C_w which is a countable union of members of $\mathfrak{W}$, contains Γ, and has $m_w(O - \Gamma) < \varepsilon/2$. Since $\mathfrak{W}$ is a field, O can be given as the union of countably many disjoint members $\{E_k, k = 1, 2, \cdots\}$ of $\mathfrak{W}$. Let E_k be given as a Borel cylinder whose base B_k is a member of $\mathfrak{B}^{n(k)}$. According to Lemma 33.7 there exists an open set B_k'' in $R^{n(k)}$ such that $B_k \subset B_k''$ and $m_w(E_k'' - E_k) < \varepsilon 2^{-(k+1)}$ where E_k'' is the Borel cylinder with B_k'' as its base. From $E_k \subset E_k''$ we have $\Gamma \subset O = \bigcup_{k=1}^\infty E_k \subset \bigcup_{k=1}^\infty E_k''$ and

$$\bigcup_{k=1}^\infty E_k'' - \Gamma = \left(\bigcup_{k=1}^\infty E_k'' - \bigcup_{k=1}^\infty E_k\right) \cup \left(\bigcup_{k=1}^\infty E_k - \Gamma\right) \subset \bigcup_{k=1}^\infty (E_k'' - E_k) \cup \left(\bigcup_{k=1}^\infty E_k - \Gamma\right),$$

so that

$$m_w\left(\bigcup_{k=1}^\infty E_k'' - \Gamma\right) \le \sum_{k=1}^\infty m_w(E_k'' - E_k) + m_w\left(\bigcup_{k=1}^\infty E_k - \Gamma\right) \le \sum_{k=1}^\infty \frac{\varepsilon}{2^{k+1}} + \frac{\varepsilon}{2} = \varepsilon.$$

Let $G = \bigcup_{k=1}^\infty E_k''$. It remains to show that $G \in \mathfrak{J}^\sigma$. Now since B_k'' is an open set in $R^{n(k)}$ it is a countable union of semiopen semiclosed intervals in $R^{n(k)}$. Since the inverse transformation of a countable union is the countable union of inverse transformations, $E_k'' \in \mathfrak{J}^\sigma$ and consequently $G \in \mathfrak{J}^\sigma$ too. □

Lemma 33.9 It $\Gamma \in \mathfrak{W}^*$ then $\Gamma = G - N$ where $G \in \mathfrak{J}^{\sigma\downarrow}$ and $N \subset G$, $N \in \mathfrak{W}^*$, with $m_w(N) = 0$.

Proof According to Lemma 33.8, for every positive integer n there exists $G_n \in \mathfrak{J}^\sigma$ such that $\Gamma \subset G_n$ and $m_w(G_n - \Gamma) < 1/n$. Let $G_n' = \bigcap_{k=1}^n G_k$. Then since $\mathfrak{J}^\sigma$ is closed under finite intersection, $G_n' \in \mathfrak{J}^\sigma$. Also $\Gamma \subset G_n'$ and $G_n' \downarrow$ as $n \to \infty$. Let $G = \lim_{n\to\infty} G_n' \in \mathfrak{J}^{\sigma\downarrow}$. Then $\Gamma \subset G$ and $m_w(G - \Gamma) \leq m_w(G_n - \Gamma) < 1/n$ for every n, so that $m_w(G - \Gamma) = 0$. By letting $N = G - \Gamma$ we have the proof. □

Theorem 33.10 (R. H. Cameron and W. T. Martin [1]) Let T be a translation of C_w defined by $Tx = x + x_0$ for $x \in C_w$ where $x_0 \in C_w$ and $x_0' \in$ B. V. [0,1]. Then $T^{-1}\Gamma$, $T\Gamma \in \mathfrak{W}^*$ for every $\Gamma \in \mathfrak{W}^*$ and

$$m_w(\Gamma) = \int_{T^{-1}\Gamma} J(x_0, x)\, m_w(dx) \tag{1}$$

where

$$J(x_0, x) = \exp\left\{-\frac{1}{2}\int_0^1 \left[x_0'(t)\right]^2 dt\right\} \exp\left\{-\int_0^1 x_0'(t)\, dx(t)\right\}. \tag{2}$$

Moreover if F is an extended real-valued Wiener measurable (i.e., $\mathfrak{W}^*$-measurable) functional on C_w then

$$\int_\Gamma F[y]\, m_w(dy) = \int_{T^{-1}\Gamma} F[x + x_0]\, J(x_0, x)\, m_w(dx) \tag{3}$$

for $\Gamma \in \mathfrak{W}^*$ in the sense that the existence of one side implies that of the other and the equality of the two.

Proof According to Theorem 33.5, if G is a real-valued functional on C_w which is continuous on C_w and bounded on every subset of C_w in the uniform topology of C_w and is furthermore integrable on C_w then

$$\int_{C_w} G[y]\, m_w(dy) = \int_{C_w} G[x+x_0]\, J(x_0, x)\, m_w(dx). \tag{4}$$

Note that by taking $G \equiv 1$ on C_w we have the Wiener integrability of $J(x_0, \cdot)$ on C_w, and in fact

$$\int_{C_w} J(x_0, x)\, m_w(dx) = 1. \tag{5}$$

We shall use (4) to show that for every $\Gamma \in \mathfrak{W}^*$, $T^{-1}\Gamma \in \mathfrak{W}^*$ as well as (1), or equivalently, in view of $\chi_{T^{-1}\Gamma}[x] = \chi_\Gamma[x+x_0]$,

$$\int_{C_w} \chi_\Gamma[y]\, m_w(dy) = \int_{C_w} \chi_{T^{-1}\Gamma}[x]\, J(x_0, x)\, m_w(dx)$$

$$= \int_{C_w} \chi_\Gamma[x+x_0]\, J(x_0, x)\, m_w(dx) \tag{6}$$

hold. In this connection note that $T^{-1}\Gamma \in \mathfrak{W}^*$ is equivalent to the Wiener measurability of $\chi_\Gamma[x+x_0]$ as a functional of x. Needless to say that $T^{-1}\Gamma \in \mathfrak{W}^*$ for every $\Gamma \in \mathfrak{W}^*$ will also imply $T\Gamma \in \mathfrak{W}^*$ for every $\Gamma \in \mathfrak{W}^*$ since $T = (T^{-1})^{-1}$ and T^{-1} is a translation given by $T^{-1}x = x - x_0$ and $-x_0$ satisfies the condition in the theorem on x_0.

Let us start with the case where $\Gamma = I \in \mathfrak{J}$ which is given by

$$I = \left\{x \in C_w;\, \alpha_i < x(t_i) \le \beta_i,\ i = 1, 2, \cdots, n\right\}$$

where $0 < t_1 < \cdots < t_n \le 1$ and $-\infty \le \alpha_i < \beta_i \le \infty$ for $i = 1, 2, \cdots, n$. For every $\epsilon > 0$, let $\varphi_{\epsilon,i}$ be a continuous and trapezoidal function on R^1 defined by

$$\varphi_{\epsilon,i}(\eta) = \begin{cases} 1 & \text{for } \eta \in [\alpha_i + \epsilon, \beta_i] \\ 0 & \text{for } \eta \in (-\infty, \alpha_i] \cup [\beta_i + \epsilon, \infty) \\ \text{linear} & \text{for } \eta \in [\alpha_i, \alpha_i + \epsilon] \text{ and for } \eta \in [\beta_i, \beta_i + \epsilon]. \end{cases}$$

Then $\varphi_{\epsilon,i}\left[y(t_i)\right]$, $y \in C_w$, is continuous in the uniform topology of C_w and so is

$$\varphi_\epsilon[y] = \prod_{i=1}^{n} \varphi_{\epsilon,i}\left[y(t_i)\right] \quad \text{for } y \in C_w.$$

Also φ_ϵ is bounded by 1 on C_w and is hence Wiener integrable on C_w. Thus by (4)

$$\int_{C_w} \varphi_\epsilon[y]\, m_w(dy) = \int_{C_w} \varphi_\epsilon[x + x_0]\, J(x_0, x)\, m_w(dx).$$

Now since $\lim_{\epsilon \downarrow 0} \varphi_\epsilon[y] = \chi_I[y]$ for every $y \in C_w$ and since the integrands in the left and right sides are bounded by 1 and $J(x_0, \cdot)$, respectively, for all $\epsilon > 0$, we have, by the Dominated Convergence Theorem,

$$\int_{C_w} \chi_I[y]\, m_w(dy) = \int_{C_w} \chi_I[x + x_0]\, J(x_0, x)\, m_w(dx). \tag{7}$$

Observe that the Wiener measurability of $\chi_I[x + x_0]$ as a function of x is implied by $\chi_I[x + x_0] = \lim_{\epsilon \downarrow 0} \varphi_\epsilon[x + x_0]$.

Next consider the case where $\Gamma = I_1 \cup I_2$ where $I_1, I_2 \in \mathfrak{J}$. Then $I_1, I_2 \in \mathfrak{B}_{t_1 \cdots t_n}$ for some $\{t_1, \cdots, t_n\} \subset [0,1]$ with $0 < t_1 < \cdots < t_n \leq 1$ and $I_1 \cup I_2$ is a Borel cylinder in C_w whose base is the union of two semiopen semiclosed intervals A_1 and A_2 in R^n. Now $A_1 \cup A_2$ can be given as the union of disjoint semiopen semiclosed intervals $B_1, \cdots, B_q$ in R^n. Let $J_1, \cdots, J_q$ be the Borel cylinders in C_w whose bases are $B_1, \cdots, B_q$, respectively. Then $\{J_1, \cdots, J_q\}$ is a disjoint collection and $\bigcup_{p=1}^q J_p = I_1 \cup I_2$ so that

$$\chi_{I_1 \cup I_2} = \sum_{p=1}^q \chi_{J_p}.$$

Applying (7) to each J_p and summing over p we have

$$\begin{aligned}
\int_{C_w} \chi_{I_1 \cup I_2}[y]\, m_w(dy) &= \sum_{p=1}^q \int_{C_w} \chi_{J_p}[y]\, m_w(dy) \\
&= \sum_{p=1}^q \int_{C_w} \chi_{J_p}[x+x_0]\, J(x_0, x)\, m_w(dx) \\
&= \int_{C_w} \chi_{I_1 \cup I_2}[x+x_0]\, J(x_0, x)\, m_w(dx). \quad (8)
\end{aligned}$$

This proves (6) for this case.

When $\Gamma = G \in \mathfrak{J}^\sigma$ then $G = \bigcup_{n=1}^\infty I_n$ where $\{I_n, n = 1, 2, \cdots\} \subset \mathfrak{J}$. Since $\chi_{\bigcup_{k=1}^n I_k}[y] \uparrow \chi_G[y]$ as $n \to \infty$ for every $y \in C_w$, and since (6) holds for $\chi_{\bigcup_{k=1}^n I_k}$ as we proved for the last case, (6) holds for χ_G also by the Monotone Convergence Theorem Theorem.

When $\Gamma = G \in \mathfrak{J}^{\sigma\downarrow}$ then G is the limit of a monotone decreasing sequence $\{G_n, n = 1, 2, \cdots\} \subset \mathfrak{J}^\sigma$, so that $\chi_{G_n}[y] \downarrow \chi_G[y]$ as $n \to \infty$ for every $y \in C_w$. Since (6) holds for χ_{G_n} by the last case, (6) holds for χ_G by the Dominated Convergence Theorem.

When $\Gamma = N \in \mathfrak{W}^*$ with $m_w(N) = 0$ then, by Lemma 33.9,

$N = G - N'$ where $G \in \mathfrak{J}^{\sigma\downarrow}$ and $N' \subset G$, $N' \in \mathfrak{W}^*$ with $m_w(N') = 0$. Then $G = N \cup N'$ so that $m_w(G) = 0$ also. Since (6) holds for χ_G by the last case, we have

$$0 = m_w(G) = \int_{C_w} \chi_G[y]\, m_w(dy) = \int_{C_w} \chi_G[x + x_0]\, J(x_0, x)\, m_w(dx).$$

Since the integrand on the extreme right is nonnegative, it must be equal to 0 for a.e. $x \in C_w$. Then since $J(x_0, x) > 0$ for every $x \in C_w$, $\chi_G[x + x_0] = 0$ for a.e. $x \in C_w$. From $N \subset G$ we have $\chi_N[x + x_0] = 0$ for a.e. $x \in C_w$. Thus

$$\int_{C_w} \chi_N[y]\, m_w(dy) = m_w(N) = 0 = \int_{C_w} \chi_N[x + x_0]\, J(x_0, x)\, m_w(dx),$$

proving (6) for this case.

Finally for $\Gamma \in \mathfrak{W}^*$, we have, by Lemma 33.9, $\Gamma = G - N$ where $G \in \mathfrak{J}^{\sigma\downarrow}$ and $N \subset G$, $N \in \mathfrak{W}^*$, with $m_w(N) = 0$. Thus we have $\chi_\Gamma[y] = \chi_G[y] - \chi_N[y]$ for $y \in C_w$ and similarly $\chi_\Gamma[x + x_0] = \chi_G[x + x_0] - \chi_N[x + x_0]$ for $x \in C_w$. From this and from the fact that (6) holds for χ_G and χ_N, it holds for χ_G also. This completes the proof of (6) in its generality and its equivalent (1). Let us remark also that the Wiener measurability of $T^{-1}\Gamma$, i.e., the Wiener measurability of $\chi_\Gamma[x + x_0]$ as a functional of x when $\Gamma \in \mathfrak{W}^*$ has been proved case by case starting from the case $\Gamma \in \mathfrak{J}$.

Now that (1) holds for any $\Gamma \in \mathfrak{W}^*$, (3) holds for a simple function F on C_w and consequently for a nonnegative Wiener measurable function F on C_w. Then (3) holds for an arbitrary extended real-valued Wiener measurable function on F on C_w in the sense that the existence of one side implies that of the other and the equality of the two. □

Corollary 33.11 Let p be a real-valued function which is continuous and of bounded variation on $[0,1]$. Then

$$\int_{C_w} \exp\left\{\zeta \int_0^1 p(t)\, dx(t)\right\} m_w(dx) = \exp\left\{\frac{\zeta^2}{2}\int_0^1 \left[p(t)\right]^2 dt\right\}$$

for $\zeta \in C$, (1)

and in particular

$$\int_{C_w} \exp\left\{i\lambda \int_0^1 p(t)\, dx(t)\right\} m_w(dx) = \exp\left\{-\frac{\lambda^2}{2}\int_0^1 \left[p(t)\right]^2 dt\right\}$$

for $\lambda \in R^1$. (2)

Thus the characteristic function $\varphi(\lambda)$, $\lambda \in R^1$, of the random variable $\int_0^1 p(t)\, dx(t)$ on the probability space $\left(C_w, \mathfrak{W}^*, m_w\right)$ is given by the right side of (2), and the random variable is distributed according to $N\left(0, \int_0^1 \left[p(t)\right]^2 dt\right)$.

Proof For $\xi \in R$ let $x_0(t) = \int_0^t -\xi\, p(s)\, ds$ for $t \in [0,1]$. Then $x_0 \in C_w$ and $x_0' = -\xi p \in$ B. V. $[0,1]$, so that for any Wiener integrable functional F on C_w we have, according to Theorem 33.10

$$\int_{C_w} F[y]\, m_w(dy) = \int_{C_w} F[x + x_0] \exp\left\{-\tfrac{1}{2}\xi^2 \int_0^1 \left[p(t)\right]^2 dt\right\}$$

$$\times \exp\left\{\xi \int_0^1 p(t)\, dx(t)\right\} m_w(dx).$$

In particular, with $F \equiv 1$ on C_w,

$$\int_{C_w} \exp\left\{\xi \int_0^1 p(t)\, dx(t)\right\} m_w(dx) = \exp\left\{\frac{\xi^2}{2}\int_0^1 \left[p(t)\right]^2 dt\right\}$$

for $\xi \in R^1$, (3)

which proves (1) for the case $\zeta \in C$.

To prove (1) for $\zeta \in C$ let us note that the right side of (1) is a holomorphic function of ζ on C. If we show that the left side of (1) is also a holomorphic function of ζ on C then the equality of the two holomorphic functions on the real axis as given by (3) implies the equality of the two on the entire complex plane. Thus, to complete the proof of (1) it remains to show that the left side of (1) is a holomorphic function of ζ on C. To show this it suffices to prove that, for any simple closed rectifiable smooth curve K on C,

$$\int_K \left[\int_{C_w} \exp\left\{ \zeta \int_0^1 p(t)\, dx(t) \right\} m_w(dx) \right] d\zeta = 0 \tag{4}$$

holds.

Let us parametrize K by the arc length s, $0 \le s \le \ell$, where ℓ is the arc length of K. Then $|\zeta'(s)| = 1$ for $s \in [0, \ell]$. Also from the fact that K is a bounded set on C we have $|\zeta(s)| \le M$ for $s \in [0, \ell]$ with some nonnegative number M. Now

$$\begin{aligned} I &\equiv \int_K \left[\int_{C_w} \exp\left\{ \zeta \int_0^1 p(t)\, dx(t) \right\} m_w(dx) \right] d\zeta \\ &= \int_0^\ell \left[\int_{C_w} \exp\left\{ \zeta(s) \int_0^1 p(t)\, dx(t) \right\} m_w(dx) \right] \zeta'(s)\, ds . \end{aligned}$$

To apply the Fubini theorem, let us observe that for $\zeta = \xi + i\eta$, where $\xi, \eta \in R^1$ and $|\zeta| \le M$, and $u \in R^1$, we have

$$|e^{\zeta u}| = e^{\xi u} \le e^{|\zeta|\,|u|} < e^{Mu} + e^{-Mu},$$

so that

$$\left| \exp\left\{ \zeta(s) \int_0^1 p(t)\, dx(t) \right\} \zeta'(s) \right|$$
$$\le \exp\left\{ M \int_0^1 p(t)\, dx(t) \right\} + \exp\left\{ -M \int_0^1 p(t)\, dx(t) \right\} .$$

According to (3),

$$\int_0^\ell \left[\int_{C_w} \exp\left\{ M \int_0^1 p(t)\, dx(t) \right\} m_w(dx) \right] ds$$
$$= \int_0^\ell \exp\left\{ \frac{M^2}{2} \int_0^1 \left[p(t) \right]^2 dt \right\} ds = \ell \exp\left\{ \frac{M^2}{2} \int_0^1 \left[p(t) \right]^2 dt \right\} < \infty ,$$

and similarly for $\exp\left\{ -M \int_0^1 p(t)\, dx(t) \right\}$. Thus the Fubini theorem is applicable to our iterated integral I, and consequently

$$I = \int_{C_w} \left[\int_0^\ell \exp\left\{ \zeta(s) \int_0^1 p(t)\, dx(t) \right\} \zeta'(s)\, ds \right] m_w(dx)$$
$$= \int_{C_w} \left[\int_K \exp\left\{ \zeta \int_0^1 p(t)\, dx(t) \right\} d\zeta \right] m_w(dx)$$
$$= \int_{C_w} 0\, m_w(dx) = 0.$$

This completes the proof. □

[IV] The Probability Measure Induced by the Translated Process

Lemma 33.12 Let μ_1 and μ_2 be finite measures on a measurable space $(X, \mathfrak{A})$ and let $\mathfrak{A}_0$ be a field of subsets of X which generates the σ-field $\mathfrak{A}$. If there is a nonnegative $\mathfrak{A}$-measurable and μ_1-integrable function f on X such that

$$\mu_2(A_0) = \int_{A_0} f(x)\, \mu_1(dx) \qquad \text{for every } A_0 \in \mathfrak{A}_0, \tag{1}$$

then μ_2 is absolutely continuous with respect to μ_1 on $(X, \mathfrak{A})$ and f is in fact a Radon-Nikodym derivative of μ_2 with respect to μ_1.

Proof Since (1) holds, for every $\epsilon > 0$ there exists $\delta > 0$ such that

$$\mu_2(A_0) < \epsilon \qquad \text{whenever } A_0 \in \mathfrak{A}_0 \text{ and } \mu_1(A_0) < \delta. \tag{2}$$

We may take $\delta < \epsilon$ without loss of generality. Now suppose $A \in \mathfrak{A}$ and $\mu_1(A) = 0$. Let $\epsilon > 0$ be arbitrarily given and let δ be chosen in accordance with (2). Since $\mu_1 + \mu_2$ is a finite measure on $\mathfrak{A}$, there exists $A_0 \in \mathfrak{A}_0$ such that $(\mu_1 + \mu_2)(A \,\Delta\, A_0) < \delta$ by Lemma 9.12, and hence

$$\mu_1(A \,\Delta\, A_0) < \delta \tag{3}$$

and

$$\mu_2(A \,\Delta\, A_0) < \delta \tag{4}$$

also. Since $\mu_1(A) = 0$, (3) implies that $\mu_1(A_0) < \delta$. Then by (2), $\mu_2(A_0) < \epsilon$. This estimate together with (4) implies that $\mu_2(A) < \epsilon + \delta < 2\epsilon$. From the arbitrariness of $\epsilon > 0$ we have then $\mu_2(A) = 0$. This proves the absolute continuity of μ_2 with respect to μ_1 on $(X, \mathfrak{A})$.

Let g be a Radon-Nikodym derivative of μ_2 with respect to μ_1 on $(X, \mathfrak{A})$. To complete the proof of the lemma it remains to show that $f = g$ a.e. on $(X, \mathfrak{A}, \mu_1)$. This we do by contradiction argument. Thus assume $f = g$ a.e. on $(X, \mathfrak{A}, \mu_1)$ is false. Then either $g(x) > f(x)$ or $g(x) < f(x)$ on some $\mathfrak{A}$-measurable set with positive μ_1-measure. Since the two cases can be handled in similar ways let us take the former of the two as an example. Then there exist $A \in \mathfrak{A}$ with $\mu_1(A) > 0$ and $\eta > 0$ such that $g(x) \geq f(x) + \eta$ for $x \in A$. Since f is μ_1-integrable on X, for $\epsilon > 0$ there exists $\delta > 0$ such that

$$\int_E f(x)\,\mu_1(dx) < \epsilon \quad \text{whenever } E \in \mathfrak{A} \text{ and } \mu_1(E) < \delta. \tag{5}$$

Let $\epsilon < \frac{1}{3}\eta\mu_1(A)$ and let δ be chosen in accordance with (5). We also take $\delta < \epsilon$. Let $A \in \mathfrak{A}_0$ be so chosen that (3) and (4) hold with our δ. Then

$$\begin{aligned} \mu_2(A) - \int_{A_0} f(x)\,\mu_1(dx) &= \mu_2(A) - \mu_2(A_0) \\ &\leq \mu_2(A \,\Delta\, A_0) < \delta < \epsilon < \tfrac{1}{3}\,\eta\mu_1(A). \end{aligned} \tag{6}$$

On the other hand

$$\mu_2(A) = \int_A g(x)\,\mu_1(dx) \geq \int_A f(x)\,\mu_1(dx) + \eta\mu_1(A),$$

while by (5)

$$\left| \int_A f(x)\,\mu_1(dx) - \int_{A_0} f(x)\,\mu_1(dx) \right| \leq \int_{A\Delta A_0} f(x)\,\mu_1(dx) < \epsilon,$$

so that

$$\begin{aligned} \mu_2(A) - \int_{A_0} f(x)\,\mu_1(dx) &\geq \eta\mu_1(A) + \int_A f(x)\,\mu_1(dx) - \int_{A_0} f(x)\,\mu_1(dx) \\ &\geq \eta\mu_1(A) - \epsilon > \tfrac{2}{3}\,\eta\mu_1(A), \end{aligned} \tag{7}$$

which contradicts (6). □

Theorem 33.13 Let T be a translation of C_w defined by $Tx = x + x_0$ for $x \in C_w$ where $x_0 \in C_w$ with $x_0' \in \text{B.V.}\,[0,1]$, and let μ_X and μ_Y be the probability measures induced on $\sigma(\mathfrak{W})$

by the Wiener process $X(t, x) = x(t)$ and the process $Y(t, x) = (Tx)(t)$ for $(t, x) \in [0,1] \times C_w$. [Thus μ_X is the restriction of m_w to $\sigma(\mathfrak{W})$.] Then μ_X and μ_Y are equivalent and

$$\frac{d\mu_Y}{d\mu_X}(x) = \frac{d\mu_Y}{dm_w}(x) = J(-x_0, x) \qquad \text{for } x \in C_w, \tag{1}$$

where J is given by (2) of Theorem 33.10. [Note that our Radon-Nikodym derivative is equal to $J(-x_0, x)$ and not $J(x_0, x)$.]

Proof In §31 we defined μ_Y on $\mathfrak{W}$ by

$$\mu_Y(F) = m_w(T^{-1}F) \qquad \text{for } F \in \mathfrak{W}. \tag{2}$$

According to Theorem 33.10, $T^{-1}\Gamma$, $T\Gamma \in \mathfrak{W}^*$ for every $\Gamma \in \mathfrak{W}^*$ and also

$$m_w(\Gamma) = \int_{T^{-1}\Gamma} J(x_0, x)\, m_w(dx),$$

and hence

$$m_w(T\Gamma) = \int_{\Gamma} J(x_0, x)\, m_w(dx) .$$

Thus if we consider the translation T^{-1} of C_w, i.e., $T^{-1}x = x - x_0$ for $x \in C_w$, then we have

$$m_w(T^{-1}\Gamma) = \int_{\Gamma} J(-x_0, x)\, m_w(dx),$$

and, from (2),

$$\mu_Y(F) = \int_F J(-x_0, x)\, m_w(dx) \qquad \text{for } F \in \mathfrak{W}.$$

Then by Lemma 33.12, μ_Y is absolutely continuous with respect to m_w on $\left(C_w, \sigma(\mathfrak{W})\right)$ and $J(-x_0, x)$ is a Radon-Nikodym derivative of μ_Y with respect to m_w. Thus

$$\mu_Y(\Gamma) = \int_\Gamma J(-x_0, x)\, m_w(dx) \qquad \text{for } \Gamma \in \sigma(\mathfrak{W}).$$

Since $J(-x_0, x) > 0$ for every $x \in C_w$, $\mu_Y(\Gamma) = 0$ for $\Gamma \in \sigma(\mathfrak{W})$ implies $m_w(\Gamma) = 0$. This proves the absolute continuity of m_w with respect to Γ on $(C_w, \sigma(\mathfrak{W}))$ and hence the equivalence of the two measures. □

§34. TRANSFORMATION OF THE WIENER MEASURE AND WIENER INTEGRALS BY LINEAR INTEGRAL EQUATIONS

[I] Introduction

Let us consider a transformation T of $x \in C_w$ by a Volterra integral equation of the second kind given by

$$(Tx)(t) = x(t) + \int_0^t K(s)\, x(s)\, ds \tag{1}$$

where K is a real-valued continuous function on $[0,1]$. Let X be the Wiener process, i.e.,

$$X(t, x) = x(t) \qquad \text{for } (t, x) \in [0,1] \times C_w \tag{2}$$

and let Y be a real-valued function defined by

$$Y(t, x) = (Tx)(t) \qquad \text{for } (t, x) \in [0,1] \times C_w. \tag{3}$$

To show that Y is a Gaussian process on $(C_w, \sigma(\mathfrak{W}), m_w)$ and $[0,1]$ observe that, from the continuity of K and x on $[0,1]$,

$$Y(t, \cdot) = X(t, \cdot) + \lim_{n\to\infty} \sum_{n=1}^{\infty} K\left(\frac{i}{n}t\right) X\left(\frac{i}{n}t, \cdot\right)\frac{t}{n} \qquad \text{for } t \in [0,1].$$

Then since $X(t, \cdot)$, $t \in [0,1]$, is a Gaussian system of random variables on $(C_w, \sigma(\mathfrak{W}), m_w)$ so is $Y(t, \cdot)$, $t \in [0,1]$, according to Theorem 16.9 and Theorem 16.11. This proves that Y is a

Gaussian process. In particular 2° of §31 is satisfied. It remains to show that T is a one-to-one transformation of C_w onto C_w. This will be done in Lemma 34.1.

Lemma 34.1 Let G be a real-valued continuous function on [0,1] and let T be a linear transformation defined on C_w by

$$y = Tx\,;\; y(t) = x(t) - \int_0^t G(s)\, x(s)\, ds \qquad \text{for } t \in [0,1] \text{ and } x \in C_w. \tag{1}$$

Then T transforms C_w one-to-one onto C_w and both T and T^{-1} are bounded linear operators on the real Banach space C_w (with the uniform norm). The inverse operator T^{-1} can be given as an integral operator in the form

$$x = T^{-1}y\,;\; x(t) = y(t) + \int_0^t H(t, r)\, y(r)\, dr$$

$$\text{for } t \in [0,1] \text{ and } y \in C_w, \tag{2}$$

where H is a real-valued continuous function defined on the domain $\Delta = \{(t, r) \in R^2;\, 0 \le r \le t \le 1\}$ as the sum of a uniformly absolutely convergent series of continuous functions

$$H(t, r) = \sum_{n=1}^{\infty} G_n(t, r) \qquad \text{for } (t, r) \in \Delta \tag{3}$$

with

$$G_1(t, r) = G(r) \qquad \text{and} \qquad G_n(t, r) = \int_r^t G(s)\, G_{n-1}(s, r)\, ds$$

$$\text{for } n = 2, 3, \cdots \tag{4}$$

and satisfies

$$H(t, r) = G(r) + \int_r^t G(s)\, H(s, r) \qquad \text{for } (t, r) \in \Delta. \tag{5}$$

Furthermore a real-valued continuous function H on Δ satisfying

(5) is uniquely determined by the given function G.

<u>Proof</u> Let us show first that for $y \in C_w$ there exists $x \in C_w$ such that $y = Tx$. Thus let

$$x_0(t) = y(t) \text{ and } x_n(t) = \int_0^t G(s)\, x_{n-1}(s)\, ds$$

$$\text{for } n = 1, 2, \cdots, \text{ where } t \in [0,1]. \tag{6}$$

Then with $B = \sup_{[0,1]} |G(t)|$, it follows by mathematical induction on n that

$$|x_n(t)| \leq |||y|||\, \frac{B^n t^n}{n!} \qquad \text{for } n = 0,1,2,\cdots . \tag{7}$$

According to the Weierstrass comparison test, (7) implies that $\sum_{n=0}^{\infty} x_n(t)$ converges uniformly absolutely for $t \in [0,1]$. Let

$$x(t) = \sum_{n=0}^{\infty} x_n(t) \qquad \text{for } t \in [0,1] . \tag{8}$$

Then by (6) and the uniform convergence in (8)

$$\begin{aligned} x(t) - \int_0^t G(s)\, x(s)\, ds &= \sum_{n=0}^{\infty} x_n(t) - \int_0^t G(s) \sum_{n=0}^{\infty} x_n(s)\, ds \\ &= \sum_{n=0}^{\infty} x_n(t) - \sum_{n=0}^{\infty} \int_0^t G(s)\, x_n(s)\, ds \\ &= \sum_{n=0}^{\infty} x_n(t) - \sum_{n=1}^{\infty} x_n(t) = x_0(t) = y(t). \end{aligned}$$

Thus $Tx = y$.

Next let us show that for $y \in C_w$ there can be only one $x \in C_w$ satisfying $y = Tx$. Suppose $u, v \in C_w$ and $y = Tu$ as well as $y = Tv$. Let $w = u - v \in C_w$. Then, by (1),

$$w(t) = \int_0^t G(s)\, w(s)\, ds,$$

from which follow

$$|w(t)| \le |||w|||\, Bt$$

and then

$$|w(t)| \le \int_0^t |||w|||\, B^2 s\, ds = |||w|||\, \frac{B^2 t^2}{2!},$$

and in general

$$|w(t)| \le |||w|||\, \frac{B^n t^n}{n!} \qquad \text{for } n = 1, 2, \cdots,\ t \in [0,1]. \tag{9}$$

Thus $w(t) = 0$ for $t \in [0,1]$ and $u = v$.

To obtain the integral representation (2) of T^{-1} let us return to the sequence $\{x_n, n = 0,1,2, \cdots\} \subset C_w$ defined by (6). Then

$$x_1(t) = \int_0^t G(s)\, y(s)\, ds,$$

$$x_2(t) = \int_0^t G(s)\, x_1(s)\, ds = \int_0^t G(s) \left\{ \int_0^s G(r)\, y(r)\, dr \right\} ds$$

$$= \int_0^t G_2(t, r)\, y(r)\, dr \qquad \text{where } G_2(t, r) = \int_r^t G(s)\, G(r)\, ds,$$

$$x_3(t) = \int_0^t G(s)\, x_2(s)\, ds = \int_0^t G(s) \left\{ \int_0^s G_2(s, r)\, y(r)\, dr \right\} ds$$

$$= \int_0^t G_3(t, r)\, y(r)\, dr \qquad \text{where } G_3(t, r) = \int_r^t G(s)\, G_2(s, r)\, ds,$$

and so on. In general

$$G_1(t, r) = G(r) \quad \text{and} \quad G_n(t, r) = \int_r^t G(s)\, G_{n-1}(s, r)\, ds$$

$$\text{for } n = 2, 3, \cdots \tag{10}$$

and

$$x_n(t) = \int_0^t G_n(t, r)\, y(r)\, dr \qquad \text{for } n = 1, 2, \cdots . \tag{11}$$

From (10) it follows by mathematical induction that

$$|G_n(t, r)| \le \frac{B^n (t - r)^{n-1}}{(n-1)!} \qquad \text{for } n = 1, 2, \cdots, \ (t, r) \in \Delta . \tag{12}$$

Let H be defined by (3). Then by the Weierstrass comparison test, H converges uniformly absolutely on T. Thus from (11), (8), and the fact that $x_0 = y$,

$$\int_0^t H(t, r)\, y(r)\, dr = \sum_{n=1}^{\infty} \int_0^t G_n(t,r)\, y(r)\, dr = \sum_{n=1}^{\infty} x_n(t) = x(t) - y(t).$$

This proves (4).

The fact that T and T^{-1} are bounded linear operators on the Banach space C_w is obvious from (1) and (2) and the boundedness of G and H.

To prove (5), note that, from (3) and (10),

$$\begin{aligned} H(t, r) &= G_1(t, r) + \sum_{n=2}^{\infty} G_n(t, r) \\ &= G(r) + \int_r^t G(s) \sum_{n=1}^{\infty} G_n(s, r)\, ds \\ &= G(r) + \int_r^t G(s)\, H(s, r)\, ds . \end{aligned}$$

Finally the uniqueness of a real-valued continuous function H on Δ satisfying (5) can be proved by an estimate analagous to (9). □

[II] Transformation Theorem for Bounded Continuous Functionals Which Vanish Outside of Bounded Sets

Definition 34.2 Let K be a real-valued function on $[0,1]$. For a positive integer n let $t_i = i/n$ and $K_i = K(t_i)$ for $i = 0,1,2,\cdots,n$. Let T_n be a transformation of $x \in C_w$ defined by

$$(T_n x)(t) = x(t) + \sum_{j=1}^{[nt]} \frac{1}{2n}\left\{K_j x(t_j) + K_{j-1} x(t_{j-1})\right\}$$

$$+ \frac{1}{2n}\left\{K_{[nt]+1}\, x(t_{[nt]+1}) + K_{[nt]}\, x(t_{[nt]})\right\}\left\{nt - [nt]\right\}$$

$$\text{for } t \in [0,1]. \tag{1}$$

Note that at $t = t_i$ we have $nt = i = [nt]$, so that

$$(T_n x)(t_i) - x(t_i) = \frac{1}{n}\sum_{j=1}^{i-1} K_j\, x(t_j) + \frac{1}{2n} K_i\, x(t_i) \qquad \text{for } i = 1,2,\cdots,n$$

$$(T_n x)(t_0) - x(t_0) = 0. \tag{2}$$

On the other hand $nt - [nt]$ is linear on $[t_{i-1}, t_i)$, vanishes at t_i, and $\lim_{t\uparrow t_i}\{nt - [nt]\} = 1$. Thus $T_n x - x$ is a polygonal function with n equal steps $[t_{i-1}, t_i]$, $i = 1,2,\cdots,n$, and its values as t_i, $i = 0,1,2,\cdots,n$, are given by (2). The function $T_n x$ is a polygonal function with n equal steps if and only if x itself is such a function.

Lemma 34.3 Let $H[\eta_1,\cdots,\eta_n]$ be a real-valued continuous function on R^n and let G be a functional on C_w defined by

$$G[y] = H\left[y\left(\frac{1}{n}\right),\cdots,y\left(\frac{n}{n}\right)\right] \qquad \text{for } y \in C_w, \tag{1}$$

then with K_i, $i = 0, 1, 2, \cdots, n$ and T_n as in Definition 34.2 we have

$$\int_{C_w} G[y] m_w(dy) = \Delta_n \int_{C_w} G[T_n x]$$
$$\times \exp\left\{-\tfrac{1}{2} \sum_{i=1}^{n} \left[x(t_i) - x(t_{i-1})\right]\left[K_i x(t_i) + K_{i-1} x(t_{i-1})\right]\right\}$$
$$\times \exp\left\{-\frac{1}{8n} \sum_{i=1}^{n} \left[K_i x(t_i) + K_{i-1} x(t_{i-1})\right]^2\right\} m_w(dx), \qquad (2)$$

with

$$\Delta_n = \prod_{i=1}^{n} \left\{1 + \frac{K_i}{2n}\right\} \qquad (3)$$

when n is so large that $|K_i|/2n < 1$ for $i = 0, 1, 2, \cdots, n$, and $\Delta_n > 0$.

Proof According to Theorem 29.6

$$\int_{C_w} G[y]\, m_w(dy)$$
$$= \left\{(2\pi)^n n^{-n}\right\}^{-\frac{1}{2}} \int_{-\infty}^{\infty} (n) \int_{-\infty}^{\infty} H[\eta_1, \cdots, \eta_n]$$
$$\times \exp\left\{-\frac{n}{2} \sum_{i=1}^{n} (\eta_i - \eta_{i-1})^2\right\} d\eta_1 \cdots d\eta_n \,. \qquad (4)$$

The linear transformation S_n of $\xi = [\xi_1, \cdots, \xi_n] \in R^n$ into $\eta = [\eta_1, \cdots, \eta_n] \in R^n$ defined by

$$\eta = S_n \xi \,;\, \eta_i = \sum_{j=1}^{i} \frac{1}{2n} \left\{K_j \xi_j + K_{j-1} \xi_{j-1}\right\} + \xi_i$$
$$= \frac{1}{n} \sum_{j=1}^{i-1} K_j \xi_j + \left\{1 + \frac{K_i}{2n}\right\} \xi_i \qquad \text{for } i = 1, 2, \cdots, n, \qquad (5)$$

has a Jacobian which is equal to Δ_n given by (3). When n is sufficiently large then $(2n)^{-1}|K_i| < 1$ for $i = 0, 1, 2, \cdots, n$, so that $\Delta_n > 0$ and S_n transforms R^n one-to-one onto R^n. Apply S_n to the right side of (4). Then

$$\int_{C_w} G[y]\, m_w(dy)$$

$$= \Delta_n \left(\frac{n}{2\pi}\right)^{\frac{n}{2}} \int_{-\infty}^{\infty} (n) \int_{-\infty}^{\infty} H\left[\left(1+\frac{K_1}{2n}\right)\xi_1, \cdots, \frac{1}{n}\sum_{j=1}^{n-1} K_j \xi_j + \left(1+\frac{K_n}{2n}\right)\xi_n\right]$$

$$\times \exp\left\{-\frac{n}{2}\sum_{i=1}^{n}\left[\left(1+\frac{K_i}{2n}\right)\xi_i - \left(1+\frac{K_{i-1}}{2n}\right)\xi_{i-1} + \frac{1}{n} K_{i-1}\xi_{i-1}\right]^2\right\} d\xi_1 \cdots d\xi_n. \tag{6}$$

The exponential factor on the right side of (6) can be written as

$$\exp\left\{-\frac{n}{2}\sum_{i=1}^{n}\left[(\xi_i - \xi_{i-1}) + \frac{1}{2n}(K_i\xi_i + K_{i-1}\xi_{i-1})\right]^2\right\}$$

$$= \exp\left\{-\frac{n}{2}\sum_{i=1}^{n}(\xi_i - \xi_{i-1})^2\right\} \exp\left\{-\frac{1}{2}\sum_{i=1}^{n}(\xi_i - \xi_{i-1})(K_i\xi_i + K_{i-1}\xi_{i-1})\right\}$$

$$\times \exp\left\{-\frac{1}{8n}\sum_{i=1}^{n}(K_i\xi_i + K_{i-1}\xi_{i-1})^2\right\}. \tag{7}$$

On the other hand by (2) of Definition 34.2 and (1)

$$G[T_n x] = H\left[(T_n x)(t_1), \cdots, (T_n x)(t_n)\right]$$

$$= H\left[\left(1+\frac{K_1}{2n}\right)x(t_1), \cdots, \frac{1}{n}\sum_{j=1}^{n=1} K_j x(t_j) + \left(1+\frac{K_n}{2n}\right)x(t_n)\right].$$

Thus if we apply Theorem 29.6 to the right side of (2), the result is equal to the right side of (6). This proves (2). □

Lemma 34.4 Let K be a real-valued continuous function on $[0,1]$ and let $t_i = i/n$ for $i = 0,1,2,\cdots,n$. Then

$$\lim_{n\to\infty} \prod_{i=1}^{n} \left\{1 + \frac{K(t_i)}{2n}\right\} = \exp\left\{\tfrac{1}{2}\int_0^1 K(t)\, dt\right\} .$$

Proof For $\xi, h \in R^1$ where $h \neq 0$ and $|h\xi| < 1$ we have

$$\log (1 + h\xi)^{1/h} = \frac{1}{h}\left\{h\xi - \tfrac{1}{2}h^2\xi^2 + \tfrac{1}{3}h^3\xi^3 - \cdots\right\} = \xi + O(h), \qquad (h \to 0).$$

Thus, with $h = 1/n$ for $n = 1,2,\cdots,$

$$1 + \frac{\xi}{n} = e^{\frac{\xi}{n} + \frac{1}{n} O\left(\frac{1}{n}\right)} = e^{\frac{\xi}{n}}\left\{1 + \frac{1}{n} O\left(\frac{1}{n}\right)\right\}, \qquad (n \to \infty).$$

Since K is bounded on $[0,1]$,

$$\prod_{i=1}^{n} \left\{1 + \frac{K(t_i)}{2n}\right\} = \prod_{i=1}^{n} \exp\left\{\frac{K(t_i)}{2n}\right\}\left\{1 + \frac{1}{n} O\left(\frac{1}{n}\right)\right\}$$

$$= \exp\left\{\sum_{i=1}^{n} \frac{K(t_i)}{2n}\right\}\left\{1 + O\left(\frac{1}{n}\right)\right\},$$

and hence the lemma holds. □

Lemma 34.5 Let K be a real-valued continuous function of bounded variation on $[0,1]$. With $K_i = K(t_i)$ where $t_i = i/n$ for $i = 1,2,\cdots,n$, define, for $x \in C_w$,

$$r_n(x) = \sum_{i=1}^{n} \left\{x(t_i) - x(t_{i-1})\right\}\left\{K_i x(t_i) + K_{i-1} x(t_{i-1})\right\}, \tag{1}$$

$$s_n(x) = \frac{1}{4n} \sum_{i=1}^{n} \left\{K_i\, x(t_i) + K_{i-1}\, x(t_{i-1})\right\}^2 . \tag{2}$$

Then

$$\lim_{n\to\infty} r_n(x) = \int_0^1 K(t)\, dx^2(t), \tag{3}$$

$$\lim_{n\to\infty} s_n(x) = \int_0^1 K^2(t)\, x^2(t)\, dt, \tag{4}$$

and

$$|r_n(x)| \le 4M^2 B \qquad \text{for } x \in C_M \text{ and } n = 1, 2, \cdots, \tag{5}$$

where

$$B = \max\left\{ \max_{[0,1]} |K(t)|, \ \operatorname*{Var}_{[0,1]} K \right\} \qquad \text{and}$$

$$C_M = \left\{ x \in C_w ;\ |||x||| \le M \right\}.$$

Proof Since $K \in$ B. V. $[0,1]$ and $x^2 \in C_w$, the Riemann-Stieltjes integral $\int_0^1 K(t)\, dx^2(t)$ exists and

$$\int_0^1 K(t)\, dx^2(t) = \lim_{n\to\infty} \rho_n(x), \tag{6}$$

where

$$\rho_n(x) = \sum_{i=1}^{n} K_i \left\{ x(t_i) + x(t_{i-1}) \right\} \left\{ x(t_i) - x(t_{i-1}) \right\}.$$

For n so large that $|x(t_i) - x(t_{i-1})| < \epsilon$ for $i = 1, 2, \cdots, n$, we have

$$|r_n(x) - \rho_n(x)| = \left| \sum_{i=1}^{n} (K_{i-1} - K_i)\, x(t_{i-1}) \left\{ x(t_i) - x(t_{i-1}) \right\} \right|$$
$$\le |||x|||\, B\epsilon.$$

Thus $\lim_{n\to\infty} r_n(x) = \lim_{n\to\infty} \rho_n(x)$, and (3) holds in view of (6). Also

$$r_n(x) = \sum_{i=1}^{n} \left\{ x(t_i) - x(t_{i-1}) \right\} K_i \left\{ x(t_i) + x(t_{i-1}) \right\}$$

$$+ \sum_{i=1}^{n} \left\{ x(t_i) - x(t_{i-1}) \right\} (K_{i-1} - K_i)\, x(t_{i-1})$$

$$= \sum_{i=1}^{n} \left\{ x^2(t_i) - x^2(t_{i-1}) \right\} K_i + \sum_{i=1}^{n} \left\{ x(t_i)\, x(t_{i-1}) - x^2(t_{i-1}) \right\} (K_{i-1} - K_i)$$

$$= x^2(t_n)\, K_n - x^2(t_0)\, K_1 - \sum_{i=1}^{n-1} x^2(t_i)(K_{i+1} - K_i)$$

$$+ \sum_{i=1}^{n} \left\{ x(t_i)\, x(t_{i-1}) - x^2(t_{i-1}) \right\} (K_{i-1} - K_i)\,.$$

From this we obtain (5) for $x \in C_M$.

To prove (4) observe that

$$s_n(x) = \frac{1}{4n} \sum_{i=1}^{n} K_i^2\, x^2(t_i) + \frac{1}{4n} \sum_{i=1}^{n} K_{i-1}^2\, x^2(t_{i-1})$$

$$+ \frac{1}{2n} \sum_{i=1}^{n} K_i\, x(t_i)\, K_{i-1}\, x(t_{i-1}). \tag{7}$$

Since $\lim_{n\to\infty} \sum_{i=1}^{n} K_i\, x(t_i)\, K_{i-1}\, x(t_{i-1}) = \int_0^1 K^2(t)\, x^2(t)\, dt$ by Duhamel's theorem, (4) follows from (7). □

Lemma 34.6 For $A_1, \cdots, A_n \neq 0$, let

$$M_n = \begin{bmatrix} A_1 & 0 & 0 & \cdots & 0 \\ a_1 & A_2 & 0 & \cdots & 0 \\ a_1 & a_2 & A_3 & \cdots & 0 \\ \vdots & \vdots & \vdots & & \vdots \\ a_1 & a_2 & a_3 & \cdots & A_n \end{bmatrix} \tag{1}$$

Then with $b_i = a_i A_i^{-1}$ and $c_i = (a_i - A_i)\, A_i^{-1}$ for $i = 1, 2, \cdots, n$, we have

$$M_n^{-1} = \begin{bmatrix} A_1^{-1} & 0 & 0 & \cdots & 0 \\ -b_1A_2^{-1} & A_2^{-1} & 0 & \cdots & 0 \\ b_1c_2A_3^{-1} & -b_2A_3^{-1} & A_3^{-1} & \cdots & 0 \\ -b_1c_2c_3A_4^{-1} & b_2c_3A_4^{-1} & -b_3A_4^{-1} & \cdots & 0 \\ \vdots & \vdots & \vdots & & \vdots \\ (-1)^{n+1}b_1c_2\cdots c_{n-1}A_n^{-1} & (-1)^{n+2}b_2c_3\cdots c_{n-1}A_n^{-1} & (-1)^{n+3}b_3c_4\cdots c_{n-1}A_n^{-1} & \cdots & A_n^{-1} \end{bmatrix} \tag{2}$$

Proof A proof of the lemma can be obtained by the direct multiplication of the two matrices.

□

Theorem 34.7 Let F be a real-valued bounded and continuous functional on C_w which vanishes outside of a bounded subset of C_w in the uniform topology. Then with the change of variable of integration

$$y = (Tx)(t) = x(t) + \int_0^t K(s)\, x(s)\, ds \tag{1}$$

where K is a real-valued continuous function of bounded variation on $[0,1]$, we have

$$\int_{C_w} F[y]\, m_w(dy) = \int_{C_w} F[Tx]\, J[K,x]\, m_w(dx), \tag{2}$$

where the "Jacobian" $J[K,\cdot]$ is given by

$$J[K,x] = \exp\left\{\tfrac{1}{2}\int_0^1 K(t)\, dt - \tfrac{1}{2}\int_0^1 K(t)\, dx^2(t) - \tfrac{1}{2}\int_0^1 K^2(t)\, x^2(t)\, dt\right\}. \tag{3}$$

Proof Let $L^{(n)}$ be the polygonalization given in Definition 33.1. According to Lemma 33.2 there exists a real-valued continuous function $H[\eta_1, \cdots, \eta_n]$ on R^n such that

$$F\left[L^{(n)}y\right] = H\left[y\left(\frac{1}{n}\right), \cdots, y\left(\frac{n}{n}\right)\right] \equiv G[y] \quad \text{for } y \in C_w,$$

so that, with T_n given by Definition 34.2,

$$G[T_n x] = H\left[(T_n x)\left(\frac{1}{n}\right), \cdots, (T_n x)\left(\frac{n}{n}\right)\right] = F\left[L^{(n)}T_n x\right] \quad \text{for } x \in C_w.$$

Thus, according to Lemma 34.3,

$$\int_{C_w} F\left[L^{(n)}y\right] m_w(dy) = \prod_{i=1}^n \left\{1 + \frac{K_i}{2n}\right\} \int_{C_w} F\left[L^{(n)}T_n x\right]$$

$$\times \exp\left\{-\tfrac{1}{2}\sum_{i=1}^n \left[x(t_i) - x(t_{i-1})\right]\left[K_i x(t_i) + K_{i-1}x(t_{i-1})\right]\right\}$$

$$\times \exp\left\{-\frac{1}{8n}\sum_{i=1}^{n}\left[K_i x(t_i) + K_{i-1}\, x(t_{i-1})\right]^2\right\} m_w(dx). \tag{4}$$

To prove (2) we let $n \to \infty$ on both sides of (4) and pass to the limit under the integral signs. This is justified in the rest of the proof.

Consider the left side of (4). Since $\lim_{n\to\infty} L^{(n)}y = y$ for every $y \in C_w$ in the uniform topology of C_w and since F is continuous in this topology, we have $\lim_{n\to\infty} F\left[L^{(n)}y\right] = F[y]$ for $y \in C_w$. From the boundedness of F, the Bounded Convergence Theorem applies, and

$$\lim_{n\to\infty} \int_{C_w} F\left[L^{(n)}y\right] m_w(dy) = \int_{C_w} F[y]\, m_w(dy). \tag{5}$$

For the first factor of the integrand on the right side of (4) let us show first that, for each $x \in C_w$,

$$\lim_{n\to\infty} \left(L^{(n)} T_n x\right)(t) = (Tx)(t) \qquad \text{uniformly in } t \in [0,1]. \tag{6}$$

Now from (1) of Definition 34.2

$$\left(L^{(n)} T_n x\right)(t) = \left(L^{(n)}x\right)(t) + \sum_{j=1}^{[nt]} \frac{1}{2n}\left\{K_j\, x(t_j) + K_{j-1}\, x(t_{j-1})\right\}$$

$$+ \frac{1}{2n}\left\{K_{[nt]+1}\, x(t_{[nt]+1}) + K_{[nt]}\, x(t_{[nt]})\right\}\left\{nt - [nt]\right\}$$

$$= \left(L^{(n)}x\right)(t) + u_n(x,t) + v_n(x,t), \tag{7}$$

where

$$u_n(x,t) = \frac{1}{n}\sum_{j=1}^{[nt]} K_j\, x(t_j) + \frac{nt - [nt]}{n} K(t)\, x(t)$$

and

$$v_n(x,t) = -\frac{1}{2n} K_{[nt]}\, x(t_{[nt]})$$

$$+ \frac{nt-[nt]}{n}\left\{\tfrac{1}{2}K_{[nt]+1}\, x(t_{[nt]+1}) + \tfrac{1}{2}K_{[nt]}\, x(t_{[nt]}) - K(t)\, x(t)\right\}.$$

Now on the right side of (7) we have first of all $\lim_{n\to\infty}\left(L^{(n)}x\right)(t) = x(t)$ uniformly in $t \in [0,1]$. Second, for an arbitrary $\epsilon > 0$

$$\left|\int_0^t K(s)\, x(s)\, ds - u_n(x,t)\right| = \left|\sum_{j=1}^{[nt]}\int_{t_{j-1}}^{t_j} K(s)\, x(s)\, ds + \int_{t_{[nt]}}^{t} K(s)\, x(s)\, ds\right.$$

$$\left. -\frac{1}{n}\sum_{j=1}^{[nt]} K_j\, x(t_j) - \frac{nt-[nt]}{n} K(t)\, x(t)\right|$$

$$\le \sum_{j=1}^{[nt]}\int_{t_{j-1}}^{t_j} \left|K(s)x(s) - K(t_j)x(t_j)\right| ds + \int_{t_{[nt]}}^{t} \left|K(s)x(s) - K(t)x(t)\right| ds < \epsilon$$

for all $t \in [0,1]$ for sufficiently large n on account of the uniform continuity of Kx on $[0,1]$. Thus we have shown that

$$\lim_{n\to\infty} u_n(x,t) = \int_0^t K(s)\, x(s)\, ds \qquad \text{uniformly in } t \in [0,1].$$

Regarding v_n we have

$$|v_n(x,t)| \le \frac{5}{2n} \max_{[0,1]} |K(t)|\ \|x\|,$$

so that

$$\lim_{n\to\infty} v_n(x,t) = 0 \qquad \text{uniformly in } t \in [0,1].$$

Thus (6) holds. Then, from the continuity of F in the uniform topology of C_w,

$$\lim_{n\to\infty} F\left[L^{(n)} T_n x\right] = F[Tx]. \tag{8}$$

Let $C_M = \left\{x \in C_w ; \;|||x||| \le M\right\}$ for $M \ge 0$. Since F vanishes outside of a bounded set in C_w, there exists $M_0 \ge 0$ such that $F[y] = 0$ for $y \notin C_{M_0}$. We proceed to show that there exist M_1 and N such that

$$F\left[L^{(n)} T_n x\right] = 0 \qquad \text{for all } n \ge N \text{ when } x \notin C_{M_1}. \tag{9}$$

Let $P^{(n)}$ be the collection of all polygonal functions with n equal steps and vanishing at $t = 0$. Then $L^{(n)} T_n x \in P^{(n)}$ for each $x \in C_w$. A member of $P^{(n)}$ is uniquely determined by its values $\xi_1, \cdots, \xi_n$ at $t_i = i/n$ for $i = 1, 2, \cdots, n$, and there is a one-to-one correspondence between the elements of $P^{(n)}$ and those of R^n. Let N_0 be so large that $|K(t)|\,(2N_0)^{-1} < 1$ for all $t \in [0,1]$. Then, as we pointed out in Lemma 34.3, the linear transformation S_n defined by (5) of Lemma 34.3 transforms R^n one-to-one onto R^n when $n \ge N_0$. The matrix of S_n is given by (1) of Lemma 34.6 with

$$A_i = 1 + \frac{K_i}{2n} \qquad \text{and} \qquad a_i = \frac{K_i}{n} \qquad \text{for } i = 1, 2, \cdots, n,$$

so that the matrix of the inverse transformation S_n^{-1} is given by (2) of Lemma 34.6 with

$$b_i = \frac{a_i}{A_i} = \left\{1 + \frac{K_i}{2n}\right\}^{-1} \frac{K_i}{2n},$$

$$c_i = \frac{a_i - A_i}{A_i} = \left\{1 + \frac{K_i}{2n}\right\}^{-1} \left\{-1 + \frac{K_i}{2n}\right\}.$$

If $n \ge N_0$ then $|K(t)|(2n)^{-1} < 1$ for $t \in [0,1]$, so that

$$\left\{1 + \frac{K_i}{2n}\right\}^{-1} = 1 - \frac{K_i}{2n} + \left\{\frac{K_i}{2n}\right\}^2 - \left\{\frac{K_i}{2n}\right\}^3 + \cdots = 1 + O\left(\frac{1}{n}\right),$$

and consequently

$$A_i = 1 + O\left(\frac{1}{n}\right),$$

$$b_i = \left\{1 + O\left(\frac{1}{n}\right)\right\} O\left(\frac{1}{n}\right),$$

$$c_i = \left\{1 + O\left(\frac{1}{n}\right)\right\} \left\{-1 + O\left(\frac{1}{n}\right)\right\} = -1 + O\left(\frac{1}{n}\right). \tag{10}$$

Let R^n be normed by the uniform norm $|||\xi||| = \max_{i=1,2,\cdots,n}|\xi_i|$ for $\xi = [\xi_1, \cdots, \xi_n] \in R^n$. If we let $\gamma_{i,j}$, $i,j = 1,2,\cdots,n$, be the entries of the matrix of S_n^{-1}, then for the norm of S_n^{-1} we have

$$\|S_n^{-1}\| \le \max_{i=1,2,\cdots,n} \sum_{j=1}^{n} |\gamma_{ij}|. \tag{11}$$

Since the matrix of S_n^{-1} is given by (2) of Lemma 34.6 with A_i, b_i, c_i given by (10) we have, in accordance with (11),

$$\|S_n^{-1}\| \le (n-1)\, O\left(\frac{1}{n}\right) \left\{1 + O\left(\frac{1}{n}\right)\right\}^{n-1} + \left\{1 + O\left(\frac{1}{n}\right)\right\}$$

$$= O(1)\left\{1 + O(1)\right\} + \left\{1 + O(1)\right\} = O(1) \qquad (n \to \infty).$$

Thus there exist $\alpha \ge 0$ and N such that $\|S_n^{-1}\| \le \alpha$ for $n \ge N$. Then

$$|||S_n^{-1}\xi||| \le \|S_n^{-1}\|\ |||\xi||| \le \alpha\ |||\xi||| \qquad \text{for all } \xi \in R^n \text{ when } n \ge N.$$

Consider S_n and S_n^{-1} as transformations of $P^{(n)}$ onto $P^{(n)}$. Then $S_n = L^{(n)}T_n$ on $P^{(n)}$. For $x \in P^{(n)} \cap C_{M_0}$ where $n \ge N$ we have $\left|(S_n^{-1}x)(i/n)\right| \le \alpha M_0$ for $i = 1,2,\cdots,n$, and hence $S_n^{-1}x \in C_{\alpha M_0}$ from the fact that $S_n^{-1}x$ is a polygonal function. Thus $S_n^{-1}\left(P^{(n)} \cap C_{M_0}\right) \subset C_{\alpha M_0}$ for all $n \ge N$. Now for $x \notin C_{\alpha M_0}$

we have $x \notin S_n^{-1}(P^{(n)} \cap C_{M_0})$ for $n \geq N$, and hence $L^{(n)} T_n x \notin P^{(n)} \cap C_{M_0}$ for $n \geq N$, i.e., $L^{(n)} T_n x \notin C_{M_0}$ for $n \geq N$, and consequently (9) holds with the choice $M_1 = \alpha M_0$.

On the right side of (4), if we consider $n \geq N$ as in (9), then $F[L^{(n)} T_n x] = 0$ for $x \notin C_{M_1}$, so that the Wiener integral on C_w reduces to an integral on C_{M_1}. The first exponential factor is bounded on C_{M_1} according to (5) of Lemma 34.5. The second exponential factor is bounded by 1. Also $F[L^{(n)} T_n x]$ is bounded from the boundedness of F. Thus if we let $n \to \infty$ then, by the Bounded Convergence Theorem, (8), Lemma 34.5, and Lemma 34.4, the right side of (4) becomes the right side of (2). This and (5) prove (2). □

[III] The Transformation Theorem

Theorem 34.8 Let K be a real-valued continuous function of bounded variation on $[0,1]$ and let T be a one-to-one transformation of C_w onto C_w, continuous with continuous inverse T^{-1} with respect to the uniform topology of C_w, which is defined by

$$(Tx)(t) = x(t) + \int_0^t K(s)\, x(s)\, ds \qquad \text{for } t \in [0,1] \text{ and } x \in C_w. \tag{1}$$

Then for every $\Gamma \in \mathfrak{W}^*$ we have $T^{-1}\Gamma$, $T\Gamma \in \mathfrak{W}^*$, i.e., the transformations T and T^{-1} are Wiener measurable and

$$m_w(\Gamma) = \int_{T^{-1}\Gamma} J[K, x]\, m_w(dx), \tag{2}$$

$$m_w(T\Gamma) = \int_{\Gamma} J[K, x]\, m_w(dx), \tag{3}$$

where

$$J[K, x] = \exp\left\{ \tfrac{1}{2}\int_0^1 K(t)\, dt - \tfrac{1}{2}\int_0^1 K(t)\, dx^2(t) - \tfrac{1}{2}\int_0^1 K^2(t)\, x^2(t)\, dt \right\}. \tag{4}$$

Moreover if F is an extended real-valued Wiener measurable functional on C_w then

$$\int_{\Gamma} F[y]\, m_w(dy) = \int_{T^{-1}\Gamma} F[Tx]\, J[K, x]\, m_w(dx), \tag{5}$$

$$\int_{T\Gamma} F[y]\, m_w(dy) = \int_{\Gamma} F[Tx]\, J[K, x]\, m_w(dx), \tag{6}$$

in the sense that the existence of one side implies that of the other and the equality of the two.

Proof The Wiener measurability of $T^{-1}\Gamma$ for $\Gamma \in \mathfrak{W}^*$ is equivalent to the Wiener measurability of $\chi_{T^{-1}\Gamma}[x]$, i.e., $\chi_\Gamma[Tx]$ as a functional of $x \in C_w$, and the Wiener measurability of $T\Gamma$ for $\Gamma \in \mathfrak{W}^*$ is equivalent to the Wiener measurability of $\chi_{T\Gamma}[y]$, i.e., $\chi_\Gamma[T^{-1}y]$ as a functional of $y \in C_w$. Now (2) and (3) are equivalent, respectively, to

$$\int_{C_w} \chi_\Gamma[y]\, m_w(dy) = \int_{C_w} \chi_{T^{-1}\Gamma}[x]\, J[K, x]\, m_w(dx), \tag{7}$$

$$\int_{C_w} \chi_{T\Gamma}[y]\, m_w(dy) = \int_{C_w} \chi_\Gamma[x]\, J[K, x]\, m_w(dx), \tag{8}$$

which are in turn equivalent respectively to

$$\int_{C_w} \chi_\Gamma[y]\, m_w(dy) = \int_{C_w} \chi_\Gamma[Tx]\, J[K, x]\, m_w(dx), \tag{9}$$

$$\int_{C_w} \chi_\Gamma[T^{-1}y]\, m_w(dy) = \int_{C_w} \chi_\Gamma[x]\, J(K, x]\, m_w(dx). \tag{10}$$

Let us prove (9) and (5) first and then (10) and (6). Let the subcollections $\mathfrak{J}$, $\mathfrak{J}^\sigma$, $\mathfrak{J}^{\sigma\downarrow}$ of members of $\sigma(\mathfrak{W})$ be as given in Definition 33.6. Consider first the case where $\Gamma = I$ where I is a member of $\mathfrak{J}$ given by

$$I = \left\{x \in C_w;\ \alpha_i < x(t_i) \le \beta_i,\ i = 1, 2, \cdots, n\right\}$$

with $0 < t_1 < \cdots < t_n \le 1$ and $-\infty \le \alpha_i < \beta_i \le \infty$ for $i = 1, 2, \cdots, n$. For every $\epsilon > 0$ let $\varphi_{\epsilon,i}[\eta]$, $\eta \in R^1$, be a trapezoidal function defined by

$$\varphi_{\epsilon,i}[\eta] = \begin{cases} 1 & \text{for } \eta \in [\alpha_i + \epsilon, \beta_i] \\ 0 & \text{for } \eta \in (-\infty, \alpha_i] \cup [\beta_i + \epsilon, \infty) \\ \text{linear} & \text{for } \eta \in [\alpha_i, \alpha_i + \epsilon] \text{ and for } \eta \in [\beta_i, \beta_i + \epsilon] \end{cases}$$

and let $\psi_\epsilon[\eta]$, $\eta \in [0, \infty)$, be a continuous function defined by

$$\psi_\epsilon[\eta] = \begin{cases} 1 & \text{for } \eta \in \left[0, \frac{1}{\epsilon}\right] \\ 0 & \text{for } \eta \in \left[\frac{1}{\epsilon} + 1, \epsilon\right) \\ \text{linear} & \text{for } \eta \in \left[\frac{1}{\epsilon}, \frac{1}{\epsilon} + 1\right) \end{cases}$$

and finally let

$$\theta_\epsilon[y] = \psi_\epsilon\left(|||y|||\right) \prod_{i=1}^{n} \varphi_{\epsilon,i}\left[y(t_i)\right] \quad \text{for } y \in C_w.$$

It is clear that, for every $y \in C_w$,

$$\lim_{\epsilon\downarrow 0} \prod_{i=1}^{n} \varphi_{\epsilon,i}\left[y(t_i)\right] = \chi_I[y], \quad \lim_{\epsilon\downarrow 0} \psi_\epsilon\left(|||y|||\right) = 1, \quad \lim_{\epsilon\downarrow 0} \theta_\epsilon[y] = \chi_I[y].$$

Now θ_ε is bounded by 1 and continuous on C_w and vanishes outside of $C_{\frac{1}{\varepsilon}+1} = \left\{x \in C_w ; \, |||x||| \le \frac{1}{\varepsilon} + 1\right\}$. Thus by Theorem 34.7

$$\int_{C_w} \theta_\varepsilon[y] \, m_w(dy) = \int_{C_w} \theta_\varepsilon[Tx] \, J[K, x] \, m_w(dx).$$

Letting $\varepsilon \to 0$ we obtain by the Bounded Convergence Theorem

$$\int_{C_w} \chi_I[y] \, m_w(dy) = \int_{C_w} \chi_I[Tx] \, J[K, x] \, m_w(dx)$$

proving (9) for the case $\Gamma = I \in \mathfrak{J}$. Concerning the Wiener measurability of $\chi_I[Tx]$ as a functional of x, or equivalently that of $T^{-1}\Gamma$, note that since $y = Tx$ is a continuous transformation of C_w and $\theta_\varepsilon[y]$ is a continuous functional on C_w, the functional $\theta_\varepsilon[Tx]$ of x is continuous in the uniform topology of C_w, so that $\theta_\varepsilon[Tx]$ is a Wiener measurable functional of x and so is $\chi_I[Tx] = \lim_{\varepsilon \downarrow 0} \theta_\varepsilon[Tx]$, and this establishes the Wiener measurability of $T^{-1}\Gamma$. Now that we have proved (9) for $\Gamma \in \mathfrak{J}$, we can proceed to the cases where $\Gamma \in \mathfrak{J}^\sigma$, $\Gamma \in \mathfrak{J}^{\sigma\downarrow}$, $\Gamma \in \mathfrak{W}^*$ with $m_w(\Gamma) = 0$ and finally $\Gamma \in \mathfrak{W}^*$ just as in the proof of Theorem 33.10. The Wiener measurability of $\chi_\Gamma[Tx]$ as a functional of x, or equivalently that of $T^{-1}\Gamma$, is also established case by case. Finally from (9) we obtain (5) by going through the cases where F is a simple function on C_w, a nonnegative Wiener measurable functional on C_w, and finally an extended real-valued Wiener measurable functional on C_w.

Let us turn now to (10) and (6). Here we have to verify the Wiener measurability of $T\Gamma$, or equivalently that of $\chi_\Gamma[T^{-1}y]$ as a functional of y. Here too we start with $\Gamma = I \in \mathfrak{J}$. Since

$\chi_I[T^{-1}y] = \lim_{\epsilon\downarrow 0} \theta_\epsilon[T^{-1}y]$, it suffices to verify the Wiener measurability of $\theta_\epsilon[T^{-1}y]$ as a functional of y. But this last follows immediately since $x = T^{-1}y$ is a continuous transformation of C_w and $\theta_\epsilon[x]$ is a continuous functional so that $\theta_\epsilon[T^{-1}y]$ is a continuous functional of y and is hence Wiener measurable. The rest of the proof of (10) can be given as in (9). Also (6) follows from (10) in the same way as (5) follows from (9). □

Corollary 34.9

$$\int_{C_w} \exp\left\{\frac{\zeta^2}{2}\int_0^1 x^2(t)\,dt\right\} m_w(dx) = \frac{1}{(\cos\zeta)^{\frac{1}{2}}}$$

$$\text{for } \zeta\in C \text{ with } \Re e\,\zeta^2 < \frac{\pi^2}{4} \tag{1}$$

where for $(\cos\zeta)^{\frac{1}{2}}$ we take the branch which is positive for $\zeta\in R^1$ with $\zeta^2 < \pi^2/4$. Thus in particular the characteristic function of the random variable $\frac{1}{2}\int_0^1 x^2(t)\,dt$ on the probability space $(C_w, \mathfrak{W}^*, m_w)$ is given by

$$\int_{C_w} \exp\left\{i\frac{\eta}{2}\int_0^1 x^2(t)\,dt\right\} m_w(dx) = \frac{1}{\left\{\cos(i\eta)^{\frac{1}{2}}\right\}^{\frac{1}{2}}} \quad \text{for } \eta\in R^1 \tag{2}$$

where for $(i\eta)^{\frac{1}{2}}$ we take the branch of $w^{\frac{1}{2}}$, $w\in C$, which is positive for positive w.

Proof For a fixed real number $\xi\in\left(-\pi/2, \pi/2\right)$, let

$$K(t) = \xi\tan\xi(t-1) \qquad \text{for } t\in[0,1]. \tag{3}$$

The function K is continuous and of bounded variation on $[0,1]$.

With the transformation T of C_w defined by

$$(Tx)(t) = x(t) + \int_0^t K(s)\, x(s)\, ds = x(t) + \int_0^t \xi \tan \xi(s-1)\, x(s)\, ds$$

and with $F[y] \equiv 1$ for $y \in C_w$, we have according to (5) and (4) of Theorem 34.8

$$\int_{C_w} \exp\left\{-\tfrac{1}{2}\int_0^1 K(t)\, dx^2(t) - \tfrac{1}{2}\int_0^1 K^2(t)\, x^2(t)\, dt\right\} m_w(dx)$$
$$= \exp\left\{-\tfrac{1}{2}\int_0^1 K(t)\, dt\right\}. \tag{4}$$

From (3) we have

$$\exp\left\{-\tfrac{1}{2}\int_0^1 K(t)\, dt\right\} = \exp\left\{-\tfrac{1}{2}\int_0^1 \xi \tan \xi(t-1)\, dt\right\}$$
$$= \exp\left\{\tfrac{1}{2} \log \cos \xi(t-1)\Big|_0^1\right\} = \frac{1}{(\cos \xi)^{\frac{1}{2}}},$$

$$\int_0^1 K(t)\, dx^2(t) = K(t)\, x^2(t)\Big|_0^1 - \int_0^1 x^2(t)\, dK(t) = -\xi^2 \int_0^1 x^2(t) \sec^2 \xi(t-1)\, dt,$$

and

$$\int_0^1 K^2(t)\, x^2(t)\, dt = \xi^2 \int_0^1 x^2(t)\left\{\sec^2 \xi(t-1)\right\} dt - \xi^2 \int_0^1 x^2(t)\, dt .$$

Substituting these in (4) we obtain

$$\int_{C_w} \exp\left\{\tfrac{1}{2}\xi^2 \int_0^1 x^2(t)\, dt\right\} m_w(dx) = \frac{1}{(\cos \xi)^{\frac{1}{2}}} \quad \text{for } \xi \in \left(-\frac{\pi}{2}, \frac{\pi}{2}\right) \tag{5}$$

where for $(\cos \xi)^{\frac{1}{2}}$ we take the positive square root since the left side of (5) is nonnegative.

Consider next

$$G(w) = \int_{C_w} \exp\left\{\tfrac{1}{2} w \int_0^1 x^2(t)\, dt\right\} m_w(dx) \quad \text{for } w \in C. \tag{6}$$

Clearly

$$|G(w) \le \int_{C_w} \exp\left\{\tfrac{1}{2} \Re e\, w \int_0^1 x^2(t)\, dt\right\} m_w(dx) . \tag{7}$$

For $\Re e w \le 0$, the Wiener integral in (7) is bounded between 0 and 1 and for $0 \le \Re e\, w < \pi^2/4$ it is bounded according to (5). Thus G is finite valued for $w \in D$ where $D = \{w \in C\,;\, -\infty < \Re e\, w < \pi^2/4\}$. If we integrate G with respect to w along a contour which lies entirely in D then we can apply the Fubini theorem to show that the contour integral vanishes. Thus G is a holomorphic function of w in D.

Let $w = \zeta^2$ where $\zeta = \xi + i\eta \in C$. Then $\Re e\, w = \Re e \zeta^2 = \xi^2 - \eta^2$. Let D_0 be the region in the complex ζ-plane bounded between the two branches of the hyperbola $\xi^2 - \eta^2 = \pi^2/4$ with foci at $(-\pi/\sqrt{2}, 0)$ and $(\pi/\sqrt{2}, 0)$. For $\zeta \in D_0$ we have $-\infty < \Re e\, \zeta^2 < \pi^2/4$ so that

$$G_0(\zeta) = \int_{C_w} \exp\left\{\tfrac{1}{2} \zeta^2 \int_0^1 x^2(t)\, dt\right\} m_w(dx) \quad \text{for } \zeta \in D_0$$

is a holomorphic function. Consider $(\cos \zeta)^{-\frac{1}{2}}$ for $\zeta \in C$. Since $\cos \zeta = 0$ for $\zeta = \frac{1}{2}(2k+1)\pi$, $k = 0, \pm 1, \pm 2, \cdots$, only, if we slit the complex ζ-plane along the real axis from $\pi/2$ to ∞ and from $-\pi/2$ to $-\infty$ then $(\cos \zeta)^{-\frac{1}{2}}$ is single valued and holomorphic once a determination is chosen. Let us choose the determination which is positive for $\zeta \in R^1$, $\zeta^2 < \pi^2/4$. Then both $G_0(\zeta)$ and $(\cos \zeta)^{-\frac{1}{2}}$ are single valued and holomorphic on D_0 and are equal for $\zeta \in R^1$,

$\zeta^2 < \pi^2/4$ according to (5). Thus by the Identity Theorem for holomorphic functions, $G(\zeta)$ and $(\cos\zeta)^{-\frac{1}{2}}$ are equal on D_0. This proves (1). It is obvious that (2) follows from (1). □

[IV] Interpretation of the "Jacobian" of the Transformation as a Radon-Nikodym Derivative

According to Lemma 34.1 if K is a real-valued continuous function on $[0,1]$ then the transformation T of C_w defined by

$$(Tx)(t) = x(t) + \int_0^t K(s)\, x(s)\, ds \qquad \text{for } x \in C_w$$

transforms C_w one-to-one onto C_w and T^{-1} is given by

$$(T^{-1}y)(t) = y(t) + \int_0^t H(t,r)\, y(r)\, dr \qquad \text{for } y \in C_w$$

where H is a real-valued continuous function on $\{(t,r) \in R^2;\ 0 \le r \le t \le 1\}$ given by

$$H(t,r) = \sum_{n=1}^{\infty} G_n(t,r)$$

with

$$G_1(t,r) = -K(r), \quad G_n(t,r) = -\int_r^t K(s)\, G_{n-1}(s,r)\, ds$$

for $n = 2, 3, \cdots$.

Consider the Wiener process

$$X(t,x) = x(t) \qquad \text{for } (t,x) \in [0,1] \times C_w$$

and the real-valued function Z defined by

$$Z(t,x) = (T^{-1}x)(t) = x(t) + \int_0^t H(t,r)\, x(t)\, dr \qquad \text{for } (t,x) \in [0,1] \times C_w .$$

Z is a Gaussian process on $(C_w, \mathfrak{W}^*, m_w)$ and $[0,1]$ since

$$Z(t,\cdot) = X(t,\cdot) + \lim_{n\to\infty} \sum_{i=1}^{n} H\left(t, \frac{i}{n}t\right) X\left(\frac{i}{n}t, \cdot\right) \frac{t}{n}.$$

Assume further that K is of bounded variation on $[0,1]$ so that Theorem 34.8 applies. The probability measure μ_Z induced on $\left(C_w, \sigma(\mathfrak{W})\right)$ by Z is then given according to §31 by

$$\mu_Z(F) = m_w(TF) = \int_F J[K,x]\, m_w(dx) \qquad \text{for } F \in \mathfrak{W}$$

with J as given in (4) of Theorem 34.8. Then by Lemma 33.12, μ_Z is absolutely continuous with respect to $\mu_X(=m_w)$ on $\left(C_w, \sigma(\mathfrak{W})\right)$ and

$$\frac{d\mu_Z}{d\mu_X}(x) = \frac{d\mu_Z}{dm_w}(x) = J[K,x] \qquad \text{for } x \in C_w.$$

§35. EVALUATION OF WIENER INTEGRALS BY MEANS OF STURM-LIOUVILLE DIFFERENTIAL EQUATIONS

As an example of application of the transformation theorem in §34 we evaluate Wiener integrals by using Sturm - Liouville differential equations. Consider the differential system of real-valued functions f on $[0,1]$ with a real parameter λ given by

$$f''(t) + \lambda p(t) f(t) = 0$$

where p is continuous and $p(t) > 0$ for $t \in [0,1]$, (D)

$$f(0) = 0, \tag{B_1}$$

$$f'(1) = 0. \tag{B_2}$$

According to the Sturm-Liouville theory (see Ince [1]), there exists a least eigenvalue λ_0 of the differential system (D), (B_1), (B_2), $\lambda_0 > 0$, and an eigenfunction corresponding to λ_0 is nonvanishing on $(0,1]$. For every $\lambda \in R^1$ there exists a nontrivial solution of (D) satisfying (B_2).

Lemma 35.1 Let $\lambda < \lambda_0$ where λ_0 is the least eigenvalue of the differential system (D), (B_1), (B_2). If f_λ is a nontrivial solution of (D) satisfying (B_2) then $f_\lambda(t) \neq 0$ for $t \in [0,1]$.

Proof Since $f_\lambda(0) = 0$ and $f'_\lambda(1) = 0$ together with the nontriviality of f_λ would contradict the fact that λ_0 is the least eigenvalue of the system (D), (B_1), (B_2), we have $f_\lambda(0) \neq 0$. Also $f_\lambda(1) = 0$ together with $f'_\lambda(1) = 0$ would imply $f_\lambda(t) \equiv 0$ for $t \in [0,1]$ according to the uniqueness of the solution of (D) with fixed λ under the boundary conditions $f_\lambda(1) = 0$ and $f'_\lambda(1) = 0$, contradicting the nontriviality of f_λ. Thus we have $f_\lambda(1) \neq 0$. Hence for our f_λ we have $f_\lambda(0) \neq 0$ and $f_\lambda(1) \neq 0$.

Let f_{λ_0} be an eigenfunction of (D), (B_1), (B_2) corresponding to the least eigenvalue λ_0. Then from

$$f''_{\lambda_0}(t) + \lambda_0 p(t) f_{\lambda_0}(t) = 0 \quad \text{and} \quad f''_\lambda(t) + \lambda p(t) f_\lambda(t) = 0$$

for $t \in [0,1]$

we obtain

$$f''_{\lambda_0}(t) f_\lambda(t) - f_{\lambda_0}(t) f''_\lambda(t) = (\lambda - \lambda_0) p(t) f_{\lambda_0}(t) f_\lambda(t)$$

for $t \in [0,1]$,

i.e.,

$$\frac{d}{dt}\left\{f'_{\lambda_0}(t)\, f_\lambda(t) - f_{\lambda_0}(t)\, f'_\lambda(t)\right\} = (\lambda-\lambda_0)\, p(t)\, f_{\lambda_0}(t)\, f_\lambda(t) \quad \text{for } t \in [0,1],$$

and then

$$\left[f'_{\lambda_0}(s)\, f_\lambda(s) - f_{\lambda_0}(s)\, f'_\lambda(s)\right]_t^1 = (\lambda-\lambda_0)\int_t^1 p(s)\, f_{\lambda_0}(s)\, f_\lambda(s)\, ds$$

$$\text{for } t \in (0,1]. \tag{1}$$

Suppose f_λ vanishes at some points $t \in [0,1]$. Let t_0 be the supremum of all such points. From the continuity of f_λ we have then $f_\lambda(t_0) = 0$. Since $f_\lambda(0) \neq 0$ and $f_\lambda(1) \neq 0$, we have $t_0 \in (0,1)$. With $t = t_0$ in (1) and from $f'_\lambda(1) = 0$, $f'_{\lambda_0}(1) = 0$, and $f_\lambda(t_0) = 0$ we have

$$f_{\lambda_0}(t_0)\, f'_\lambda(t_0) = (\lambda-\lambda_0)\int_{t_0}^1 p(s)\, f_{\lambda_0}(s)\, f_\lambda(s)\, ds. \tag{2}$$

Now since f_{λ_0} never vanishes on $(0,1]$, either $f_{\lambda_0}(t) > 0$ for $t \in (0,1]$ or $f_{\lambda_0}(t) < 0$ for $t \in (0,1]$. From the definition of t_0, $f_\lambda(t) > 0$ for $t \in (t_0, 1]$ or $f_\lambda(t) < 0$ for $t \in (t_0, 1]$. Let us consider one of the four possible cases, say, the case where $f_{\lambda_0}(t) > 0$ for $t \in (0,1]$ and $f_\lambda(t) > 0$ for $t \in (t_0, 1]$. Then (2) yields $f'_\lambda(t_0) < 0$. This and $f_\lambda(t_0) = 0$ together contradict the fact that $f_\lambda(t) > 0$ for $t \in (t_0, 1]$. The other three cases can be handled similarly. Thus f_λ can not vanish on $[0,1]$. □

Lemma 35.2 Let $\lambda < \lambda_0$ where λ_0 is the least eigenvalue of the differential system (D), (B_1), (B_2) and let f_λ be a nontrivial solution of (D) satisying (B_2). Then the transformation T of C_w defined by

$$(Tx)(t) = x(t) + \int_0^t K(s)\, x(s)\, ds \qquad \text{for } t \in [0,1] \text{ and } x \in C_w \tag{1}$$

where

$$K(t) = -\frac{f'_\lambda(t)}{f_\lambda(t)} \qquad \text{for } t \in [0,1] \tag{2}$$

transforms C_w one-to-one onto C_w, and T^{-1} is given by

$$(T^{-1}y)(t) = y(t) + \int_0^t H(t, s)\, y(s)\, ds, \tag{3}$$

where

$$H(t, s) = \frac{f_\lambda(t)\, f'_\lambda(s)}{\left[f_\lambda(s)\right]^2} \qquad \text{for } 0 \le s \le t \le 1. \tag{4}$$

Both T and T^{-1} are continuous in the uniform topology of C_w. They are also Wiener measurable transformations.

Proof Note that, according to Lemma 35.1, $f_\lambda(t) \neq 0$ for $t \in [0,1]$ so that K in (2) and H in (4) are defined. Let us prove our lemma by using Lemma 34.1 in showing that K is continuous and of bounded variation on $[0, 1]$. The continuity of K is obvious from (2). Also from (2) and (D)

$$K'(t) = \frac{-1}{\left[f_\lambda(t)\right]^2} \left\{ f_\lambda(t)\, f''_\lambda(t) - \left[f'_\lambda(t)\right]^2 \right\}$$

where $f''_\lambda(t) = -\lambda p(t)\, f_\lambda(t)$,

so that K' is continuous on $[0,1]$ and consequently K is of bounded variation on $[0,1]$. Thus according to Lemma 34.1, T maps C_w one-to-one onto C_w and both T and T^{-1} are continuous in the uniform topology of C_w. They are Wiener measurable transformations according to Theorem 34.8.

The integral representation (3) of T^{-1} can be obtained directly as follows. Let

$$y(t) = (Tx)(t) = x(t) - \int_0^t \frac{f'_\lambda(s)}{f_\lambda(s)}\, x(s)\, ds$$

for $t \in [0,1]$ and $x \in C_w$.

Then

$$\frac{f'_\lambda(t)}{\left[f_\lambda(t)\right]^2}\, y(t) = \frac{f'_\lambda(t)}{\left[f_\lambda(t)\right]^2} \left\{ x(t) - \int_0^t \frac{f'_\lambda(s)}{f_\lambda(s)}\, x(s)\, ds \right\}$$

$$= \frac{d}{dt}\left\{ \frac{1}{f_\lambda(t)} \int_0^t \frac{f'_\lambda(s)}{f_\lambda(s)}\, x(s)\, ds \right\},$$

and hence

$$f_\lambda(t) \int_0^t \frac{f'_\lambda(s)}{\left[f_\lambda(s)\right]^2}\, y(s)\, ds = \int_0^t \frac{f'_\lambda(s)}{f_\lambda(s)}\, x(s)\, ds = x(t) - y(t),$$

so that (3) and (4) hold. □

<u>Theorem 35.3</u> (R. H. Cameron and W. T. Martin [3]) Let p be a positive-valued continuous function on $[0,1]$: let λ_0 be the least eigenvalue of the differential system (D), (B_1), (B_2), let $\lambda < \lambda_0$; and let f_λ be a nontrivial solution of (D) satisfying (B_2). If G is an extended real-valued Wiener measurable functional on C_w then

$$\int_{C_w} G[x] \exp\left\{ \frac{\lambda}{2} \int_0^1 p(t)\, x^2(t)\, dt \right\} m_w(dx)$$

$$= \left[\frac{f_\lambda(1)}{f_\lambda(0)} \right]^{\frac{1}{2}} \int_{C_w} G\left[y(\cdot) + f_\lambda(\cdot) \int_0^{(\cdot)} \frac{f'_\lambda(s)}{\left[f_\lambda(s)\right]^2}\, y(s)\, ds \right] m_w(dy) \tag{1}$$

in the sense that the existence of one side implies that of the other and the equality of the two. In particular with $G[x] \equiv 1$ for $x \in C_w$ we have

$$\int_{C_w} \exp\left\{\frac{\lambda}{2}\int_0^1 p(t)\, x^2(t)\, dt\right\} m_w(dx) = \left[\frac{f_\lambda(1)}{f_\lambda(0)}\right]^{\frac{1}{2}}. \tag{2}$$

Proof The transformation T of Lemma 35.2 satisfies the conditions of Theorem 34.8. Let us calculate the "Jacobian" $J[K, \cdot]$ as given by (4) of Theorem 34.8 with our K, i.e.,

$$J[K, x] = \exp\left\{\tfrac{1}{2}\int_0^1 K(t)\, dt - \tfrac{1}{2}\int_0^1 K(t)\, dx^2(t) - \tfrac{1}{2}\int_0^1 K^2(t)\, x^2(t)\, dt\right\}$$

for $x \in C_w$, (3)

where

$$K(t) = -\frac{f_\lambda'(t)}{f_\lambda(t)} \qquad \text{for } t \in [0,1]. \tag{4}$$

From (4),

$$\exp\left\{\tfrac{1}{2}\int_0^1 K(t)\, dt\right\} = \exp\left\{-\tfrac{1}{2}\int_0^1 \frac{f_\lambda'(t)}{f_\lambda(t)}\, dt\right\} = \exp\left\{-\tfrac{1}{2}\Big[\log f_\lambda(t)\Big]_0^1\right\} = \left[\frac{f_\lambda(0)}{f_\lambda(1)}\right]^{\frac{1}{2}}$$

and

$$\exp\left\{-\tfrac{1}{2}\int_0^1 K(t)\, dx^2(t) - \tfrac{1}{2}\int_0^1 K^2(t)\, x^2(t)\, dt\right\}$$

$$= \exp\left\{\tfrac{1}{2}\int_0^1 \frac{f_\lambda'(t)}{f_\lambda(t)}\, dx^2(t) - \tfrac{1}{2}\int_0^1 \left[\frac{f_\lambda'(t)}{f_\lambda(t)}\, x(t)\right]^2 dt\right\}$$

$$= \exp\left\{\tfrac{1}{2}\left[\frac{f_\lambda'(t)}{f_\lambda(t)}\, x^2(t)\right]_0^1 - \tfrac{1}{2}\int_0^1 x^2(t)\, d\left[\frac{f_\lambda'(t)}{f_\lambda(t)}\right] - \tfrac{1}{2}\int_0^1 \left[\frac{f_\lambda'(t)}{f_\lambda(t)}\, x(t)\right]^2 dt\right\}$$

$$= \exp\left\{-\tfrac{1}{2}\int_0^1 x^2(t)\,\frac{f_\lambda(t)\,f''_\lambda(t) - \left[f'_\lambda(t)\right]^2}{\left[f_\lambda(t)\right]^2}\,dt - \int_0^1\left[\frac{f'_\lambda(t)}{f_\lambda(t)}\,x(t)\right]^2 dt\right\}$$

$$= \exp\left\{-\tfrac{1}{2}\int_0^1 x^2(t)\,\frac{f''_\lambda(t)}{f_\lambda(t)}\,dt\right\} = \exp\left\{\tfrac{1}{2}\int_0^1 x^2(t)\,\lambda p(t)\,dt\right\},$$

so that from (3)

$$J[K,x] = \left[\frac{f_\lambda(0)}{f_\lambda(1)}\right]^{\frac{1}{2}} \exp\left\{\frac{\lambda}{2}\int_0^1 p(t)\,x^2(t)\,dt\right\}. \tag{5}$$

Let F be an extended real-valued Wiener measurable functional on C_w, then by (5) of Theorem 34.8

$$\int_{C_w} F[y]\,m_w(dy)$$

$$= \int_{C_w} F[Tx]\left[\frac{f_\lambda(0)}{f_\lambda(1)}\right]^{\frac{1}{2}} \exp\left\{\frac{\lambda}{2}\int_0^1 p(t)\,x^2(t)\,dt\right\} m_w(dx) \tag{6}$$

in the sense that the existence of one side implies that of the other and the equality of the two. With our G, write

$$G[x] = G[T^{-1}Tx] = F[Tx] \qquad \text{where } F = GT^{-1}. \tag{7}$$

Since T^{-1} is a Wiener measurable transformation of C_w onto C_w and G is a Wiener measurable functional on C_w, F is Wiener measurable. We also have

$$F[y] = F[TT^{-1}y] = G[T^{-1}y]. \tag{8}$$

With our F, (6) becomes

$$\int_{C_w} G[T^{-1}y]\,m_w(dy) = \int_{C_w} G[x]\left[\frac{f_\lambda(0)}{f_\lambda(1)}\right]^{\frac{1}{2}} \exp\left\{\frac{\lambda}{2}\int_0^1 p(t)\,x^2(t)\,dt\right\} m_w(dx). \tag{9}$$

Using expressions (3) and (4) of Lemma 35.2 for $T^{-1}y$ in (9) we obtain (1). □

Theorem 35.4 (R. H. Cameron and W. T. Martin [3]) Let p, λ_0, λ, and f_λ be as in Theorem 35.3. If g is a real-valued continuous function on $[0,1]$ and H is an extended real-valued Baire function on R^1 then

$$\int_{C_w} \exp\left\{\frac{\lambda}{2}\int_0^1 p(t)\, x^2(t)\, dt\right\} H\left[\int_0^1 g(t)\, x(t)\, dt\right] m_w(dx)$$
$$= \left\{\frac{1}{2\pi}\, \frac{f_\lambda(1)}{f_\lambda(0)}\right\}^{\frac{1}{2}} \int_{R^1} H(bu)\, e^{-u^2/2}\, m_L(du)\,, \tag{1}$$

where

$$b = \left\{\int_0^1 \left[\frac{1}{f_\lambda(t)}\int_1^t g(s)\, f_\lambda(s)\, ds\right]^2 dt\right\}^{\frac{1}{2}} \tag{2}$$

in the sense that the existence of one side of (1) implies that of the other and the equality of the two.

Proof The Riemann integral $\int_0^1 g(t)\, x(t)\, dt$ is a Wiener measurable functional on C_w and so is $H\left[\int_0^1 g(t)\, x(t)\, dt\right]$. According to (1) of Theorem 35.3,

$$\int_{C_w} \exp\left\{\frac{\lambda}{2}\int_0^1 p(t)\, x^2(t)\, dt\right\} H\left[\int_0^1 g(t)\, x(t)\, dt\right] m_w(dx)$$
$$= \left\{\frac{f_\lambda(1)}{f_\lambda(0)}\right\}^{\frac{1}{2}} \int_{C_w} H\left[\int_0^1 g(t)\left[y(t) + f_\lambda(t)\int_0^t \frac{f_\lambda'(s)}{\left[f_\lambda(s)\right]^2}\, y(s)\, ds\right] dt\right] m_w(dy) \tag{3}$$

in the sense that the existence of one side implies that of the other and the equality of the two. We proceed to reduce the right side of (3) to that of (1).

Since $d\left[f_\lambda(t)\right]^{-1}/dt = -\left[f_\lambda(t)\right]^{-2} f'_\lambda(t)$ is continuous on $[0,1]$, $\left[f_\lambda(t)\right]^{-1}$ is absolutely continuous and, in particular, of bounded variation there. Thus by integration by parts of the Riemann-Stieltjes integral we have

$$\int_0^1 g(t)\left\{y(t) + f_\lambda(t)\int_0^t \frac{f'_\lambda(s)}{\left[f_\lambda(s)\right]^2}\, y(s)\, ds\right\} dt$$

$$= \int_0^1 g(t)\, y(t)\, dt + \int_0^1 g(t)\, f_\lambda(t)\left\{\int_0^t y(s)\, d_s\left[-\frac{1}{f_\lambda(s)}\right]\right\} dt$$

$$= \int_0^1 g(t)\, y(t)\, dt + \int_0^1 g(t)\, f_\lambda(t)\left\{\left[-\frac{y(s)}{f_\lambda(s)}\right]_0^t + \int_0^t \frac{1}{f_\lambda(s)}\, dy(s)\right\} dt$$

$$= \int_0^1 g(t)\, y(t)\, dt - \int_0^1 g(t)\, f_\lambda(t)\, \frac{y(t)}{f_\lambda(t)}\, dt + \int_0^1 g(t)\, f_\lambda(t)\left\{\int_0^t \frac{1}{f_\lambda(s)}\, dy(s)\right\} dt$$

$$= \int_0^1 g(t)\, f_\lambda(t)\left\{\int_0^t \frac{1}{f_\lambda(s)}\, dy(s)\right\} dt. \tag{4}$$

Let

$$G(t, \lambda) = \int_1^t g(s)\, f_\lambda(s)\, ds\ .$$

Since $d\, G(t, \lambda)/dt = g(t)\, f_\lambda(t)$ we have, by integration by parts of the Riemann integral

$$\int_0^1 g(t)\, f_\lambda(t)\left\{\int_0^t \frac{1}{f_\lambda(s)}\, dy(s)\right\} dt$$

$$= \left[G(t, \lambda)\int_0^t \frac{1}{f_\lambda(s)}\, dy(s)\right]_0^1 - \int_0^1 G(t, \lambda)\frac{1}{f_\lambda(t)}\, dy(t) = -\int_0^1 \frac{G(t, \lambda)}{f_\lambda(t)}\, dy(t). \tag{5}$$

Note that $G(t,\lambda)\left[f_\lambda(t)\right]^{-1}$ is absolutely continuous and is of bounded variation on $[0,1]$ from the absolute continuity of $G(t,\lambda)$ and $\left[f_\lambda(t)\right]^{-1}$ there. Using (4) and (5) in (3) we reduce (3) to

$$\int_{C_w} \exp\left\{\frac{\lambda}{2}\int_0^1 p(t)\, x^2(t)\, dt\right\} H\left[\int_0^1 g(t)\, x(t)\, dt\right] m_w(dx)$$

$$= \left\{\frac{f_\lambda(1)}{f_\lambda(0)}\right\}^{\frac{1}{2}} \int_{C_w} H\left[-\int_0^1 \frac{G(t,\lambda)}{f_\lambda(t)}\, dy(t)\right] m_w(dy) \,. \tag{6}$$

Now according to Theorem 29.7, if φ is of bounded variation on $[0,1]$ and $\int_0^1 \varphi^2(t)\, m_L(dt) = 1$ then, for any extended real-valued Baire function F on R^1, $F\left[\int_0^1 \varphi(t)\, dy(t)\right]$ is a Wiener measurable function of $y \in C_w$ and

$$\int_{C_w} F\left[\int_0^1 \varphi(t)\, dy(t)\right] m_w(dy) = \frac{1}{\sqrt{2\pi}} \int_{R^1} F(u)\, e^{-u^2/2}\, m_L(du) \tag{7}$$

in the sense that the existence of one side implies that of the other and the equality of the two. As we pointed out, $G(t,\lambda)\left[f_\lambda(t)\right]^{-1}$ is of bounded variation on $[0,1]$. Let

$$b = \left\{\int_0^1 \left[\frac{G(t,\lambda)}{f_\lambda(t)}\right]^2 dt\right\}^{\frac{1}{2}} = \left\{\int_0^1 \left[\frac{1}{f_\lambda(t)}\int_1^t g(s)\, f_\lambda(s)\, ds\right]^2 dt\right\}^{\frac{1}{2}} .$$

Applying (7) to the Wiener integral on the right side of (6) we have

$$\int_{C_w} H\left[-\int_0^1 \frac{G(t,\lambda)}{f_\lambda(t)}\, dy(t)\right] m_w(dy)$$

$$= \int_{C_w} H\left[-b\int_0^1 \frac{1}{b}\frac{G(t,\lambda)}{f_\lambda(t)}\, dy(t)\right] m_w(dy) = \frac{1}{\sqrt{2\pi}}\int_{R^1} H(-bu)\, e^{-u^2/2}\, m_L(du)$$

$$= \frac{1}{\sqrt{2\pi}}\int_{R^1} H(bu)\, e^{-u^2/2}\, m_L(du)\ . \tag{8}$$

Using (8) in (6) we have (1). □

A SYNOPSIS OF PROBABILITY THEORY

§A.1 PROBABILITY SPACE AND FINITE-DIMENSIONAL RANDOM VECTORS

Definition A1.1 A probability space is a measure space $(\Omega, \mathfrak{B}, P)$ in which $P(\Omega) = 1$. The set Ω is called the sample space, every member A of the σ-field $\mathfrak{B}$ is called a measurable event, and $P(A)$ is called the probability of A.

Definition A1.2 Given a probability space $(\Omega, \mathfrak{B}, P)$. A system $\{A_\lambda, \lambda \in \Lambda\} \subset \mathfrak{B}$ where Λ is an arbitrary index set is said to be independent if for every finite subset $\{\lambda_1, \cdots, \lambda_k\} \subset \Lambda$ the equality

$$P\left(\bigcap_{i=1}^{k} A_{\lambda_i}\right) = \prod_{i=1}^{k} P(A_{\lambda_i})$$

holds.

Theorem A1.3 (Borel-Cantelli) Given a probability space $(\Omega, \mathfrak{B}, P)$ and a sequence $\{A_n, n = 1,2, \cdots\} \subset \mathfrak{B}$. If $\sum_{n=1}^{\infty} P(A) < \infty$ then $P\left(\lim_{n\to\infty} \sup A_n\right) = 0$. If $\sum_{n=1}^{\infty} P(A_n) = \infty$ and $\{A_n, n = 1,2, \cdots\}$ is an independent system then $P\left(\lim_{n\to\infty} \sup A_n\right) = 1$.

Definition A1.4 A probability space $(R^k, \mathfrak{B}^k, \Phi)$ where R^k is the k-dimensional Euclidean space and $\mathfrak{B}^k$ is the σ-field of Borel sets in R^k is called a k-dimensional probability space and Φ is called a k-dimensional probability distribution. When Φ is absolutely continuous with respect to the Lebesgue measure m_L on $(R^k, \mathfrak{B}^k)$ the Radon-Nikodym derivative $d\Phi(x)/dm_L$, $x \in R^k$, is called the density function of Φ. It is determined up to a null set with respect to $(\mathfrak{B}^k, m_L)$.

Definition A1.5 By a k-dimensional random vector on a probability space $(\Omega, \mathfrak{B}, P)$ we mean a measurable transformation X of $(\Omega, \mathfrak{B})$ into $(R^k, \mathfrak{B}^k)$. The set function Φ_X on $\mathfrak{B}^k$ defined by $\Phi_X(E) = P\left(X^{-1}(E)\right)$, $E \in \mathfrak{B}^k$, is a probability measure on $(R^k, \mathfrak{B}^k)$ and is called the k-dimensional probability distribution determined by the random vector X. When $k = 1$, X is called a random variable. By a complex random variable we mean a complex-valued function on $(\Omega, \mathfrak{B}, P)$ whose real imaginary parts are random variables. By the expectation $E(X)$ of a real or complex random variable X we mean $E(X) = \int_\Omega X(\omega)\, P(d\omega)$ if this integral exists.

Theorem A1.6 Let X be a k-dimensional random vector on a probability space $(\Omega, \mathfrak{B}, P)$ and let f be a real or complex Baire (i.e., $\mathfrak{B}^k$-measurable) function on R^k. Then $Y = f \circ X$ is a real or complex random variable on $(\Omega, \mathfrak{B}, P)$ and

$$E(Y) = \int_{R^k} f(x)\, \Phi_X(dx)$$

in the sense that the existence of one side implies that of the other and the equality of the two.

Theorem A1.7 Let X be a k-dimensional random vector on a probability space $(\Omega, \mathfrak{B}, P)$ and let Φ_X be absolutely continuous with respect to m_L on $(R^k, \mathfrak{B}^k)$. If T is a nonsingular linear transformation of R^k onto R^k then $Y = TX + b$, $b \in R^k$, is a k-dimensional random vector on $(\Omega, \mathfrak{B}, P)$ and Φ_Y is absolutely continuous with respect to m_L on $(R^k, \mathfrak{B}^k)$. Furthermore for the density functions $f(x) = d\Phi_X(x)/dm_L$, $x \in R^k$, and $g(y) = d\Phi_Y(y)/dm_L$, $y \in R^k$, we have

$$g(y) = \frac{1}{|\det T|} f\left(T^{-1}(y - b)\right).$$

Theorem A1.8 Given a k-dimensional probability space. $(R^k, \mathfrak{B}^k, \Phi)$. Let $C_0(R^k)$ be the collection of real-valued continuous functions with compact support on R^k. Then the real-valued functional L on $C_0(R^k)$ defined by

$$Lf = \int_{R^k} f(x)\, \Phi(dx), \qquad f \in C_0(R^k) \tag{1}$$

satisfies the following conditions:

1° $f, g \in C_0(R^k)$, $a, b \in R^1 \Rightarrow L(af + bg) = aLf + bLg$

2° $f \in C_0(R^k)$, $f \geq 0 \Rightarrow Lf \geq 0$

3° $\{f_n, n = 1, 2, \cdots\} \subset C_0(R^k)$, $f_n \uparrow 1 \Rightarrow Lf_n \uparrow 1$.

Conversely if a real-valued functional L on $C_0(R^k)$ satisfies 1°, 2°, 3° then there exists a unique k-dimensional probability distribution Φ such that (1) holds.

Definition A1.9 Let Φ be a k-dimensional probability distribution. The distribution function of Φ is the real-valued function F on R^k defined by

$$F(x) = \Phi\Big((-\infty, x_1] \times \cdots \times (-\infty, x_k]\Big) \qquad \text{for } x = (x_1, \cdots, x_k) \in R^k.$$

By the distribution function of a k-dimensional random vector we mean the distribution function of the k-dimension probability distribution determined by the random vector.

Theorem A1.10 If F is the distribution function of a 1-dimensional probability distribution, it satisfies the following conditions:

1° monotonicity; $x' < x'' \Rightarrow F(x') \le F(x'')$

2° right-continuity; $x \downarrow a \Rightarrow F(x) \downarrow F(a)$

3° bounded and normalized; $\lim_{x \downarrow -\infty} F(x) = 0$, $\lim_{x \uparrow \infty} F(x) = 1$.

Conversely if a real-valued function F on R^1 satisfies 1°, 2°, 3° then there exists a unique 1-dimensional probability distribution Φ which has F as its distribution function.

An analogous theorem holds for the k-dimensional case.

§A2. CHARACTERISTIC FUNCTIONS OF PROBABILITY DISTRIBUTIONS

Definition A2.1 The characteristic function of a k-dimensional probability distribution Φ is a complex-valued function φ on R^k defined by

$$\varphi(y) = \int_{R^k} e^{i(x,y)}\, \Phi(dx), \qquad \text{for } y \in R^k,$$

where $(x, y) = \Sigma_{j=1}^{k} x_j, y_j$. By the characteristic function of a k-dimensional random vector we mean the characteristic function of the k-dimensional probability distribution determined by the random vector.

Definition A2.2 A complex-valued function $\varphi(y)$, $y \in R^k$, is said to be positive definite if, for an arbitrary positive integer n and arbitrary $\{y_1, \cdots, y_n\} \subset R^k$ and $\{\zeta_1, \cdots, \zeta_n\} \subset C$,

$$\sum_{j=1}^{n} \sum_{\ell=1}^{n} \varphi(y_j - y_\ell)\, \zeta_j \overline{\zeta_\ell} \geq 0 .$$

From this inequality it follows that $\varphi(0) \geq 0$, $\varphi(-y) = \overline{\varphi(y)}$, $|\varphi(y)| \leq \varphi(0)$ for $y \in R^k$.

Theorem A2.3 (Bochner's theorem) Let $\varphi(y)$, $y \in R^k$, be the characteristic function of a k-dimensional probability distribution Φ. Then

1° φ is positive definite

2° $\varphi(0) = 1$

3° φ is continuous at $y = 0$

4° φ is uniformly continuous on R^k.

Conversely if φ is a complex-valued function on R^k satisfying 1°, 2°, 3° then there exists a unique k-dimensional probability distribution which has φ as its characteristic function (so that φ satisfies 4° also).

Theorem A2.4 (Lévy inversion formula) Let $F(x)$, $x \in R^1$, and $\varphi(y)$, $y \in R^1$, be the distribution function and the characteristic function, respectively, of a 1-dimensional probability distribution. Let $\widetilde{F}(x) = \frac{1}{2}\{F(x-0) + F(x)\}$ for $x \in R^1$. Then for $x', x'' \in R^1$, $x' < x''$,

$$\tilde{F}(x'') - \tilde{F}(x') = \lim_{c\to\infty} \frac{1}{2\pi} \int_{-c}^{c} \frac{e^{-ix''y} - e^{-ix'y}}{-iy} \varphi(y)\, dy$$

holds.

A similar formula holds for the k-dimensional case.

§A3. MOMENTS OF PROBABILITY DISTRIBUTIONS

Definition A3.1 The pth moment $M^p(\Phi)$, $p = 1,2,\cdots$, of a 1-dimensional probability distribution Φ is defined by

$$M^p(\Phi) = \int_{R^1} x^p \Phi(dx)$$

provided the integral exists. The pth absolute moment $\overline{M}^p(\Phi)$, $p = 1,2,\cdots$, of Φ is defined by

$$\overline{M}^p(\Phi) = \int_{R^1} |x|^p \Phi(dx).$$

The 1st moment of Φ, $M^1(\Phi)$ is also called the mean of Φ. If $M^1(\Phi)$ exists and is finite then

$$V(\Phi) = \int_{R^1} \left\{x - M^1(\Phi)\right\}^2 \Phi(dx) = M^2(\Phi) - \left\{M^1(\Phi)\right\}^2$$

is called the variance of Φ. The moments $M^p(X)$, the absolute moments $\overline{M}^p(X)$, and the variance $V(X)$ of a random variable X on a probability space $(\Omega, \mathfrak{B}, P)$ are defined by

$$M^p(X) = M^p(\Phi_X), \quad \overline{M}^p(X) = \overline{M}^p(\Phi_X), \quad V(X) = V(\Phi_X),$$

where Φ_X is the 1-dimensional probability distribution determined by X.

In view of Theorem A1.6 we have

$$M^p(X) = \int_{R^1} x^p \Phi_X(dx) = E(X^p),$$

$$\overline{M}^p(X) = \int_{R^1} |x|^p \Phi_X(dx) = E\left(|X|^p\right),$$

$$V(X) = \int_{R^1} \{x - E(X)\}^2 \Phi_X(dx) = E\left[\{X - E(X)\}^2\right].$$

As immediate consequences of the above definition we have

Chebyshev inequality: $P\{\omega \in \Omega;\ |X(\omega) - E(X)| \geq c\} \leq \frac{V(X)}{c^2}$ for $c > 0$

Markov inequality : $P\{\omega \in \Omega;\ |X(\omega)| \geq c\} \leq \frac{\overline{M}^p(X)}{c^p}$ for $c > 0$.

Theorem A3.2 Let Φ be a 1-dimensional probability distribution and let φ be its characteristic function. If $\overline{M}^q(\Phi) < \infty$ for some positive integer q then the derivatives $\varphi^{(p)}$, $p = 1, 2, \cdots, q$, exist on R^1 and are given by

$$\varphi^{(p)}(y) = \int_{R^1} (ix)^p e^{iyx} \Phi(dx), \quad \text{for } y \in R^1.$$

In particular

$$\varphi^{(p)}(0) = i^p M^p(\Phi).$$

Definition A3.3 For a k-dimensional probability distribution Φ the moments $M^{p_1, \cdots, p_k}(\Phi)$ and the absolute moments $\overline{M}^{p_1, \cdots, p_k}(\Phi)$, $p_1, \cdots, p_k = 1, 2, \cdots$, are defined by

$$M^{p_1, \cdots, p_k}(\Phi) = \int_{R^k} x_1^{p_1} \cdots x_k^{p_k} \Phi(dx)$$

if the integral exists and by

$$\overline{M}^{p_1, \cdots, p_k}(\Phi) = \int_{R^k} |x_1|^{p_1} \cdots |x_k|^{p_k} \Phi(dx) .$$

The moments $M^{p_1, \cdots, p_k}(X)$ and the absolute moments $\overline{M}^{p_1, \cdots, p_k}(X)$ of a k-dimensional random vector X on a probability space are defined by

$$M^{p_1, \cdots, p_k}(X) = M^{p_1, \cdots, p_k}(\Phi_X) \qquad \text{and}$$

$$\overline{M}^{p_1, \cdots, p_k}(X) = \overline{M}^{p_1, \cdots, p_k}(\Phi_X) ,$$

where Φ_X is the k-dimensional distribution determined by X.

Theorem A3.4 Let Φ be a k-dimensional probability distribution and let φ be its characteristic function. If $\overline{M}^{p_1, \cdots, p_k}(\Phi) < \infty$ for all $p_1 = 1,2, \cdots, q_1; \cdots ; p_k = 1,2, \cdots, q_k$ then $\partial^{p_1 + \cdots + p_k} \varphi / \partial y_1^{p_1} \cdots \partial y_k^{p_k}$ exists on R^k for $p_1 = 1,2, \cdots, q_1 ; \cdots ;$ $p_k = 1,2, \cdots, q_k$ and

$$\frac{\partial^{p_1 + \cdots + p_k}}{\partial y_1^{p_1} \cdots \partial y_k^{p_k}} \varphi(y) = \int_{R^k} (ix_1)^{p_1} \cdots (ix_k)^{p_k} e^{i(y,x)} \Phi(dx), \qquad \text{for } y \in R^k.$$

In particular

$$\frac{\partial^{p_1+\cdots+p_k}}{\partial y_1^{p_1}\cdots\partial y_k^{p_k}}\varphi(0) = i^{p_1+\cdots+p_k} M^{p_1,\cdots,p_k}(\Phi) .$$

§A4. CONVERGENCE OF PROBABILITY DISTRIBUTIONS

Definition A4.1 Let $\{\Phi_n, n=0,1,2,\cdots\}$ be a sequence of k-dimensional probability distributions. We say that Φ_n converges to Φ_0 and write $\lim_{n\to\infty}\Phi_n = \Phi_0$ if

$$\lim_{n\to\infty}\int_{R^k} f(x)\,\Phi_n(dx) = \int_{R^k} f(x)\,\Phi_0(dx)$$

for every $f \in C_0(R^k)$,

where $C_0(R^k)$ is the collection of real-valued continuous functions with compact support on R^k.

When $\lim_{n\to\infty}\Phi_n = \Phi$ and $\lim_{n\to\infty}\Phi_n = \Psi$ also then $\Phi = \Psi$.

Theorem A4.2 Let $\{\Phi_n, n=0,1,2,\cdots\}$ be a sequence of k-dimensional probability distributions and let $\{F_n, n=0,1,2,\cdots\}$ and $\{\varphi_n, n=0,1,2,\cdots\}$ be the corresponding sequences of distribution functions and characteristic functions respectively. The following conditions are all equivalent:

[A] $\lim_{n\to\infty}\Phi_n = \Phi_0$.

[B] $\lim_{n\to\infty}\int_{R^k} f(x)\,\Phi_n(dx) = \int_{R^k} f(x)\,\Phi_0(dx)$ for every real-valued bounded continuous function f on R^k.

[C] $\lim_{n\to\infty} \Phi_n(E) = \Phi_0(E)$ for every $E \in \mathfrak{B}^k$ with $\Phi_0(E^i) = \Phi_0(\overline{E})$ where E^i is the interior of E.

[D] $\lim_{n\to\infty} F_n(x) = F_0(x)$ at every point of continuity x of F_0.

[E] $\lim_{n\to\infty} \varphi_n(y) = \varphi_0(y)$ at every $y \in R^k$.

Theorem A4.3 Let $\{\Phi_n, n = 0,1,2,\cdots\}$ be a sequence of k-dimensional probability distributions and let $\{\varphi_n, n = 0,1,2,\cdots\}$ be the corresponding sequence of characteristic functions.

(1) (P. Lévy). If $\lim_{n\to\infty} \Phi_n = \Phi_0$ then $\lim_{n\to\infty} \varphi_n(y) = \varphi_0(y)$, $y \in R^k$, where the convergence is uniform on every compact subset of R^k.

(2) (V. Glivenko). If $\lim_{n\to\infty} \varphi_n(y) = \varphi_0(y)$, $y \in R^k$, then $\lim_{n\to\infty} \Phi_n = \Phi_0$.

(3) (P. Lévy). If $\varphi(y) = \lim_{n\to\infty} \varphi_n(y)$, $y \in R^k$, and φ is continuous at $y = 0$ then φ is the characteristic function of a k-dimensional probability distribution Φ and $\Phi = \lim_{n\to\infty} \Phi_n$.

§A5. CONVERGENCE OF RANDOM VECTORS

Theorem A5.1 Let $\{X_n, n = 0,1,2,\cdots\}$ be a sequence of k-dimensional random vectors on a probability space $(\Omega, \mathfrak{B}, P)$. If

$$\sum_{n=1}^{\infty} P\left\{\omega \in \Omega;\ |X_n(\omega) - X_0(\omega)| \geq \varepsilon_n\right\} < \infty$$

for some sequence of positive numbers ε_n which converges to 0 then X_n converges to X_0 a.e., on Ω.

Theorem A5.2 Let $\{X_n, n = 1,2,\cdots\}$ be a sequence of k-dimensional random vectors on a probability space $(\Omega, \mathfrak{B}, P)$. If

$$\sum_{n=1}^{\infty} P\left\{\omega \in \Omega ; |X_n(\omega)| \geq \varepsilon_n\right\} < \infty$$

for some convergent series of positive numbers $\sum_{n=1}^{\infty} \varepsilon_n$ then the series $\sum_{n=1}^{\infty} |X_n|$ converges a.e., on Ω.

Definition A5.3 Given a sequence of k-dimensional random vectors $\{X_n, n = 0,1,2,\cdots\}$ on a probability space $(\Omega, \mathfrak{B}, P)$.

(1) If $E\left(|X_n|^p\right) < \infty$, $n = 0,1,2,\cdots$, for some positive integer p and $\lim_{n\to\infty} E\left(|X_n - X_0|^p\right) = 0$ we say that X_n converges to X_0 in the pth moment. This is the convergence of a sequence in $L_p(\Omega) = L_p(\Omega, \mathfrak{B}, P)$ to a member in $L_p(\Omega)$ in the L_p norm.

(2) If for every $\eta > 0$, $\lim_{n\to\infty} P\left\{\omega \in \Omega ; |X_n(\omega) - X_0(\omega)| \geq \eta\right\} = 0$ then we say that X_n converges in probability to X_0 and write $X_0 = P - \lim_{n\to\infty} X_n$.

(3) Let Φ_{X_n} be the k-dimensional probability distribution determined by X_n, $n = 0,1,2,\cdots$. If $\lim_{n\to\infty} \Phi_{X_n} = \Phi_{X_0}$ we say that X_n converges in distribution to X_0.

Theorem A5.4 Given a sequence of k-dimensional random vectors $\{X_n, n = 0,1,2,\cdots\}$ on a probability space $(\Omega, \mathfrak{B}, P)$.

(1) If X_n converges a.e. on Ω to X_0 then X_n converges to X_0 in probability.

(2) If X_n converges in the L_p norm to X_0 then X_n converges to X_0 in probability.

(3) If X_n converges in probability to X_0 then X_n converges in distribution to X_0.

§A6. INDEPENDENT SYSTEMS OF RANDOM VECTORS

Definition A6.1 A system of random vectors $\{X_\lambda, \lambda \in \Lambda\}$, X_λ being a k_λ-dimensional random vector, on a probability space $(\Omega, \mathfrak{B}, P)$ is said to be independent if for any X_{λ_j}, $j = 1,2,\cdots,n$, from the system and any $E_j \in \mathfrak{B}^{\lambda_j}$, $j = 1,2,\cdots,n$, the system of members of $\mathfrak{B}$, $\left\{X_{\lambda_j}^{-1}(E_j),\ j = 1,2,\cdots,n\right\}$, is independent, i.e.,

$$P\left(\bigcap_{j=1}^{n} X_{\lambda_j}^{-1}(E_j)\right) = \prod_{j=1}^{n} P\left(X_j^{-1}(E_j)\right),$$

in other words

$$P\left\{\omega \in \Omega ; X_{\lambda_j}(\omega) \in E_j, j = 1,2,\cdots,n\right\} = \prod_{j=1}^{n} P\left\{\omega \in \Omega ; X_{\lambda_j}(\omega) \in E_j\right\}.$$

Theorem A6.2 Let X_j be a k_j-dimensional random vector on a probability space $(\Omega, \mathfrak{B}, P)$ and let Φ_{X_j} be the k_j-dimensional probability distribution determined by X_j for $j = 1,2,\cdots,n$. Let $k = k_1 + \cdots + k_n$ and let Φ_X be the k-dimensional probability distribution determined by the k-dimensional random vector $X = (X_1, \cdots, X_n)$. Then the system $\{X_j, j = 1,2,\cdots,n\}$

is independent if and only if Φ_X is the product measure of $\Phi_{X_1}, \cdots, \Phi_{X_n}$.

<u>Theorem A6.3</u> Let X_j be a k_j-dimensional random vector on a probability space $(\Omega, \mathfrak{B}, P)$ and let $f_j(x_j)$, $x_j \in R^{k_j}$, be a real- or complex-valued Baire function with $E\left(|f_j(X_j)|\right) < \infty$ for $j = 1,2,\cdots,n$. If $\{X_j, j = 1,2,\cdots,n\}$ is an independent system then $E\left(|f_1(X_1) \cdots f_n(X_n)|\right) < \infty$ and

$$E\left[f_1(X_1) \cdots f_n(X_n)\right] = E\left[f(X_1)\right] \cdots E\left[f(X_n)\right].$$

<u>Theorem A6.4</u> Let X_j be a k_j-dimensional random vector on a probability space $(\Omega, \mathfrak{B}, P)$ and let $\varphi(y_j)$, $y_j \in R^{k_j}$, be its characteristic function for $j = 1,2,\cdots,n$. Let $\varphi(y)$, $y = (y_1, \cdots, y_n) \in R^k$, $k = k_1 + \cdots + k_n$, be the characteristic function of the k-dimensional random vector $X = (X_1, \cdots, X_n)$. Then the system $\{X_j, j = 1,2,\cdots,n\}$ is independent if and only if $\varphi(y) = \prod_{j=1}^{n} \varphi_j(y_j)$.

<u>Theorem A6.5</u> Let $\left\{X_{m,n}, n = 1,2,\cdots,N(m); m = 1,2,\cdots,M\right\}$ be a system of random vectors on a probability space $(\Omega, \mathfrak{B}, P)$, $X_{m,n}$ being a $k_{m,n}$-dimensional random vector. Let $X_m = \left(X_{m,1}, \cdots, X_{m,N(m)}\right)$ for $m = 1,2,\cdots,M$:

(1) If $\left\{X_{m,n}, n = 1,2,\cdots,N(m); m = 1,2,\cdots,M\right\}$ is an independent system then $\{X_m, m = 1,2,\cdots,M\}$ is an independent system.

(2) If $\{X_m, m = 1,2,\cdots,M\}$ is an independent system and for each m $\{X_{m,n}, n = 1,2,\cdots,N(m)\}$ is an independent system then $\{X_{m,n}, n = 1,2,\cdots,N(m); m = 1,2,\cdots,M\}$ is an independent system.

Theorem A6.6 Let $\{X_j, j = 1,2,\cdots n\}$ be an independent system of random vectors on a probability space $(\Omega, \mathfrak{B}, P)$, X_j being a k_j-dimensional random vector. Let T_j be a Baire transformation of R^{k_j} into R^{ℓ_j} $\left[\text{i.e., a measurable transformation of } \left(R^{k_j}, \mathfrak{B}^{k_j}\right) \text{ into } \left(R^{\ell_j}, \mathfrak{B}^{\ell_j}\right)\right]$ and let $Y_j = T_j(X_j)$, an ℓ_j-dimensional random vector, for $j = 1,2,\cdots,n$. Then $\{Y_j, j = 1,2,\cdots,n\}$ is an independent system.

Theorem A6.7 Let $\{X_{m,n}, n = 1,2,\cdots; m = 1,2,\cdots,M\}$ be an independent system of random vectors on a probability space $(\Omega, \mathfrak{B}, P)$, $X_{m,n}$ being a k_m-dimensional random vector for $n = 1,2,\cdots$. If $X_m = P\text{-}\lim_{n\to\infty} X_{m,n}$ then $\{X_m, m = 1,2,\cdots,M\}$ is an independent system.

§A.7 CONVOLUTION

Definition A7.1 Given two 1-dimensional probability distributions Φ_1 and Φ_2. The 1-dimensional probability distribution $\Phi_1 * \Phi_2$ defined by

$$(\Phi_1 * \Phi_2)(E) = \int_{R^2} \chi_E(x+y)(\Phi_1 \times \Phi_2)\big(d(x,y)\big), \qquad E \in \mathfrak{B}^1$$

is called the convolution of Φ_1 and Φ_2.

Definition A7.2 Let F_1 and F_2 be 1-dimensional distribution functions (i.e., real-valued functions on R^1 satisfying 1°, 2°, 3° of Theorem A1.10). The 1-dimensional distribution function $F_1 * F_2$ defined by

$$(F_1 * F_2)(z) = \int_{R^1} F_1(z - y)\, dF_2(y) \qquad \text{for } z \in R^1$$

is called the convolution of F_1 and F_2. Here the integration is with respect to the Borel measure on $\mathfrak{B}^1$ determined by F_2.

The above two definitions are equivalent in the sense that if Φ_1, Φ_2, Φ are 1-dimensional probability distributions and F_1, F_2, F are their distribution functions then $\Phi = \Phi_1 * \Phi_2$ if and only $F = F_1 * F_2$. From this and from $\Phi_1 * \Phi_2 = \Phi_2 * \Phi_1$ follows $F_1 * F_2 = F_2 * F_1$.

Theorem A7.3 Let Φ_1 and Φ_2 be 1-dimensional probability distributions. Then for every real- or complex-valued Baire function f on R^1 we have

$$\int_{R^1} f(z)(\Phi_1 * \Phi_2)(dz) = \int_{R^2} f(x+y)(\Phi_1 \times \Phi_2)\big(d(x,y)\big)$$

in the sense that the existence of one side implies that of the other and the equality of the two.

Theorem A7.4 Let Φ_1, Φ_2, Φ be 1-dimensional probability distributions and let $\varphi_1(y), \varphi_2(y), \varphi(y)$, $y \in R^1$ be their characteristic functions, then $\Phi = \Phi_1 * \Phi_2$ if and only if $\varphi(y) = \varphi_1(y)\, \varphi_2(y)$, $y \in R^1$.

Theorem A7.5 For 1-dimensional probability distributions the following hold:

(1) $\Phi_1 * \Phi_2 = \Phi_2 * \Phi_1$.

(2) $\Phi_E * \Phi = \Phi$ where Φ_E is the unit distribution, i.e., $\Phi_E\big(\{0\}\big) = 1$.

(3) $(\Phi_1 * \Phi_2) * \Phi_3 = \Phi_1 * (\Phi_2 * \Phi_3)$.

(4) $\lim_{n\to\infty} \Phi_n = \Phi_0$ and $\lim_{n\to\infty} \Psi_n = \Psi_0$ imply $\lim_{n\to\infty} (\Phi_n * \Psi_n) = \Phi_0 * \Psi_0$.

(5) If $\varphi_1(y)$ and $\varphi_2(y)$, $y \in R^1$, are characteristic functions of 1-dimensional probability distributions then so is $\varphi_1(y)\,\varphi_2(y)$, $y \in R^1$.

Theorem A7.6 Let X and Y be random variables on a probability space $(\Omega, \mathfrak{B}, P)$. Let $\Phi_X, \Phi_Y, \Phi_{X+Y}$ be the 1-dimensional probability distributions determined by $X, Y, X+Y$, respectively. If $\{X, Y\}$ is independent then $\Phi_X * \Phi_Y = \Phi_{X+Y}$.

§A8. SERIES OF INDEPENDENT RANDOM VARIABLES

Theorem A8.1 (P. Lévy) Let $\{X_n, n = 1,2,\cdots\}$ be a sequence of independent random variables on a probability space and let $X_N = \sum_{n=1}^{N} X_n$ for $N = 1,2,\cdots$. Then the following statements are all equivalent:

[A] X_N converges a.e. to a random variable as $N \to \infty$.

[B] X_N converges in probability to a random variable as $N \to \infty$.

[C] The probability distribution of X_N converges to a 1-dimensional probability distribution as $N \to \infty$.

BIBLIOGRAPHY

Baxter, G., [1]. A strong limit theorem for Gaussian processes. Proc. Amer. Math. Soc., 7, (1956), pp. 522-527.

Billingsley, P., [1]. Convergence of Probability Measures, Wiley, New York, 1968.

Cameron, R. H. and W. T. Martin, [1]. Transformations of Wiener integrals under translations. Ann. Math., 45, (1944), pp. 386-396.

Cameron, R. H. and W. T. Martin, [2]. Transformations of Wiener integrals under a general class of linear transformations. Trans. Amer. Math. Soc., 58, (1945), pp. 184-219.

Cameron, R. H. and W. T. Martin, [3]. Evaluation of various Wiener integrals by use of certain Sturm-Liouville differential equations. Bull. Amer. Math. Soc., 51, (1945), pp. 73-89.

Cameron, R. H. and W. T. Martin, [4]. The behavior of measure and measurability under change of scale in Wiener space. Bull. Amer. Math. Soc., 53, (1947), pp. 130-137.

Doob, J. L., [1]. Stochastic processes depending on a continuous parameter. Trans. Amer. Math. Soc., 42, (1937), pp. 107-140.

Doob, J. L., [2]. Stochastic Processes, Wiley, New York, 1953.

Dunford, N. and J. Schwartz, [1]. Linear Operators, Vol. I, Wiley-Interscience, New York, 1958.

Feldman, J., [1]. Equivalence and perpendicularity of Gaussian processes. Pacific J. Math., 8, (1958), pp. 699-708; correction, ibidem, 9, (1959), pp. 1295-1296.

Gelfand, I. M. and A. M. Yaglom, [1]. Integration in function spaces and its applications in quantum physics (in Russian), Usp. Mat. Nauk, 11, (1956), pp. 77-114.

Gelfand, I. M. and N. Ya Vilenkin, [1]. Generalized Functions, Vol. 4 (in Russian), Gosudarstvennoe Izdatelstvo, Moscow, 1961.

Hájek, J., [1]. A property of J-divergences of marginal probability distributions. Czech. Math. J., 8, (1958), pp. 460-463.

Hájek, J., [2]. On a property of normal distributions of an arbitrary stochastic process. Czech. Math. J., 8, (1958), pp. 610-618.

Halmos, P., [1]. Measure Theory, Van Nostrand, Princeton, New Jersey, 1950.

Hewitt, E. and K. Stromberg, [1]. Real and Abstract Analysis, Springer-Verlag, New York, 1969.

Ince, E., [1]. Ordinary Differential Equations, London, 1927.

Itô, K., [1]. Stochastic integral. Proc. Imperial Acad., Tokyo, 20, (1944), pp. 519-524.

Itô, K., [2]. Probability Theory (in Japanese) Iwanami, Tokyo, 1953.

Itô, K., [3]. Lectures on Stochastic Processes, Tata Institute for Fundamental Research, Bombay, 1961.

Gnedenko, B. V., [1]. A Course in Probability Theory, 4th ed., (in Russian) Nauka, Moscow, 1965.

Kac, M., [1]. Probability and Related Topics in Physical Sciences, Wiley-Interscience, New York, 1959.

Kac, M. and A. J. F. Siegert, [1]. An explicit representation of stationary Gaussian processes. Ann. Math. Statistics, 18, (1947), pp. 438-442.

Kolmogorov, A. N., [1]. Grundbegriffe der Wahrscheinlichkeitsrechnung, Ergebnisse der Mathematik und ihrer Grenzgebiete, Julius Springer, Berlin, 1933.

Kovalchik, I. M., [1]. Wiener integral (in Russian). Usp. Mat. Nauk, 109, (1963), pp. 97-134.

Krickeberg, K., [1]. Wahrscheinlichkeitstheorie, Teubner, Stuttgart, 1963.

Lévy, P., [1]. Le mouvement brownien plan. Amer. J. Math., 62, (1940), pp. 487-550.

Lévy, P., [2]. Processus Stochastiques et Mouvement Brownien, 2nd ed., Gauthier-Villars, Paris, 1965.

Loéve, M., [1]. Probability Theory, 3rd ed., Van Nostrand, Princeton, New Jersey, 1963.

Schatten, R., [1]. Norm Ideals of Completely Continuous Operators, Ergebnisse der Mathematik und ihrer Grenzgebiete, Springer-Verlag, Berlin, 1960.

Shepp, L. A., [1]. Radon-Nikodym derivatives of Gaussian measures. Ann. Math. Statistics, 37, (1966), pp. 321-354.

Smithies, F., [1]. Integral Equations, Cambridge Univ. Press, London and New York, 1962.

Tucker, H. G., [1]. A Graduate Course in Probability, Academic Press, New York, 1967.

Varberg, D. E., [1]. Some Radon-Nikodym derivatives associated with stochastic processes. Ph.D. Thesis, University of Minnesota, 1959.

Wiener, N., [1]. Generalized harmonic analysis. Acta Math., 55, (1930), pp. 117-258.

Yaglom, A. M., [1]. On the equivalence and perpendicularity of two Gaussian probability measures in function space. Proceedings of the Symposium on Time Series Analysis held at Brown University, 1962, pp. 327-346.

Yeh, J., [1]. Differentiability of sample functions in Gaussian processes. Proc. Amer. Math. Soc., 18, (1967), pp. 105-108; correction, 19, (1968), p. 843.

Yeh, J., [2]. Singularity of Gaussian measures on function spaces induced by Brownian motion processes with nonstationary increments. Illinois J. Math., 15, (1971), pp. 37-46.

Yosida, K., [1]. Lectures on Differential and Integral Equations, Wiley-Interscience, New York, 1960.

Yosida, K., [2]. Functional Analysis, Springer-Verlag, Berlin, 1965.

ADDENDA

To [III] of §16, pp. 241-247, we add the following:

Theorem 16.11a Let $\{X_n, n = 1, 2, \cdots\}$ be a sequence of random variables on a probability space $(\Omega, \mathfrak{B}, P)$ and let the probability distribution of X_n be $N(m_n, v_n)$ for $n = 1, 2, \cdots$. If $X_0 = P - \lim_{n\to\infty} X_n$ exists then X_0 is normally distributed, $m_0 = \lim_{n\to\infty} m_n$ and $v_0 = \lim_{n\to\infty} v_n$ exist in R^1 and the probability distribution of X_0 is given by $N(m_0, v_0)$. Furthermore

$$\lim_{n\to\infty} \| X_n - X_0 \| = 0 \tag{1}$$

where $\| \cdot \|$ is the L_2-norm in $L_2(\Omega)$. Thus if $\{X_n, n = 1, 2, \cdots\}$ is a sequence of random variables on $(\Omega, \mathfrak{B}, P)$ each of which is normally distributed then the sequence converges to a random variable X_0 in the L_2-norm if and only if it converges to X_0 in probability. Consequently the sequence is a Cauchy sequence in the L_2-norm if and only if it is a Cauchy sequence with respect to convergence in probability.

Proof If $X_0 = P - \lim_{n\to\infty} X_n$ then the probability distributions of $\{X_n, n = 1, 2, \cdots\}$ converge to that of X_0 by Theorem A5.4. Then by Lemma 16.10, the probability distribution of X_0 is a normal distribution $N(m_0, v_0)$ and $\lim_{n\to\infty} m_n = m_0$ and $\lim_{n\to\infty} v_n = v_0$.

To prove (1) let us consider first the case where $m_n = 0$ for $n = 1, 2, \cdots$ and consequently $m_0 = 0$ as well. Take an arbitrary subsequence $\{n_k, k = 1,2, \cdots\}$. Since $X_0 = P - \lim_{k\to\infty} X_{n_k}$ there exists a subsequence $\{n_{k_\ell}, \ell = 1,2, \cdots\}$ such that $X_0(\omega) = \lim_{\ell\to\infty} X_{n_{k_\ell}}(\omega)$ for a.e. $\omega \in \Omega$. Then since $\lim_{\ell\to\infty} v_{n_{k_\ell}} = v_0$ is equivalent to $\lim_{\ell\to\infty} \| X_{n_{k_\ell}} \| = \| X_0 \|$ and since convergence a.e. and convergence of the L_2-norms together imply convergence in the L_2-norm we have

$$\lim_{\ell\to\infty} \| X_{n_{k_\ell}} - X_0 \| = 0 .$$

Now consider the sequence of real numbers $a_n = \| X_n - X_0 \|$, $n = 1,2, \cdots$. As we have just seen an arbitrary subsequence $\{a_{n_k}, k = 1,2, \cdots\}$ contains a subsequence $\{a_{n_{k_\ell}}, \ell = 1,2, \cdots\}$ which converges to 0. Thus the sequence $\{a_n, n = 1,2, \cdots\}$ itself converges to 0 and we have (1) for the special case in which we assume that $m_n = 0$, $n = 1,2, \cdots$.

Let us now remove the assumption that $m_n = 0$, $n = 1,2, \cdots$. Let $Y_n = X_n - m_n$, $n = 0,1, \cdots$. Then $E(Y_n) = 0$, $n = 0,1, \cdots$, so that from the last case we have

$$\lim_{n\to\infty} \| Y_n - Y_0 \| = 0.$$

But

$$\| X_n - X_0 \| = \| (Y_n + m_n) - (Y_0 + m_0) \| \le \| Y_n - Y_0 \| + | m_n - m_0 |.$$

Then from $\lim_{n\to\infty} m_n = m_0$ we have (1).

The rest of the theorem is obvious in view of Theorem A5.4. □

Definition 16.11b Let $\mathfrak{X}$ be the linear space whose elements are the equivalence classes of random variables on a probability space $(\Omega, \mathfrak{B}, P)$, the equivalence relation being that of a.e. equality on Ω, and in which addition and scalar multiplication are defined by

$$(X+Y)(\omega) = X(\omega) + Y(\omega), \qquad X, Y \in \mathfrak{X}$$

$$(\alpha X)(\omega) = \alpha X(\omega), \qquad \alpha \in R^1, \; X \in \mathfrak{X}.$$

Let $L_2(\Omega)$ be the Hilbert space consisting of $X \in \mathfrak{X}$ such that

$$\|X\|^2 = \int_\Omega \left[X(\omega)\right]^2 P(d\omega) < \infty .$$

By a Gaussian space on $(\Omega, \mathfrak{B}, P)$ we mean a closed linear subspace of $L_2(\Omega)$ (so that it is a Hilbert space itself) which is also a Gaussian system. The smallest Gaussian space on $(\Omega, \mathfrak{B}, P)$ which contains a Gaussian system on $(\Omega, \mathfrak{B}, P)$ is called the Gaussian space generated by the Gaussian system.

Theorem 16.11c Let $\mathfrak{G}$ be a Gaussian system of random variables on a probability space $(\Omega, \mathfrak{B}, P)$. Let $\mathfrak{L}$ be the collection of all linear combinations of members of $\mathfrak{G}$ and let $\mathfrak{H}$ be the collection of all limits of convergence in probability of sequences of members of $\mathfrak{L}$. Then $\mathfrak{H}$ is the Gaussian space generated by $\mathfrak{G}$.

Proof $\mathfrak{L}$ is a Gaussian system by Theorem 16.9 and consequently $\mathfrak{H}$ is a Gaussian system by Theorem 16.11. Clearly $\mathfrak{L}$ is a linear subspace of $L_2(\Omega)$. Now according to Theorem 16.11a, $\mathfrak{H}$ consists of all limits in the L_2-norm of sequences of members of $\mathfrak{L}$. Thus $\mathfrak{H}$ is a linear subspace of $L_2(\Omega)$. To show that $\mathfrak{H}$ is a closed linear subspace of $L_2(\Omega)$ let

$\{Z_n, n = 1,2, \cdots\} \subset \mathfrak{H}$ be a Cauchy sequence in $L_2(\Omega)$ and let $Z_0 \in L_2(\Omega)$ be such that $\lim_{n\to\infty} \|Z_n - Z_0\| = 0$. Now for each n, since $Z_n \in \mathfrak{H}$ we have $Y_n \in \mathfrak{L}$ such that $\|Z_n - Y_n\| < 1/n$. Then

$$\lim_{n\to\infty} \|Y_n - Z_0\| \leq \lim_{n\to\infty} \left\{\|Y_n - Z_n\| + \|Z_n - Z_0\|\right\} = 0$$

so that $\lim_{n\to\infty} \|Y_n - Z_0\| = 0$ and consequently $Z_0 \in \mathfrak{H}$. Thus $\mathfrak{H}$ is a closed linear subspace of $L_2(\Omega)$. This establishes the fact that $\mathfrak{H}$ is a Gaussian space on $(\Omega, \mathfrak{B}, P)$. It is obvious that $\mathfrak{H}$ is the smallest Gaussian space on $(\Omega, \mathfrak{B}, P)$ which contains $\mathfrak{G}$. □

Theorem 16.11d Let $\mathfrak{G}$ be a Gaussian system of random variables on a probability space $(\Omega, \mathfrak{B}, P)$ and let $\mathfrak{G}_1$ be the collection of random variables on $(\Omega, \mathfrak{B}, P)$ obtained by adjoining to $\mathfrak{G}$ the constant random variable which is identically equal to 1 on Ω. Then $\mathfrak{G}_1$ is a Gaussian system on $(\Omega, \mathfrak{B}, P)$ and the Gaussian space generated by it contains all the constant random variables.

Proof Consider $\alpha_0 \cdot 1 + \alpha_1 X_1 + \cdots + \alpha_n X_n$ where $\{X_1, \cdots, X_n\} \subset \mathfrak{G}$ and $\{\alpha_0, \cdots, \alpha_n\} \subset R^1$. Since $\mathfrak{G}$ is a Gaussian system, the probability distribution of $\alpha_1 X_1 + \cdots + \alpha_n X_n$ is a normal distribution $N(m, v)$ by Theorem 16.4. Then the probability distribution of $\alpha_0 \cdot 1 + \alpha_1 X_1 + \cdots + \alpha_n X_n$ is the normal distribution $N(m + \alpha_0, v)$. Thus $\mathfrak{G}_1$ is a Gaussian system by Theorem 16.4. The rest of the theorem follows from Theorem 16.11c. □

INDEX

R

S

U

V

W

Other books of interest to you...

Because of your interest in our books, we have included the following catalog of books for your convenience.

Any of these books are available on an approval basis. This section has been reprinted in full from our ***mathematics/ statistics*** catalog.

If you wish to receive a complete catalog of MDI books, journals and encyclopedias, please write to us and we will be happy to send you one.

mathematics statistics

BABAKHANIAN *Cohomological Methods in Group Theory*

(Pure and Applied Mathematics Series, Volume 11)

by ARARAT BABAKHANIAN, *University of Illinois, Urbana*

254 pages, illustrated. 1972.

Provides the reader with the basic tools in cohomology of groups and illustrates their use in obtaining group theoretic results, and may be used as a text for graduate students who have taken one course in algebra. Also recommended to group theorists interested in employing cohomological methods in their research.

CONTENTS: Elements of homological algebra • Cohomology of finite groups • Computations • Lower central series and dimension subgroups • Relations with subgroups and quotient groups • Finite p-nilpotent groups • Cup products • Spectral sequences • Descending central series • Galois groups.

BARROS-NETO *An Introduction to the Theory of Distributions*

(Pure and Applied Mathematics Series, Volume 14)

by JOSE BARROS-NETO, *Rutgers—The State University, New Brunswick, New Jersey*

232 pages, illustrated. 1973

Provides an introduction to the theory of distributions as it is derived from the general theory of topological vector spaces. Specially designed for the student who has taken courses on advanced calculus, linear algebra, and general topology, and who is familiar with Lebesgue integration theory and Banach and Hilbert spaces, including the Hahn-Banach theorem. Problems at the end of each chapter serve to help the reader check his comprehension of the subject matter.

CONTENTS: Locally convex spaces • Distributions • Convolutions • Tempered distributions and their Fourier transforms • Sobolev spaces • On some spaces of distributions • Applications.

BOOTHBY and WEISS *Symmetric Spaces: Short Courses Presented at Washington University*

(Pure and Applied Mathematics Series, Volume 8)

edited by WILLIAM M. BOOTHBY and GUIDO L. WEISS, *Washington University, St. Louis, Missouri*

504 pages, illustrated. 1972

Contains material presented in a series of short courses on the geometry and harmonic analysis of symmetric spaces given by well known authorities in the field. This text is of great interest to graduate students and professional mathematicians working in the areas of harmonic analysis, differential geometry, topological groups, and symmetric spaces.

CONTENTS: Minimal immersions of symmetric spaces into spheres, *N. R. Wallach.* Spherical functions on semisimple Lie groups, *R. Gangolli.* Spectra of discrete uniform subgroups of semisimple Lie groups, *R. Gangolli.* Fourier decompositions of certain representations, *K. I. Gross and R. A. Kunze.* Conical distributions and group representations, *S. Helgason.* Geometric ideas in Lie group harmonic analysis theory, *R. Hermann.* Bounded symmetric domains and holomorphic discrete series, *A. W. Knapp.* Schwarz lemma, *S. Kobayashi.* On tube domains, *Y. Matsushima.* Fine structure of Hermitian symmetric spaces, *J. A. Wolf.* Boundaries of Riemannian symmetric spaces, *H. Furstenberg.* Harmonic functions on symmetric spaces, *A. Koranyi.* Fatou's theorem for symmetric spaces, *N. J. Weiss.* New and old results in invariant theory with applications to arithmetic groups, *S. J. Rallis.* Topics on totally discontinuous groups, *H.-C. Wang.*

BURCKEL *Characterizations of C(X) Among Its Subalgebras*

(Lecture Notes in Pure and Applied Mathematics Series, Volume 6)

by R. B. BURCKEL, *Kansas State University, Manhattan*

176 pages, illustrated. 1972

(continued)

BURCKEL *(continued)*

Gives a detailed account of some recent results about subalgebras of C(X). Readers should have completed a course in real-variables and should have some acquaintance with functional analysis and complex-variables. Of interest to advanced undergraduates, graduate students, and professional mathematicians alike.

CONTENTS: Bishop's Stone-Weierstrass theorem • Restriction algebras determining C(X) • Wermer's theorem on algebras with multiplicatively closed real part • The work of Alain Bernard • The theorems of Gorin and Čirka • Bounded approximate normality, the work of Badé and Curtis • Katznelson's bounded idempotent theorem • Characterization of C(X) by functions which operate.

CHAVEL *Riemannian Symmetric Spaces of Rank One*

(Lecture Notes in Pure and Applied Mathematics Series, Volume 5)

by ISAAC CHAVEL, *City College of the City University of New York*

96 pages, illustrated. 1972

Provides an introduction to results on Riemannian symmetric spaces of rank one. A unified treatment aimed at the student familiar with the fundamentals of Riemannian geometry.

CONTENTS: Variational theory and comparison theorems • ¼-Pinched manifolds • Riemannian homogeneous spaces • Riemannian symmetric spaces of rank one.

DIEUDONNÉ *Introduction to the Theory of Formal Groups*

(Pure and Applied Mathematics Series, Volume 20)

by J. DIEUDONNÉ, *University of Nice, France*

248 pages, illustrated. 1973

CONTENTS: Definition of formal groups • Infinitesimal formal groups • Infinitesimal commutative groups • Representable reduced infinitesimal groups.

DORNHOFF *Group Representation Theory*

In 2 Parts

(Pure and Applied Mathematics Series, Volume 7)

by LARRY DORNHOFF, *University of Illinois, Urbana*

Part A ***Ordinary Representation Theory***
264 pages, illustrated. 1971

Part B ***Modular Representation Theory***
266 pages, illustrated. 1972

Provides a readable account of several major applications of representation theory to the structure of finite groups. Serves well as a textbook for a graduate course in representation theory and is useful for individual study by graduate students and mathematicians wishing to familiarize themselves with the subject.

CONTENTS:

Part A: Introduction • Theory of semisimple rings • Semisimple group algebras • Splitting fields and absolutely irreducible modules • Characters • Burnside's $p^a q^b$ theorem • Multiplicities, generalized characters, character tables • Representations of Abelian groups • Induced characters • Representations of direct products • Permutation groups • T. I. sets and exceptional characters • Frobenius groups • Clifford's theorem • M-groups • Brauer's characterization of characters • Brauer's theorem on splitting fields • Normal p-complements and the transfer • Generalized quaternion Sylow 2-subgroups • A theorem of Tate • Mackey decomposition • Itô's theorem on character degrees • Algebraically conjugate characters • The Schur index • Projective representations • The finite two-dimensional linear groups • Special conjugacy classes • A characterization via centralizers of involutions • Primitive complex linear groups • Jordan's theorem à la Blichfeldt • Extra-special p-groups • Normal p-subgroups of primitive linear groups • The Frobenius-Schur count of involutions • Primitive solvable linear groups • Simplicity of $PSL(n,F)$ and $PSp(2m,F)$ • Jordan's theorem for solvable groups • Itô's theorem on characters of solvable groups • Characters of $SL(2, p^n)$.

Part B: Indecomposable modules and chain conditions • The radical of a ring • Idempotents • Completeness • Unique decomposition theorems • Lifting idempotents • Principal indecomposable modules • Cartan invariants • The number of irreducible modules • Decomposition numbers • Finite extensions of complete local domains • Existence of a suitable ring: p-adic integers • Relatively projective RG-modules • Green's theorem • Vertices and sources • Defect groups • Central characters • The Brauer homomorphism • The Brauer correspondence • Brauer's first main theorem • Brauer characters • Orthogonality relations • Characters in blocks • Blocks of defect zero • Higher decomposition numbers; Brauer's second main theorem • Extension of the first main theorem to $DC_G(D)/D$ • The principal block • Quaternion Sylow 2-subgroups • The Z*-theorem of Glauberman • Blocks with cyclic defect group • Brauer: Groups of degree $<(p-1)/2$ • Feit and Thompson: Groups of degree $<(p-1)/2$ • p-blocks of $SL(2, p)$ • p-blocks of p-solvable groups.

GILMER *Multiplicative Ideal Theory*

(Pure and Applied Mathematics Series, Volume 12)

by ROBERT GILMER, *The Florida State University, Tallahassee*

624 pages, illustrated. 1972

Presents a comprehensive and detailed account of some of the important aspects of commutative algebra. Contains over 1,000 exercises and a bibliography of more than 300 entries. Directed to graduate students in mathematics and mathematicians concerned with commutative algebra.

CONTENTS: Basic concepts • Integral dependence • Valuation theory • Prüfer domains • Polynomial rings • Domains of classical ideal theory.

GRAY and SCHUCANY *The Generalized Jackknife Statistic*

(Statistics Series, Volume 1)

by H. L. GRAY, *Texas Tech University, Lubbock,* and W. R. SCHUCANY, *Southern Methodist University, Dallas, Texas*

320 pages, illustrated. 1972

Explores the theory surrounding the jackknife method and gives examples of its applications. Written from a theoretical and practical point of view and serves both the research statistician and the practitioner. Directed to statisticians, economists, professors in business colleges, psychologists, biometricians, and mathematicians.

CONTENTS: Reduction of bias by jackknifing • Applications to biased estimators • Asymptotic distributions • Jackknifing stochastic processes • The $J_{\infty}^{(2)}$-estimator.

HERMANN *Geometry, Physics, and Systems*

(Pure and Applied Mathematics Series, Volume 18)

by ROBERT HERMANN, *Rutgers—The State University, New Brunswick, New Jersey*

Part I in preparation. 1973

Deals with the interaction between geometry and physics and related disciplines, such as optimal control and systems theory, and continuum mechanics. Emphasizes the role of the theory of linear differential operators on manifolds, Ehresmann's theory of jets, and the geometric contributions of Sophus Lie and Elei Cartan. Requires only basic knowledge of differential and integral calculus on manifolds.

CONTENTS:

Part I: Algebraic concepts of manifold theory of differential operators • General differential-geometric form of the equations of motions of particle mechanics • Contact transformations and differential equations • Symmetries of variational problems • The theory of exterior differential systems • The mathematics of thermodynamics.

HIRZEBRUCH, NEUMANN, and KOH *Differentiable Manifolds and Quadratic Forms*

(Lecture Notes in Pure and Applied Mathematics Series, Volume 4)

by FRIEDRICH E. HIRZEBRUCH and WALTER D. NEUMANN, *University of Bonn, Germany,* and SEBASTIAN S. KOH, *West Chester State College, Pennsylvania*

128 pages, illustrated. 1971

Based on Sebastian Koh's notes on Friedrich Hirzebruch's lecture series given at Brandeis University and at the University of California at Berkeley. Explores invariants of quadratic forms and the calculation of some Grothendieck rings of quadratic forms. Also deals with manifolds and invariants defined by their quadratic forms.

CONTENTS: Quadratic forms • The Grothendieck ring • Certain arithmetical properties of quadratic forms • Integral unimodular quadratic forms • Quadratic forms over Z(p); the genus of integral forms • The quadratic form of a 4k-dimensional manifold • An application of Rohlins theorem; μ-invarients • Plumbing • Complex manifolds of complex dimension 2 • A theorem of Kervaire and Milnor.

JACOBSON *Exceptional Lie Algebras*

(Lecture Notes in Pure and Applied Mathematics Series, Volume 1)

by NATHAN JACOBSON, *Yale University, New Haven, Connecticut*

136 pages, illustrated. 1971

Presents a set of models for the exceptional Lie algebras over algebraically closed fields of characteristic 0 and over the field of real numbers. An excellent tool for the mathematical public in general — especially those interested in the classification of Lie algebras or groups — and for theoretical physicists.

CONTENTS: Jordan algebras of symmetric bilinear forms • Cayley algebras • Exceptional Jordan algebras • Automorphisms of $\mathcal{D}_4$'s • f_4 and $\mathcal{E}^6$ • Lie algebras of type E_6 • Some Exceptional Lie algebras of type D_4 • Roots of applications of Galois cohomology • Lie alge-

(continued)

JACOBSON *(continued)*
bras of type E_7 • Tits' second construction • Calculation of the Killing forms • Models of the real forms.

KOBAYASHI *Hyperbolic Manifolds and Holomorphic Mappings*

(Pure and Applied Mathematics Series, Volume 2)

by SHOSHICHI KOBAYASHI, *University of California, Berkeley*

160 pages, illustrated. 1970

Presents a coherent account of intrinsic pseudo distances on complex manifolds and their applications to holomorphic mappings. Of value to graduate students and research mathematicians interested in differential geometry, complex analysis, and related fields.

CONTENTS: The Schwarz lemma and its generalizations • Volume elements and the Schwarz lemma • Distance and the Schwarz lemma • Invariant distances on complex manifolds • Holomorphic mappings into hyperbolic manifolds • The big Picard theorem and extension of holomorphic mappings • Generalization to complex spaces • Hyperbolic manifolds and minimal models • Miscellany.

KSHIRSAGAR *Multivariate Analysis*

(Statistics Series, Volume 2)

by ANANT M. KSHIRSAGAR, *Texas A&M University, College Station*

552 pages, illustrated. 1972

Deals with the advanced theory of multivariate analysis and describes how multivariate techniques may be applied to practical problems in anthropometry, econometrics, psychometry, agriculture, and biometry.

Excellent as a one- or two-semester textbook for graduate students interested in multivariate analysis and also of importance to students and research scientists in statistics, and those dealing with statistical problems in anthropology, biology, and the agricultural and medical sciences.

CONTENTS: Regression and correlation among several variables • Multivariate normal distribution • The Wishart distribution • Distributions associated with regression • Hotelling's T^2 and its applications • Discriminant analysis • Canonical variables and canonical correlations • Wilks' Λ criterion • Multivariate analysis of variance and discrimination in the case of several groups • Likelihood ratio tests • Principal components.

LARSEN *Functional Analysis*

(Pure and Applied Mathematics Series, Volume 15)

by RONALD LARSEN, *Wesleyan University, Middletown, Connecticut*

512 pages, illustrated. 1973

A text which provides the basic theories, results, and techniques of functional analysis, as well as a sampling of its various applications to problems in functional analysis and other areas of mathematics. Includes problem sets for each chapter. For graduate and advanced undergraduate students who are acquainted with point set topology, linear algebra, complex analysis, and measure and integration theory.

CONTENTS: Semi-normed and normed linear spaces • Topological linear spaces • Linear transformations and linear functionals • The Hahn-Banach theorem: Analytic form • The Hahn-Banach theorem: Geometric form • The uniform boundedness theorem • The open mapping theorem and the closed graph theorem • Reflexity • Weak topologies • The Krein-Smulian theorem and the Eberlein-Smulian theorem • The Krein-Mil'man theorem • Fixed point theorem • Hilbert space.

LINDAHL and POULSEN *Thin Sets in Harmonic Analysis*

(Lecture Notes in Pure and Applied Mathematics, Volume 2)

edited by L.-Å. LINDAHL, *Uppsala University, Sweden,* and F. POULSEN, *University of Aarhus, Denmark*

200 pages, illustrated. 1971

Based on a seminar on thin sets presented at the Institute Mittag-Leffler, Djursholm, Sweden, during the year 1969-70. Valuable as an introduction to the field and as a text on which to base seminars.

CONTENTS: Dirichlet, Kronecker, and Helson sets, *L.-Å. Lindahl.* Bernard's theorem, *T. W. Körner.* Harmonic synthesis of Kronecker sets, *U. Tewari.* Continuous curves whose graphs are Helson sets, *T. Hedberg.* Sidon sets, *J.-E. Björk.* Combinatorial methods and Sidon sets, *F. Poulsen.* The characters of S(K) and the union problem for a Kronecker set and a point, *N. Th. Varopoulos.* Bochner's theorem for S(K), *N. Th. Varopoulos.* The group $S^*(X,\mu)$, *N. Th. Varopoulos.* The union problem for Helson sets, *N. Th. Varopoulos.* The embedding of A(E) into $\tilde{A}(E)$, *N. Th. Varopoulos.* Unbounded synthesis, *N. Th. Varopoulos.* Relations between Dirichlet, Kronecker, and Helson sets, *T. W. Körner.* Ultrathin symmetric sets and harmonic analysis, *Y. Meyer.* Pisot numbers and the problem of synthesis, *Y. Meyer.*

MATSUSHIMA *Differentiable Manifolds*

(Pure and Applied Mathematics Series, Volume 9)

by YOZO MATSUSHIMA, *University of Notre Dame, Indiana*

translated by EDWARD KOBAYASHI

320 pages, illustrated. 1972

An introduction to the theories of differentiable manifolds and Lie groups. Designed as a continuation of advanced calculus.

CONTENTS: Introduction • Differentiable manifolds • Differential forms and tensor fields • Lie groups and homogeneous spaces • Integration of differential forms and their applications.

MENDEL *Discrete Techniques of Parameter Estimation:* *The Equation Error Formulation*

(Control Theory Series, Volume 1)

by JERRY M. MENDEL, *McDonnell Douglas Astronautics Company, Huntington Beach, California*

408 pages, illustrated. 1973

Provides a solid analytical foundation for the estimation techniques of generalized least-squares, unbiased minimum-variance, deterministic-gradient, and stochastic-gradient. Presents these techniques from a unified point of view made possible by the use of the Equation Error Method as the basis for problem formulation. Problems accompany each chapter. Valuable as a graduate text in a course on techniques of parameter estimation and also of interest to statisticians, econometricians, and aerospace and control engineers.

CONTENTS: Equation error formulation of parameter estimation problems • Least-squares parameter estimation • Minimum-variance parameter estimation • Deterministic-gradient parameter estimation • Stochastic-gradient parameter estimation • Estimation of time-varying parameters.

NACHBIN *Convolutions and Holomorphic Mappings*

(Pure and Applied Mathematics Series)

by LEOPOLDO NACHBIN, *University of Rochester, New York*

in preparation. 1973

The first part of the text describes the work by C. P. Gupta and the author on nuclearly entire functions on a complex Banach space and the approximation of solutions of a convolutional equation by finite sums of exponential-polynomials. The second part surveys work by S. B. Chae, S. Dineen and the author on topological properties of locally convex spaces of holomorphic mappings between Banach spaces.

CONTENTS (partial): Convolutions on nuclearly entire functions • Spaces of holomorphic mappings.

NARICI, BECKENSTEIN, and BACHMAN *Functional Analysis and Valuation Theory*

(Pure and Applied Mathematics Series, Volume 5)

by LAWRENCE NARICI, *St. John's University, Jamaica, New York,* EDWARD BECKENSTEIN and GEORGE BACHMAN, *Polytechnic Institute of Brooklyn, New York*

200 pages, illustrated. 1971

"It is clearly written. . . . Exceptionally well supplied with exercises. . . . The material is well chosen and at a high scientific level."—Jack Schwartz, *Courant Institute*

CONTENTS: Topological results • Completeness • Normed linear spaces • Normed algebras.

NEY and PORT *Advances in Probability and Related Topics*

a series edited by PETER NEY, *University of Wisconsin, Madison,* and SIDNEY PORT, *University of California, Los Angeles*

Vol. 1 236 pages, illustrated. 1970

Vol. 2 264 pages, illustrated. 1970

Vol. 3 in preparation. 1973

A series consisting of research articles and critical reviews that treat current work in probability and related topics. Directed to research mathematicians.

CONTENTS:

Volume 1: Random walks and discrete subgroups of Lie groups, *H. Furstenberg.* The technique of using random measures and random sets in harmonic analysis, *J. Kahane.* Recent developments in the theory of finite Toeplitz operators, *I. Hirschman, Jr.* Matching theory, an introduction, *G. Rota and L. Harper.*

Volume 2: Ergodic properties of operators in Lebesgue space, *M. A. Akcoglu and R. V. Chacon.* The role of reproducing kernel Hilbert spaces in the study of Gaussian processes, *G. Kallianpur.* The sums of iterates of a positive operator, *D. Ornstein.* Boundary decomposition of locally-Hunt processes, *A. O. Pittenger.* Some new stochastic integrals and Stieltjes integrals, Part I. Analogues of Hardy-Littlewood classes, *L. C. Young.*

PASSMAN ***Infinite Group Rings***

(Pure and Applied Mathematics Series, Volume 6)

by DONALD S. PASSMAN, *University of Wisconsin, Madison*

160 pages, illustrated. 1971

Offers a coherent account of the basic results in this field. Of value as a text for second year graduate students and will interest all mathematicians working with infinite group rings.

CONTENTS: Linear identities • Bounded representation degree • Nil and nilpotent ideals • Idempotents and annihilators • Research problems.

PROCESI ***Rings with Polynomial Identities***

(Pure and Applied Mathematics Series, Volume 17)

by CLAUDIO PROCESI, *University of Pisa, Italy*

192 pages, illustrated. 1973

Presents a comprehensive account of the results obtained in the last twenty years on the theory of rings with polynomial identities. Directed to graduate students and research mathematicians.

CONTENTS: Polynomial identities in algebras • Structure theorems • The identities of matrix algebras • Representations and their invariants • Finitely generated algebras and extensions • Finiteness theorems • Intrinsic characterization of Azumaya algebras • The center of a PI-ring.

PSHENICHNYI ***Necessary Conditions for an Extremum***

(Pure and Applied Mathematics Series, Volume 4)

by BORIS N. PSHENICHNYI, *Institute of Cybernetics, Kiev, U.S.S.R.*

translated by KAROL MAKOWSKI

translation edited by LUCIEN W. NEUSTADT

248 pages, illustrated. 1971

Deals with the basic principles of the modern theory of necessary conditions for an extremum. Logically develops the needed mathematical apparatus starting with very basic concepts, so that no advanced mathematical knowledge is required of the reader.

SATAKE ***Classification Theory of Semi-Simple Algebraic Groups***

(Lecture Notes in Pure and Applied Mathematics Series, Volume 3)

by ICHIRO SATAKE, *University of California, Berkeley*

160 pages, illustrated. 1971

Explains the general principle of classification theory of semi-simple algebraic groups. Includes an appendix written by M. Sugiura of the University of Tokyo simplifying previous methods of classifying real semi-simple algebraic groups. Directed toward graduate students working in algebraic groups and related areas.

CONTENTS: Preliminaries on Algebraic Groups • General Principles of Classification.

SATAKE ***Linear Algebra***

(Pure and Applied Mathematics Series)

by ICHIRO SATAKE, *University of California, Berkeley*

in preparation. 1973

Presents a self-contained account of the basic concepts of linear algebra. Employs modern algebraic methods and emphasizes their usefulness in other branches of mathematics. An excellent textbook for undergraduate students, and a useful guide for self-study.

VAISMAN ***Cohomology and Differential Forms***

(Pure and Applied Mathematics Series, Volume 21)

by IZU VAISMAN, *Semiarul Matematic Universitate, Iasu, Romania*

304 pages, illustrated. 1973

Studies cohomology spaces in three important situations: the sheaf of germs of locally constant functions on a differentiable manifold; the sheaf of germs of differentiable functions which are constant on the leaves of a foliation; and the sheaf of germs of holomorphic functions on a complex manifold. Develops the necessary subjects of homological algebra, algebraic topology, and differential geometry, and includes problems and applications. Especially written for graduate students and research workers in the various domains of differential geometry and global analysis. Also useful to any mathematician interested in categories, homological algebra, and algebraic topology.

CONTENTS: Categories and functions • Sheaves and cohomology • Fiber and vector bundles • Differential geometry • Cohomology classes and differential forms.

VLADIMIROV *Equations of Mathematical Physics*

(Pure and Applied Mathematics Series, Volume 3)

by VASILIY S. VLADIMIROV, *Steklov Institute of Mathematics, Moscow, U.S.S.R.*

translated by AUDREY LITTLEWOOD

translation edited by ALAN JEFFREY

428 pages, illustrated. 1971

Examines classical boundary value problems for differential equations of mathematical physics, using the concept of the generalized solution instead of the traditional means of presentation. Devotes a special chapter to the theory of generalized functions and may be used as a graduate text.

CONTENTS: Formulation of boundary value problems in mathematical physics • Generalized functions • Fundamental solutions and the Cauchy problem • Integral equations • Boundary value problems for elliptic equations • The mixed problem.

WALLACH *Harmonic Analysis on Homogeneous Spaces*

(Pure and Applied Mathematics Series, Volume 19)

by NOLAN WALLACH, *Rutgers—The State University, New Brunswick, New Jersey*

352 pages, illustrated. 1973

CONTENTS: Vector bundles • Elementary representation theory • Basic structure theory of compact Lie groups and semi-simple Lie algebras • The topology and representation theory of compact Lie groups • Harmonic analysis on a homogeneous vector bundle • Holomorphic vector bundles over flag manifolds • Analysis on semi-simple Lie groups • Representations of semi-simple Lie groups.

WARD *Topology: An Outline for a First Course*

(Pure and Applied Mathematics Series, Volume 10)

by LEWIS E. WARD, JR., *University of Oregon, Eugene*

128 pages, illustrated. 1972

A textbook designed for a one-year introductory course in topology. Uses the Socratic method in which students provide proofs of theorems and solutions to problems without the assistance of other materials. Emphasizes the development of deductive reasoning and includes numerous examples as an additional teaching aid.

CONTENTS: Prerequisites • Topological spaces • Connected sets • Compact sets • Separation axioms • Mappings • Product spaces • Countability axioms • Complete spaces and perfect sets • Inverse limits • Quotient spaces • Nets and compactness • Embedding and metrization • Locally compact spaces • Continua • Cutpoints and arcs • Indecomposable continua • Locally connected spaces • Arcs and mapping theorems • Partially ordered spaces • The Brouwer fixed-point theorem • Homotopy • The fundamental group.

YANO *Integral Formulas in Riemannian Geometry*

(Pure and Applied Mathematics Series, Volume 1)

by KENTARO YANO, *Tokyo Institute of Technology, Japan*

168 pages, illustrated. 1970

CONTENTS: Fundamental concepts and formulas in Riemannian geometry • Harmonic 1-forms and Killing vector fields • Riemannian manifolds admitting an infinitesimal conformal transformation • Harmonic forms and Killing tensor fields • Hypersurfaces of Riemannian manifolds • Closed hypersurfaces of a Riemannian manifold with constant mean curvature • Harmonic 1-forms and Killing vector fields in Riemannian manifolds with boundary • Harmonic forms and Killing tensor fields in Riemannian manifolds with boundary.

YANO and ISHIHARA *Differential Geometry of Tangent and Cotangent Bundles*

(Pure and Applied Mathematics Series, Volume 16)

by KENTARO YANO and S. ISHIHARA, *Tokyo Institute of Technology, Japan*

392 pages, illustrated. 1973

A summation of the results on tangent and cotangent bundles known up to the present time. Not only gives a clear insight to classical results, but also provides many new problems in the study of modern differential geometry, encouraging further investigation of this new branch of an old discipline.

CONTENTS: Vertical and complete lifts from a manifold to its tangent bundle • Horizontal lifts from a manifold to its tangent bundle • Cross-sections in the tangent bundle • Tangent bundle of Riemannian manifolds • Prolongations of G-structures to tangent bundles • Non-linear connections in tangent bundles •

(continued)

YANO and ISHIHARA *(continued)*

Vertical and complete lifts from a manifold to its cotangent bundle • Horizontal lifts from a manifold to its cotangent bundle • Tensor fields and connections on a cross-section in the cotangent bundle • Prolongations of tensor fields and connections to the tangent bundle of order 2 • Prolongations of tensor fields, connections, and G-structures to the tangent bundle of higher order.

YEH *Stochastic Processes and the Wiener Integral*

(Pure and Applied Mathematics Series, Volume 13)

**price to be announced*

by JAMES J. YEH, *University of California, Irvine*

560 pages, illustrated. 1973

A self-contained treatise of a range of closely related topics on the space of sample functions of a stochastic process. Based on courses taught by the author at the University of California at Irvine. Of particular value as a textbook for students with knowledge of real analysis and some measure theoretic probability theory.

CONTENTS: Stochastic processes • Martingales • Additive processes • Gaussia processes • Stochastic integrals • Gaussian measures in function spaces • Wiener measure and Wiener integral • Transformations of Wiener integrals.

OTHER BOOKS OF INTEREST

EL BAZ and CASTEL *Graphical Methods of Spin Algebras in Atomic, Nuclear, and Particle Physics*

by EDGARD EL BAZ, *Claude Bernard University of Lyon, France,* and BORIS CASTEL, *Queen's University, Kingston, Canada*

444 pages, illustrated. 1972

HEINMETS *Concepts and Models of Biomathematics: Simulation Techniques and Methods*

(Biomathematics Series, Volume 1)

edited by F. HEINMETS, *U.S. Army Natick Laboratories, Natick, Massachusetts.*

302 pages, illustrated. 1969

JOURNALS OF INTEREST

COMMUNICATIONS IN STATISTICS

editor: DONALD B. OWEN, *Southern Methodist University, Dallas, Texas*

Communications in Statistics is devoted to presenting the formulation and discussion of problems and their solutions, whether elegant or practical. The communication of interesting applications of known methods to real problems in industry and government will be as important as those articles having a strong mathematical orientation that have an impact on the field of statistics. The journal is reproduced directly from manuscripts submitted by authors, enabling the editor to publish articles from three to five months from the time of their receipt. *Communications in Statistics* is a vehicle for the rapid dissemination of new ideas in all areas of statistics.

6 issues per volume

TRANSPORT THEORY AND STATISTICAL PHYSICS
An International Journal for Rapid Communication in Irreversible Statistical Mechanics

editor: PAUL ZWEIFEL, *Virginia Polytechnic Institute, Blacksburg*

This new journal will be devoted primarily to those areas of irreversible statistical mechanics which are generally known as transport theory and kinetic theory. It will include papers on transport of neutral particles, dynamics of simple liquids, kinetic theory of liquids and plasmas, gas dynamics, and correlation functions.

4 issues per volume

An examination copy of any journal is available upon request.